Cellular Ultrastructure
of Woody Plants

Sponsored by the State University of New York College of Forestry at Syracuse University and supported by a National Science Foundation Grant through The Research Foundation of State University of New York, Albany, New York.

Cellular Ultrastructure
of Woody Plants

Proceedings of the
Advanced Science Seminar
Pinebrook Conference Center
Upper Saranac Lake, New York
September, 1964

Edited by WILFRED A. CÔTÉ, JR.
Professor of Wood Technology
Department of Wood Products Engineering
State University of New York College of Forestry
at Syracuse University

SYRACUSE UNIVERSITY PRESS   1965

DEDICATED TO

PROFESSOR IRVING WIDMER BAILEY
whose pioneering researches on
woody plants have served as
a continuous source of
information and inspiration

PREFACE

During the week of September 20 to 26, 1964, a group of fifty academic, industrial, and government research and teaching personnel met at Syracuse University's Pinebrook Conference Center, Upper Saranac Lake, New York. With the primary objective of an improved understanding of the woody cell wall, the topic "Cellular ultrastructure of woody plants" was explored from the standpoint of certain key disciplines: physiology, chemistry, anatomy, and biophysics. The papers that appear in this volume were presented at this interdisciplinary conference. They are being published so that the many interested people who could not attend the conference will have access to the material that developed at these meetings.

Support for the conference came from the National Science Foundation under the Advanced Science Seminar Program, Grant No. GE4831. It was sponsored by State University of New York College of Forestry at Syracuse University, Syracuse, New York, with the cooperation of Syracuse University and their Adirondack Conference Center staff. This volume was made possible by support received from National Science Foundation and the cooperation of Syracuse University Press.

I would like to thank the many people who contributed to the success of the conference. Without the cooperation and efforts of the authors, the conference and this volume of proceedings would not have been possible. Special thanks are extended to Dr. H. Harada and Dr. T. E. Timell for assistance and advice with editorial matters, to Miss Judy Barton for the many stenographic tasks performed during the planning phases of the conference as well as in preparing manuscript for the publisher, and to Mr. Arnold Day who contributed in countless ways to the operation of the conference and to the mechanical details of preparing material for this volume.

December, 1964   WILFRED A. CÔTÉ, JR.

ACKNOWLEDGMENTS

Grateful acknowledgment is made to the following for permission to publish figures that have appeared previously in other publications. Page and figure references in this list are to the present volume.

Academic Press, Inc., (New York). P. 53, Figs. 1, 2, 3; P. 65, Figs. 2, 3; P. 172, Fig. 16; P. 377, Fig. 3; P. 381, Fig. 6; P. 384, Fig. 8.

Almqvist and Wiksell, (Uppsala, Sweden). P. 588, Fig. 12.

American Journal of Botany. P. 343, Fig. 1.

Prof. I. W. Bailey, Harvard University. P. 306, Fig. 1; P. 351, Fig. 5.

Birkhäuser Verlag, (Basel, Switzerland). P. 160, Fig. 3.

Chapman & Hall, Ltd., (London). P. 5, Fig. 1; P. 8, Fig. 4; P. 12, Fig. 7; P. 15, Fig. 10.

Deutsche Botanische Gesellschaft, (Berlin-Zehlendorf). P. 257, Fig. 7.

Forest Products Journal. P. 410, Fig. 18; P. 413, Fig. 19; P. 415, Figs. 21, 22; P. 417, Fig. 23; P. 418, Fig. 25; P. 546, Fig. 2.

Prof. Dr.-Ing. G. Jayme, Institut für Cellulosechemie, (Darmstadt). P. 309, Fig. 3.

Journal of Polymer Science. P. 359, Fig. 11.

MacMillan & Company, Ltd., (London). P. 264, Fig. 16.

Pergamon Press, Limited, (London). P. 92, Fig. 26; P. 128, Fig. 1; P. 174, Fig. 20.

Publishing House of the Czechoslovak Academy of Sciences, (Prague). P. 277, Fig. 5; P. 281, Figs. 9, 10.

Pulp and Paper Magazine of Canada. P. 202, Fig. 1; P. 203, Fig. 2; P. 204, Fig. 3; P. 206, Fig. 5; P. 207, Fig. 6.

Rockefeller Institute Press, (New York). P. 55, Fig. 4.

Springer-Verlag, (Heidelberg). P. 252, Fig. 2; P. 265, Fig. 17; P. 273, Fig. 2; P. 298, Fig. 8; P. 299, Figs. 9, 10; P. 300, Fig. 11.

Springer-Verlag, (Berlin). P. 366, Fig. 12; P. 590, Fig. 13.

Technischer Verlag Herbert Cram, (Berlin). P. 176, Fig. 22.

Verlag Georg Fromme & Co., (Vienna). P. 158, Fig. 1; P. 159, Fig. 2.

Wissenschaftliche Verlagsgesellschaft m. b. H., (Stuttgart). P. 275, Fig. 4; P. 292, Fig. 1; P. 293, Fig. 2.

LIST OF CONTRIBUTORS

S. K. Asunmaa, Fundamental Research, Owens-Illinois Technical Center, 1700 N. Westwood Avenue, Toledo, Ohio

J. Ross Colvin, Biophysics Section, Division of Biosciences, National Research Council, Ottawa 2, Canada

Wilfred A. Côté, Jr., Department of Wood Products Engineering, State University College of Forestry at Syracuse University, Syracuse, New York 13210

D. R. Cowdrey, The Astbury Department of Biophysics, The University, Leeds 2, England

Ellis B. Cowling, Greeley Memorial Laboratory, School of Forestry, Yale University, New Haven, Connecticut 06511

James Cronshaw, Department of Biology, Osborne Memorial Laboratories, Yale University, New Haven, Connecticut 06511

Arnold C. Day, Department of Wood Products Engineering, State University College of Forestry at Syracuse University, Syracuse, New York 13210

D. T. Dennis, Department of Chemistry, University of California, Los Angeles, California

Carl de Zeeuw, Department of Wood Products Engineering, State University College of Forestry at Syracuse University, Syracuse, New York 13210

Everett L. Ellis, Department of Wood Technology, School of Natural Resources, University of Michigan, Ann Arbor, Michigan

Katherine Esau, Department of Biological Sciences, University of California, Santa Barbara, California 93106

J. L. Farrar, Faculty of Forestry, University of Toronto, Toronto 5, Canada

William L. Galligan, Wood Technology Laboratory, Division of Industrial Research, Washington State University, Pullman, Washington

H. Harada, Wood Technology Institute, Department of Forestry, Kyoto University, Kyoto, Japan

G. Ifju, Department of Forestry and Wildlife, Virginia Polytechnic Institute, Blacksburg, Virginia 24061

R. W. Kennedy, Faculty of Forestry, University of Toronto, Toronto 5, Canada

Zoltán Kórán, Pulp and Paper Research Institute of Canada, 3240 University Street, Montréal 2, Canada

K. KRATZL, Organisch-Chemisches Institut der Universität Wien, Wien 9, Austria, Währingerstrasse 38

WALTER LIESE, Lehrstuhl für Holzwirtschaft (Holzbiologie) der Universität Hamburg, 2057 Reinbek, Schloss, Germany

RICHARD MARK, School of Forestry, Yale University, New Haven, Connecticut 06511

D. C. McINTOSH, Central Research Laboratories, The Mead Corporation, Chillicothe, Ohio

KURT MÜHLETHALER, Laboratorium für Elektronenmikroskopie, Institut für Allgemeine Botanik, Eidgenössische Technische Hochschule, Zürich 6, Switzerland, Universitätstrasse 2

ARTHUR F. NOSKOWIAK, Department of Forestry and Range Management, Washington State University, Pullman, Washington

R. D. PRESTON, The Astbury Department of Biophysics, The University, Leeds 2, England

IRVING B. SACHS, U. S. Forest Products Laboratory, Madison, Wisconsin 53705

ROSWITHA SCHMID, Forstbotanisches Institut der Universität München, München 13, Germany, Amalienstrasse 52

D. W. SCHWAB, Fundamental Research, Owens-Illinois Technical Center, 1700 N. Westwood Avenue, Toledo, Ohio

T. E. TIMELL, Department of Forest Chemistry, State University College of Forestry at Syracuse University, Syracuse, New York 13210

GEORGE TSOUMIS, School of Forestry, The Pennsylvania State University, University Park, Pennsylvania 16802

A. B. WARDROP, Department of Botany, University of Tasmania, Hobart, Tasmania, Australia

R. W. WELLWOOD, Faculty of Forestry, University of British Columbia, Vancouver 8, Canada

J. W. WILSON, Faculty of Forestry, University of British Columbia, Vancouver 8, Canada

CONTENTS

xi

Cellular Ultrastructure
of Woody Plants

Interdisciplinary Approaches to Wood Structure

R. D. PRESTON, F.R.S.

The Astbury Department of Biophysics
The University of Leeds

I do not need to stress at a conference devoted to its study that wood is among the most remarkable products of this earth with a range of properties which makes it unique among the materials around us and virtually irreplaceable for the uses it finds. Nor do I need to dwell upon the circumstance that, although nowadays we know a great deal about wood, we are still far from understanding the derivation of almost any of its properties from its structure. Rather do I want to attempt to outline some of the difficulties we meet in working with this material and to try to define the approaches which must be made to its study in the future if wood is eventually to take its place among materials whose properties can be tailored in a predictable fashion for particular needs.

The complexity of wood arises from three general circumstances. Firstly, wood is heterogeneous at all levels of examination and in several ways. Consisting as it does of some four basic cell types—vessels, tracheids (including fibers, fiber-tracheids, and so on, if I may be allowed to group these together), wood parenchyma cells, and ray cells—each with its own structural peculiarities, wood is variable from species to species dependent upon the relative proportion and mutual distribution within it of these types of cells. Further, the cells within each group are variable in character so that even within one single tree, with roughly the same distribution of cell types throughout, the wood is different between inner and outer annual rings, between branches and trunks, and even to some extent from the top to the bottom of the trunk itself. A single piece of wood as small as a matchstick and even a single slice of it is still visually heterogeneous, consisting as it does of wood substance perfused by pores (the cell lumina) varying in diameter from about 20 μ to about 100 μ. Even the smallest fragment still recognizable as wood, in which porosity of this order plays no part, is still heterogeneous both chemically and physically. The integrated effect of all these forms of heterogeneity needs to be taken into account in assessing the physical properties of a timber. Secondly, wood is anisotropic and the basis for the anisotropy is complex. The shape of its constituent cells with their

1

lumina in general elongated and parallel to each other confers immediately upon the wood an anisotropy of structure which is clearly the basis
upon which depends, at least in part, the anisotropy of some properties
(e.g., thermal conductivity, permeability), but not necessarily of all. At a
more sophisticated level, the wood substance itself is anisotropic down to
the finest detail of its structure. The properties of wood in one direction
do not therefore necessarily have any bearing on the properties of the
same wood in some other direction. Thirdly, wood is a substance produced by a living organism and therefore subject in its "manufacture" to
factors which are not, at present at least, subject to close control.

On the one hand, therefore, wood cannot be treated solely as a physical
entity like a piece of copper, or even of granite, with complete disregard
for its biological origin without serious risk of errors such as are already
contained in the literature. Nor on the other hand can it be regarded,
any more than any other biological tissue can be regarded, as solely the
preserve of the botanist (as we at present know him) without regard to the
physical and chemical nature of its substance.

It is quite clear therefore that the study of wood should properly be
examined against the whole background of "classical" anatomy, and of
the wide range of disciplines applicable to the study of the structure of
matter up to the most sophisticated modern treatments; and that all the
methods involved should be applied rigidly and together. Wood presents,
in other words, a striking example of the dilemma facing the whole of
botany today—the need somehow to develop side by side both the new
approaches which modern physics and chemistry allow to biology and the
older, well tried methods of "classical" botany itself. A comprehensive
understanding of wood therefore necessitates an interdisciplinary approach wider than that of any substance now known.

This need is all the more strengthened by the diversity of the things we
need to know about a wood by virtue of its multitudinous uses. Most
timbers are not of themselves durable and must therefore, for prolonged
use, be protected against decay. Here knowledge of mycology, of ento-
mology, and of wood chemistry are involved in determining the course of
attack on timber by a variety of microorganisms and by insects. In protection by current methods much more is needed to be known about the
porosity of wood and of the channel of flow by which large amounts of
liquid may be moved into and out of wood. Looking towards the future,
methods must be sought, and are being sought, of chemically so modifying the wood substance itself as to make it immune to such attack. In
structural use, the mechanical properties of wood need to be known—
and predictable for any given wood structure—and the degree of swelling and shrinkage needs to be controlled; and both of these depend upon

a thorough and detailed knowledge of the structure of wood down to the finest limits attainable.   Similarly, the production of paper and other forms of "pulverized" wood increasingly demands knowledge of chemistry and fine structure. In short, the use of wood presupposes a knowledge of the behavior of wood under a wide variety of conditions and this demands investigations by many disciplines.

In the past few years in particular, we have gone a long way in determining the structure of wood both in the physical and in the chemical sense. But the crux of the matter is that however far we go it seems that for the foreseeable future the heterogeneity of wood is such that it will not do merely to know the structure of wood in general in however detailed a way. Insofar as the study of any wood property presupposes a knowledge of the structure of the specimen in hand, the detailed structure of this particular specimen must be known.

It is the purpose of this article to discuss in a general way the application of a variety of physical methods in the determination of the structure of wood and to outline the advantages and disadvantages of each. It is not for a moment to be supposed that chemical investigations are of less importance from the fact that they will be mentioned here only as and when necessary. Even if space would allow, the author is not qualified to deal with the purely chemical studies of wood components.

The Light Microscope and Its Modifications

It is probable that wood was the first plant tissue to be looked at when the compound microscope was first invented almost three hundred years ago, the observations of Henshaw on walnut antedating the historic observations on cork by Robert Hooke possibly by about six years. During the years since then, up to this very moment and beyond, wood has been subjected to continuous scrutiny by this remarkable instrument. It is not the purpose here to examine even in outline the anatomy revealed in this way but to deal with some of the features which make this instrument quite unique as a tool of investigation.

The detail which can be resolved with any instrument using radiation for the production of a real image is limited by the wave length of radiation used, following the well known relation

$$r = \frac{0.61\lambda}{n \sin \beta}.$$

A bright point on the object becomes through (unavoidable) diffraction a small bright circle surrounded by rings of diminishing brightness separated by narrow dark annuli. It is taken that if two points on the object are so close together that the central disc of the image of one falls squarely on the first dark annulus of the other then the two points can *just* be resolved. The distance apart of the points is then given by *r* in the above relation and this imposes a limit on all the image-forming instruments we shall deal with. With visible radiation the resolving power is usually taken at 0.1 μ or 1000 Å.

This means that even the thinnest of cell walls in plants can readily be observed and sharply focused. Since, moreover, the image is produced by refraction and absorption of light, details of structure within cell walls can be resolved down to this limit, if there is a suitable difference of refractive index or opacity, so that wall lamellae are easily resolved. This makes the light microscope unique among image-forming instruments since such detail may be observed in fresh specimens with no pretreatment other than sectioning. Moreover, histochemistry allows the spatial distribution of some chemical substances also down to this fine detail and no other instrument is available which can do this.

Beyond this the normal light microscope cannot go without assistance. Once the fine structures underlying the microscopic appearance is known, however, as it is today by other methods, then the light microscope can be used again to define some features of this fine structure. Thus, striations in cell walls are known to lie parallel to the cellulose microfibrils of the wall lamellae in which they are observed. The preferred orientation of microfibrils which are not themselves visible can therefore be determined and the remarkably short focal depth of high-powered optical lenses allows also the lamella itself, within which these microfibrils occur, to be identified. In the absence of striations, the major axis of slit pits, or the direction of cracks running from the margin of pits also give a guide to the microfibril direction (Preston, 1947). Again, the incorporation of silver grains into a wall can sometimes be used for the same purpose (Frey-Wyssling, 1937), though here there is some danger of distortion. Failing all else, swelling in a suitable reagent increases artificially the size of small details which can then be seen, though this is of less value owing to the much grosser distortions which must take place on swelling. Familiarity with modern more sophisticated tools should not blind us therefore to the remarkable powers of the light microscope.

THE POLARIZING MICROSCOPE

The light microscope reaches its peak, however, in the form of the polarizing microscope. In the hands of Carl von Nägeli during the last quarter of the nineteenth century, this instrument served not only to add new vistas to our knowledge of cell walls, but to lay the foundation of the physical chemistry of matter in the colloidal state among which wood cell walls must be included. The underlying theory may be read in any one of a number of excellent texts (e.g., Burri, 1950; Hartshorne and Stuart, 1960; Bloss, 1961) and a simplified account dealing with cell walls in particular has already been given (Preston, 1952). The basis upon which this instrument stands may be seen schematically as follows. In a beam of polarized light the electric vector vibrates with simple harmonic motion in a single plane, represented by the arrow in Figure 1, the direction of propagation of the light being normal to the page. Imagine this beam passing through a body consisting of diatomic molecules lying parallel to each other and oriented as in Figure 1a. Then at a given instant of time each atom will be polarized as indicated. Notice that, since the charges nearest to each other are of opposite sign, the polarization of each atom *increases* the polarization of the other—the polarization is high. If the body is turned through 90°, as in Figure 1b, the closest charges are of opposite sign and the polarization of each atom *reduces* the polarization of the other—the polarization is low. In each orientation the polarization increases the refractive index above that for a vacuum. The refractive index is, however, greater in position a than in position b, and the direction of the greater refractive index, and therefore of the bond between the atoms, can be determined.

With cellulose, the crystalline component of cell walls, the direction of the linear molecular chains (Fig. 2), if they tend to be parallel to each other, may be determined in this way. Let us notice what happens as a random mat of chains is gradually converted into a strictly parallel array as, for instance, by stretching the mat in one direction. When completely random (Fig. 3A), the refractive index for light propagated in a direc-

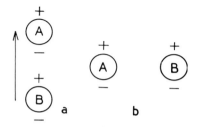

FIG. 1. A diagrammatic representation of the momentary effect of a beam of plane polarized light on a diatomic molecule. The arrow shows the direction of vibration of the beam of light. A and B are the atoms joined together in a single diatomic molecule AB. In *a* the polarization of the molecule is high and in *b* the polarization of the molecule is low (from Preston, 1952).

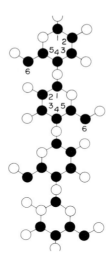

FIG. 2. Diagrammatic representation of a section of a cellulose chain molecule. The solid circles represent carbon, the open circles oxygen, and hydrogen atoms are omitted.

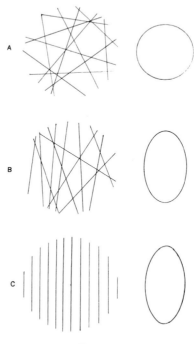

FIG. 3.

tion normal to the page is invariate with vibration direction, the material is isotropic and its optical properties may be represented by a circle each radius of which is formally equal to the refractive index (n) for light vibrating in that direction. If the mat is slightly extended (Fig. 3B), so that the chains are not quite at random, then the refractive index is greater for vibrations parallel to the direction of stretch than it is at right angles and the optical properties are represented by an ellipse of low eccentricity, the major and minor axes of which correspond to the higher (n_γ') and the lower (n_α') values of the refractive index. When the chains are completely parallel (Fig. 3C), the ellipse has the highest possible eccentricity and the refractive indices n_γ and n_α are as high, and as low, respectively, as they can be. In cases B and C the direction of the greater refractive index gives the *preferred* direction of the chains; the refractive indices n_γ' and n_α' (or, better because more easily measured, the difference (n_γ' − n_α') [the *birefringence*]) give a measure of the degree of parallelism, other things being equal.

One further feature must be added at this point. In a perfect crystal (e.g., Fig. 3C) the light can vibrate within the crystal only in the two directions given by n_γ and n_α and in no others. If we think now of the parallel array of chain molecules in Figure 3C as a solid body, by superposing one array upon another, then the ellipse becomes an ellipsoid (Fig. 4) with major axis n_γ and minor axes (in the median circular section of the ellipsoid) n_α. To determine the vibration directions and refractive indices for light propagated at any direction θ to the major axis (and therefore to the chains), the ellipsoid is cut by a plane ABCO whose normal is the direction of propagation X; the vibration directions are then OA and OB and the refractive indices given by OA ($= n_\gamma$) and OB ($= n_\alpha$). Clearly if n_γ' and n_α are measured, then θ, and hence the true direction of the chains can be calculated.

These principles are applied in microscopy by making certain changes in the standard light microscope. A rotatable polaroid (the polarizer) is placed in the substage of the microscope to convert the light to plane-polarized light and a second polaroid (the analyzer), which can be removed from the light path at will, in the body tube. The objective lens is chosen to be completely free of strain and the stage is rotatable with a graduated edge and a vernier. With this simple instrument it was early shown (for what follows see references in Preston, 1952) that

a. In walls seen in edge view in longitudinal sections the direction of vibration with the greater refractive index (called, for technical reasons, the major extinction position, m.e.p.) lies parallel to wall surface, i.e., longitudinally.

b. In single cell walls of tracheids and fibers, seen in face view, the m.e.p. lies at an angle θ to the cell length.

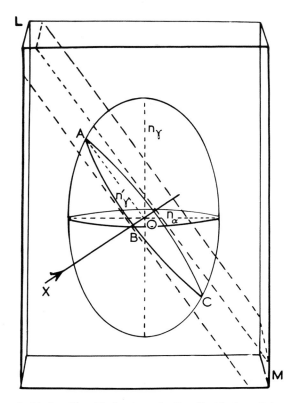

Fig. 4. The optical index ellipsoid of a piece of cell wall with the cellulose chains vertical. The refractive indices of the cellulose are given by the major and minor axes of the ellipsoid respectively, i.e., by n_γ and n_α. When a section LM of the wall is examined normal to the face of the section, i.e., along the direction X, the refractive indices of the section are given by the major and minor axes of the ellipse $ABCO$ which is the intersection of the ellipsoid with a plane through O parallel to LM. The refractive indices are therefore n'_γ and n_α (from Preston, 1952).

These observations demonstrate clearly that in a whole tracheid or fiber the m.e.p., and therefore the general run of the cellulose chains, lies helically around the cell. As long ago as 1934 it was demonstrated that the angle which the helical winding makes to the long axis of the cell varies with cell length. This was shown by comparing the average length L with the average angle θ in the early wood of a series of annual rings from inside to outside. It then appeared that L is related linearly with cot θ. By examining individual cells in a mass of macerated fibers, and using the cracks at the end of slit pits (proved to correspond to the m.e.p.), it was shown (Preston, 1947) (Fig. 5) that for individual cells, even within one annual ring, L varies with θ according to the relationship

$$L = a + b\cot\theta.$$

This type of relation has since been shown applicable in other timbers and phloem fibers. Examination of cross sections under the polarizing microscope showed, however, that the value of θ is not uniform throughout the secondary walls of these wood cells; the wall normally consists of three

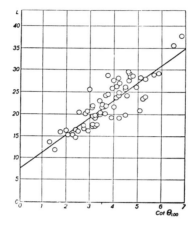

FIG. 5. The relationship between tracheid length L and Cot θ in tracheids of *Pinus radiata*. The values of L are in arbitrary units.

layers named by Bailey and his co-workers S_1, S_2, and S_3 (from the outside of the cell to the lumen), θ being larger in S_1 and S_3 than in S_2. By the use of the polarizing microscope alone, Wardrop and Preston were able to show that nevertheless the value of θ for each layer individually varies with L much as shown above, though the constants a and b are of course different. The model of the wall structure of tracheids and fibers obtained in this way was presented in 1951 by Wardrop and Preston (Fig. 6); it was similar to the model presented some years before by I. W. Bailey, differing mainly in the steepness of the helix in S_1 and S_3 and in the variability in the steepness of all three helices with tracheid length.

Both these models were reached by the use of the light microscope only, through the ability conferred by polarization optics to deduce the organization of wall constituents which are below the limits of direct visibility. The polarizing microscope properly used is possibly the most pow-

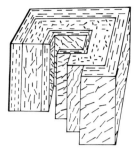

FIG. 6a. Diagrammatic representation of the model of the wall structure of wood tracheids and fibers given by Wardrop and Preston before the use of electron microscopy. The
figure shows a short section of a cell dissected to show the structure of the three layers of
the secondary wall. The direction of the crystallites in each layer of the wall are shown by
the short full lines.

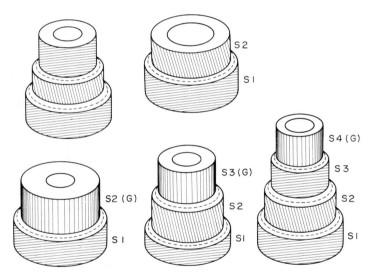

FIG. 6b. More recent representations of the variations in the structure of tracheids and
fibers (after A. B. Wardrop). (a) Normal three-layered structure of secondary wall. (b)
Two-layered structure of secondary wall in compression wood tracheid. (c) Two-layered
structures in tension wood fibers. (d) Three layered structures in tension wood fibers.
(e) Four-layered structures in tension wood fibers.

erful single tool in the hands of the cell wall investigator. It must, however, be used with some caution because, unless something is already
known through the use of other techniques (see below) about the general
structure of the material studied, there is risk of serious error. Some of
the major points to be watched are as follows:

1. If a material consists of submicroscopic crystallites lying completely at random it will be optically isotropic. Absence of birefringence does not necessarily mean lack of crystallinity but only lack of orientation. The crystallinity should be checked by some other method, such as X-ray diffraction analysis.

2. If the crystallites in a cell wall are arranged almost at random, but not quite, then the material will be birefringent and the direction of the m.e.p. can be determined. In this sense the microscope is very sensitive to orientation, and the determination of the m.e.p. alone means no more than a *tendency* for the crystallites to lie in this direction. A clear example of this occurs in the green alga *Bryopsis,* in which the material is strongly and sharply birefringent though the appearance in the electron microscope shows that the constituent microfibrils show scarcely a sign of orientation. Only if the birefringence ($n_\gamma - n_\alpha$) is measured and compared with that of a known well oriented sample can any estimate be made of the degree of orientation.

3. If the crystallites (e.g., the microfibrils in the cell wall) are well oriented but the material consists of two lamellae with different orientations, then, if the angle ϕ between these two directions is less than 90°, the material will be birefringent in face view (Fig. 7) and the m.e.p. will lie in the acute angle between the two microfibril directions. There are several special cases.

a. If the two lamellae are identical, the m.e.p. bisects the angle ϕ. This is the case when whole (macerated) tracheids are examined since the two walls, upper and lower, are identical. It is usually the case also if in a longitudinal section the walls of two neighboring cells attached by the middle lamella are examined in face view.

b. If one lamella for any reason (e.g., greater thickness, higher crystallinity) is more strongly birefringent than the other, then the m.e.p. will be displaced from the acute bisector towards the direction of the microfibrils in the more strongly birefringent lamella. This is the general case. A single cell wall of any tracheid or fiber examined in face view falls into this category; the m.e.p. of the whole wall is seldom more than a few degrees away from the microfibril direction in the S_2 layer.

c. If the two lamellae are identical and $\phi = 90°$ the composite body is isotropic. This holds, for instance, when a whole tracheid is examined for which the helical angle of the m.e.p. for each wall (upper and lower) is 45°.

d. If the lamellae are not identical and $\phi = 90°$ the m.e.p. defines the microfibril direction of the lamellae which is more strongly birefringent.

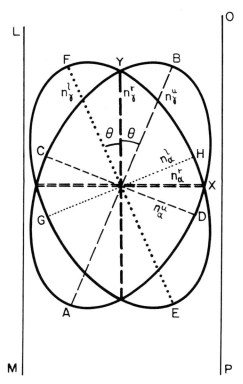

FIG. 7. The optics of a crossed crystalline plate as represented by a whole conifer tracheid in longitudinal view. LM and OP represent the side walls. The ellipse $ABCD$ represents the trace in the plane of the wall of the index ellipsoid of the upper wall, and the ellipse $EFGH$ represents the trace in the plane of the wall of the index ellipsoid of the lower wall. n_γ^u and n_α^u are the two refractive indices of the upper wall and n_γ^l and n_α^l are the refractive indices of the lower wall. These compound to give the two refractive indices n_γ^r and n_α^r. The direction of n_γ^r bisecting the directions EF and AB represents the resultant major extinction position of the double wall, parallel to the length of the cell (from Preston, 1952).

In such cases the composite body is indistinguishable, unless other evidence is available, from a single crystal, in our case a wall in which the chain direction is uniform throughout. The other evidence necessary can be obtained by X-ray diffraction analysis and for these purposes polarization microscopy and X-ray diffraction analysis are complementary. Usually the m.e.p. of a whole wall is not more than $\pm 2°$ removed from the m.e.p. of the S_2 layer alone. Alternatively, examination of cross sections, as used qualitatively by Bailey and quantitatively by Wardrop and Preston (and for bamboo fibers by Preston and Singh, 1952) will give the answer; or if the wall can be torn so that one lamella protrudes from an edge, the optical characteristics of the second lamella may be calculated from those of the protruding lamella and of the whole wall as demonstrated by Preston (1947).   This is satisfactory only if the second lamella is homogeneous.

THE INTERFERENCE MICROSCOPE

In using the polarizing microscope it is often necessary to measure refractive indices. This may be done tediously by measuring n_γ and n_α separately, or very quickly by determining the difference $(n_\gamma - n_\alpha)$. This is done by measuring the path difference of the specimen $(n_\gamma - n_\alpha)d$ where d is the specimen thickness. In the past d has been difficult to measure accurately; it can now be determined both accurately and quickly in the interference microscope.

The interference microscope has many important uses in biology but for present purposes its outstanding feature is that it can measure optical thickness. This is achieved by superposing in the eyepiece two fields of view, one with and one without the object. Apart from disturbances due to the object the phase difference between the two images will be zero, or have a variable known value, and the conditions are such that interference will occur. The phase difference between the object and the field is given by a simple measurement of length and from this the thickness of the object can be calculated. The method is standard and will be found in any one of a number of standard texts. It is therefore to be recommended that users of the polarizing microscope should also have available an interference microscope.

X-RAY DIFFRACTION ANALYSIS

Polarization microscopy suffers, however, from the limitation that it cannot define the form of the anisotropic bodies, except in a general way, and cannot usually be used with any certainty to define the nature of substance under observation. It reaches its highest powers, therefore, when used in conjunction with other physical methods of investigation and one such method is that of X-ray diffraction analysis, the method of investigation which has contributed so much in the past forty years or so to our knowledge of matter in the solid state (see, e.g., Bunn, 1961).

X-ray diffraction analysis is concerned, like polarization microscopy, with matter in the crystalline state. Now, however, the degree of organization needs to be much more perfect than with polarization microscopy.

Not only must molecular chains now lie parallel to each other but they must both be in some sort of register and be regularly packed side by side over an appreciable volume. A beam of X-radiation of wave length about 1 Å passed through such an array of chains will be diffracted just as a beam of light is diffracted by a diffraction grating the lines of which are spaced apart a distance comparable with the wave length of the light. A photographic plate placed in the path of these diffracted rays then records the position of the rays, as illustrated in Figure 8. Such diffraction diagrams are the raw material to which a crystallographer can apply his calculations.

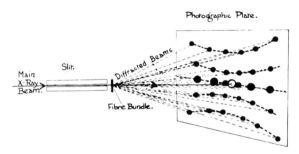

FIG. 8. Diagrammatic representation of the method used in obtaining the x-ray diagram of a piece of wood. The piece of wood is held immediately before a circular slit in a brass rod along which is propagated a beam of X-radiation in such a way that the beam lies normal to the grain. Most of the beam passes through the wood and is held back from the photographic plate beyond by means of a small lead cup in order to prevent complete blackening of the film. The refracted beams are received by the photographic plate, causing blackening of the plate at the appropriate loci as shown.

Each arc on the diagram can be regarded as the result of diffraction from a certain set of planes in the material examined, spaced regularly the same distance d apart (Fig. 9). The diagram in Figure 9 corresponds to a set of cellulose crystallites in wood lying approximately parallel to the longer edge of the page. The arcs along the horizontal central line (the equator) therefore correspond to planes which lie parallel to chain length; those along the vertical line (the meridian) correspond to planes lying perpendicular to chain length; and the obliquely placed arcs correspond to oblique planes. The photograph presents us with a set of d values from which the parameters of the lattice may be calculated, namely (Fig. 10),

1. the closest distances of approach of two chains in the lattice (a = 8.35 Å, c = 7.9 Å),
2. the distance along the chains between two *identically situated* points (b = 10.3 Å),
3. the angles between a and b (= 90°), b and c (= 90°), c and a (= 84°).

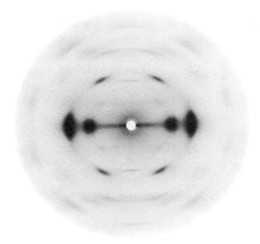

FIG. 9. The X-ray diagram of a bundle of cellulosic fibers, obtained as shown in Figure 8, with the cellulose crystallites lying approximately parallel to the fiber length (and to the longer edge of the page). For further explanation see text.

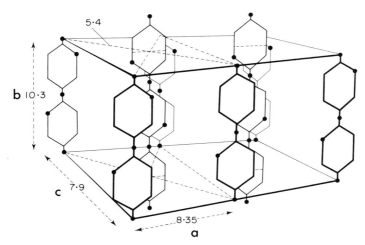

FIG. 10. Diagrammatic representation of the crystal lattice of cellulose after Meyer and Misch (1937). The figure shows two unit cells side by side. The cellobiose units are shown in skeleton outlines only (from Preston, 1952).

The density of cellulose shows that the *unit cell* defined by *a, b,* and *c* must contain two cellobiose units, and consideration of the reflections shows that one must be central and that four others (each shared by four unit cells) must be placed along the four *b* edges. By definition the central

chain must be different from the corner chains and for crystallographic
and other reasons the central chain is placed upside down with reference
to the edge chains and displaced along the *b* axis by a distance *b*/4.

Ideally, the next step is to determine the relative intensity of the scattered beams which produce the arcs on the diagram and to proceed to calculate from these the position of all the atoms in the unit cell. This cannot
be done with cellulose partly because the arcs on the diagram are so few.
We have at the moment to be satisfied with the observation that the length
of the cellobiose unit is close to 10.3 Å (the *b* axis) and that in a scale
model the chains fit nicely together with appropriate hydrogen bonding.
Though the unit cell proposed by Meyer and Misch (1937) (Fig. 10.) may
need correction in detail—for instance, it is still not proved that the central chain in the unit cell is antiparallel—it may therefore be accepted as
in general correct.

The disposition of the reflections in the diagram of Figure 9 is typical
of cellulose, with arcs corresponding to spacings (listed in Meyer and
Mark, 1930) diagnostic of this substance. The spacings vary a little according to the source of the cellulose but, normally, if spacings are observed close to 3.9 Å, 5.4 Å, 6.1 Å (particularly if along the equator in an
oriented diagram), and to 5.15 Å and 2.58 Å (particularly if along the
meridian in an oriented diagram), then it can be accepted that the substance involved is cellulose. This is, however, of little consequence for
our present purpose since in wood the major crystalline substance is always cellulose.

The most important feature for the purposes of wood structure analysis
is that since the arcs at 3.9 Å, 5.4 Å, and 6.1 Å lie along a line perpendicular to chain direction then they define this direction. If, for instance, they
lie along a single line at right angles to the direction of the grain of the
wood then the chains lie more or less longitudinally in the individual
cells. If, on the other hand, they form complete rings (Fig. 11) then the
crystallites in the specimen lie at random in a plane normal to the X-ray
beam.

The common condition is that they are spread into arcs of appreciable
angular width, tailing off into a complete ring of lower intensity (Fig. 12).
Interpretation of such a diagram cannot be made with complete certainty
and it is normally necessary in such cases to call in the help of the polarization microscope.

To follow the deductions which may be made by X-ray analysis alone,
however, we first take note of the diagram in which the arcs are widely
spread (Fig. 13). Each lateral arc is then most intense at either end
and there is no doubt of the interpretation. The cellulose crystallites lie

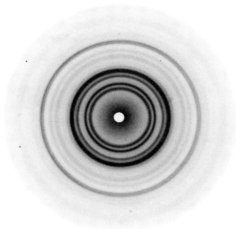

FIG. 11. The X-ray diagram of cellulosic material (*Chaetomorpha melagonium*) in which the cellulose crystallites lie completely at random. The arcs are now spread into complete circles. This is a typical powder diagram of cellulose.

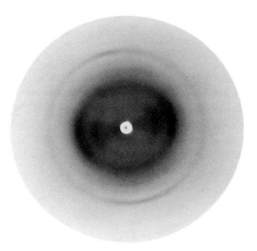

FIG. 12. The X-ray diagram of a piece of wood of *Pseudotsuga*. Note that the lateral arcs are drawn out considerably and can be traced, at low intensity, almost through a complete circle. This is the typical condition for wood.

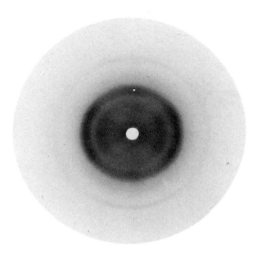

FIG. 13. X-ray diagram of a piece of wood of *Juniperus virginiana*. Note that in this specimen the lateral arcs are drawn out widely and that for each of these lateral arcs the intensity is the highest at each end of the arc. This is typical of specimens in which the helix of the microfibrils is relatively slow.

in a helix around each of the elongated cells in the wood (fiber or tracheid), and the angular distance between the most intense parts of the arc, corrected for the glancing angle, gives a direct measure of the average helical angle in the specimen (Preston, 1946). This has been verified by obtaining diagrams of artificial helices of known angle; Figure 14 presents one such, which may be compared with Figure 13. This presents the best method of determining the angle θ averaged over a fairly large piece of wood (say, 0.5 mm³), since the method is nondestructive and the investigator can then proceed to examine the relevant physical properties of identically the same specimen.

If now we move to specimens in which the spread of the arcs is less and less, there comes a point at which the two intenser ends fuse and each lateral arc is then most intense at the equator. A photometric curve of the X-ray intensity distribution over this arc would then appear, as in Figure 15. It is customary to take the angular distance between the two points of this curve which show 40% of the central maximum intensity as twice the helical angle. This should always be checked against the average angle determined under the polarizing microscope.

If the investigation involves the examination of many samples of wood, then the photographic method of recording is usually too slow. Exposure

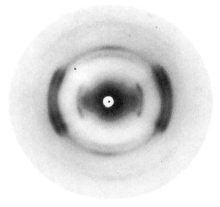

FIG. 14. X-ray diagram of an artificial helix prepared by winding threads of regenerated cellulose around a horse hair as format. The angle of the helical winding to the length of the helix is 30°. Note that the lateral arcs are widely drawn out with the intensity the highest at each end of each arc. This illustrates the genesis of the so-called spiral diagram.

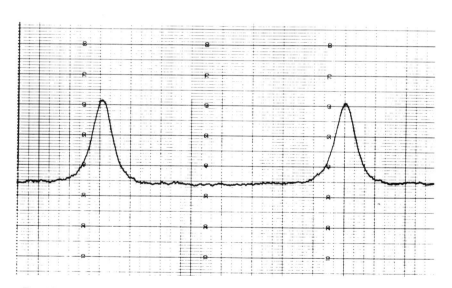

FIG. 15. A scan of the X-ray intensity around a circle on Figure 13 containing the outer-most intense lateral arc. The two peaks correspond to the two lateral arcs and the distance between the two maxima represents therefore 180°. The curve was obtained from a specimen of wood 150 μ thick, using a Geiger counter spectrometer.

of the film will occupy five to ten hours, drying several hours, and scanning on a densitometer perhaps thirty minutes. There is then still some considerable calculation to do since the densitometer reading is not a direct measure of the intensity of the beam. A better, because quicker, method is to record the reflections on a recording Geiger counter X-ray spectrometer. This gives within a few minutes a curve (e.g., Fig. 15) from which the required angle can be read off directly.

It must be remembered that when the cellulose crystallites lie sensibly parallel to the long axis of a cell, as they do in very long fibers such as ramie, the lateral arcs are still considerably spread. This is because the crystallites do not lie exactly parallel to each other, their directions being spread over a finite solid angle. This angular dispersion must be taken into account in assessing the reliability of helical angle measurements by the X-ray method; the angle cannot be regarded even under the best circumstances as reliable to within less than $\pm$ 2°.

X-ray diffraction analysis, unlike polarization microscopy, allows a measure to be made of crystal size. This is possible even with diagrams as presented in Figure 9, if certain assumptions are made. The arcs in the diagram have a finite width along a line drawn radially through each of them. Line broadening of this kind can be due to the small width of the crystallites along the line of the corresponding spacing, and the width of the crystallites can be calculated from the relation deduced by Scherrer:

$$\beta = \frac{0.9\lambda}{t} \sec \theta$$

where β = angular line width at half peak intensity,
t = thickness of crystallite, and θ = glancing angle.

In this way it was originally deduced by Hengstenberg and Mark that the crystallite of cellulose is at least 600 Å long along chain length; the breadth varies according to the source of the cellulose from about 30 Å to about 200 Å, normally with wood about 50 Å. This deduction is valid only if it is known that line broadening is due to crystallite size—there are other explanations. Observations in the electron microscope fortunately do support this assumption.

A better method for the deduction of crystallite size consists in the examination of the low angle scattering near the center of the diagram. This scattering, representing longer spacings, depends upon the size and shape of the crystallites and under appropriate conditions may be used to derive values for these parameters.

Polarization microscopy and X-ray diffraction analysis are the two major methods available for crystal structure investigation in wood. Together they can serve to present a detailed picture of wall architecture—not a direct visual picture such as given by the electron microscope, it is true, but in some ways more reliable and more informative. The techniques are simple, the apparatus relatively cheap, and, within the limits needed for examination of wood, interpretation is relatively straightforward. Apart from their continued use in attempts to define in more detail the crystal structure of wood, these methods are involved—and are being used—in attempts to solve a number of problems.

1. Variations in the measurable properties of wood occur independently of any easily measurable wood characteristic, such as density or proportion of cell types. It is therefore worthwhile to examine the possibility that these variations are associated with differences in wall structure, particularly with differences in the average helical fibril angle. This is especially true if the property is anisotropic. Such properties as swelling and shrinkage, thermal conductivity and diffusivity, tensile strength, Young's Modulus (see references in Preston, 1963; and p. 479, this volume) are all associated with structure though in each case the detailed relations remain to be worked out. In this category also falls the recognition of differences between normal wood and reaction wood.

2. Breakdown of wood by wood-destroying fungi involves attack by the fungus of cellulose or hemicellulose or lignin or all three together, depending on the particular species of fungus involved. Such breakdown is identified and followed most readily, of course, by chemical methods which are no part of our concern here. Nevertheless crystallographic methods can be used with revealing results. Perhaps the most striking are the cavities produced in the S_2 layer of wood fibers and tracheids by soft rot fungi such as *Chaetomium globosum*. These were seen and figured many years ago by Bailey and Vestal in the light microscope. More recently Levi (1964), in a study of the decomposition of beech wood by *Chaetomium* which is mainly chemical in nature, has found advantage in characterizing the nature of the attack by observation of wood at all stages under the polarizing microscope (Fig. 16). This is because those areas from which cellulose has been removed are less birefringent and the typical pointed cavities therefore show up most clearly. Similarly, in the unpublished work of Finlay and Preston, when beech wood is attacked by *Poria monticola* the first part of the cellulose to disappear can be shown by X-ray diffraction methods to be the amorphous or less crystalline parts. Polarization microscopy would no doubt have shown similar effects.

3. Similarly, crystallographic methods supplement chemical methods in the examination of wood degraded in the apparent absence of microorganisms. It has been observed with British soils that if wood is buried under water-logged conditions it becomes slowly degraded in the apparent absence of fungi and bacteria. After about 2,000 years, i.e., for wood buried about Roman times, the wood has the consistency of butter but

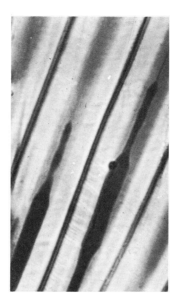

FIG. 16. Photo-micrograph obtained under a polarization microscope with crossed polaroids of a longitudinal section of beech wood during attack by the soft rot fungus *Chaetomium globosum*. Note the prominent cavities produced by the organism, with sharply conical ends. The cavities are distinctly visible within them because the cellulose, the only crystalline compound present, has been removed or disorganized.

some cellulose still remains. Both X-ray analysis and polarization microscopy shows, however, that long before this the wood is no longer crystalline so that the chains have become disordered before breakdown. In other conditions this particular type of breakdown takes much longer. In unpublished work of Chowdhury and Preston, for instance, wood taken from the gem pits in Ceylon, and dated by C^{14} at 25,000 years old, is still birefringent and gives an X-ray diagram even sharper than that of new wood, i.e., amorphous materials have been removed preferentially (Chowdhury and Preston, *unpublished*). Wood dated at 70,000 years, on the other hand, though still containing 34% of its weight as "cellulose," shows no birefringence and no X-ray diagram. This slow change in the cellulose component might well repay study from the point of view of timber preservation.

ELECTRON MICROSCOPY

X-ray diffraction analysis thus produces an image of the structure of matter with a resolving power of the order of 1 Å. It is not, however, by its nature a good method for the delineation of structure of the order of

100 Å in dimension. At the other end of the scale the light microscope can resolve two particles only if they are of the order of 1000 Å apart. This leaves therefore a gap in dimensions between a few Å's and 1000 Å which is closed to either of these two techniques. The electron microscope is important because it bridges this gap so that matter can be observed now by a range of instruments with a resolving power from about 1 Å upwards continuously. All these instruments are necessary for a complete determination of structure. Their respective ranges may be put into perspective by relating them to the X-ray diagram. A photographic film 5 cm in radius, 3 cm from an irradiated specimen, will record spacings down to about 1.5 Å. The information conveyed by an electron microscope whose resolving power is 20 Å is contained in a central circle on the film about 0.25 cm radius; that conveyed by a light microscope is contained in a circle of only 0.005 cm radius.

Soon after the electron microscope became available it was used in an examination of cell walls to show for the first time that the lamellae of a cellulosic wall are not smooth and featureless but consist of a series of long, thin threads called microfibrils lying in an amorphous matrix. It was not long before the microfibrils could be identified specifically as cellulose (Preston and Ripley, 1954) and the observations were generalized to cover the wood cell wall (Hodge and Wardrop, 1950; Wardrop and Dadswell, 1957; Frei et al., 1957; Harada et al., 1958). The microfibrils vary in thickness from species to species of plant, ranging from, say, about 80 Å to about 250 Å, and are about a half as thick as wide (Preston, 1951). The range in width parallels the range in dimension of the crystallites determined by X-ray diffraction analysis, the width of the crystallite being somewhat less than that of the microfibril. In wood the microfibrils are commonly around 100 Å wide. Wherever the appropriate determinations have been found possible, the microfibrils have been shown crystallographically to lie with their flat faces in the planes of the wall as was demonstrated in the unpublished work of Frei and Preston. This has not yet been found possible to test with wood cells but there seems no reason to expect that such uniplanar orientation does not occur there also.

The identification of the microfibrils as the cellulose-containing components has made it possible for the first time to estimate the "purity" of cellulose fraction extracted from walls. Any standard method for the removal of noncellulosic wall constituents leaves behind a mass of microfibrils only, with little sign of amorphous material. This mass constitutes the material known as cellulose. On hydrolysis this material yields not only glucose but other sugars as well, ranging up to 50% of xylose in some plant species (Cronshaw et al., 1958). Even beech wood cellulose contains about 15% of mannan. This has, of course, been recognized for a long time but these smaller amounts of nonglucose sugars have been regarded as a residue of the hemicelluloses not extracted. Now that they are known to be an integral part of the microfibril it is a little difficult to harmonize the use of the word *cellulose* for this material while retaining the same word for the *cellulose* of the crystallographer which contains only glucose residues. In point of fact one small group of plants, all seaweeds, contain microfibrils which hydrolize to give glucose only. These are therefore pure cellulose and it has been proposed that these should be termed *eucellulose* microfibrils (Myers and Preston, 1959). This would contrast them with all other microfibrils which could still be said to contain cellulose, which now however must be defined as a family of polysaccharides containing a large amount of glucose. It has since that time been shown that when microfibrils are broken down into rodlets by the method of Rånby the rodlets themselves hydrolize to give glucose only. On the basis of this and other evidence, the microfibril is considered to be constituted as represented diagramatically in Figure 17, with a central crystalline core of eucellulose. It is this central crystalline core which gives rise

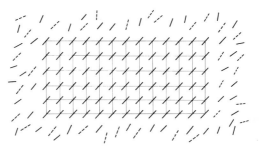

FIG. 17. Diagrammatic representation of the cross section of a cellulose microfibril. The oblique full lines represent the trace in the plane of the page of cellulose chains which pass through the microfibril normal to the page surface. The central area is hatched to represent the central crystalline core. The short dotted lines outside this central crystalline core represent the trace of chains of sugar residues other than glucose.

to the X-ray diagram described above. There is good reason to believe that the anisotropy which gives rise to the effects seen under a polarizing microscope has contributions from the nonmicrofibrillar wall components. In molecular species outside the microfibrils which have unbranched chains, or in which there are considerable lengths of chain unbranched, the chains are considered to lie parallel to each other (p. 191) though not regularly spaced. Comparisons between crystal size as determined by X-ray diffraction and microfibril size as seen in the electron microscope leads to the belief that all microfibrils are built in this way and that the wider microfibrils are not aggregates of smaller microfibrils.

In untreated wood walls the microfibrils are not easily visible; they can be clearly delineated only if the wood has been at least slightly delignified. This should not arouse any concern whether the microfibrils really exist as separate entities in the untreated wall. There are walls of many non-woody plants which show the same phenomenon and also many others in which the microfibrils are perfectly clear in completely untreated material, and it is not to be anticipated that this represents any fundamental structural difference. It harmonizes with the old observation that wood does not normally stain for cellulose unless injured or delignified. The structure is clearly such that wood microfibrils are imbedded in a material (e.g., lignin), which, with the same chemical elements as in cellulose, has the same scattering power. It is this lack of contrast which makes ultra-thin sections virtually useless in wall studies. One might indeed here propound a principle which goes far beyond the bounds of wood studies or even of cell wall organization, and it is this. If logical deduction from secure premises says that a structure must be there, and it is not visible in the electron microscope, the observation and not the deduction must be at fault.

Fortunately, direct observation of the wood cell wall, at the hands largely of Wardrop and his collaborators and of Frei et al. (1959) and Harada et al. (1958), has fully confirmed—though it has also of course extended—the image of structure deduced by the indirect methods of polarization microscopy and X-ray analysis. The details are well known and need not be repeated here. One or two points might, however, be made concerning the structures observed in the electron microscope which had not been—and could not have been—deduced.

The S_1 layer, deduced from polarization microscopy to consist of a single helix of cellulose chain aggregates, has been shown by electron microscopy to contain two helices of about the same pitch but opposite in sign, one often containing more microfibrils than the other (Fig. 18). Reverting to p. 11, we see that the m.e.p. would then lie in the acute angle between these (i.e., towards the transverse plane) but closer to the direction with more abundant microfibrils than towards that with less. There was therefore no way of deducing the presence of the second helix. The low birefringence ($n_\gamma - n_\alpha$) of the S_1 layer (0.02 instead of 0.06) was seen to imply the presence of crystallites with directions lying far from the m.e.p., but again presented no way of assessing the nature of this divergence. It is surely, however, striking that a polarizing microscope, costing nowadays, say, about £400, came so close to the answer given by an electron microscope costing, say £12,000. Indeed the repeated observation that the m.e.p. in S_1 is always, or almost always, helically arranged and not transverse means that one set of microfibrils always dominates, and

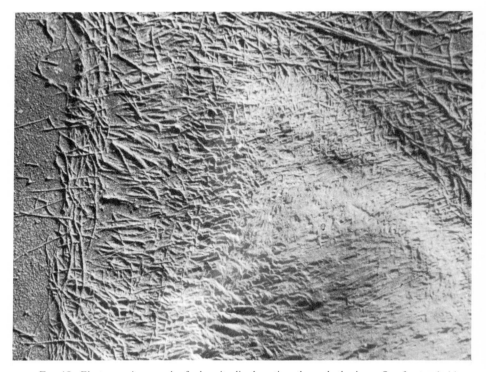

Fig. 18. Electron micrograph of a longitudinal section through the layer S_1 of a tracheid of *Pinus radiata*. X 22,700, shadowed Pd/Au. The edge of the tracheid may be seen on the lefthand side.

defines the dominant set; this cannot easily be done with an electron microscope. It might indeed perhaps be noted that had it not happened that cellulose chains are organized into microfibrils, the electron microscope might have been of less use than the polarizing microscope.

Similarly the S_2 layer is finely lamellated and in each lamella the microfibrils, while steeply helical, lie in a slightly different direction from those in the next. This again could not have been deduced from either polarization microscopy or X-ray analysis.

Finally, it is useful to note, from the point of view of wood formation, that the existence of microfibrils containing crystalline cellulose alone demonstrates something definite about the course of wall synthesis. The cellulose in the microfibrils occurs in a specific lattice symbolized by the Roman numeral I—it is cellulose I. If the constituent chains are separated and then allowed to recrystallize they form a different crystalline compound, cellulose II. It follows that the original microfibril could not have been formed by aggregation of preformed chains. The only alternative seems to be that they are formed by end synthesis through, therefore, an enzyme complex situated at one or both ends. There is indeed strong supporting evidence in favor of such a type of synthesis (Colvin, 1964; Preston, 1964).

INFRARED SPECTROPHOTOMETRY

The three structural research methods dealt with so far thus form, taken together, a unit capable of displaying the architecture of wood cell walls down to very fine detail. There still remain, however, gaps and one of these is the precise configuration of the chains of cellulose in the unit cell. Fortunately a new research tool has been rapidly developed over the past few years which is complementary to the method of X-ray analysis and is already, in the hands of Marchessault (Marchessault and Liang, 1962), closing this gap. This is the method of infrared spectrophotometry, particularly powerful when using polarized radiation.

Infrared spectrophotometry is a method whereby the presence of certain groups of atoms can be recognized, e.g., C—OH, C=O, N—H. These groups of atoms have characteristic vibration frequencies which lie in the infrared region. When, therefore, a beam of infrared radiation of wave length continuous from, say, about 2 μ to about 15 μ is passed through a substance containing these groups, wave lengths of the corresponding frequencies are absorbed. The infrared spectrophotometer is a machine which picks out and records these absorbed frequencies and therefore can detect the presence of these groups. This is already an advantage because this enables a special sort of chemical analysis to be achieved quickly and without necessarily destroying the material. In particular it allows the presence of H bonds to be detected from the changed frequency of the OH groups.

More particularly, and of special importance perhaps in linear macromolecules including cellulose, these groups absorb with different strengths at different azimuths to the plane of the bond joining two atoms, of a plane polarized beam of infrared. The direction of these bonds relative to the chain length can thus in principle be determined. In this way Marchessault has reached tentative conclusions concerning the orientation of the —CH$_2$OH group on the fifth carbon atom on each glucose residue in cellulose. This promises a marked advance towards a realization of the detailed structure of this compound. By similar methods he has shown that in the whole wood the linear xylan chains among the hemicelluloses lie parallel to the cellulose microfibrils, and this is one of the pieces of evidence referred to above.

Bonding in Cell Walls

Infrared spectroscopy should also in principle be useable in detecting the nature of interchain bonding in the walls, about which little is as yet known. It has, indeed, already been argued that certain infrared spectra favor a hemiacetal bond between lignin and some wall polysaccharide, though this is said on chemical gounds to be unlikely. The structure of the wall as delineated today makes it unlikely that a cellulose-to-cellulose bond is frequent. It would seem rather that the bonds may be of the types cellulose-hemicellulose-hemicellulose-cellulose with lignin inserted between any pair. One line of investigation which would seem to be relevant here would be the application of electron spin resonance (ESR). ESR is a powerful tool for the detection of unpaired electrons such as occur momentarily when a bond is broken. The method is too recent to allow any evaluation even of its potential today. It has already been applied, however, in a recent attack on the problem of bond breaking in protein fibers and it could well be that this is a tool of the future in cellulose research. Similarly, nuclear magnetic resonance, by allowing the specification of protons, may well also come to be applied in this field.

Porosity

This leaves to be examined the spaces in the walls of wood cells which are not filled with macromolecular complexes and which indeed have contents that are free to move. Crystal structure investigations are not of much use here since knowledge of the structure of a material is irrelevant to the size of pores passing through it; though crystals can be grown in the pores and their sizes estimated by crystal analysis or otherwise (Fig. 19), there is no guarantee that the size of the crystal gives the size of the pore or that the size is too small or too large. Electron microscopy as so far practiced is not of much use either. By the time a wall element can be looked at, it is dessicated and collapsed and this, together with the huge depth of focus of the microscope, superposing images in all planes one over the other, makes it impossible to be sure of the size of intermicellar spaces. In any case these appear as spaces only because they contain no recognizable structure; they may still contain amorphous solid material. Even with the large "pores" through the membrane of bordered pits, examined mostly in conifers, there is still some controversy as to whether the appearance in the electron microscope proves the absence of a membrane across them. There is perhaps some hope in the comparatively new method of negative staining, but I am not sure if this has yet been tried.

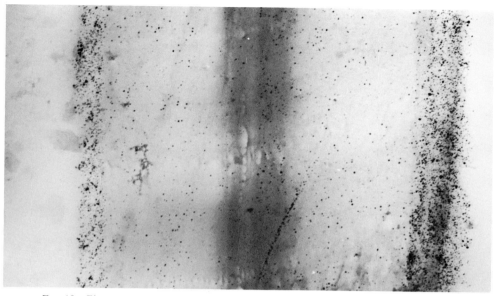

FIG. 19. Electron micrograph of a transverse section of the double wall between two tracheids of Sitka Spruce stained with silver. Notice the innumerable black granules in the cell wall, particularly crowded towards the inner faces of the wall; these are silver grains presumably representing in location the position of pores in the wall. X 14,000.

There seems therefore, at the moment, no method available for the visual estimation of pore size in wood cell walls. Even if there were, it is difficult to imagine how such a method could be used for the quantitative estimation of the frequency distribution of pore size and pore length, such as is required for problems involving movement of liquids through wood. There is, therefore, no alternative to indirect methods such as observation of flow rates through wood and setting up and testing flow equations. These methods have already been used extensively by Stamm but there is no doubt that a good deal more needs to be done.

There seem to be basically two difficulties in this approach. First, wood is extremely heterocapillary with pores ranging in size from, say, 50 Å to, say, 0.1 mm (1,000,000 Å) in radius and, say, 1 μ to 1 cm in length. This means that flow equations are complex and usually involve assumptions or simplifications which are from the outset suspect. Second, it seems highly likely that the capillaries are unstable and will change diameter as the permeating liquid is changes; in particular they will be sensitive to the water balance.

For this reason there is a marked tendency to use dry wood permeated by a rare gas in studying problems of flow. This provides a satisfying physical approach and has given average values for pore size at about the size of the pores in pit membranes. It seems hardly likely that these values are applicable to flow of liquids and particularly of water.

The major problem at the moment is whether most of the water flowing through wood does so via the large pores in pit membranes or whether an appreciable part of it passes along the (more numerous though finer) wall capillaries. The studies which have been made on this problem have recently been reviewed by Jensen *et al.* (1960). The original observation by Bailey (1913) that when carbon black suspensions are perfused through wood the particles are accumulated in the pit chambers has been repeatedly confirmed (Buro and Buro, 1959; Wardrop and Davies, 1961; Côté and Krahmer, 1962) and is taken to imply that the major flow path lies through pit membranes. While the interpretations reached by these workers seem reasonable, they cannot be regarded as final until it has been proved that the pores in pit membranes are real pores and not closed off by a membrane and until rational flow formulae have been developed for all three definitive directions in wood.

REFERENCES

Bailey, I. W. (1913) "The preservative treatment of wood. II. The structure of the pit membranes in the tracheids of conifers, and its relation to the penetration of gases, liquids and finely divided solids into green and seasoned wood." *Forestry Quarterly* 11:12–20.

Bloss, F. D. (1961) *Introduction to the methods of optical crystallography.* Prentice Hall, Englewood Cliffs, N.J.

Bunn, C. W. (1961) *Chemical Crystallography.* Oxford University Press, New York.

Buro, A., and Buro, E. A. (1959) "Beitrag zur Kenntnis der Eindringwege der Flüssigkeiten in Kiefernholz." *Holzforschung* 13:71–77.

Burri, C. (1950) *Das Polarisationsmikroskop.* Birkhaüser, Basel.

Colvin, J. Ross (1964) "The biosynthesis of cellulose." In *The Formation of Wood in Forest Trees* (M. H. Zimmermann, ed.), pp. 189–201. Academic Press, New York.

Côté, W. A., and Krahmer, R. L. (1962) "The permeability of coniferous pits demonstrated by electron microscopy." *Tappi* 45:119–122.

Cronshaw, J., Myers, A., and Preston, R. D. (1958) "A chemical investigation of the cell walls of some marine algae." *Biochim. Biophys. Acta* 27:89–103.

Frei, Eva, Preston R. D., and Ripley, G. W. (1957) "The fine structure of the walls of conifer tracheids VI. Electron microscope investigations of sections." *J. Exp. Botany* 8:139–146.

Frey-Wyssling, A. (1937) "Ueber die röntgenometrische Vermessung der submikroskopischen Raüme in Gerüstsubstanzen." *Protoplasma* 27:372–411.

Harada, H., Myazaki, Y., and Wakashima, T. (1958) "Electronmicroscopic investigation on the cell wall structure of wood." Bulletin of the Govt. Forest Experiment Station, No. 104 (Meguro, Tokyo, Japan).

Hartshorne, N. H., and Stuart, M. J. (1960) *Crystals and the Polarizing Microscope.* Arnold, London.

Hodge, A. J., and Wardrop, A. B. (1950) "Electron microscope investigation of the cell wall organisation of conifer tracheids and conifer cambium." *Australian J. Sci. Res.* 3:265–269.

Jensen, W., Fogelberg, B. C., and Johanson, M. (1960) "Use of radioactive tracers to follow path of working liquors into wood." *Paperi Puu* 42:393–400.

Levi, M. P. (1964) Ph.D. Thesis, University of Leeds, England.

Marchessault, R. H., and Liang, C. Y. (1962) "The infrared spectra of crystalline polysaccharides. VIII. Xylans." *J. Polymer Sci.* 59:357–378.

Meyer, K. H., and Mark, H. (1930) *Der Aufbau der Hochpolymeren Organischen Naturstoffe.* Akademische Verlagsgesellschaft M.B.H., Leipzig.

———, and Misch, L. (1937) "Positions des atomes dans le nouveau modele spatial de la cellulose." *Helv. Chim. Acta* 20:232–244.

Myers, A., and Preston, R. D. (1959) "Fine structure in the red algae. II. The structure of the cell wall in *Rhodymenia palmata.*" *Proc. Roy. Soc. (London), Ser.* 150:447–455, 456–459.

Preston, R. D. (1946) "The fine structure of the wall of the conifer tracheid. I. The X-ray diagram of conifer wood." *Proc. Roy. Soc. (London), Ser. B* 133:327–348.

——— (1947) "The fine structure of the walls of the conifer tracheid. II. Optical properties of dissected cells in *Pinus insignis.*" *Proc. Roy. Soc. (London), Ser. B* 134:202–218.

——— (1950) "Fibrillar units in the structure of native cellulose." In *The Size and Shape Factor in Colloidal Systems.* Discussions of the Faraday Society No. 11, p. 165. Faraday Society, Aberdeen.

——— (1952) *The Molecular Architecture of Plant Cell Walls.* Chapman and Hall, London.

——— (1963) "Observed fine structure in plant fibres." In *Fibre Science* (J. W. S. Hearle and R. H. Peters, ed.), Chapter 7. Butterworths, London.

——— (1964) "Structural and mechanical aspects of plant cell walls with particular reference to synthesis and growth." In *The Formation of Wood in Forest Trees* (M. H. Zimmermann, ed.), pp. 169–188. Academic Press, New York.

——— and Ripley, G. W. (1954) "Electron diffraction diagrams of cellulose microfibrils in *Valonia.*" *Nature* 174:76

——— and Singh, K. (1952) "The fine structure of bamboo fibres." *J. Exp. Botany* 3:162–169.

Wardrop, A. B., and Dadswell, H. E. (1957) "Variations in the cell wall organization of tracheids and fibres." *Holzforschung* 11:33–41.

——— and Davies, G. W. (1961) "Some anatomical factors relating to the penetration of water in xylem of gymnosperms." *Australian J. Botany* 6:96–102.

——— and Preston, R. D. (1951) "The submicroscopic organisation of the cell wall in conifer tracheids and wood fibres." *J. Exp. Botany* 2:20–30.

PART I

Wood Cells—*Their Formation, Growth, and Differentiation*

On the Anatomy of the Woody Plant

KATHERINE ESAU

Department of Biological Sciences
University of California, Santa Barbara

The purpose of this presentation is not to review the familiar features of tree anatomy but to focus attention on matters that either continue to cause controversy or merit more consideration than they receive in discussions of the anatomy of the seed plant. I am referring here to seed plants in general because most of the topics to be discussed pertain to both the woody and the herbaceous plants. The chief distinction between the woody and the herbaceous dicotyledons is largely quantitative; the herbaceous species have less secondary growth.

The question about the relationship between the woody and the herbaceous plant, especially with regard to their phylogeny, is still controversial. This subject is concisely reviewed by Metcalfe and Chalk (1950, pp. xxxii-xxxix). In concluding the discussion the authors suggest that some herbaceous plants have evolved from arboreal ancestors by reduction of cambial activity, but others may have had herbaceous ancestors which did not include any arboreal or woody forms. Metcalfe and Chalk's discussion does not include reference to the data from xylem studies that have a bearing on the phylogeny of herbaceous plants. According to these data, vessels of dicotyledons arose in the woody plants— and subsequently became specialized—beginning with the secondary xylem, then in succession in the late and the early metaxylem and the protoxylem (Cheadle, 1956). Research on the phylogeny of xylem has clarified many misconceptions regarding the origin of dicotyledonous herbs. But the study of herbs is still far from complete.

LEAF TRACES

The familiar descriptions of the primary vascular system in the shoot as composed of bundles, or fascicles, separated by interfascicular regions and leaf gaps, give a highly simplified account of the structure of this system. If one examines the woody shoots in the primary state of growth, or at least before much secondary growth has occurred, he can observe

35

conspicuous variations in the pattern formed by the vascular bundles in
transections (Figs. 1, 2). Basically these variations are referable to the
form, number, and size of the bundles, and to their relations to the leaves.
In Figure 1 (*Trochodendron*, Trochodendraceae) is an example of a shoot
in which each leaf has 5 to 7 bundles, or traces (Bailey and Nast, 1945),
whereas Figure 2 (*Cinnamomum*, Lauraceae) shows one with a single trace
to a leaf (Sinnott, 1914). In *Trochodendron* the bundles are much narrower and more discrete than those in *Cinnamomum*. In the latter the leaf
traces are extended tangentially and therefore form an apparently continuous cylinder close to the apical meristem.

The relation between the leaves and the units of the vascular system in
the stem is one of the fundamental aspects in the interpretation of the
morphology of the shoot of a fern or a seed plant, herbaceous or woody.
Considerable space is devoted in the older literature to the question as to
whether the vascular system of these plants consists wholly of leaf traces
or whether it contains vascular tissue pertaining to the stem; and this
question has been raised anew in the modern literature on morphogenesis
(cf. Wardlaw, 1952). In some experiments, dealing mainly with ferns, leaf
primordia were prevented from developing and, as a result, the vascular
system of the axis became reduced either to a medullated or nonmedul-
lated column lacking extensions corresponding to leaf traces. This development was interpreted as a fundamental change proving that the stele
is truly a cauline structure and not merely a collection of decurrent leaf
traces (Wetmore and Wardlaw, 1951, p. 273).

The results of defoliation can be interpreted in another way. One
should consider the question whether the leaf traces and the stem bundles
are indeed distinct entities morphologically. The commonly accepted
concept that early plants were leafless axes and that the leaves of the fern
and the seed plant arose from branches makes the leafy shoot a unit structure and the division into leaf and stem an arbitrary matter. The same
conclusion may be arrived at by reference to the ontogeny and the mature
structure.

The organization of the vascular system reflects this unity of stem and
leaf. In the stem of a lower plant having very small leaves or none, as well
as in the root, the vascular system differentiates as an independent axial
system. In the leafy shoot of a fern or a seed plant the vascular system of
the stem differentiates in relation to the leaves. In other words, the leaves
influence the differentiation of the vascular system of the stem. The presence of bundles recognizable as leaf traces is an expression of this influence. If leaf development is reduced or suppressed, experimentally or
normally (leafless scapes, rhizomes), the influence of the leaf diminishes or
is eliminated. The experiments on destruction of the prospective leaves

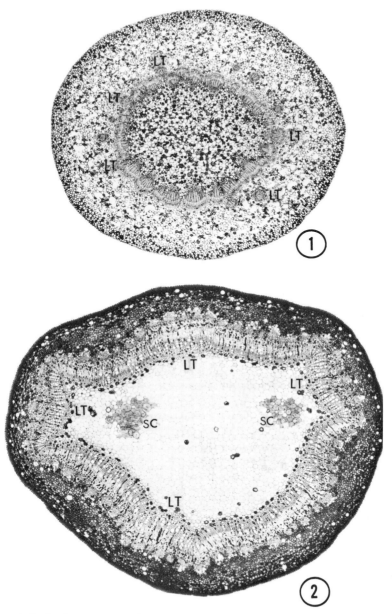

FIGS. 1–2. Leaf-trace concept in stem structure. Fig. 1. One-year-old *Trochodendron aralioides* stem in transection. Beginning of secondary growth. Leaf traces (some are marked LT) and leaf-trace sympodia constitute the primary vascular system. Fig. 2. One-year-old *Cinnamomum camphora* stem in transection. Beginning of secondary growth. Wide leaf traces (LT) and leaf-trace sympodia make the primary vascular system appear continuous. Groups of sclereids at SC. Fig. 1, X 22; Fig. 2, X 32.

teach us this much and no more. No fundamental change is involved and the discussion whether the stem has its own vascular tissue or not is futile. Vascular tissue is present in the stem and in the leaf and the two are associated developmentally and physiologically. The leaf traces "belong" to the leaf as much as they do to the stem.

The concept of the leaf trace is not merely of theoretical interest. If it is not used literally, to mean that the leaf trace pertains only to the leaf, the concept is most useful for interpreting the primary vascular differentiation and its relation to the secondary growth. The leaf traces form characteristic patterns of interconnections that can be expressed in terms of designations used in discussions of phyllotaxis. Reference to leaf traces helps one to understand the variation in the composition of the primary xylem that faces the pith. The leaf traces to the nearest leaves (LT in Figure 2) contain protoxylem (Fig. 6); in the sympodia of leaf traces (stem bundles of some authors) metaxylem only represents the primary xylem (Fig. 16). Similarly, the understanding of leaf-trace interrelations enables one to explain the distribution of the primary phloem and its varied associations with the xylem along the circumference of the stem (O'Neill, 1961).

As is well known, the protoxylem of leaf traces of normally elongating shoots matures in stem parts that have not yet elongated, and its tracheary elements are destroyed during the elongation of the internodes. The earliest elements are stretched and crushed (Fig. 5, arrows). The later ones are stretched but may not be completely crushed (Fig. 6, arrows and lower T's). These changes obscure the nature of the tissue and cause the protoxylem often to remain unrecognized in older stems. A close inspection, however, reveals the difference between the regions containing protoxylem (Fig. 6) and those where metaxylem is next to the pith (Fig. 16).

THE DELIMITATION OF THE VASCULAR REGION

Consideration of the primary vascular system is important with regard to another concept pertinent to the anatomy of the woody plant, the stele. Despite the general familiarity of plant anatomists with this term, it is rarely used in its original connotation, namely, as the central column of vascular and associated nonvascular tissues. In most modern papers the term is used as a substitute for the vascular system.

The stelar theory is closely associated with the concept of the pericycle, originally defined as ground tissue delimiting the stele from the cortex. Intensification of research on primary phloem since the thirties of this century (cf. Blyth, 1958 and Esau, 1950) has brought the recognition that in the majority of dicotyledons the so-called pericycle is primary phloem

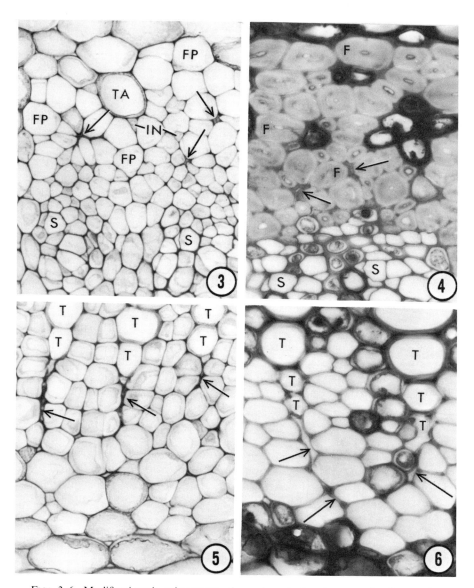

FIGS. 3–6. Modifications in primary vascular regions during stem growth. Transections from *Tilia* stem in first (Figs. 3, 5) and second (Figs. 4, 6) years of growth. Fig. 3. Fiber primordia (FP) with crushed sieve elements (arrows) among them. Ends of intrusively growing fiber primordia at IN, sieve tubes at S, tannin cell at TA. Fig. 4. Mature fibers (F) above, functioning phloem with sieve tubes (S) below. Arrows, crushed cells. Figs. 5 and 6. Protoxylem regions with some tracheary elements still open (T), others crushed or pulled apart (arrows). The secondary walls in the tracheary elements in Figure 5 were retouched. All, X 670.

modified during the later stages of stem development. The fibers that commonly occur on the periphery of the vascular region are protophloem fibers.

Figure 3 shows the early stage of development of protophloem fibers in *Tilia*. The earliest sieve tubes have been crushed (arrows) and the fiber primordia (FP) are enlarged. The young fibers also have undergone intrusive growth as indicated by the small transectional views of cells with somewhat dense cytoplasm (IN). In Figure 4 the fibers are mature; they have fully developed secondary walls. The remnants of crushed phloem elements are not discernible in the oldest phloem but may be recognized in the subjacent tissue (Fig. 4, arrows).

Thus the protophloem and protoxylem are profoundly modified in older stems (Figs. 4,6) and require developmental studies to reveal their identity. But despite their short functional life they cannot be ignored in discussions of anatomical and physiological aspects of the structure of the woody plant because they constitute the conducting tissues of the youngest parts of the plant.

The term pericycle was introduced by reference to the stem of *Cucurbita* in which the cylinder of sclerenchyma surrounding the vascular region arises outside the phloem, as it does in the stem of *Aristolochia* (Fig. 9). If the term pericycle is to be maintained for the anatomic description of stems, *Cucurbita* and *Aristolochia* may be said to have such a region (as originally defined) since the starch sheath, which is one of the manifestations of endodermis, occurs outside these fibers (Fig. 9, EN).

The endodermis also plays an important role in discussions regarding the stele. This tissue region was originally given a morphological meaning and was considered indispensable for the development of the stelar theory. As is well known, the manifestations of this layer are varied. The endodermis may have a special wall structure or it may be a starch sheath. The intensive studies of Van Fleet (1961) have made it possible to put the significance of the endodermis in proper perspective. The endodermis is a physiological limit between the vascular and nonvascular tissues in which the substances originating in the vascular tissues react with those from the cortex—two biochemically distinct tissue regions. These reactions make possible a histochemical recognition of this layer whether or not it shows morphologic differentiation. Similar reactions occur in all parts of the plant wherever vascular and nonvascular tissues are contiguous.

CAMBIAL SECONDARY GROWTH

Our notions about secondary growth are derived chiefly from studies of conifers and dicotyledons of the temperate zone. This familiar type of secondary growth is classified as normal in contrast to the less familiar type, the anomalous. Yet in the tropical countries anomalous formations are common among the dicotyledons and the monocotyledons. Obaton (1960), for example, found anomalous structure in 108 species of woody lianas belonging to 21 different families of dicotyledons growing in Western Africa. The concentration of studies on a certain group of plants apparently has caused the development of the concepts of normal and anomalous types of growth.

Some of the genera studied by Obaton were not described before and in some the type of anomaly was new. She recognized seven types of anomalous growth. Usually the anomalous growth resulted from irregular functioning of the cambium and was often followed by considerable development of parenchyma.

Figures 7-11 gives examples of anomalous secondary growth. *Leptadenia spartium* (Asclepiadaceae; Fig. 7) is a shrub with included phloem (PH2), that is, phloem which is periodically formed by the cambium on the side of the xylem. A continuous vascular cambium on the periphery of the xylem produces phloem in normal position (PH1). *Tiliacora acuminata* (Menispermaceae; Fig. 8) is a vine with successive layers of cambia that produce strands combining xylem and phloem (PH) and the intervening ground tissue. Within the bundles the cambium is located between the xylem and the phloem. This type of anomaly is rather familiar since it occurs in our Amaranthaceae and Chenopodiaceae (sugar beet). *Aristolochia* (Aristolochiaceae; Fig. 9) is sometimes described as anomalous chiefly because of its wide rays, the crushing of rays, and the type of dilatation growth (see below).

Figures 10-13 illustrate the remarkable resemblance between *Bougainvillea lateritia* (Nyctaginaceae; Figs. 10, 11), a dicotyledon vine, and *Dracaena ensifolia* (Agavaceae; Figs. 12, 13), a monocotyledon, with regard to primary and secondary organization. In both the primary vascular bundles have a scattered arrangement (Fig. 11 and Fig. 13, lower half), the secondary tissues consist of bundles imbedded in ground tissue, and the cambium produces no phloem to the outside. But in *Dracaena* the secondary bundles are amphivasal, whereas they are collateral and have some cambium in *Bougainvillea*.

DILATATION GROWTH

We tend to identify secondary growth with cambial activity (vascular cambium and phellogen). But other types of growth phenomena often occur in the plant body after it has completed its primary extension (internodal elongation in shoots). One cannot properly call primary the dilata-

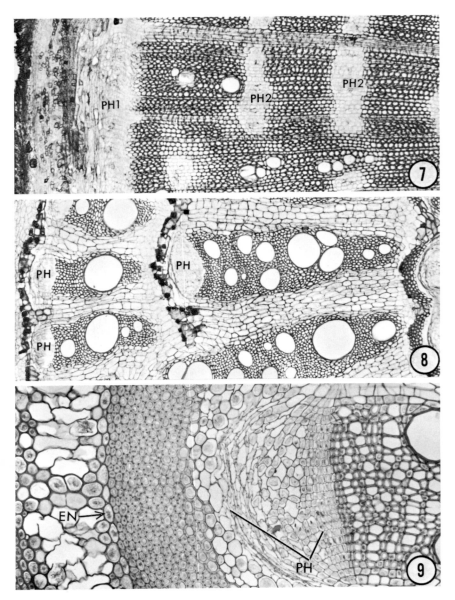

Figs. 7–9. Secondary growth. Fig. 7. *Leptadenia spartium*, stem transection. Cambium forms secondary phloem toward outside (PH1), xylem and included phloem (PH2) toward the inside. Fig. 8. *Tiliacora acuminata*, stem transection. Separate cambia produce successive layers of collateral vascular bundles, with phloem at PH, imbedded in ground tissue. Fig. 9. *Aristolochia*, stem transection, first year of growth. Part of continuous cylinder of sclerenchyma at the right of endodermis (EN), phloem at PH, crushed to the left. Figs. 7, 8, X 50; Fig. 9, X 168.

42

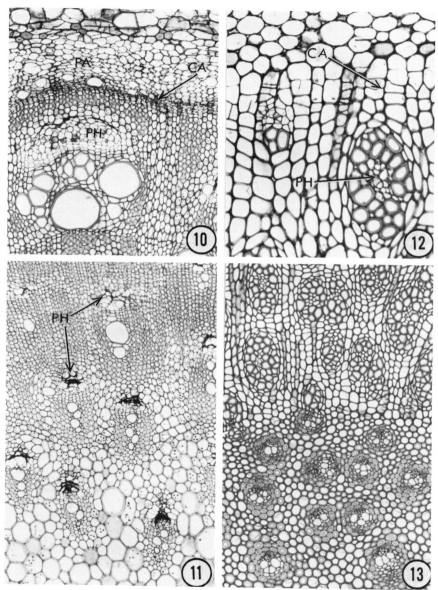

FIGS. 10–13. Secondary growth. Figs. 10, 11. *Bougainvillea lateritia*, stem transections, Fig. 10 in cambial region (CA) and Fig. 11 at margin of primary (below) and secondary (above) growth. Parenchyma at PA, phloem at PH. Figs. 12, 13. *Dracaena ensifolia*, stem transections, Fig. 12 in cambial region (CA) and Fig. 13 at margin of primary (below) and secondary (above) growth. Phloem (PH) surrounded by xylem (Fig. 12), amphivasal bundle. Fig. 10, X 84; Fig. 11, X 60; Fig. 12, X 140; Fig. 13, X 60.

tion growth that affects the phloem and the cortex of many dicotyledons and the proliferation of parenchyma that occurs in some fleshy storage organs, often in combination with anomalous secondary growth. Tomlinson (1961) has called attention to noncambial growth in thickness of palms and termed it diffuse secondary growth.

Dilatation of stems and roots outside the vascular cambium is also noncambial secondary growth but diffuse would not be an entirely proper term for it. It may be called intercalary secondary growth as contrasted with cambial secondary growth.

Figure 14 illustrates the familiar example of dilatation growth of the phloem rays of *Tilia* in a later stage of development, Figure 15 in an early stage. Cells of a biseriate ray (Fig. 15, R) have enlarged tangentially and divided anticlinally. In later stages, divisions may continue in the median position of the ray giving the impression of a localized meristem (Fig. 14, arrows). Such localization of divisions concerned with dilatation of rays may be quite pronounced (Schneider, 1955). Dilatation may affect phloem parenchyma also (Chattaway, 1955).

The dilatation growth in *Aristolochia* is highly complex because it is preceded by a rupture of the initially continuous cylinder of sclerenchyma located outside the phloem (Fig. 9). Eventually, usually beginning in the second year, this cylinder is fragmented and the gaps filled with parenchyma in which the cells undergo anticlinal divisions (Fig. 17, left).

The dilatation parenchyma in *Aristolochia* is derived from parenchyma bordering the sclerenchyma cylinder on the inside and the outside. It fills the ruptures by intrusive growth and then proliferates. A perusal of the literature indicates that this information dates back to De Bary (1884) and that apparently no later studies were carried out to substantiate the interpretation. In seeing only the advanced stages of dilatation (Fig. 17) it is difficult to accept the invasion concept but earlier stages do indeed furnish proof of intrusive growth. Such growth begins when the crack between sclerenchyma cells is barely perceptible (Fig. 19, arrow). The sclerenchyma cells separate along the middle lamella and the crack steadily enlarges. The invading part of the cell becomes longer and then divides periclinally. The result is the establishment of a row of cells as at X in Figure 17. Another evidence of invasion is the nonconformity sometimes perceptible in the wall contacts between the intruding cells and the scler-

FIGS. 14–16. Secondary modifications in stems. Transections of *Tilia* stem, four-year-old (Fig. 14) and one-year-old (Figs. 15, 16). Dilatation of phloem rays in advanced (Fig. 14) and early (Fig. 15) stages. Arrows in Fig. 14, rows of recently divided cells. Fibers at F, rays at R, xylem at X. Fig. 16. Primary xylem region lacking protoxylem. No crushing of tracheary elements (T). Fig. 14, X 73; Fig. 15, X 560; Fig. 16, X 670.

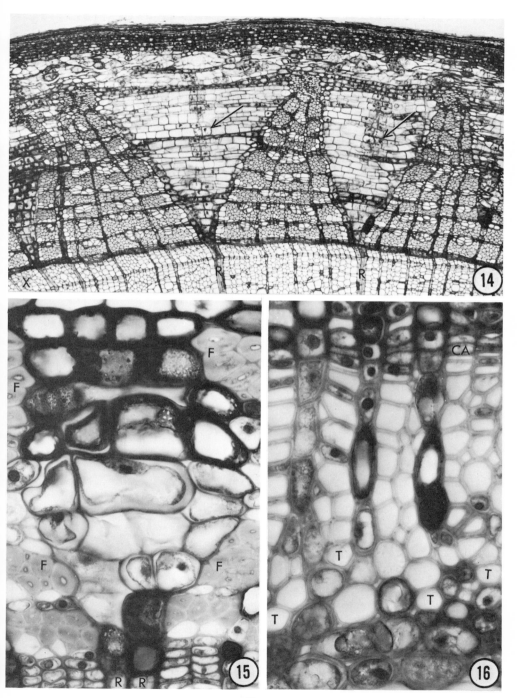

45

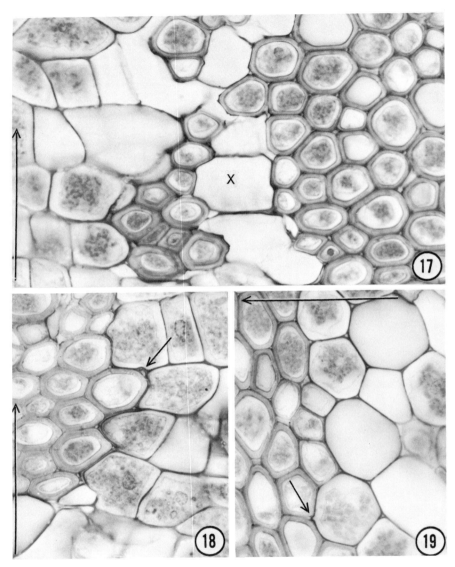

FIGS. 17–19. Dilatation in second year of growth in stem of *Aristolochia* as seen in transections. Fig. 17. Part of sclerenchyma cylinder with dilatation parenchyma (left) having undergone anticlinal divisions. At X row of ontogenetically related cells of dilatation parenchyma. Fig. 18. Margin between sclerenchyma (left) and dilatation parenchyma (right) with remains of old middle lamella between the two. Short arrow, fold in middle lamella. Fig. 19. Margin between sclerenchyma and subjacent parenchyma showing contact between ontogenetically related cells. Short arrow, beginning of intrusive growth. Long arrows are directed toward stem periphery. All, X 670.

46

enchyma. Figure 19 shows a normal contiguity between parenchyma and sclerenchyma as they develop side by side from meristematic tissue. Figure 18, on the other hand, shows the contact established between the dilatation parenchyma and the sclerenchyma. The parenchyma is applied against the old middle lamella (probably compound middle lamella). At arrow in Figure 18 a piece of the middle lamella became bent.

The alternative to intrusive growth would be removal of secondary walls in the sclerenchyma and resumption of growth by the cells. The sclerenchyma cells in *Aristolochia* are living and their ability to remove secondary walls cannot be ruled out because this type of dedifferentiation has been reported in several plants in connection with wound healing (Bloch, 1941). But signs of dedifferentiation of sclerenchyma were not detected in any of the available material of *Aristolochia*.

The panels of dilatation parenchyma in this vine are at least several millimeters high, and before they widen they resemble rays in tangential sections. Some of these parenchyma cells differentiate into sclereids.

Cellular Adjustments during Growth

The adjustments resulting from dilatation growth appear rather spectacular. More subtle adjustments occur throughout the growth and differentiation of plant tissues. Some of the common examples are differential elongation and increase in width of cells. A common type of elongation is one involving no intrusive growth. A cell can thus elongate if the adjacent cells continue to divide and enlarge between divisions. Elongation by intrusive growth has received more attention and anatomists agree that commonly such elongation occurs at the tips of the cells and involves a separation of cells in front of the invading tip. This separation occurs along the middle lamella but the causal mechanism of this separation is apparently not known.

Intrusive growth also characterizes the enlargement of wide vessels in the xylem. The disjunctive tracheids and parenchyma cells develop in response to such growth. The enlarging vessel forces the adjacent cells apart (Fig. 20, arrow, disjunction of cells in row 1). The disjoined cells may remain partially attached to one another and at these points the cells continue to grow and form protuberances.

The expansion of vessels involves another type of adjustment; cessation of production of new cells in one or more rows in the cambium behind the vessel. In Figure 20, left, rows 2 and 3 appear to have had a reduction in rate of cell production to make room for the expanding vessel. To the right, only row 2 seems to have reduced its activity whereas rows 1 and 3

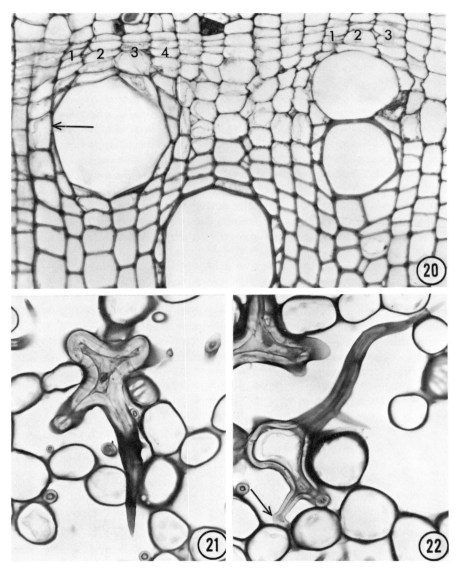

FIGS. 20–22. Growth adjustments in cell differentiation. Fig. 20. Differentiating xylem in transection of stem of *Boehmeria nivea*. Cellular adjustments in relation to vessel differentiation. Numbers, rows of cells involved in adjustments. Arrow, disjunction of cells in row 1. Figs. 21 and 22. Sclereids from transection of stem of *Trochodendron aralioides* showing results of intrusive growth: penetration between cells and diversion from straight path (Fig. 22, arrow). Fig. 20, X 350; Figs. 21, 22, X 375.

were only somewhat displaced. The vessels to the right are narrower than those to the left.

More remarkable adjustments occur when sclereids, especially astroclereids (Figs. 21, 22), embark upon their highly individualistic growth. In the meristematic state the sclereid primordia do not differ from contiguous cells, but during the enlargement they grow much faster than their neighbors, form protuberances ("arms") in all directions, invade intercellular spaces, and intrude between cells (Fig. 21). If they meet an obstacle in the form of a wall, they change their direction of growth (Fig. 22, arrow). Sclereids may push between the epidermal cells and reach the cuticle or protrude between stomata (Foster, 1947).

Students of morphogenesis stress that the plant is organized and aim to uncover the basis of this organization. Some factors having morphogenetic effects have been disclosed, notably those hormonal in nature. Developmental anatomists discuss polar distribution of hormones, the establishment of gradients in relation to anatomic barriers, and differential distributions of cell contents during cytokinesis. But the ultimate origin of patterns in plant development still eludes the investigator. The ability of the cell to produce a whole plant when isolated from the tissue complex in which it has developed in the plant (Steward *et al.*, 1964) suggests that, within the plant, the cells are under the control of some unknown mechanism that synchronizes various processes and establishes positional relations among cells. Even with regard to such apparently individualistic cells as the sclereid positional relation in differentiation has been suggested (Foard, 1959). Many aspects at various cellular and subcellular levels must continue to be investigated for a more complete understanding of the plant as a whole organism.

REFERENCES

Bailey, I. W., and Nast, C. G. (1945) "Morphology and relationship of *Trochodendron* and *Tetracentron.* I. Stem, root, and leaf." *J. Arnold Arboretum* 26:143–154.

Bloch, Robert (1941) "Wound healing in higher plants." *Botan. Rev.* 7:110–146.

Blyth, Amélie (1958) "Origin of primary extraxylary fibers in dicotyledons." *Univ. Calif. (Berkeley) Publ. Botany*, 30:145–232.

Chattaway, M. M. (1955) "The anatomy of bark. IV. Peppermints, boxes, ironbarks, and other eucalypts with cracked and furrowed barks." *Australian J. Botany* 3:170–176.

Cheadle, V. I. (1956) "Research on phloem and xylem—progress in fifty years." *Am. J. Botany* 43:719–731.

De Bary, A. (1884) *Comparative Anatomy of the Vegetative Organs of the Phanerogams and Ferns.* (Translated from the German.) Clarendon Press, Oxford University Press.

Esau, Katherine (1950) "Development and structure of the phloem tissue. II." *Botan. Rev.* 16:67–114.

50 K. ESAU

Foard, D. E. (1959) "Pattern and control of sclereid formation in the leaf of *Camellia japonica.*" *Nature* (London) 184:1663–1664.

Foster, A. S. (1947) "Structure and ontogeny of the terminal sclereids of *Mouriria Huberi* Cogn." *Am. J. Botany* 34:501–514.

Metcalfe, C. R., and Chalk, L. (1950) *Anatomy of the Dicotyledons.* Vol. 1. Clarendon Press, Oxford University Press.

Obaton, Madeleine (1960) "Les lianes ligneuses a structure anormale des forêts denses d'Afrique occidentale." *Ann. Sci. Nat. Botan. Biol. Végétale,* Ser. 12, 1:1–220.

O'Neill, T. B. (1961) "Primary vascular organization of *Lupinus* shoot." *Botan. Gaz.* 123:1–9.

Schneider, Henry (1955) "Ontogeny of lemon tree bark." *Amer. J. Botany* 42:893–905.

Sinnott, E. W. (1914) "The anatomy of the node as an aid in the classification of angiosperms." *Am. J. Botany* 1:303–322.

Steward, F. C., with Mapes, M. O., Kent, A. E., and Holsten, R. D. (1964) "Growth and development of cultured plant cells." *Science* 143:20–27.

Tomlinson, P. B. (1961) *Anatomy of the Monocotyledons. II. Palmae.* Clarendon Press, Oxford University Press.

Van Fleet, D. S. (1961) "Histochemistry and function of the endodermis." *Botan. Rev.* 27:165–220.

Wardlaw, C. W. (1952) *Phylogeny and Morphogenesis.* Macmillan, London.

Wetmore, R. H., and Wardlaw, C. W. (1951) "Experimental morphogenesis in vascular plants." *Ann. Rev. Plant Physiol.* 2:269–292.

Growth Theories and the Development
of the Cell Wall

KURT MÜHLETHALER

Electron Microscopy Laboratory,
Swiss Federal Institute of Technology, Zürich

It has long been known that cell walls are deposited by intussusceptional and appositional growth. At first the primary wall is laid down; it contains a matrix of polyuronides and hemicellulose strengthened by a loose network of cellulose microfibrils. During cell growth this framework expands and is strengthened by the addition of new cellulose fibrils. In contrast to the secondary wall, the cellulose threads are interwoven in a fabric-like manner. In contradiction to older views, it can be shown that the deposition of the secondary wall begins before the cell has reached its final size. At short intervals a large number of individual lamellae, in which the cellulose fibrils are arranged in a parallel manner, are deposited.

Many processes involved in cell wall growth still cannot be explained with the help of either the light or the electron microscope. For instance, there is much discussion as to the extent of protoplasmic involvement in wall formation. Also it cannot be determined if the synthesis of the wall material takes place in the outer region of the protoplasm, at the surface of the plasmalemma, or in the wall itself. If we study the literature on this subject, we find that all three areas could be responsible for the cell wall synthesis. There is little doubt that the living cell is responsible for the synthesis of the wall substances. It is also likely that such elaborate structures cannot be formed without the guiding influence of the living matter. On the other hand, only small amounts of protein are detectable in the walls, indicating that the protoplasm does not penetrate into these lamellae. The formation of cellulose remote from the living cell has been shown to be possible in cultures of *Bacterium xylinum* (Mühlethaler, 1949; Colvin and Beer, 1960). The cellulose deposit, however, does not show an ordered structure comparable to the lamellae of secondary walls. These observations lead to the hypothesis that the plasmalemma is guiding the process of wall formation.

Recently we were able to obtain some information which sheds new light on these problems. In most of our previous studies we used young parenchyma cells, but they provided us with little new information on the

51

process of wall formation. They are excellent subjects for the study of the changes in texture which occur during growth. Such a system is so complex that the basic processes: formation, deposition, orientation, and so on, cannot be studied independently from each other. An object is needed which can be cultured first without a wall and then subsequently influenced to produce one. There are a few possibilities of observing wall formation from the very beginning. One is the synthesis of the new cell wall in the cell plate. Also, we know of a few organisms which are naked at first and form their walls during later differentiation. For example, there are the swarmers in the algae, the free-living soil amoeba, and some slime molds. It is also possible to work with plasmolyzed cells because they are able to form a new wall around the shrunken protoplasm.

For our investigations we have used dividing cells in the root tips of *Phalaris canariensis* and *Allium cepa* (Frey-Wyssling *et al.*, 1964). For the study of the formation of the outer membrane, we have used a free-living *Acanthamoeba*. The beginning of the new cell wall appears in early telophase as a free-floating lamella. From the center of the equatorial plane of the spindle the cell plate grows peripherally until it reaches the longitudinal wall of the mother cell. The area in which the cell plate is formed is termed the phragmoplast. With the help of the light microscope, Becker (1932) was able to see small vesicles whose contents can be stained with the same dyes as those used in the vital staining of vacuoles. He also described the merging of these granules by lateral coalescence. Investigations with the electron microscope, published by Whaley and Mollenhauer (1963), have shown that in root cells the Golgi vesicles might be the precursors of the cell plate. This conclusion has been confirmed in our laboratory by Frey-Wyssling *et al.* (1964). Porter and Caulfield (1960) have also observed bodies, which they termed phragmosomes, during cell plate formation. They apparently originate as blisters of the ER (endoplasmic reticulum) and are larger than the Golgi vesicles. According to their size and structure, it seems more likely that these phragmosomes are identical with the lysosomes discovered by de Duve (1959). These particles carry lytic enzymes, which could be released to open up a gap in the phragmoplast for the formation of the cell plate.

Before the cell plate is formed, the Golgi vesicles migrate to the equator (Fig. 1), where they fuse by lateral coalescence (Fig. 2). At certain points, strands of the ER prevent this fusion and provide capillaries for future plasmodesmata. Since the cell plate and the bulk of the primary wall consists of a mixture of highly hydrated uronides and hemicelluloses, it seems likely that the Golgi vesicles contain the precursors for these substances. After their incorporation into the cell wall these molecules become highly polymerized and insoluble in water. Whaley and Mollen-

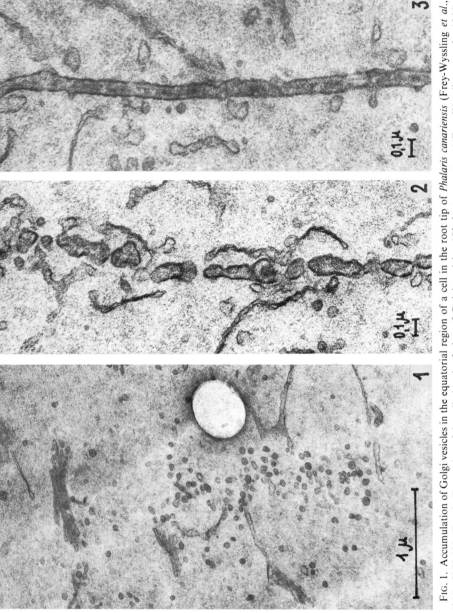

FIG. 1. Accumulation of Golgi vesicles in the equatorial region of a cell in the root tip of *Phalaris canariensis* (Frey-Wyssling *et al.*, 1964). X 30,000. FIG. 2. Formation of the cell plate by fusion of Golgi vesicles (*Phalaris canariensis*)(Frey-Wyssling *et al.*, 1964). X 50,000. FIG. 3. Middle lamella and primary wall. Additional matrix substances are incorporated by Golgi vesicles (Frey-Wyssling *et al.*, 1964). X 50,000.

hauer (1963) have demonstrated that in root cap cells also, Golgi vesicles move into the cell wall. The same process has been demonstrated by Sievers (1963) in root hairs. From these results we may conclude that the so-called matrix substances (polyuronides, polyoses, and hemicelluloses) are synthesized in the Golgi apparatus.

Until now we have discussed only the relationship between the contents of the Golgi vesicles and the cell wall matrix. However, the fate of the vesicle membrane must be considered. Our observations showed that during the coalescence of the vesicles, the plasmalemma becomes visible (Fig. 3). We must assume that the membrane of the Golgi vesicles forms this semipermeable layer. With the ordinary preparation techniques used in electron microscopy, only the usual dark and light layers of the unit membrane can be detected. In order to obtain a more detailed view of this region, we used our new freeze-etching method (Moor et al., 1961), which allows surface views of the cell surface and the plasmalemma. The first pictures were obtained (Fig. 4) using yeast cells (Moor and Mühlethaler, 1963). On the plasmalemma there are a large number of particles having a diameter of about 150 Å. In some areas these particles are arranged in a hexagonal lattice containing 20–50 units. The electron micrographs showed that the lattices are connected to the cell wall by a number of small fibrils. The fibrils have a diameter of about 50 Å and therefore correspond in size with the glucan fibrils described by Houwink and Kreger (1953) in hydrolyzed yeast cell walls. We regard these areas as specialized centers, involved in the synthesis of glucan threads. Between the ordered areas, there are single particles distributed at random over the entire plasmalemma (Moor and Mühlethaler, 1963). Their concentration is in the order of about 1000 particles per square micron. No fibrils have been observed on or associated with the isolated globules. We concluded that the randomly distributed particles are not able to form fibrils. They may, however, polymerize glucose to form amorphous glucan. The particles concentrated in patterns are responsible for the production of fibrils. Only about one fourth of all the particles are found to be regularly arranged, a fact which coincides with the observation that only a small amount of the glucans are crystallized. In some preparations the particles have been partly removed. When this occurs, holes having the same diameter as the missing particles become visible in the plasmalemma. This confirms that the globules do not simply adhere to the surface but are part of it.

These observations on yeast cell surfaces would mean little if similar particles were absent in various plant cells. We found, however, that they are always present on the plasmalemma of all plant cells we have examined. In onion root cells (Fig. 5) Branton and Moor, (1964) ob-

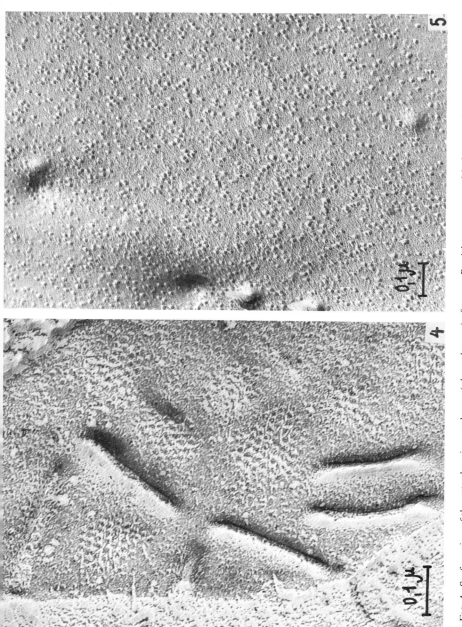

FIG. 4. Surface view of the cytoplasmic membrane (plasmalemma) of yeast. Particles are arranged in hexagonal patterns (Moor and Mühlethaler, 1963). X 135,000. FIG. 5. Cytoplasmic membrane of a parenchyma cell in onion root (*Allium cepa*). The whole surface is covered with particles. (Photo by Branton.) X 90,000.

served them scattered over the entire surface. Regular patterns have not been observed as yet; but perhaps because only young membranes were studied. Similar globules are also present on the surface of the soil amoeba *Acanthamoeba*. Tomlinson and Jones (1962) have shown that these free-living *Acanthamoeba* form a cellulose membrane if they are transferred from a rich medium, containing proteose peptone, dextrose, vitamins, and salts, to a poor medium with salts only. Before the first cellulose fibrils become apparent, the plasmalemma becomes covered by an increasing number of particles. They are piled up in a dense layer upon the plasmalemma and there we also observed the cellulose fibrils. When the same specimens are fixed with osmium or permanganate, no particles are seen. With these fixatives we have found particles only in the late stage of sperm formation in the spermatogenetic cells of chara. In the phase where the cell contracts, thin protoplasmic threads covered by a regular pattern of particles (Fig. 6) can be seen. It is not yet certain, however, that these units are identical with the particles seen after freeze-etching.

The origin of the membrane particles may be in the Golgi vesicles. It was found that the membrane of these vesicles contains particles similar to those found on the plasmalemma (Figs. 7 and 8). In the phragmoplast the

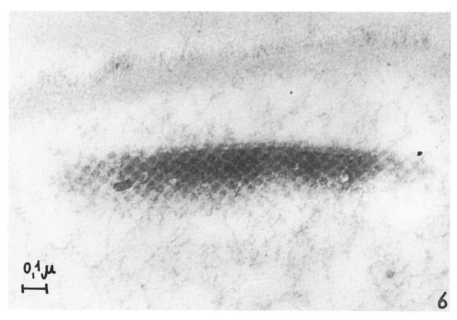

0,1μ

6

FIG. 6. Surface view of the cytoplasmic membrane of a maturing cell in a spermatogenous filament of *Chara*. X 60,000.

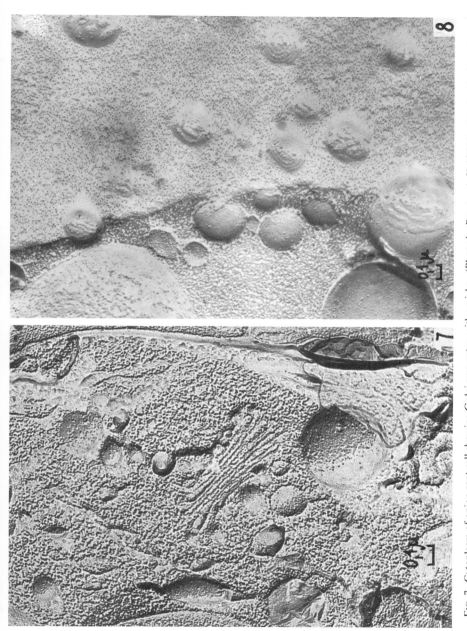

FIG. 7. Cytoplasm of onion root cell showing Golgi apparatus with vesicles. (Photo by Branton.) X 50,000.   FIG. 8.   Surface view of the cytoplasmic membrane showing the penetration of Golgi vesicles (Branton and Moor, 1964).   X 43,000.

Golgi vesicles merge together to form the new middle lamella and the plasmalemma of the newly formed daughter cells. This leads to the conclusion that the cell controls wall synthesis with its Golgi system.

So far we have discussed only where the cell wall originates and which elements are involved in the synthesis of wall material. We have not yet considered an additional feature of the membrane, namely, the orientation of the cellulose fibrils. Unfortunately we have no results that would enable us to decide which of the extant theories is correct. For this reason I will restrict myself to a critical discussion of the recent hypothesis. In general, the numerous concepts may be divided into two main groups: those which attribute orientation to purely mechanical factors, and those which consider the protoplasm as the guiding force. According to the multi-net growth theory (Houwink and Roelofsen, 1954), which has been confirmed by several authors, the wall can be expanded by stretching forces induced by the hydrostatic pressure of the turgid cell. This process is a passive one because the membrane structure was determined before the stretching forces extended the wall. Castle (1937) and van Iterson (1927) believed that the orientation of the fibrils could be caused by the wall stress. It can be calculated that the tension in the wall caused by turgor pressure is twice as great in the transverse as in the perpendicular plane (Frey-Wyssling, 1959). In fact it can be shown that most of the microfibrils in newly deposited lamellae of elongating cylindrical cells tend to be oriented transversely. A detailed study, however, showed that the microfibrils along the cell edges are laid down in the axial direction, and therefore perpendicularly to the direction of maximum stress. Also in bordered pits the cellulose threads around the pore and in the torus are arranged circularly, an orientation which cannot be explained by the action of mechanical forces. The stress theory has also been tested by Green and Chen (1960). When *Nitella* internodes were grown under longitudinal stress by a floating diver with a strong uplift, the deposition of the transverse microfibrils continued without change. They believe that the strain caused by passive cell expansion is the acting force in determining fibrillar orientation. It does not seem appropriate to explain orientation by exogenous mechanical forces like stress and strain only (Frey-Wyssling, 1962). We must consider the cause and effect of these established interrelations. In young meristems the cells are approximately isodiametric, which means that each can be compared with a sphere.

If we assume that the stress and strain theory is correct, they ought to expand uniformly in all directions. In order to form a cylindrical cell, derived from a sphere, the microfibrils must first be arranged in an appropriate manner. As a consequence of the transverse orientation of the fibrils, a stress anisotropy arises which deforms the sphere to a cylinder. From such considerations, we must assume that the living substance is guiding the development of the membrane and not mere exogenous mechanical forces alone.

Let us now discuss the influence which the protoplasm could have on the fibrillar arrangement. In a number of kinds of cells the direction of protoplasmic streaming coincides with the direction of fibrillar orientation (Probine and Preston, 1958). Our observations with the electron microscope showed very clearly that cell wall formation takes place outside the plasmalemma. An ordering influence could occur if the plasmalemma would move along the stream, a possibility which seems very unlikely. Recently Ledbetter and Porter (1963) have described new cell elements in the cell cortex, which they called microtubules. These elements are 230–270 Å in diameter and of undetermined length. In cross section they appear as hollow cylinders or tubules, limited by a dense wall about 70 Å thick. These tubules are found close to the plasmalemma, where they may appear aligned in parallel array. A direct connection between them and the cell surface has not been observed. Their disposition mirrors the orientation of the cellulose fibrils in the secondary walls on the other side of the plasma membrane (Hepler and Newcomb, 1964). When considered with our results it seems very unlikely that these elements are involved in cellulose synthesis, because it would be difficult to understand how the long threads could move through the plasmalemma. As recently published by Dannell (1964) tubules of similar dimension may be responsible for the contractility of the protoplast.

If the globules which we found on the plasmalemma are responsible for cellulose synthesis, we may assume that the arrangement of the particles determines the orientation of the fibrils. A scattered arrangement of particles could be related to the primary wall, in which the fibrils are deposited at random. The parallel-oriented threads of the secondary wall could be formed by a particle population arranged in a regular pattern. These considerations led us to a model which is, in general, similar to the one postulated recently by Preston (1964). If we assume that the formation of fibrils in different directions follows one or another row of particles, we still arrive at the same question. How is the change in direction of deposition of the cellulose strands coordinated with the role of the plasmalemma in strand formation? It seems that this and related questions can be answered, but it will take some time.

REFERENCES

Becker, W. A. (1932) "Recherches expérimentales sur la cytocinèse et la formation de la plaque cellulaire dans la cellule vivante." *Compt. Rend. sc. Ac. Sci.* 194:1850.

Branton, D. and Moor, H. (1964) "The fine structure of freeze-etched *Allium cepa* root tips." *J. Ultrastruct. Res.* 11:401–411.

Castle, E. S. (1937) "Membrane tension and orientation of structure in the plant cell wall." *J. Cellular Comp. Physiol.* 10:113–121.

Colvin, J. R., and Beer, M. (1960) "The formation of cellulose microfibrils in suspensions of *Acetobacter xylinum.*" *Can. J. Microbiol.* 6:631–637.

Dannell, S. (1964) "Identifizierung der kontraktilen Elemente im Cytoplasma von *Amoeba proteus.*" *Naturwiss.* 51: 368–369.

Duve, C. de, (1959) "A new group of cytoplasmic particles." In *Subcellular Particles* (T. Hayashi, ed.), p. 128. Ronald Press, New York.

Frey-Wyssling, A. (1959) *Die pflanzliche Zellwand.* Springer Verlag, Berlin-Göttingen-Heidelberg.

―――(1962) "Interpretation of the ultrastructure in growing plant cell walls." In *Symp. Intern. Soc. Cell Biol.,* Vol. 1, pp. 307–323. Academic Press, New York.

―――, López-Sáez, J. F., and Mühlethaler, K. (1964) "Formation and development of the cell plate." *J. Ultrastruct. Res.* 10:422–432.

Green, P. B., and Chen, J. C. W. (1960) "Concerning the role of wall stresses in the *Nitella* cell." *Z. Wiss. Mikroskopie.* 64:482–488.

Hepler, P. K., and Newcomb, E. H. (1964) "Microtubules and fibrils in the cytoplasm of *Coleus* cells undergoing secondary wall deposition." *J. Cell Biol.* 20: 529–533.

Houwink, A. L., and Kreger, D. R. (1953) "Observations on the cell wall of yeasts." *Antonie van Leeuwenhoek,* 19:1–24.

―――, and Roelofsen, P. A. (1954) "Fibrillar architecture of growing plant cell walls." *Acta Botan. Neerl.* 3:385–395.

Iterson, G. van, (1927) "De wording van den plantaardigen celwand." *Chem. Weekbl.* 24:166.

Ledbetter, M. C., and Porter, K. R. (1963) "A 'Microtubule' in plant cell fine structure." *J. Cell Biol.* 19:239–250.

Moor, H., Mühlethaler, K., Waldner, H., and Frey-Wyssling, A. (1961) "A new freezing-ultramicrotome." *J. Biophys. Biochem. Cytol.* 10:1–13.

――― and ――― (1963) "Fine structure in frozen etched yeast cells." *J. Cell Biol.* 17:609–628.

Mühlethaler, K. (1949) "The structure of bacterial cellulose." *Biochim. Biophys. Acta* 3:527–535.

Porter, K. R., and Caulfield, J. B. (1960) "The formation of the cell plate during cytokinesis in *Allium cepa L.*" *4. Intern. Kongr. Elektronenmikroskopie Berlin Verhandl.,* Vol 2, pp. 503–507. Springer-Verlag, Berlin.

Preston, R. D. (1964) "Structural and mechanical aspects of plant cell walls with particular reference to synthesis and growth." In *The Formation of Wood in Forest Trees* (M. H. Zimmermann, ed.), pp. 169–188. Academic Press, New York.

Probine, M. C., and Preston, R. D. (1958) "Protoplasmic streaming and wall structure in *Nitella.*" *Nature* 182:1657–1658.

Sievers, A. (1963) "Beteiligung des Golgi-Apparates bei der Bildung der Zellwand von Wurzelhaaren." *Protoplasma* 56:188–192.

Tomlinson, G., and Jones, E. A. (1962) "Isolation of cellulose from the cyst wall of a soil amoeba." *Biochim. Biophys. Acta* 63:194–200.

Whaley, G. W., and Mollenhauer, H. H. (1963) "The Golgi apparatus and cell plate formation—a postulate." *J. Cell Biol.* 17:216–225.

Cellular Differentiation in Xylem

A. B. WARDROP

Division of Forest Products, Commonwealth Scientific and Industrial Research Organization
South Melbourne, Australia
Present address: Department of Botany,
University of Tasmania

The criteria by which mature cells are distinguished from each other are their function, form, and the structure and composition of the cell wall. The process of differentiation which results in the characteristic form and structure of different xylem elements may, for convenience, be regarded as consisting of three phases, which follow cell division. They are as follows:

1. the phase of surface growth of cells, during which their dimensions and form are determined;

2. the phase of wall thickening, during which any wall sculpturing is elaborated; and

3. the phase of lignification.

As shown in the following discussion the process of wall thickening may commence before surface growth has ceased, and lignification begins before the wall is completely thickened, so that the phases are arbitrarily distinguished and not strictly consecutive.

In the following discussion consideration is given to the change in organization of the cytoplasm and the cell wall, and to the relation of the cell wall and the cytoplasm during the differentiation of xylem elements, so that the contribution of studies in fine structure to our understanding of these structural aspects of the processes of differentiation can be assessed.

THE EXTRA-CAMBIAL GROWTH OF DIFFERENTIATING XYLEM ELEMENTS

A comparison of the dimensions of mature cells of xylem with those of the initials from which they are derived indicates that fibers and tracheids grow both in length and in diameter during differentiation. In angiosperms the fibers may measure up to five times the length, and between

61

two and five times the diameter, of the cambial initials from which they were derived (Bailey, 1920a).

In gymnosperms the tracheids increase up to 20% in length compared with the cambial initials and the change in lateral dimensions is of the same order as that of angiosperm fibers.

Optical studies have yielded some information on the sequence of changes which take place during the phases of surface growth and secondary wall formation. Thus in a study of the differentiating storied xylem of *Papuodendron lepidotum* (Wardrop, 1964), it was observed that, in cross sections of the zone of differentiation, the numbers of fiber tips increased progressively in xylem of increasing maturity, so that it was concluded that the lateral expansion of the differentiating fibers preceded their longitudinal growth.

That the longitudinal growth of the cells is confined to the region near their tips was concluded from observations such as the occurrence of cells with bifurcated or distorted tips which are not present in the parent initials, and from the observation of Schoch-Bodmer (1960) that the areas of pits in fibers and fiber tracheids corresponded with the length of the vessel segments (i.e., the length of the cambial initials). A similar conclusion was reached by Bannan and Bayly (1956), on the basis of their studies on the intercellular readjustments which accompany differentiation of conifer tracheids. Furthermore, the recent study of Foster and Wardrop (unpublished) of the variation in the pattern of microfibril orientation on the surface of mature fibers of *Papuodendron* also suggests that longitudinal growth is confined to a region immediately behind the cell tips (see below).

In further studies on the differentiating fibers of *Papuodendron* (Wardrop, 1964), it was shown from measurements of the cell perimeter and from the optical properties of the cells seen in transverse section that the fibers reached the lateral dimensions of the mature cells before secondary wall formation began.

Thus it appears that surface growth of the fibers proceeds at first laterally, that this growth is followed by longitudinal growth at the cell tips, and that secondary thickening begins when these processes have been completed, at least locally in the cell (see below).

CHANGES IN CELL WALL ORGANIZATION DURING THE PHASE OF SURFACE GROWTH

Studies of the organization of the primary wall of differentiating fibers and tracheids show that the microfibril orientation on the inner surface was approximately transverse but differed from this orientation on the outer surface (Wardrop, 1958). This observation was similar in kind to that which led to the formulation of the multi-net hypothesis by Roelofsen and Houwink (1953), on the basis of studies on elongated parenchyma and hair cells.

Further investigation (Wardrop and Harada, 1964; Foster and Wardrop, unpublished) showed that the microfibril orientation on the outer surface of mature fibers was not uniform. In this study the method of Probine and Preston (1961) was employed. The percentage of microfibrils oriented in a series of directions with reference to the fiber axis was determined. The directions were separated by equal angular intervals. From the results obtained microfibrial distribution curves could be constructed for points on the fiber surface. For a mature fiber of *Papuodendron lepidotum* the general form of a series of such distribution curves is shown in Figure 1.

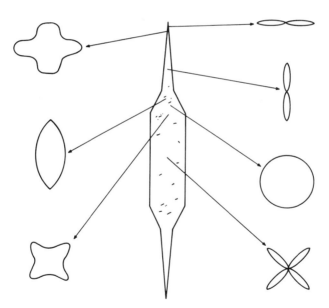

FIG. 1. A diagrammatic representation of the variation in the microfibril distribution curves at points on the surface of a mature fiber of *Papuodendron lepidotum*.

The almost axial orientation in the narrow tip region suggests that this was a zone of extension growth. The nearly transverse arrangement at the apex suggests that elongation did not occur and the initial transverse orientation was retained. The crossed arrangement in the central region most probably reflects the result of both lateral and longitudinal growth during symplastic readjustment of the cells following cambial division and before further growth occurred. This is suggested by the observation of Frey-Wyssling (1962) that this type of microfibril arrangement is characteristic of cells in which both lateral and longitudinal growth has taken place. Further detailed interpretation of the variation of microfibril orientation would perhaps be premature at this stage; it requires a more exact description of cell form and of the initial arrangement of the microfibrils, which often appears not to be truly transverse but to consist of a crossed structure in which each direction of orientation approaches the transverse direction. In general, however, these observations are consistent with the multi-net mechanism in that the final orientation observed on the outer surface of the cells reflects the extent and polarity of the growth which has occurred.

In other studies it was shown that, as in extending parenchyma, the incorporation of labeled carbon into differentiating fibers and tracheids was uniform over their surface (Wardrop and Harada, 1964), so that although wall synthesis was uniform the surface growth of the cells was localized at their tips. This being so, it is to be expected that the wall would become thicker in regions where surface growth has ceased. This was shown by Wardrop and Dadswell (1953), the wall being thicker near the center of the cell, and in fact this represents the initiation of secondary thickening. In these terms it would thus appear that the classical concepts of intussusception in primary walls and apposition in secondary walls represent a single process of wall formation, and that the resultant structure differs depending on whether the process proceeds on an expanding or a stationary surface.

The Pattern of Secondary Wall Formation

It is consistent with the above argument that the optical properties of differentiating fibers and tracheids (Wardrop and Harada, 1964) and direct electron microscopic examination (Wardrop, 1964) indicate that formation of the secondary wall, the organization of which is shown in Figure 2, begins near the middle of the differentiating fibers and extends towards their tips. Since all layers of the secondary wall are lamellated it is reasonable to suppose that the sheets of microfibrils constituting the lamellae extend by the tip growth of the microfibrils. This process of the formation of successive lamellae is shown in Figure 3. Such a process has interesting implications in relation to the nature of the orienting mechanism. Thus if it is supposed that the layer S_1 were undergoing formation,

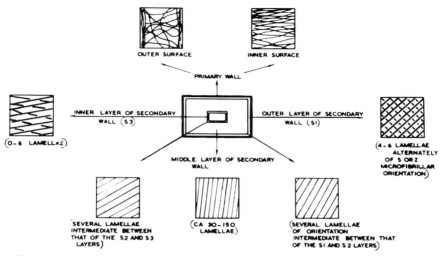

FIG. 2. A diagrammatic representation of the cell wall organization of a typical fiber or tracheid showing the texture of the different cell wall layers. (from Wardrop, 1964)

within which alternately the lamellae are of opposed helical orientation (Fig. 2), and further, that at stage 3 (Fig. 3) the cytoplasm in the region 1–2 was depositing a Z helix of microfibrils in the first lamella, then in the region 2–3 there would be an S helix in the second lamella and a Z helix in the third lamella. These observations imply that there is no over-all

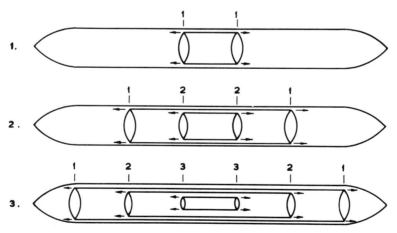

FIG. 3. A diagrammatic representation of the formation of three successive lamellae of the outer layer of the secondary wall of a differentiating fiber. It is assumed that the primary wall did not grow at the cell tips during the process. (from Wardrop, 1964)

template governing orientation. The process can, however, be understood in terms of the concept of Preston (1964), which is discussed further below.

The Cytology of Xylem

Before considering recent evidence of the relation of the cell wall to the cytoplasm during cell differentiation, the general cytoplasmic organization in differentiating xylem may be reviewed. The observations presented were made on *Acacia longifolia* and *Eucalyptus elaeophora* after permanganate fixation (Wardrop, 1964). Pioneering optical studies of xylem cytology were made by Bailey (1919; 1920a, b), in which the nature of cell division, the formation of the cell plate, and the variable vacuolate condition of the cambium were recognized and described. Electron-optical studies have been made by Hohl (1960) on *Datura*, by Esau (1963) and Esau *et al.* (1963) on *Cucurbita,* and by Cronshaw and Wardrop (1964) on *Pinus radiata.*

The Cytoplasm during Primary Wall Formation

In cells which were enclosed by only the primary wall, the conspicuous vacuolation described in optical studies by Bailey (1920b) was apparent (Fig. 4). The newly formed cell walls were thinner than other walls and were associated with aggregations of organelles (Figs. 4 and 5). The organelles present were similar in form and structure to those observed in other studies of higher plants. The proplastids and plastids showed considerable internal elaboration of the membrane system. The nucleus was large and often appeared to occupy about half of the cross-sectional area of the cells. Some evidence of intercellular cytoplasm at the cell corners was obtained (cf. Wardrop and Davies, 1964).

Fig. 4. A transverse section of the cambium zone showing several cells with newly formed walls (arrows). The highly vacuolate condition of the cells is apparent and several large nuclei can be seen.

The electron micrograph in Figure 4 is from material in the zone of xylem differentiation of *Acacia longifolia,* and that in Figure 17 is of a mature parenchyma cell of an oat coleoptile. All other electron micrographs refer to the zone of xylem differentiation in *Eucalyptus goniocalyx.* Reference symbols are as follows: g—Golgi apparatus, m—mitochondrion, n—nucleus, p—plastid, pl—plasmalemma, pp—proplastid, v—vacuole, F—fibers, PW—primary wall, S_1—first layer of secondary wall, S2G—second layer of secondary wall in a tension wood fiber (the "gelatinous layer"), T—tannin, V—vessel, W—cell wall.

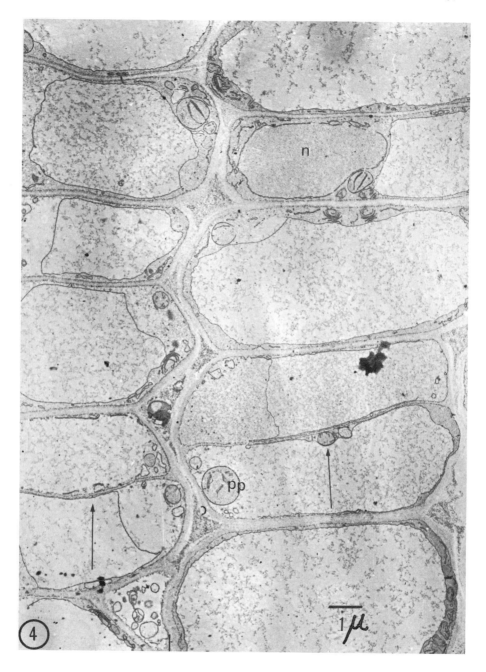

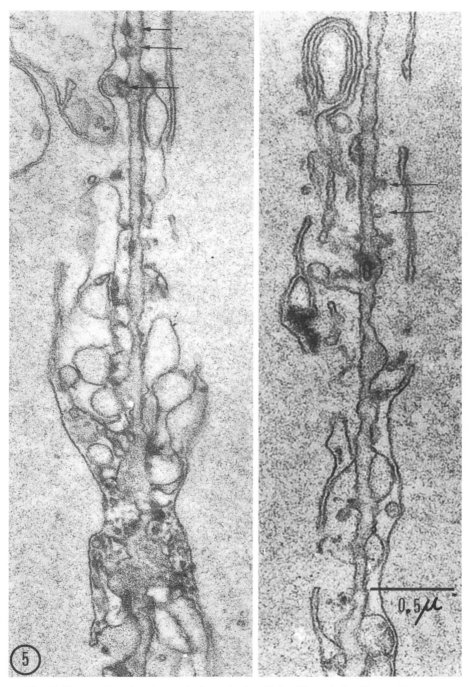

FIG. 5. Two sections showing newly formed cell walls in differentiating fibers. Numerous vesicular bodies in close association with the newly formed walls can be seen and appear to be in process of incorporation into it (arrows).

THE CYTOPLASM DURING SECONDARY WALL FORMATION

The Fibers. In fibers undergoing secondary wall formation the cytoplasm was variously and conspicuously vacuolate. In general vacuolation did not extend to the cell tips (Figs. 6 and 8) and in some cells was not apparent, or numerous small vacuoles were present (Fig. 7, lower left). Some vacuoles appeared empty while others contained granular deposits (Fig. 6). What may have been a vacuole undergoing formation in a profile of the ER (endoplasmic reticulum) is indicated by an arrow in Figure 7. As in the cambium, the nucleus was large with well developed pores.

The organelles were generally few in number but near the tips of the cell they appeared more crowded and smaller than elsewhere (Figs. 6 and 8). Mitochondria, proplastids, Golgi apparatus, and well developed ER could be recognized. The ER frequently appeared to lie parallel to the wall surface.

Between the fibers bordered pits were present (Fig. 6), in the membranes of which well developed plasmodesmata could be seen (Fig. 9). The plasmodesmata consisted of a canal ca. 400 Å in diameter, which was apparently lined by the plasmalemmae of adjacent cells. In the canal, strands of what appeared to be extensions of the ER measuring ca. 80 Å in diameter could be seen. These observations closely resemble those of Kollmann and Schumacher (1962) on the parenchyma of *Metasequoia*. The ER strands appeared to be continuous between the cells.

Vessels. In early stages of secondary wall formation the cytoplasm of vessels was extremely rich in organelles, particularly Golgi apparatus and mitochondria (Fig. 10). This may reflect a high metabolic rate associated with their rapid differentiation. Evidence of this could be seen in the presence of mature vessels with well developed vestured pits lying adjacent to living ray parenchyma. The vestures appeared to be continuous with the pit membrane and pit border.

Ray Parenchyma. The ray parenchyma contained well developed vacuoles with large tannin deposits (Fig. 11). The plastids of the ray parenchyma of large stems were similar to those described for other tissues. However, in epicormic shoots in which the bark was green (up to 2.5 cms in diameter), numerous plastids were present which closely resembled chloroplasts in their organization. These plastids had internal membranes arranged in groups of four to six double lamellae arising from the inner plastid membrane in the same manner as the grana of chloroplasts (Fig. 12).

It is interesting that the plastids showed no features of disorganization of the grana observed by Klein (1960) in etiolated plants. It was observed that the absorption spectra and chromatograms of methanol extracts of the leaves, bark, and xylem were identical and the main absorption peaks

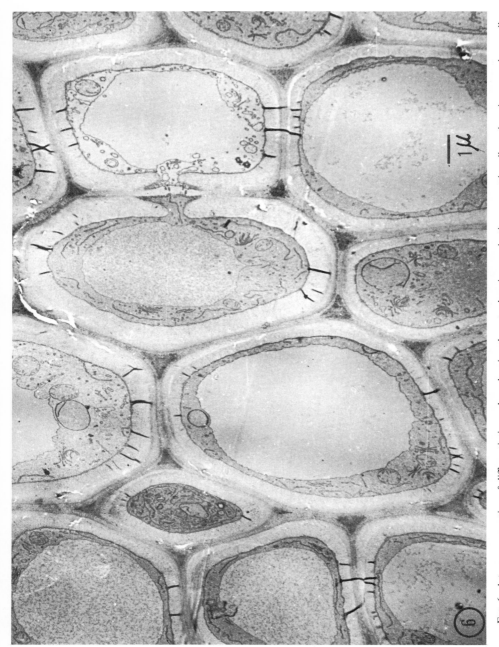

Fig. 6. A transverse section of differentiating xylem showing the cytoplasmic organization present in cells undergoing secondary wall formation. Note the variation in the apparent content of the vacuoles and the absence of vacuolation near the cell tips.

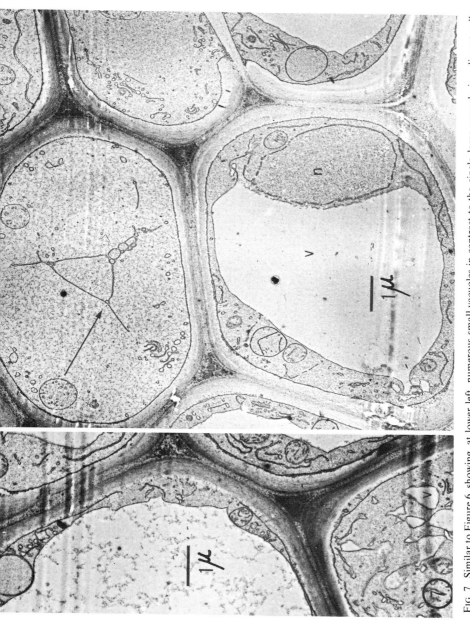

Fig. 7. Similar to Figure 6, showing, at lower left, numerous small vacuoles in contrast to the single large vacuole in adjacent cells and in the section at right. In the latter section a triangular element of the endoplasmic reticulum can be seen. At the point marked by an arrow a region where a new vacuole may have been undergoing formation can be seen.

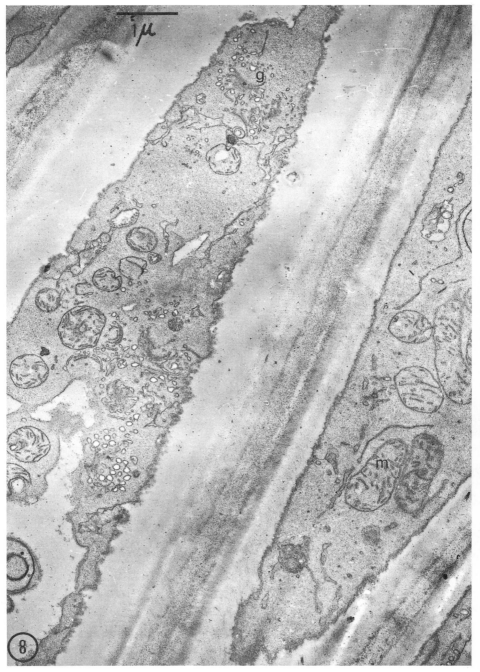

FIG. 8. A longitudinal section showing the absence of vacuolation near the tip of a differentiating fiber and the accumulation of organelles in this region. Note the smaller size of the organelles.

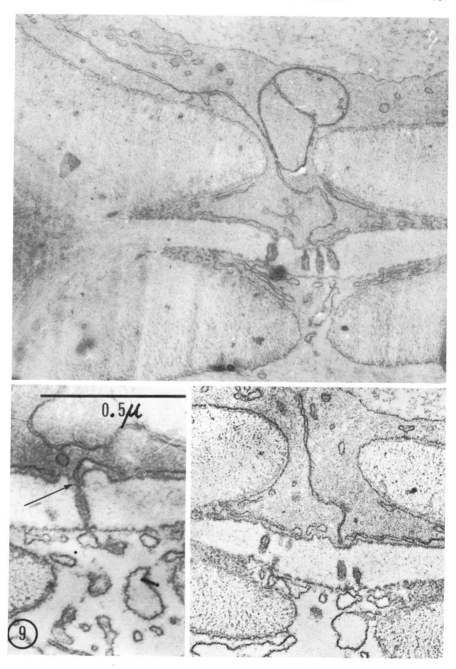

FIG. 9. Three sections through bordered pits between fibers showing plasmodesmata in the pit membrane and the entry of the endoplasmic reticulum into the canal of the plasmodesma (arrow). The canals of the plasmodesmata appear to be lined by the plasmalemmae of adjacent cells.

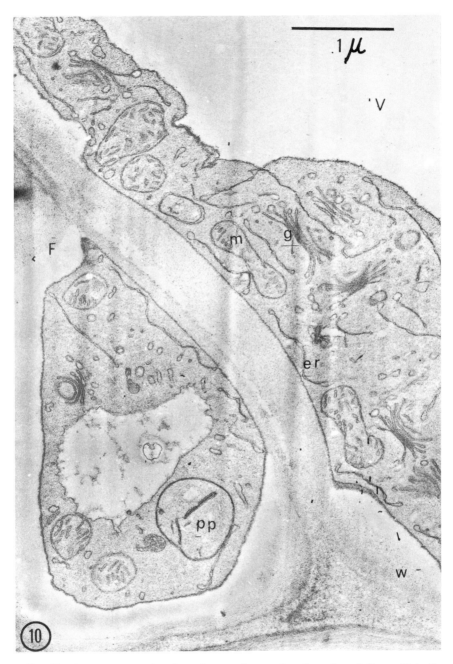

FIG. 10. A transverse section through part of a vessel and a adjacent fiber. Note the numberous organelles in the cytoplasm of the vessel and the prominence of the mitochondria and Golgi apparatus.

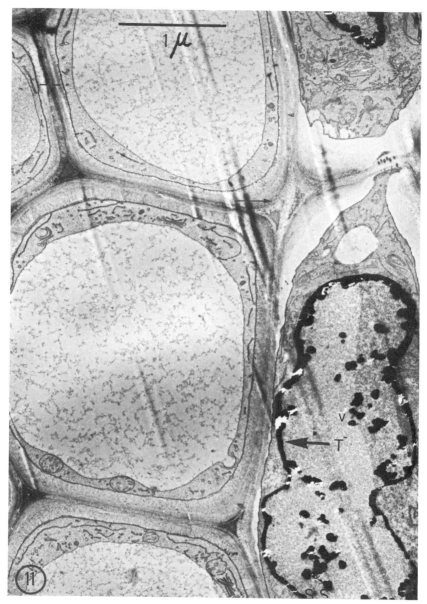

FIG. 11. A transverse section through two ray cells of adjacent fibers showing the large vacuoles of the ray parenchyma with accumulated tannin and the presence of plasmodesmata.

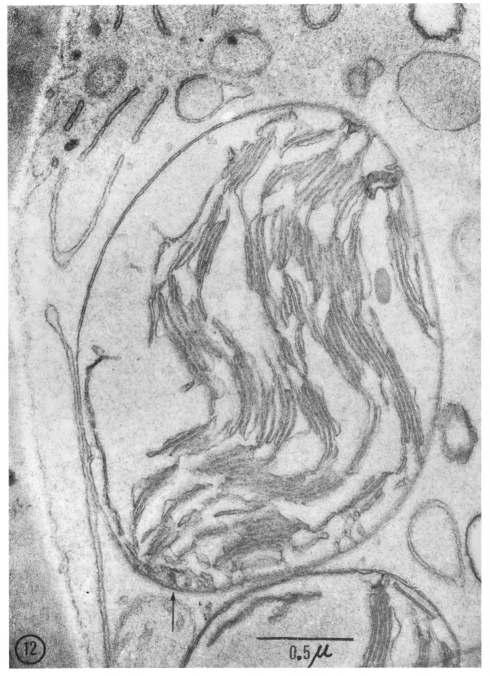

Fig. 12. A chloroplast present in ray parenchyma. Well developed grana can be seen which appear to arise from the invagination of the inner membrane of the plastid.

FIG. 13. Two sections cut parallel the length of the plasmodesmata between adjacent ray cells, showing the central strands of the endoplasmic reticulum passing through the canal of the plasmodesmata. At points marked by an arrow it appears that the central strand is continuous with the reticulum of the adjacent cells.

corresponded to these chlorophyll. The extent to which the ray parenchyma in such stems is photosynthetic has not yet been established.

Plasmodesmata were present and were similar in structure and dimensions to those described between fibers. They are shown in longitudinal
section in Figure 13 and in transverse section in Figure 14. As with the
fibers, there appeared to be continuity of the ER between adjacent cells.

Before concluding this brief cytological survey, it may be noted that the
basic organization of the cytoplasm was not markedly different in cells
undergoing primary wall formation from those undergoing secondary wall
formation. The generalization that functional specialization involves
considerable changes in cytoplasmic organization is well illustrated in ray
parenchyma with its specialized plastids and the secretion of tannins, and
in the early elaboration of the Golgi apparatus associated with vessel
differentiation. It is considered that the results presented demonstrate
the essential continuity of the ER between like cells, even in cells at an
advanced stage of secondary wall formation. Although plasmodesmata
have been observed between cells differing in type (e.g., between fibers and
ray parenchyma), the continuity of the ER between such cells has not been
established. In view of the technical difficulties involved, however, it cannot be said that continuity of the ER does not exist between dissimilar
cells. It is to be emphasized that the presence of plasmodesmata does not
necessarily imply this. Should further observations confirm that the ER
is continuous between like cells but discontinuous between unlike cells,
such a conclusion could well form the basis of an understanding of one
of the structural factors which may govern the homogeneity of cellular
differentiation.

CELL WALL FORMATION IN DIFFERENTIATING XYLEM

In studies of the cell wall–cytoplasm relation, several phenomena which
appear to be associated with wall formation have been described. Thus
Mollenhauer et al. (1961) and Sievers (1963a, b) have referred to the
secretion of vesicles arising from the Golgi apparatus into the developing

FIG. 14. *Upper:* A general view of a section through a ray parenchyma cell and part of
an adjacent fiber. In the lower part of the photograph a number of plasmodesmata can
be seen in the ray cell and part of the cytoplasm. In the upper part of the figure the
double nature of the cell wall—cytoplasm interface can be seen with vesicles approaching
the plasmalemma.

Lower left: A section normal to the plasmodesmata, showing the plasmalemma lining
the canals of the plasmodesmata and the central strand of endoplasmic reticulum.

Lower right: Similar to the previous section but in a deeper plane of section showing
the surface of the plasmalemma. Note its granular appearance.

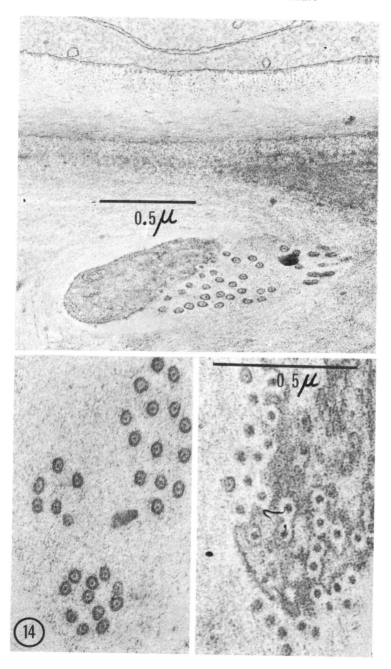

0.5 μ

0.5 μ

14

wall, and Porter and Machado (1960) have described the initiation of the cell wall as arising from the vesicles formed from the ER. In addition Myers *et al.* (1956) and Porter (1961) have presented evidence suggesting that the formation of the lamellated wall involves the formation of microfibrils near the wall cytoplasm interface, that a new plasmalemma is formed behind the newly formed lamella of microfibrils, and that these together with the associated plasmalemma are incorporated into the wall. More recently Hepler and Newcombe (1964) have described the formation of fibrillar bundles within the cytoplasm, which they postulate are subsequently incorporated into the developing wall.

In the present study, evidence has been obtained which suggests that both vesicular secretion and lamellar apposition are involved in the process of wall formation. Evidence for lamellar apposition was, as may be expected, found in cells undergoing secondary wall formation. Generally the wall cytoplasm interface had a three-layered organization consisting of strongly stained dark (D) inner membrane, a clear region (L), and a less regular and sometimes discontinuous strongly stained outer membrane (D) (Figs. 15 and 16). It may be noted that the width of the L region was similar to that between lamellae of the cell wall and was only slightly thicker than that of the isolated microfibrils measured by negative staining (80 Å). Near the tips of the cells the outer membranes measured 70–100 Å in thickness. It will be clear that each of the stained membranes was approximately the thickness of the normal three-layered "unit" cytoplasmic membranes.

A similar structure was observed in differentiating vessels and parenchyma undergoing secondary wall formation in *Avena* coleoptiles (Wardrop and Foster, 1964) (Fig. 17). In Figure 17 however, the sequence D L D is elaborated so that the structures D L D L D and D L D L D L D can be seen. These observations, together with those described above for *Eucalyptus* and the fact that similar observations were made on longitudinal sections, make it reasonable to postulate that a process of lamellar apposition is involved in secondary wall synthesis. This process may be represented diagramatically, as in Figure 18. It will be appreciated that, on such an hypothesis, the cytoplasmic components carried into the wall must be incorporated in it, or resorbed by the cytoplasm. This hypothesis would be consistent with the pattern of secondary wall formation involving the progressive growth of lamellae towards the cell tips (Fig. 3).

In addition to these observations evidence of vesicular secretion into the wall was also obtained. This was most apparent in the very young newly formed primary walls but could also be seen during secondary wall formation and during the development of bordered pits. In the primary walls what appeared to be stages of vesicular incorporation could be observed (Fig. 5, arrows). In cells with developing secondary walls, vesicles

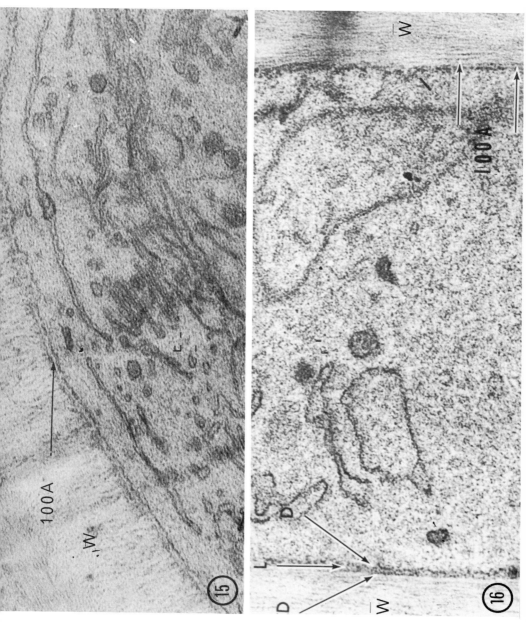

FIG. 15. Part of a transverse section of a fiber near the tip of the cell showing the three-layered structure of the cytoplasm-wall interface. Each of the dark regions corresponds in dimensions to that of a unit membrane.

FIG. 16. Similar to Figure 15, showing the cytoplasm wall interface. Note that the dimensions of the dark (D) light (L) dark (D) zone of the interface corresponds in thickness with the distance between adjacent lamellae of the cell wall (lower right).

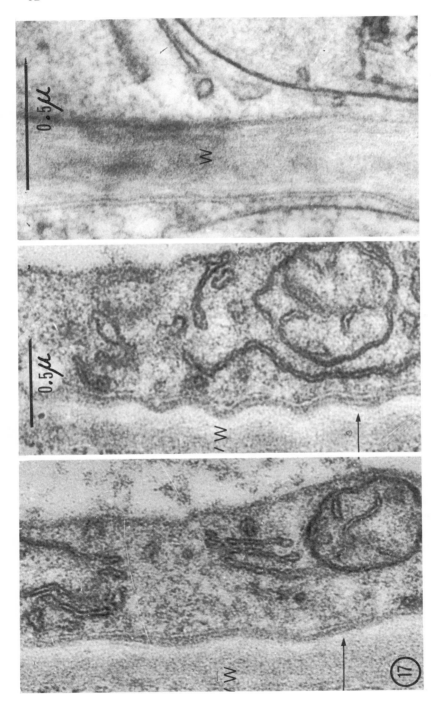

FIG. 17. Three sections cut through the cytoplasm-wall interface of *Avena* coleoptile parenchyma undergoing secondary wall formation. It can be seen (left and center) that the pattern of the interface is elaborated from that seen in Figures 15 and 16 and that in the section at the right. (See text.)

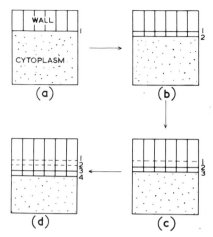

FIG. 18. A diagrammatic representation of the process of lamellar apposition involved in secondary wall formation. 1 − 4 = successively formed plasmalemmae.

which had apparently passed through the plasmalemma (Fig. 19) or were about to pass through it (Fig. 20) could also be seen. In these instances it was noted that the arrival of the vesicles at the wall cytoplasm interface frequently seemed to result in the partial breakdown of the plasmalemma and of the vesicles (Fig. 20). Since vesicular secretion was observed most frequently in young primary walls of cambium and of parenchyma in *Avena* coleoptiles (Wardrop and Foster, 1964), it is suggested that this phenomenon is involved in the incorporation of wall constituents most probably into the wall matrix rather than the framework.

Vesicular secretion was especially apparent in the developing pit borders. It was observed (Figs. 21–23) that in these structures the plasmalemma did not follow the contour of the developing border but passed from the inner edge of the border to the pit membrane, leaving a gap in the pit chamber. This region was occupied by numerous vesicles which sometimes assumed a somewhat tubular form (Fig. 23) and which appeared to be arranged in some degree of order (Fig. 21). It appears significant to recognize that there was no definite membrane separating these vesicular aggregations from the developing border, so that it might be argued that the vesicles were in process of incorporation into the cell wall. An almost mature cell is shown in Figure 24.

In the present series of observations there was little to indicate the origin of the cytoplasmic vesicles, but it is perhaps relevant that vesicular secretion was common in differentiating compression wood tracheids which contained numerous cellular organelles (Wardrop and Davies,

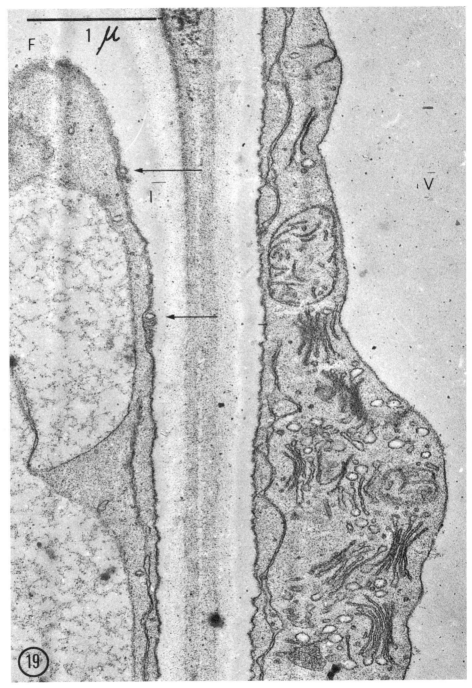

FIG. 19. A transverse section showing part of a vessel and an adjacent fiber. The presence of vesicles which have passed through the plasmalemma of the fiber is indicated (arrows). Note the profusion of organelles in the cytoplasm of the adjacent vessel.

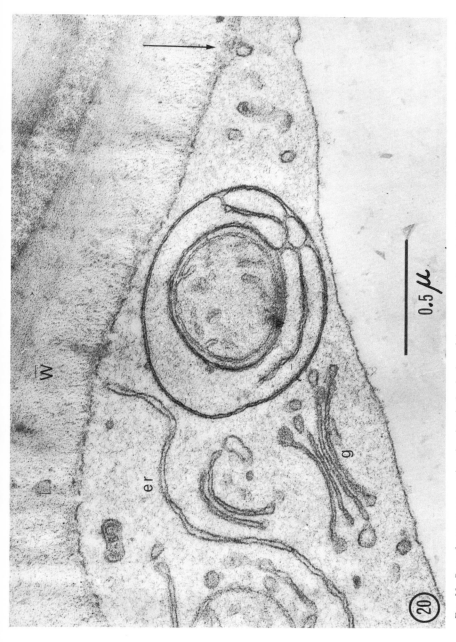

FIG. 20. Part of a transverse section showing the beginning of the passage of a vesicle through the plasmalemma into the cell wall (arrow). Note the elaboration of the internal membrane system of the plastid in the center of the photograph. At the left the origin of vesicles from the Golgi apparatus is apparent.

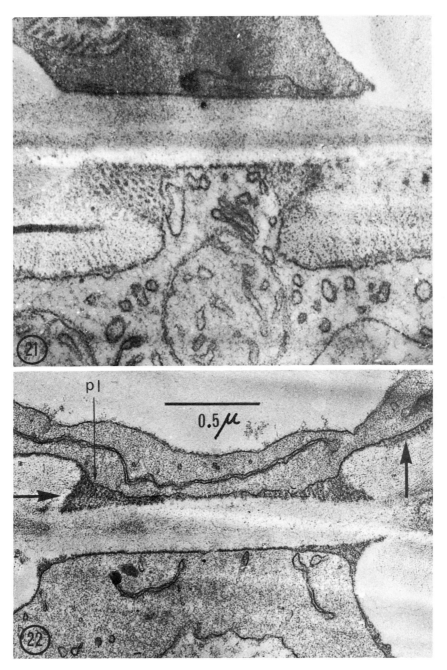

FIGS. 21–23. Transverse sections through bordered pits between adjacent fibers. Note that the plasmalemma does not follow the contour of the pit border and that in the space between the plasmalemma and the pit border numerous vesicles are present. In Figure 21 these appear to have some regularity of arrangement and in Figure 23 they appear to be tubular in form. In Figure 22 vesicular aggregates not in the pit chamber can be seen (arrow).

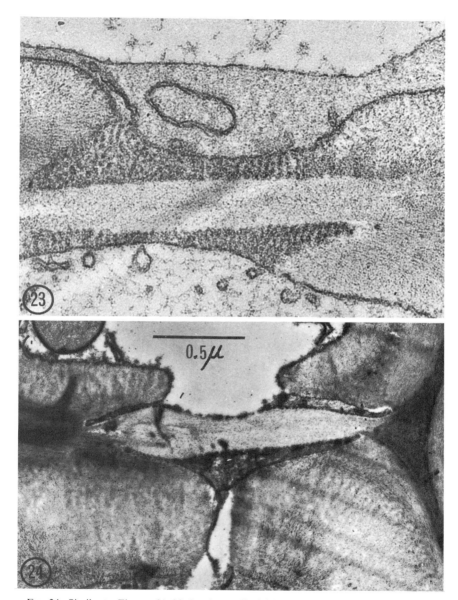

FIG. 24. Similar to Figures 21–23, but in a cell which was almost mature. Note the absence of staining in the pit membrane and the tangential continuity between the accumulated vesicles and the highly lignified region of the corner thickening of the middle lamella, and primary wall.

1964) and in which the wall is rich in matrix components. On the other hand, in differentiating tension wood in which the SG layer is rich in cellulose often only elements of the ER could be seen (Fig. 25) and vesicular secretion was not observed.

From the foregoing observations it would seem at this stage reasonable to postulate that, insofar as the phenomena of vesicular secretion and lamellar apposition are involved in wall synthesis, the former is effective in the incorporation of matrix and incrusting constituents into the wall and the latter in elaborating the cellulose framework.

If the process of lamellar apposition is considered in further detail, it will be apparent that it would involve the incorporation, at least temporarily, of cytoplasmic components into the cell wall. This conclusion is obviously of interest in relation to the recent work of Lamport and Northcote (1960), in which hydroxyproline was demonstrated to exist in cell walls of xylem and even in samples of α-cellulose. Furthermore, the work of Steward and Pollard (1959) showed that, once formed, the hydrooxyproline-rich proteins of the cell do not participate further in its metabolism. Both of these lines of work may thus be regarded as indicating a possible structural function in the wall of the hydroxyproline-containing proteins. In terms of the above observations it will be apparent that the operation of the process of lamellar apposition would prove a mechanism by which the incorporation of protein into the wall could take place.

Of the phenomona of vesicular secretion and lamellar apposition described, the evidence is undoubtedly stronger for the former. The possibility that the presence of the D L D structure, on which the concept of lamellar apposition is based, could be an artifact arising from the incipient plasmolysis of the cells was considered; but since it appeared only in cells undergoing secondary wall formation, and because of the apparent elaboration of this structure seen in oat coleoptiles (Fig. 17), it appears justifiable to consider it as a possible mechanism of wall formation, which is consistent with the evidence at this stage of the investigation.

It is of interest to consider the significance of vesicular secretion, not only as a process of incorporating new material into the cell wall but in relation to the growth of the cell wall. Thus it is now widely accepted that surface growth is essentially an osmotic phenonemon, and that coincident with uptake of water into the vacuole, there is relaxation of wall pressure which permits the cell to expand. In relation to such a mechanism vesicular secretion could be simply a means by which new components could be added to the matrix to keep pace with the increasing area of the wall. Obviously, however, other functions are possible: the vesicles may carry enzymes or ions capable of changing the physical texture of the matrix, leading to a change in the physical properties of the wall which must be involved in a relaxation of wall pressure.

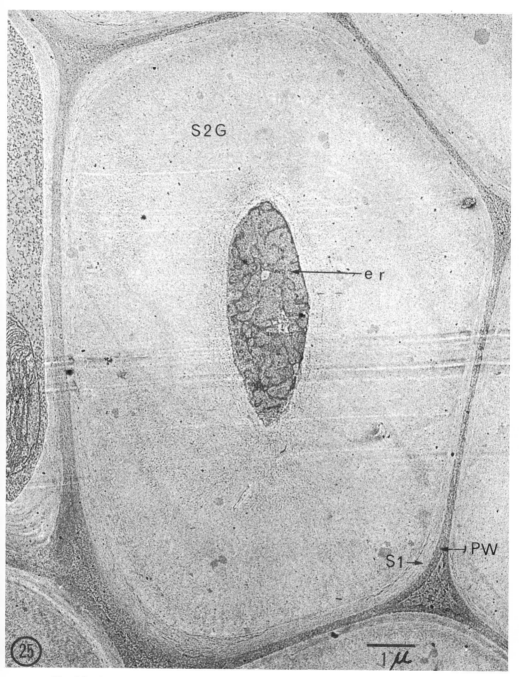

FIG. 25. A transverse section of an almost mature tension wood fiber, showing the persistent endoplasmic reticulum and the absence of other organelles from the cytoplasm.

On the other hand, there is the possibility that the vesicles secreted into the wall may not be simply involved in the incorporation of new wall constituents, but that when their contents are released they may participate in the active *in situ* synthesis of wall components, i.e., growth could occur as a result of the active growth of the wall itself. This possibility was advanced by Frey-Wyssling (1952) in relation to growth in algal cells and of reaction wood (q.v.). Other evidence has been reviewed by Mühlethaler (1961).

Although the above comments refer to walls growing in surface area, it is of interest that in thickening secondary walls the incorporation of lignin into the inter-microfibrillar regions in some instances causes measurable swelling of the wall (see the contribution on reaction wood by the writer in this symposium), which must exert forces on adjacent cells. It is thus not unreasonable to suppose that incorporation of new material into the inter-microfibrillar regions could produce forces resulting in the expansion of the wall during the phase of surface growth.

In general, however, the cell wall has not been considered to be the source of forces involved in cell growth; but in considering the possible role of vesicular secretion in wall growth, it is perhaps a concept worthy of further consideration.

Although the preceding observations provide some evidence of the mechanisms of wall formation, they give no indication of the processes governing microfibril orientation. It is of interest, however, that the "microtubules" described by Ledbetter and Porter (1963) and by Hepler and Newcombe (1964) in glutaraldelyde-fixed material, frequently lie parallel to the direction of orientation of the microfibrils, although Hepler and Newcombe (1964) have described instances where this parallelism was not observed. On the other hand, the hypothesis of Preston (1964) that the cytoplasmic surface consists of an ordered array of enzymatic synthetic centers receives some support from studies of the organization of the cytoplasmic surface by Moor and Mühlethaler (1963). The further postulation of Preston (1964) that orientation is determined by the directed tip growth of the microfibrils through regularly arranged synthetic centers in the cytoplasmic surface, is obviously consistent with the pattern of secondary wall formation described above and shown in Figure 3. However, if the development of the wall takes place by a process of lamellar apposition, it will be clear that the synthesizing-orientating interface will be removed as each lamella is added to the wall.

The model of Preston constitutes a reasonable hypothesis of the manner in which microfibril orientation may be determined, and the operation of a process of lamellar apposition would provide a means by which the ordered sequence of formation of lamellae and layers of the wall would remain under control of the cytoplasm. The mechanism which governs the extreme changes in microfibril orientation between lamellae and layers of the wall has yet to be elucidated.

In general it can be seen that, on the assumption that vesicular secretion is involved in the formation of matrix components and that lamellar apposition involves an elaboration of the cellulose framework, it is understandable that the former process should be more obvious during primary wall formation, since the framework represents only a minor component of the developing wall. Similarly, it is understandable that evidence of lamellar apposition was not obtained in primary walls, since the "lamellae" would be immediately dispersed as a result of surface expansion of the cell by the process of multi-net growth. Thus in these terms the observations on the cell wall and on the cytoplasm are in general agreement.

LIGNIFICATION

From chemical, X-ray diffraction, and electron microscopic studies it is known that the lignin of the cell wall exists in close association, or in combination, with the matrix constituents, and so lies between the microfibrils of cellulose. This evidence has been reviewed by Wardrop and Bland (1959). It is also probable that some lignin may penetrate interstices within the microfibrils and be in close association with the paracrystalline phase of cellulose.

In early histochemical investigations it was shown that the lignin was present mainly in the middle lamella and primary wall, although some was dispersed through the secondary wall. This was confirmed and quantitatively studied by Lange (1950) and Asunmaa and Lange (1952), using the technique of ultraviolet microspectrophotometry. More recently the technique of interference microscopy has been applied by Lange and Kjaer (1957). These investigations showed that in gymnosperms *ca.* 70% of the lignin lay outside the second layer of the secondary wall, i.e., in the layer S_1, primary wall, and middle lamella. In angiosperms the value was *ca.* 80%.

More recently Frey-Wyssling (1964) has reviewed the problem with special reference to the ultraviolet fluorescence studies of Ruch and Hentgartner (1960). In this work it was shown for jute that most of the lignin is present in the primary wall and middle lamella. This conclusion is in agreement with recent studies using electron-staining procedures (Wardrop, 1963).

In secondary xylem the concentration of lignin in the middle lamella is greater between radial walls than between tangential walls. The pit membranes appear to be unlignified (Bamber, 1961).

The early investigations of Sachs (1874) and Sanio (1873) showed that lignification began in the region of the middle lamella and subsequently extended to the secondary wall. This has been confirmed by later studies using ultraviolet microscopy. Lignin deposition was observed first at the cell corners in the primary wall. Lignification then extended to the middle lamella and in newly formed regions of the secondary wall. The initiation of the process, however, appeared to take place cell by cell. This process was followed during the development of the secondary wall, and the lignification was observed to lag somewhat behind the synthesis of cellulose. It was of interest, however, that lignification took place simultaneously in the middle lamella and in newly formed regions of the secondary wall. Thus it was shown (Wardrop and Bland, 1959) in one specimen of *Pinus radiata* that the formation of the S_3 could be seen in cell 38 counted from the cambium. In this cell little lignification of the S_2 layer had taken place. In cells 44 and 45, however, all secondary wall layers had formed and lignification appeared complete. Photometric examination showed that in the mature cells (44-45) the absorption had increased not only in the secondary wall but also in the middle lamella, compared with absorption in these regions in cells 38 and 39 (Fig. 26), so the process must be regarded as proceeding simultaneously in the cell wall and middle lamella.

The seasonal variation in the pattern of lignification has also been studied by Wardrop (1957). As already stated, lignification appeared to begin at the cell corners and the cessation of lignification which accompanies the cessation of differentiation during winter appeared to take place cell by

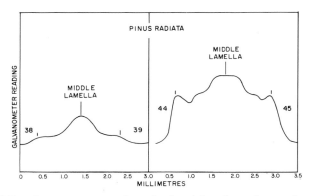

FIG. 26. Microphotometer traces through ultraviolet photomicrographs showing the greater absorption of the middle lamella in the more mature cells (44–45). (See text.) (from Wardrop and Bland, 1959)

cell, i.e., there was no evidence that lignification was an histological as distinct from a cellular process. It may be noted that this cellular aspect of lignification is apparent in the formation of isolated lignified cells following wounding of the cambium, and in the primary xylem in which only the helical thickenings become lignified and the primary wall and middle lamella remain unlignified.

The chemical and biochemical aspects of lignification have been elucidated mainly as a result of the work of Freudenberg (1952) and coworkers and of Manskaya (1948). According to the view of Freudenberg (1952), lignin precursors in the form of glycosides such as coniferin are formed in the cambium, where they are hydrolyzed by glycosidases. The phenylpropane units then move into the differentiating xylem where they are oxidized by peroxidases and other phenoloxidases and polymerized to form lignin. This view receives strong support from observations such as the complementary distribution of lignin and peroxidase in differentiating xylem, and the known presence of glycosidases; from tracer experiments in which labeled precursors were incorporated into the xylem under appropriate experimental conditions; and from the observed gradient of lignin concentration in the differentiating xylem.

It will be appreciated that these biochemical and chemical studies of lignification imply that the process is essentially a histological one, in that on the evidence presented the process could proceed only in the cell wall and the concept does not demand the active participation of the cytoplasm except insofar as this may condition the cell wall so that lignification may occur. Thus the anatomical evidence suggests that lignification involves the active cytoplasmic participation of the cell in which it takes place, whereas in biochemical studies this is not necessarily so or the participation of the cytoplasm is only indirect. It may be noted, however, that on the basis of staining experiments using phloroglucinol and the Maule reaction, Barskaya (1962) has suggested that there are two processes involved in lignification. Thus it was observed that in cells in which the whole cell wall showed a positive staining reaction with the Maule reaction, with phloroglucinol only the middle lamella was stained. This led to the conclusion that two components were involved in lignification, one arising within the cytoplasm and the other originating in the cambium zone, as proposed by Freudenberg. These observations are open to objection in that the two reactions are of greatly differing sensitivity, and so the results are ambiguous. However, they do provide further evidence for the possibility of cytoplasmic participation in the lignification process.

The above considerations make clear the desirability of cytological studies directed to the elucidation of this point. In this context it may be

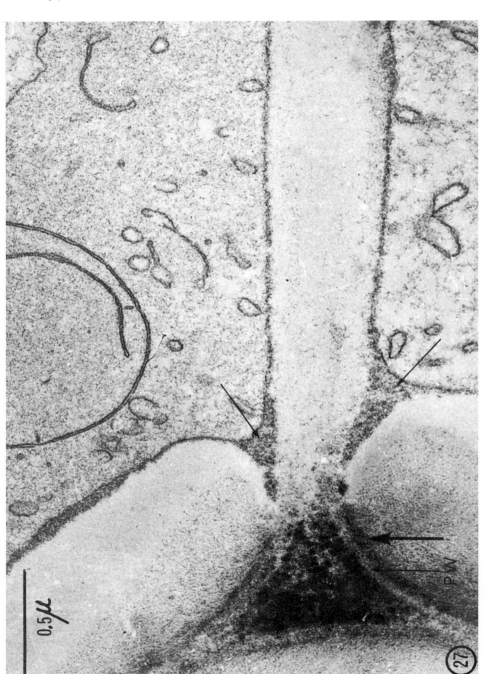

FIG. 27. Similar to Figures 21 to 24, showing the apparent tangential continuity of vesicles (light arrows) secreted in the region of the pit border, with the heavily staining region of the cell wall (heavy arrow) internal to the primary wall.

recalled that, although the vesicular secretion is involved in wall formation, there is little to indicate the nature of the vesicles beyond the circumstantial evidence that they are involved in the elaboration of the wall matrix. This does not exclude the possibility that they are involved in lignification. Although it may well be coincidence, it may be noted that in Figures 24 and 27 the zone of secreted vesicles in the region of the pit border appears to be almost continuous with the heavily stained region in the S_1 layer adjacent the wall. It will be recalled from the work of Crocker (1921) that potassium permanganate acts as a lignin stain because of its reduction by lignin to manganese dioxide, so that the stained region referred to can reasonably be supposed to be one of high lignin concentration, especially as the middle lamella at the cell corners was also heavily stained. It may be noted in addition that the intensity of lignification in the corner thickenings decreases towards the pit membrane (cut obliquely), which, in agreement with the optical observations of Bamber, appears unlignified. This is also apparent in mature cells (Fig. 24).

Although the above observations do not justify the conclusion that lignification proceeds by a process of vesicular secretion, they are sufficiently cogent to make further experimental inquiry desirable. One obvious approach at present under investigation is to study, at the electron microscopic level, the incorporation of labeled substances which are known to be incorporated into lignin.

The function of lignin is largely unknown but it has been suggested (Wardrop, 1957) that, in view of its location and the time of the initiation of lignification, it may serve to limit the growth of the differentiating cells by immobilizing the matrix components of the cell wall. Unquestionably the deposition of lignin greatly influences the mechanical properties of the cell walls, especially their resistance to compressive stresses.

From the above survey it can be seen that studies of the fine structure of cells not only contribute significantly to elucidating the organization of cell walls and the changes in their structure which accompany their differentiation, but also are of value in the study of the relation of the cell wall to the cytoplasm, and in this field are complementary to biochemical studies of the process of wall formation.

REFERENCES

Asunmaa, S., and Lange, P. W. (1952) "Distribution of the carboxyl groups in the cell wall of spruce and birch holecellulose and cotton." *Svensk. Papperstid.* 55:217–223.

Bailey, I. W. (1919) *Proc. Nat. Acad. Sci.* 5:283.

———— (1920a) "The cambium and its derivative tissues. II. Size variations of cambial initials in gymnosperms and angiosperms." *Am. J. Botany.* 7:355–367.

—— (1950b) *Proc. Nat. Acad. Sci.* 6:197.

Bamber, R. K. (1961) "Staining reaction of the pit membrane of wood cells." *Nature* 191:409–410.

Bannan, M. W., and Bayly, I. L. (1956) "Cell size and survival in conifer cambium." *Can. J. Botany* 34:769–776.

Barskaya, E. I. (1962) "Histochemical study of lignification during maturation of wood." *Fiziol. Rast.* 9:210–221.

Crocker, E. C. (1921) "Significance of 'lignin' color reactions." *Ind. Eng. Chem.* 13: 625–627.

Cronshaw, J., and Wardrop, A. B. (1964) "The organization of cytoplasm in differentiating xylem." *Australian J. Botany* 12: 15–23.

Esau, K. (1963) "Ultrastructure of differentiated cells in higher plants." *Am. J. Botany* 50: 495–506.

——, Cheadle, V. I., and Risley, E. B. (1963) "A view of ultrastructure of *Cucurbita* xylem." *Botan. Gaz.* 124: 311–316.

Foster, R. C., and Wardrop, A. B. (1964) *Australian J. Botany.* In press.

Freudenberg, K. (1952) "Die Entstehung des Lignins in der Pflanze." *Holzforschung* 3: 37–42.

Frey-Wyssling, A. (1952) "Wachstumsleistungen des Pflanzlichen Zytoplasmas." *Ber. Schweiz. Botan. Ges.* 62:583.

—— (1962) "Interpretation of ultratexture in growing plant cell walls." In *The Interpretation of Ultrastructure* (R. J. C. Harris, ed.), Vol. 1, p. 307. Academic Press, London.

—— (1964) "Ultraviolet and fluorescence optics of lignified cell walls." In *The Formation of Wood in Forest Trees.* (M. H. Zimmermann, ed.), pp. 153–167. Academic Press, N. Y.

Hepler, P. K., and Newcombe, E. H. (1964) "Microtubules and fibrils in the cytoplasm of *Coleus* cells undergoing secondary wall deposition." *J. Cell Biol.* 20:529–533.

Hohl, H. R. (1960 "Über die submikroskopische Struktur normaler und hyperplastischer Gewebe von *Datura stramonium* L. I. Teil: Normalgewebe." *Ber Schweiz. Botan. Ges.* 70:395–439.

Klein, S. (1960) "The effect of low temperature on the development of the lamellar system in chloroplasts." *J. Biophys. Biochem. Cytol.* 8:529–538.

Kollmann, R., and Schumacher, W. (1962) "Über die Feinstruktur des Phloems von *Metasequoia glyptostroboides* und seine Jahreszeitlichen Veranderungen. II. Mitteilung. Verglichende Untersuchungen des Plasmatischen verbindungsbrücken in Phloemparenchymzellen und Siebzellen." *Planta* 58:366–386.

Lamport, D. T. A., and Northcote, D. H. (1960) "Hydroxyproline in primary cell walls of higher plants." *Nature* 188:665–666.

Lange, P. W. (1950) "Kvantitativ kemisk analys av cellväggens delar i ved- och cellulosafibrer med användning av interferens-mikroskopi." *Svensk. Papperstid.* 53:749.

——, and Kjaer, A. (1957) "Quantitative chemical analysis of the different parts of the woody cell wall in wood and cellulose fiber with the interference microscope." *Norsk Skogind.* 11:425–432.

Ledbetter, M. C., and Porter, K. R. (1963) "A 'microtubule' in plant cell fine structure." *J. Cell Biol.* 19:239–250.

Manskaya, S. M. (1948) *Dikl. Akad. Nauk USSR* 62-369.

Mollenhauer, H. H., Whaley, W. G., and Leech, J. H. (1961) "A function of the golgi apparatus in outer rootcap cells." *J. Ultrastruc. Res.* 5:193–200.

Moor, H., and Mühlethaler, K. (1963) "Fine structure in frozen yeast cells." *J. Cell Biol.* 17:609–628.

Mühlethaler, K. (1961) "Plant cell walls." In *The Cell*. J. Brachet and A. E. Mirsky, ed.), Vol. 2. Academic Press, N. Y.

Myers, A., Preston, R. D., and Ripley, G. W. (1956) "Fine structure in the red algae. I. X-ray and electron microscope investigatiion of *Griffithsia flosculosa*." *Proc. Roy. Soc. (London), Ser. B* 144:450.

Porter, K. R. (1961) "The endoplasmic reticulum: some current interpretations of its form and functions." In *Biological Structure and Function* (T. W. Goodwin and O. Lindberg, ed.), Vol. 1, pp. 127–155. Academic Press, N. Y.

———, and Machado, R. D. (1960) "Studies on the endoplasmic reticulum. IV. Its form and distribution during mitosis in cells of onion root tip." *J. Biophys. Biochem. Cytol.* 7:167–180.

Preston, R. D. (1964) "Structural and mechanical aspects of plant cell walls with particular reference to synthesis and growth." In *Formation of Wood in Forest Trees* (M. H. Zimmermann, ed.), pp. 169–188. Academic Press, N. Y.

Probine, M. C., and Preston, R. D. (1961) "Cell growth and the structure and mechanical properties of the wall in internodal cells of *Nitella opaca*. I. Wall structure and growth." *J. Exp. Botany* 12:261–282.

Roelofsen, P. A., and Houwink, A. L. (1953) "Architecture and growth of the primary cell wall in some plant hairs and in the Phycomyces sporangiophore." *Acta Botan. Neerl.* 2:218–225.

Ruch, F., and Hentgartner, H. (1960) "Quantitative Bestimmung der Ligninverteilung in der pflanzlichen Zellwand." *Z. Schweiz. Forstv.* 30:75–90.

Sachs, J. (1874) *Lehrbuch der Botanik.*

Sanio, K. (1873) "Anatomie der gemeinen Kiefer (*Pinus silvestris* L.)" *Jahrb. Wiss. Botan.* 9:50–126.

Schoch-Bodmer, H. (1960) "Spitzenwachstum und Tupfelverteilung bei sekundaren Fasern von *Sparmannia."* *Z. Scheiz. Forstv.* 30:107–112.

Sievers, A. (1963a) "Beteiligung des Golgi-Apparates bei der Bildung der Zellwand von Wurzel-haaren." *Protoplasm* 56:188–192.

——— (1963b) *S. Naturforsch.* 18:830.

Steward, F. C., and Pollard, J. K. (1959) "Protein synthesis in higher plants: Concepts derived from the study of growing cells in tissue cultures." In *Proc. Intern. Congr. Biochem., 4th, Vienna, 1958,* Vol. 6, pp. 193–206. Pergamon Press, London.

Wardrop, A. B. (1957) "The phase of lignification in the differentiation of wood fibres." *Tappi* 40:225–243.

——— (1958) "Organization of the primary wall in differentiating conifer tracheids." *Australian J. Botany* 6:299–305.

——— (1963) "Morphological factors involved in the pulping and beating of wood fibres." *Svensk Papperstid.* 66:231–247.

——— (1964) "The structure and formation of the cell wall in xylem." In *Formation of Wood in Forest Trees* (M. H. Zimmerman, ed.). Academic Press, N. Y.

———, and Bland, D. E. (1959) "The process of lignification in woody plants." In *Proc. Intern. Congr. Biochem. 4th, Vienna, 1958,* Vol. 2, pp. 93–116. Pergamon Press, London.

———, and Dadswell, H. E. (1953) "The development of the conifer tracheid." *Holzforschung* 7:33–39.

———, and Davies, G. W. (1964) "The nature of reaction wood. VIII. The structure and differentiation of compression wood." *Australian J. Botany* 12:24–38.

———, and Foster, R. C. (1964) *Australian J. Botany.* In press.

———, and Harada, H. (1964) *J. Exp. Botany.* In press.

Cytoplasmic Fine Structure and Cell Wall Development in Differentiating Xylem Elements

JAMES CRONSHAW

Department of Biology, Yale University

The major structural features of the cell walls of mature xylem elements and the changes in wall organization which occur during their differentiation are well established, e.g., Roelofson (1959). Attention can now be directed to the more fundamental question of the involvement of the cytoplasm in cell wall production and cellular differentiation. The present article attempts to examine the cell wall cytoplasmic relationship and the organization of the cytoplasm during the development of xylem elements from the structural point of view.

The early light microscope work of Cruger (1855) showed a possible relationship between localized cell wall thickening, cytoplasmic structure, and the direction of protoplasmic streaming. This work was followed by several accounts which described bands of dense cytoplasm in which localized cell wall thickenings developed (Schmitz, 1880; Strasburger, 1882; Dippel, 1868; Barkley, 1927; Sinnott and Bloch, 1945). In addition Dippel (1868) noted that the direction of protoplasmic streaming was correlated to the larger refractive index of cellulose.

The electron microscope enabled more detailed studies of the cytoplasm of cells actively engaged in wall thickening to be made. In view of the known synthetic function of the endoplasmic reticulum (Porter, 1961a), observations made on its organization in differentiating cells are of interest. Esau *et al.*, (1963) observed a change in the form of the endoplasmic reticulum, from a cisternoid to a vesicular type, during maturation of *Cucurbita* xylem elements. A patterning of the endoplasmic reticulum with respect to wall deposition in onion root tip cells was noted by Porter and Machado (1960a) and Porter (1961b). In xylem elements of onion root tips Porter (1961b) suggested that residual elements of endoplasmic reticulum which were observed had a relationship with the annular thickenings of the wall. Hepler and Newcombe (1963, 1964) have described a concentration of organelles, vesicles, and tubules in the cytoplasmic band within which the secondary wall thickenings are formed in differentiating parenchyma cells of *Coleus*.

99

A study of differentiating ray parenchyma cells and tracheids of *Pinus radiata* showed no spatial organization of organelles, although a complex cellulose wall was being formed in each case (Cronshaw and Wardrop, 1964). However, the rapid vacuolation of the tracheids resulted in a change in the arrangement of the organelles until the elements of the endoplasmic reticulum and the dictyosomes aligned themselves parallel to the wall, and the plastids tended to become more ellipsoidal with their major axis parallel to the wall. Later observations (Cronshaw and Bouck, 1965) in other cell systems have revealed no gross accumulation of cytoplasm associated with cell wall deposition. Structural features of the cytoplasm do exist, however, which suggest that specific cytoplasmic components are functionally involved in cell wall synthesis and orientation. Currently, observations are being made on primary xylem elements which exhibit localized thickening patterns, and on differentiating cambial derivatives.

PRIMARY XYLEM ELEMENTS OF *Avena*

Observations have been made on differentiating primary xylem elements of *Avena sativa* (var. victory) coleoptiles (see Cronshaw and Bouck, 1965) and attention will first be directed to them. The characteristic patterns of localized secondary wall thickening identify the xylem elements and indicate their state of differentiation. At an early stage of differentiation, before secondary wall deposition has commenced, the cells have dense cytoplasmic contents and the vacuolar system is confined to numerous small vacuoles. The vacuolar membranes are triple-layered structures which may be resolved as two electron opaque lines separated by a less opaque region. A section including part of three cells at this early stage is shown in Figure 1.

The nuclei are elongated and may be multi-lobed. They are surrounded by the usual double membrane which has pores and is connected to the endoplasmic reticulum. Internally the nuclei have several granular nucleoli and regions of chromatin which stain densely (Fig. 1).

Mitochondria, plastids, endoplasmic reticulum, dictyosomes, and lipid droplets are present, and the ground substance is densely packed with ribosomes (Fig. 1). The plasma membrane has a triple-layered structure and is closely applied to the cell wall. It is continuous around the cells except at the region of the plasmodesmata, where it forms a tube which is continuous from cell to cell through the wall. The tube always contains an electron opaque core separated from the plasma membrane by a less opaque region (Fig. 2).

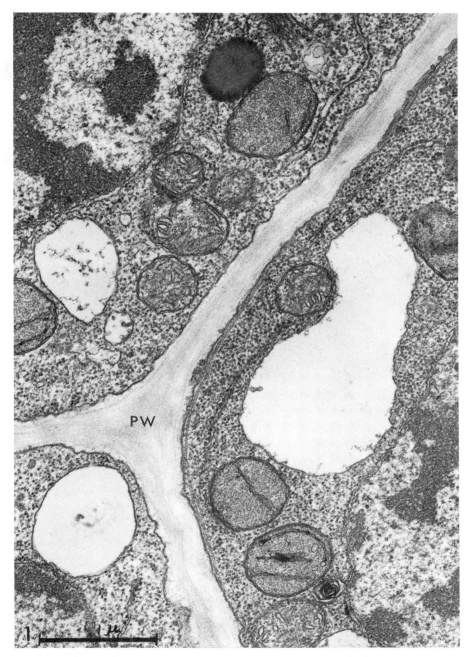

FIG. 1. *Avena sativa.* Transverse section through the vascular strand of a 1 cm coleoptile showing part of three undifferentiated cells. Long microtubules are present in the peripheral cytoplasm parallel to the plasma membrane and the cell wall. PW—Primary wall. Glutaraldehyde-osmium fixation X 32,000.

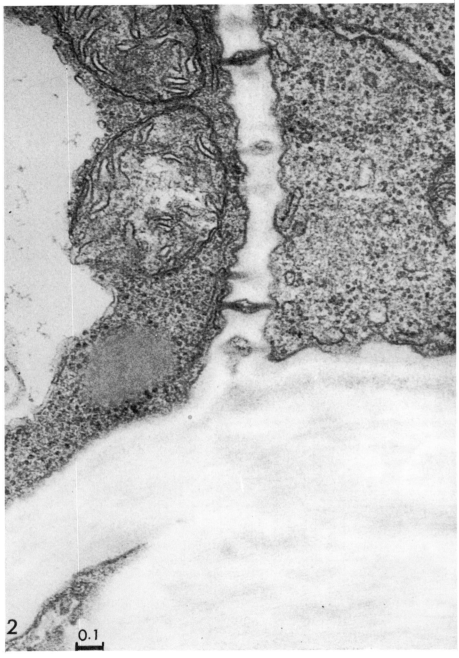

2

0.1

Fig. 2. *Avena sativa.* Transverse section through three cells of the vascular strand of a 1 cm coleoptile. One cell is a partially differentiated xylem element with an annular or spiral wall thickening. The other two cells are undifferentiated and the wall between them shows several plasmodesmata cut in longitudinal section. Glutaraldehyde-osmium fixation X 65,000.

In the region immediately within the plasma membrane ribosomes tend to be excluded and long microtubules (Ledbetter and Porter, 1963) may be observed (Fig. 1). These microtubules are *ca.* 250 Å in diameter, may be as long as 3 μ, and are oriented parallel to the direction of the microfibrils in the most recently deposited part of the cell wall. Thus in a cross section of a developing vascular strand (Fig. 1) they are seen in longitudinal view parallel to the plasma membrane.

Organization of the Cytoplasm at the Time of Secondary Wall Deposition

The small vacuoles of the young *Avena* xylem cells expand as the cells differentiate and may eventually fuse to form a large vacuole. Since many elements with well developed secondary wall thickenings have no large central vacuole, fusion, when it takes place, must occur at an advanced stage in the development of the xylem elements. Thus, at the time when wall thickenings are laid down the xylem elements have dense cytoplasmic contents, and these contents are bounded by the plasma membrane.

The Plasma Membrane. Except for the inclusions described below, the plasma membrane is adjacent to the cell wall and usually closely applied to it. It occupies a critical position in relation to cell wall development and to the movement of substances in and out of the cell in general. At all stages in the development of the xylem elements the membrane may be resolved as the usual triple-layered structure with two electron opaque lines separated by a less opaque region (Fig. 5). The appearance of the structure at regions where localized thickenings are being deposited is identical with its appearance adjacent to the primary wall. Thicker areas of the plasma membrane, however, have been observed, and may occur adjacent to either the secondary thickenings or the primary wall. This variation from the normal plasma membrane system may be important if enzyme systems concerned with wall deposition are located at its surface. A similar thickened structure has also been observed in differentiating phloem elements of pea (Bouck and Cronshaw, 1965) but at the present time it is not clear whether this thickened structure is in fact a variation of the normal membrane structure or a fixation artifact.

Inclusions, which may be tubular or vesicular, are often observed between the plasma membrane and the cell wall. Such an inclusion, which consists of a system of tubules, may be readily observed in Figure 9 in a region where the cytoplasm has pulled away from the wall. The individual tubules are of similar dimensions to the microtubules seen in the peripheral cytoplasm. Frei and Preston (1961) observed an oriented cytoplasmic component on the inner wall surface of *Chaetomorpha* and suggested that this component may be responsible for the orientation of the deposited wall. The structure they observed may well be similar in nature to the inclusions that we observe between the plasma membrane and the wall.

The nature and the continuity of the plasma membrane suggests that the final elaboration of the cell wall components takes place outside it. It is difficult to see how polymerized wall materials can be passed through this structure. This suggestion is supported by the work of Colvin *et al.*, (1957), who showed that in *Acetobacter xylinum* the cells are capable of producing an enzyme system and precursors which move outside the cell and synthesize cellulose microfibrils. Furthermore there are an increasing number of reports of enzyme systems and proteins in plant cell walls (Lamport and Northcote, 1960; Kivilaan *et al.*, 1961; Honda, 1955; Mertz, 1961). Another possibility, suggested by Myers *et al.*, (1956), is that new plasma membranes can be formed within the cytoplasm, externalizing a peripheral region which might include polymerized wall materials.

The Endoplasmic Reticulum. The endoplasmic reticulum is a possible site for the synthesis of precursors of wall polysaccharides or the enzyme system capable of producing them and possibly provides a transport pathway to the cell surface. Porter and Machado (1960b) and Whaley *et al.*, (1960) have demonstrated an anastomosing system of tubular endoplasmic reticulum which appeared to be involved in cell plate formation. Residual elements of endoplasmic reticulum near the wall of developing xylem cells of *Allium* root tips were observed by Porter and Machado (Porter and Machado, 1960a; Porter, 1961b), who suggested that they were related to the developing annular thickenings. Numerous profiles of endoplasmic reticulum may be observed throughout the cytoplasm of the developing xylem elements of *Avena* coleoptiles at the time of active wall deposition. The most common of these take the form of two parallel membranes which are interpreted as cross sections through lamellar vesicles (Fig. 3). Ribosomes are associated with the outer surface of these membranes and are usually arranged in groups (Fig. 5). A surface section through the ribosomes and the associated membrane demonstrates that the ribosomes are usually spirally arranged within the groups (Fig. 5). These elements of rough endoplasmic reticulum with attached polyribosomes are particularly abundant when the cells are involved in secondary wall formation.

Other elements of endoplasmic reticulum are devoid of ribosomes though they are seen to connect in places with the rough variety. Sections of this smooth form of endoplasmic reticulum show numerous tubular elements which are joined together into an anastomosing system.

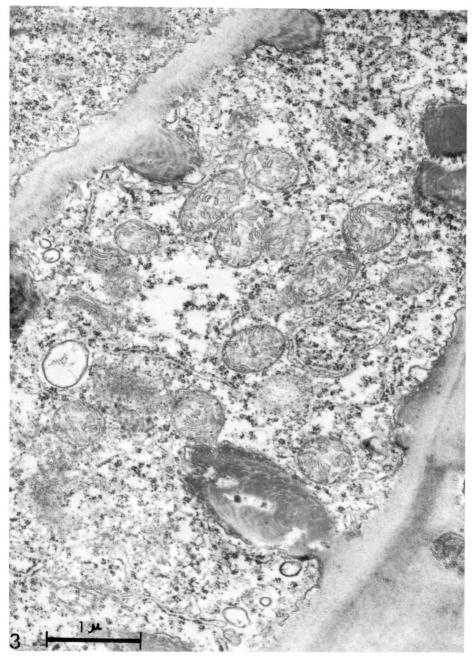

FIG. 3. *Avena sativa*. Longitudinal section through a differentiating xylem element from a 1 cm coleoptile. There is no apparent organization of the cytoplasmic components in the region of the developing thickenings. Osmium fixation X 24,000.

The role of ribosomes in protein synthesis is well known, and the synthetic function of the endoplasmic reticulum and the sequestering of proteins by its membranes has been discussed at length by Porter (1961a). In the xylem cells the enzyme systems concerned with wall deposition may be synthesized and transported to the cell surface by the well developed system of endoplasmic reticulum and the attached polyribosomes. However, although elements of endoplasmic reticulum are often seen adjacent to developing cell walls, at the present time there does not seem to be a preferred orientation of the endoplasmic reticulum with respect to the localized thickenings in the xylem elements of *Avena*.

Dictyosomes.   The linking of Golgi bodies in animal cells with secretory and excretory activities is not new (Dalton, 1961).   Recent observations suggest that dictyosomes may also have a secretory function in various types of plant cells (Bouck, 1962; Mollenhauer and Whaley, 1962 and 1963; Bonneville and Voeller, 1963; Manton, in press).   This secretory activity of the dictyosomes gives them a possible role in cell wall formation.   Mollenhauer and Whaley (1962) observed that dictyosomes are oriented in the region of cell plate formation and vesicles derived from them aggregate to form the initial stage of the cell plate.   These workers also report that the plate is extended by the fusion of vesicles at the edges, which indicates that the dictyosomes are contributing both wall material and material to extend the plasma membrane.   In xylem elements of *Avena* which are undergoing secondary wall formation dictyosomes are prominent throughout the cytoplasm.   They consist of stacks of flattened sacs (usually about five) and associated vesicles.   A small proportion of the associated vesicles have electron opaque contents; the others are apparently empty.   Similar vesicles with or without electron opaque contents and not associated with the dictyosomes, occur throughout the cytoplasm and may be very numerous.   The disassociated vesicles with electron opaque contents are here at least as numerous as those without contents. These two types of vesicles are characteristic of the differentiating xylem elements and their abundance in the developing xylem elements may be functionally significant in relation to cell wall deposition.

Microtubules.   Ledbetter and Porter (1963, 1964) have described a system of microtubules in plant cells which they state may either exert an influence over the disposition of cell wall materials or govern cytoplasmic streaming.   Hepler and Newcomb (1964) have described similar microtubules in redifferentiating parenchyma cells of *Coleus* in which localized wall thickenings are formed.   The tubules are oriented in the same direction as the cellulose microfibrils of the developing thickenings, and a system of fibrils oriented at right angles to these is confined within cisternae of the endoplasmic reticulum.

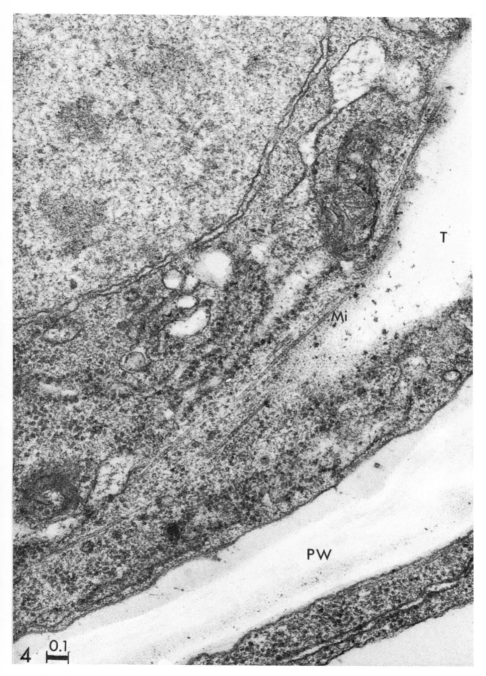

FIG. 4. *Avena sativa.* Transverse section of part of a developing xylem element from a 1 cm coleoptile. The section is cut at an angle to the thickening. Numerous microtubules are oriented in a direction parallel to that of the microfibrils in the developing wall thickening. PW—Primary wall, T—Wall thickening, Mi—Microtubules. Glutaraldehyde-osmium fixation X 54,000.

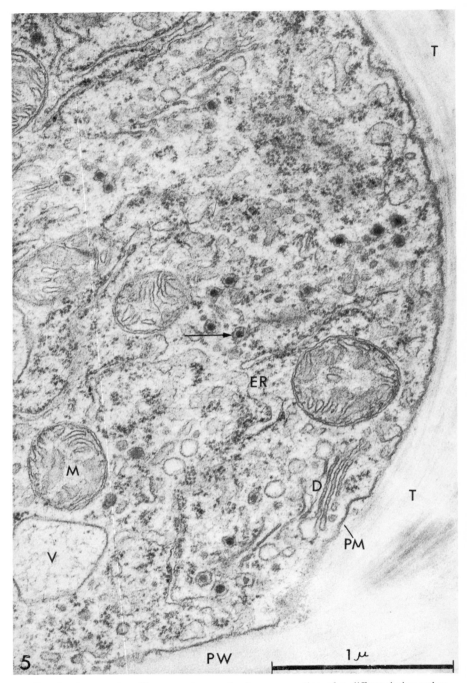

Fig. 5. *Avena sativa*. Electron micrograph of a cross section of a differentiating xylem element with a well-developed wall thickening from 1 cm coleoptile. There are numerous vesicles with electron opaque contents (arrow). PW—primary wall, T—wall thickening, PM—plasma membrane, M—mitochondrion, V—vacuole, ER—Endoplasmic reticulum. Osmium fixation X 48,000.

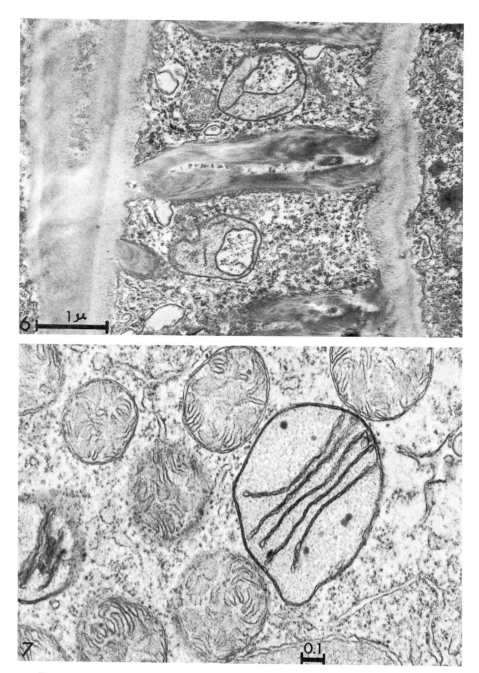

Fig. 6. *Avena sativa*. Longitudinal section through a differentiating xylem element from a 1 cm coleoptile. The section is near to the side wall and the annular thickenings are shown in longitudinal section. Plastids may be observed between the thickening bands. Osmium fixation X 18,000.

Fig. 7. *Avena sativa*. Plastid and mitochondria in a transverse section of a developing xylem element. The plastid has a group of internal lamellae. Osmium fixation X 48,000.

At all stages of differentiation of the *Avena* xylem elements, numerous microtubules are observed in the peripheral cytoplasm and are oriented in a direction parallel to the microfibrillar direction of the most recently deposited region of the wall. In particular, groups of microtubules are associated with the localized wall thickenings. Thus they are arranged in a characteristic pattern which reflects that of the developing wall thickenings. This arrangement can readily be seen in transverse sections of the developing vascular strand, where an annular or a spiral wall thickening may be cut at an angle towards its surface (Fig. 4). At the edge of the thickening several microtubules are observed in the surrounding cytoplasm which are arranged in directions parallel to the long axis of the thickening and to the cellulose microfibrils in it.

The close association of the microtubules with the developing wall thickenings, and the orientation of the microtubules in a direction similar to that of the microfibrils in the developing wall, suggests that either they are functionally involved in cell wall orientation or they are subject to the orienting forces which are operative to determine wall organization. In the latter case the orienting forces must be operative in the cytoplasm.

Mitochondria. At all stages of differentiation of the xylem element mitochondria are found scattered throughout the cytoplasm. They are surrounded by a double membrane, the innermost of which is infolded to form numerous plate-like cristae which may extend approximately half the diameter of the mitochondrion. The mitochondria are the last organelles to persist in the xylem elements and are often observed apparently intact in the cell lumen following the disorganization of the rest of the protoplasm (Fig. 8).

Plastids. Plastids are observed in most sections of the differentiating xylem elements and are surrounded by a double membrane (Figs. 6 and 7). Internally they show various substructures. Most commonly there is a system of tubules which are infoldings of the inner of the double limiting membranes. In other cases there are groups of parallel lamellae which may be in stacks of up to four or five in number (Fig. 7). Starch is absent from the plastids of the xylem elements though abundant in the plastids of the surrounding parenchyma cells. The membrane system of the plastids stains more intensely than other membrane systems of the cells.

FIG. 8. *Avena sativa.* Transverse section of part of two mature xylem elements. The thickenings have a banded appearance consisting of electron opaque and electron transparent regions which are extended in the direction of the microfibrils. The lumen of one cell contains mitochondria. Osmium fixation X 25,000.

FIG. 9. *Avena sativa.* Transverse section of a differentiating xylem element. The plasma membrane has pulled away from the cell wall and the area between shows numerous "tubules." PW—primary wall, T—wall thickening, Mi—microtubules, TU—tubules. Glutaraldehyde osmium fixation X 36,000.

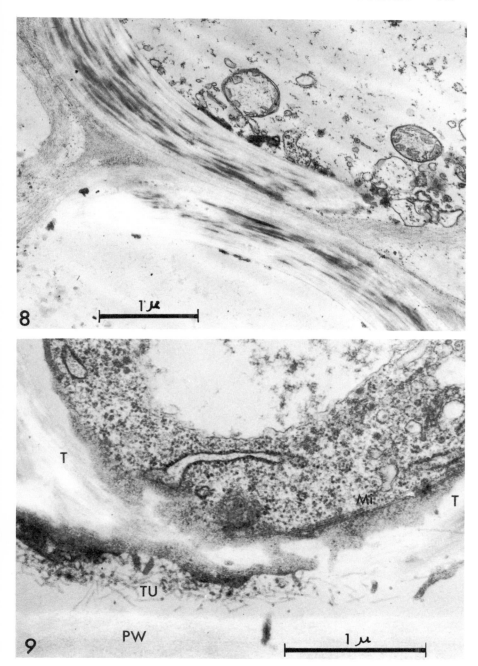

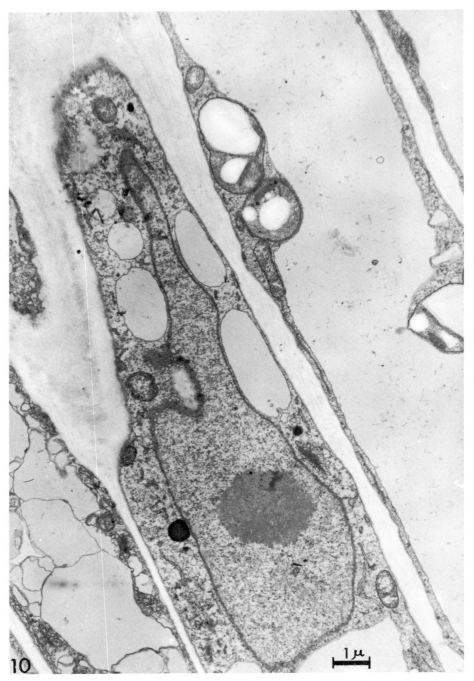

10

1 μ

Fɪɢ. 10. *Acer rubrum*. Longitudinal section of the cambial region. The cambial derivatives are at a very early stage of wall thickening. The nucleus contained in the section is
elongated and nuclear pores can be seen both in cross section and in surface view. Microtubules are apparent in the peripheral cytoplasm. Glutaraldehyde osmium fixation X 9,000.

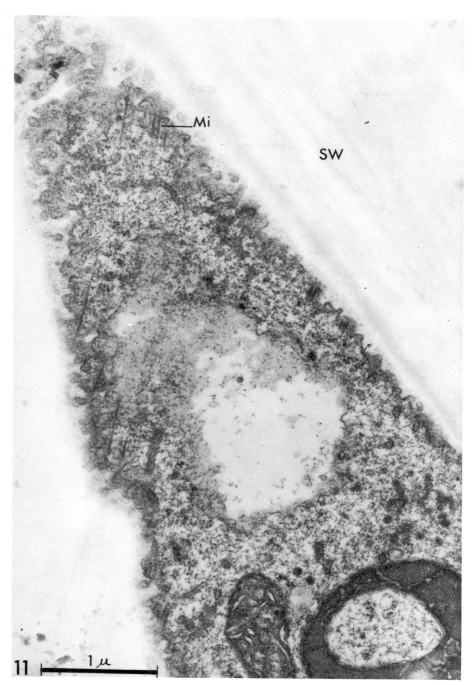

Fig. 11. *Acer rubrum*. Longitudinal section of part of a fiber with S_2 well developed. Microtubules in the peripheral cytoplasm are seen in the section as short segments in a parallel arrangement at an angle to the fiber axis. This is consistent with a helical arrangement in the intact cell. Mi—microtubules, SW—middle layer of the secondary wall. Glutaraldehyde osmium fixation X 30,000.

Crystal-Containing Bodies and Lipid Droplets. The xylem cells may contain single-membrane-bounded bodies with a crystalline core. The crystalline cores have regularly spaced electron opaque bands with a mean center to center distance *ca.* 150 Å (Cronshaw, 1964; Thornton and Thimann, 1964). There is a matrix substance between the crystal body and the limiting membrane. These bodies have been interpreted as photoreceptors by Thornton and Thimann (1964), or as storage granules that contain an organized condensation of macromolecules (either protein or lipoprotein) which may be enzymes, by the author (Cronshaw, 1964).

Lipid droplets are rarely seen in the xylem elements when secondary wall thickening is taking place although they are abundant in the cytoplasm of the surrounding parenchyma cells.

CAMBIAL DERIVATIVE OF *ACER RUBRUM*

The cells within the meristem are themselves differentiated, fusiform initials and ray initials being present. Considerable changes in dimension occur as these cells develop and the massive layered and lamellate secondary walls are laid down. The greatest bulk of the cell wall of the wood fibers is found in the layer S_2, which contains a high proportion of cellulose microfibrils, and these microfibrils are oriented in a steep helix around the cell. Figure 10 is an electron micrograph of a longitudinal section through the cambial region, which shows a cambial initial with its primary wall and differentiating adjacent cells whose walls are being elaborated. The nucleus contained in the section is elongated and has a double membrane with pores. The pores can be seen in cross section and in surface view. Mitochondria, plastids, endoplasmic reticulum, dictyosomes, ribosomes, microtubules, and lipid droplets are present and the cells have a large central vacuole and usually several smaller vacuoles.

Microtubules. During cell wall thickening a consistent feature of the cytoplasm is the large number of microtubules present which are oriented parallel to the cellulose microfibrils of the most recently deposited area of wall (Figs. 11, 12, and 13). Thus, at the time when the layer S_2 is devel-

---

FIG. 12. *Acer rubrum.* Transverse section of part of a fiber with a well developed S_2 layer. Microtubules in the peripheral cytoplasm are cut in cross section. Mi—microtubules, PM—plasma membrane, SW—secondary wall. Glutaraldehyde osmium fixation X 100,000.

FIG. 13. *Acer rubrum.* Longitudinal section of part of a fiber with a partially formed S_2 layer. Microtubules are oriented parallel to the striation direction in the wall. The dark region is the plasma membrane. SW—middle layer of the secondary wall. Glutaraldehyde osmium fixation X 50,000.

FIG. 14. *Acer rubrum.* Longitudinal section of a partially differentiated fiber. Vesicles appear to be arising from the plasma membrane. SW—secondary wall, PM—plasma membrane. Glutaraldehyde osmium fixation X 64,000.

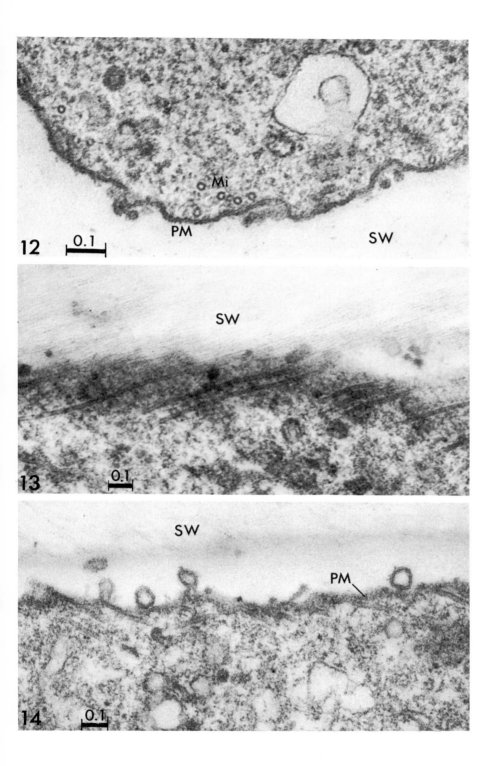

oping, these microtubules are oriented in the peripheral cytoplasm in a helical direction around the cells (Figs. 11, 13, and 15). The microtubules may be organized into small groups, usually of two or three in number, and their orientation and parallel arrangement is quite striking. They are connected to the plasma membrane, and at places the striation directions in the secondary wall appear to be continuous with the electron opaque region of the microtubules (Fig. 13). In some electron microscope images the less electron opaque region in the center of the microtubule appears to be continuous with the area outside the plasma membrane.

Endoplasmic Reticulum. The appearance of the endoplasmic reticulum in the cells at the stage when S_2 is being deposited is quite characteristic. There are numerous profiles of double membranes with attached ribosomes which are observed when the lamellar vesicles are cut in cross section, and there are also surface sections of the endoplasmic reticulum membranes with attached ribosomes which show that the groups of ribosomes are spirally arranged. At advanced stages of cell wall elaboration there are very few free ribosomes in the ground substance of the cytoplasm. The cambial cells, however, have a dense population of free ribosomes.

Another form of endoplasmic reticulum is devoid of attached ribosomes and is in the form of anastomosing tubules, which have densely staining contents following the fixation procedures used (Fig. 16). This anastomosing tubular system of the endoplasmic reticulum is most evident when sections are cut glancing towards the developing secondary wall. These sections show that the endoplasmic reticulum system is in very close proximity to the plasma membrane, and in some electron images tubules of the endoplasmic reticulum with densely staining contents can be seen apparently passing through the plasma membrane.

The Plasma Membrane. The plasma membrane has a triple-layered structure consisting of two electron opaque lines with a less opaque region between them. At regions there is an infolding of this plasma membrane. In cross section this gives the appearance of a multiple plasma membrane at the cell wall cytoplasmic interface (Fig. 18) and in longitudinal section gives the appearance of a ballooning inwards of the plasma membrane into the cytoplasm (Fig. 17). A feature of the cytoplasm adjacent to the infolded plasma membrane is that the microtubules in the peripheral cytoplasm remain oriented parallel to the cellulose microfibrils in the developing wall, suggesting that the infolding of the plasma membrane is not an artifact due to the preparation procedures (Fig. 17). The apparent space between the cell wall and the infolded plasma membrane often contains numerous tubular elements and vesicles. In fact, in many areas between the cell wall and the plasma membrane of the cell inclusions of this

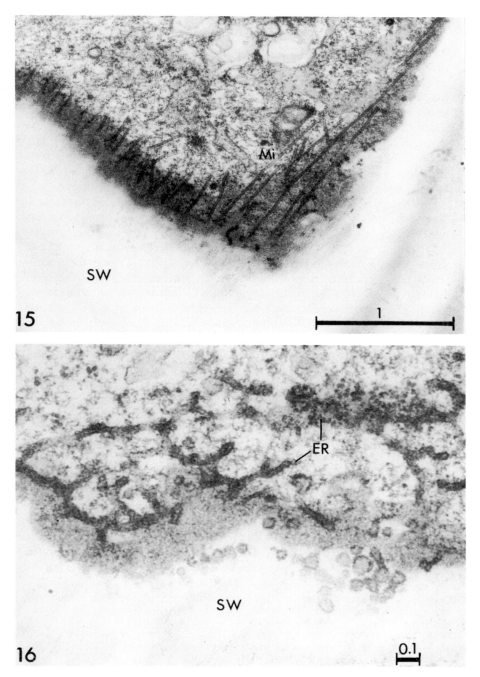

FIG. 15. *Acer rubrum.* Oblique longitudinal section of a partially differentiated fiber. The dark region is the plasma membrane. Mi—microtubules, SW—middle layer of the secondary wall. Glutaraldehyde osmium fixation X 36,000.

FIG. 16. *Acer rubrum* Transverse section of a partially differentiated fiber. The endoplasmic reticulum is associated with the cell surface. ER—endoplasmic reticulum, SW—secondary wall. Glutaraldehyde osmium fixation X 54,000.

nature are quite common. Sometimes small vesicular elements that are present between the plasma membrane and the wall may be seen to be connected to the plasma membrane, which suggests that the plasma membrane is giving rise to some of these small vesicles (Fig. 14). Also, these vesicles have the triple-layered structure similar to that of the plasma membrane (Fig. 14). Infoldings of the plasma membrane which contain vesicles and tubular elements are particularly common in the pit cavities.

Thus in these cells the cell wall cytoplasmic interface is structurally complex. The plasma membrane is in contact with tubular elements of the endoplasmic reticulum and with numerous microtubules. Further, it is not a very stable structure but probably in a continual state of breakdown and repair, allowing numerous vesicles and packets of substance to pass out of the cells.

Dictyosomes. Dictyosomes are observed, though not in abundance, throughout the differentiating wood fibers (Fig. 10). Where they occur, they have the familiar appearance of a group of flattened sacs and associated vesicles. In some sections the vesicles appear free of contents; in other sections the vesicles may have slightly electron opaque contents. There is, however, no differentiation into two types of vesicles, as was seen in the differentiating xylem elements of *Avena*. Vesicles similar to those associated with the dictyosomes are seen throughout the cytoplasm and have already been mentioned. These vesicles appear to fuse with the plasma membrane and give their contents to the wall side or appear to pass through the plasma membrane intact.

Plastids. Plastids are always observed in the differentiating xylem elements and have a complex structure (Fig. 11). They are surrounded by the usual double membrane, the innermost of which is usually infolded to form a network of tubules. The matrix of the plastids is always densely staining. In the newly formed cambial derivatives starch is often seen in the plastids, whereas xylem elements at a later stage of differentiation rarely have starch in the plastids. The plastids often show numerous large dense globuli.

Crystal-containing bodies. A consistent feature of the xylem elements at an advanced stage of differentiation is the appearance of numerous single-membrane-bounded, crystal-containing bodies (Fig. 19). Similar

FIG. 17. *Acer rubrum.* Longitudinal section of a differentiating fiber. The plasma membrane is infolded and the microtubules are oriented. SW—middle layer of the secondary wall. Glutaraldehyde osmium fixation X 45,000.

FIG. 18. *Acer rubrum.* Transverse section of a partially differentiated fiber. Several triple-layered plasma membranes are evident. SW—middle layer of the secondary wall. Glutaraldehyde osmium fixation X 100,000.

FIG. 19. *Acer rubrum.* Transverse section of a differentiating fiber. The single-membrane-bounded body has a crystalline core. Mean center to center distance of the electron opaque bands is 125 Å. SW—secondary wall. Glutaraldehyde osmium fixation X 54,000.

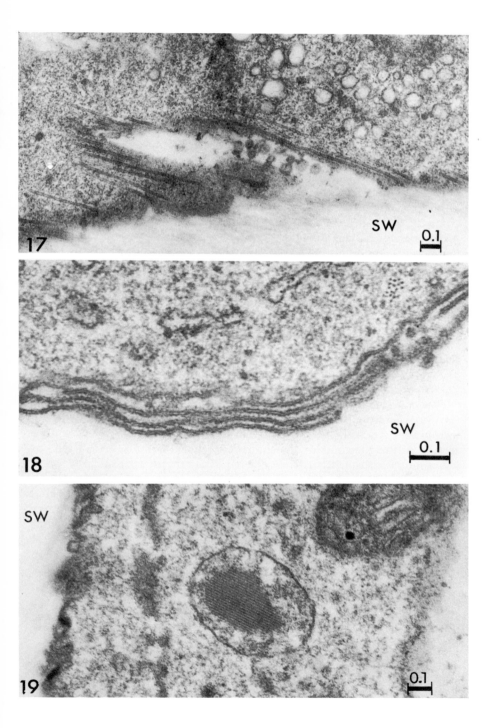

structures have already been described in the differentiating xylem elements of *Avena* and may be observed in phloem parenchyma of cells of *Acer* and in free cell cultures of *Eucalyptus camaldulensis* (Cronshaw, 1964). The crystal cores of these bodies in the cambial derivatives may have different lattice spacings even within the same cell. In a differentiating fiber containing three of these structures, the mean center to center spacings of the electron opaque bands was 180 Å, 120 Å, and 80 Å. Thus, if these bodies contain condensations of protein or lipoprotein which may be enzymatic in nature (see Cronshaw, 1964), different substances would be contained within different bodies. If these bodies are able to pass their contents through the plasma membrane, this may be one possible mechanism whereby enzymes are liberated into the cell wall. Some evidence in favor of this hypothesis has been presented from the phloem parenchyma cells of *Acer* (Cronshaw, 1964).

Lignification. Lignification of the wood fibers commences at the cell corners in the region of the primary wall (Wardrop, 1957). The primary walls and middle lamellae following the fixation procedures are densely staining. In some sections following osmium fixation, localized areas of staining are seen in the secondary wall adjacent to the primary wall region (Fig. 22). These localized areas of staining are interpreted as the first signs of lignification in the secondary wall, which may be either staining of lignin itself or the enzyme system which is about to deposit lignin.

Plasmodesmata. No cell wall thickening takes place at the region of the pits where the plasmodesmata are located. At this region the plasma membrane passes through the wall in a series of tubes. A longitudinal section of the plasmodesmata shows two cross sections of the plasma membrane with the usual triple-layered structure and a central electron opaque core (Fig. 20). It is of interest that the plasma membrane in this region has an asymmetrical structure, the inner dense layers appearing thicker or more heavily stained than the outer dense regions. Cross sections through the primary wall containing the plasmodesmata show rings of plasma membrane, again with a triple-layered structure and the central electron opaque cores (Fig. 21). These central electron opaque cores are surrounded by a uniform area of less opaque material and always appear

---

FIG. 20. *Acer rubrum.* Oblique section of a pit between two ray cells. Plasmodesmata are cut in longitudinal section. The triple-layered structure of the plasma membrane lining the plasmodesmata can be resolved and also the electron opaque core. Glutaraldehyde osmium fixation X 90,000.

FIG. 21. *Acer rubrum.* Oblique section of a vessel element wall. A pit with numerous plasmodesmata is included in the section. Osmium fixation X 60,000.

FIG. 22. *Acer rubrum.* Transverse section of a fiber with a well formed S_2 layer. Localized areas of staining are evident in S_2 adjacent to the primary wall. Osmium fixation X 40,000.

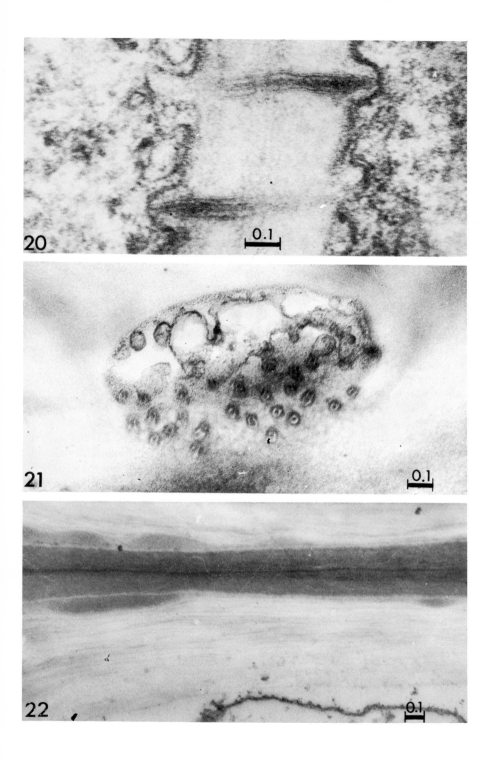

central in a true cross section. Longitudinal sections of the plasmodesmata show that they sometimes branch within the wall, and this branching
most often occurs in the middle lamella region.

GENERAL COMMENTS

Structural features of the cytoplasm have been described which suggest
that specific cytoplasmic components are functionally involved in cell wall
synthesis and orientation. The observations indicate the following points:

1. The endoplasmic reticulum is abundant in cells whose major activity
at the time of fixation is cell wall deposition; it has in some cases a morphological association with the developing wall and may contribute enzyme systems or even precursors to the wall. Its form in the cells is well
suited to transport of materials to the cell surface.

2. The dictyosomes, known to have a secretory function in other cell
systems, may contribute wall materials by means of the dictyosome-de-
rived vesicles. In view of the known involvement of these vesicles in cell
plate formation, in the xylem elements the activity of the dictyosomes may
be restricted to matrix materials of the wall.

3. The plasma membrane is not a static structure and is involved in
passing materials out of the cell. The microtubules are anchored to it and
the endoplasmic reticulum is closely associated with it.

4. Microtubules in the peripheral cytoplasm are always oriented parallel to the direction of the microfibrillar direction of the most recently
deposited wall material. Thus they are transversely oriented around xylem
elements which have only a primary wall, oriented parallel to the thickenings of primary xylem elements, and oriented helically in wood fibers
which are developing the S_2 layer. The morphological association of the
microtubules with the developing walls may be functionally significant
with respect to the orientation of the microfibrils. This function may be
passive in that they form an oriented skeleton in the cytoplasm which may
trap and direct wall metabolites, or they may be actively involved in that
they provide the site of a motivating force for cytoplasmic movement.
The other possibility is that the microfibrils in the cell wall and the microtubules are subject to the same orienting mechanism. If this is the case
then this general orienting mechanism must reside in the cytoplasm and
not outside the plasma membrane.

ACKNOWLEDGMENT

These investigations were supported by grant No. GM11215 from the
Division of General Medical Sciences, National Institute of Health.

REFERENCES

Barkley, G. (1927) "Differentiation of vascular bundle of *Trischosanthes anguina*." Botan. Gaz. 83:173–184.

Bonneville, M. A., and Voeller, B. R. (1963) "A new cytoplasmic component of plant cells." *J. Cell Biol.* 18:703–708.

Bouck, G. B. (1962) "Chromatophore development, pits, and other fine structure in the red alga, *Lomentaria baileyana* (Harv.) Farlow." *J. Cell Biol.* 12:553–569.

————, and Cronshaw, J. (1965) "The fine structure of differentiating phloem elements." *J. Cell Biol. 25*:1

Colvin, J. R., Bayley, S. T., and Beer, M. (1957) "The growth of cellulose microfibrils from *Acetobacter xylinum*." *Biochim. Biophys. Acta* 23:652–653.

Cronshaw, J. (1964) "Crystal containing bodies of plant cells." *Protoplasma. 59*:318.

————, and Bouck, G. B. (1965) "The fine structure of differentiating xylem elements," *J. Cell Biol.* 24:415.

————, and Wardrop, A. B. (1964) "The organization of cytoplasm in differentiating xylem." *Australian J. Botany* 12:15–23.

Cruger, H. (1855) "Zur Entwicklungsgeschichte der Zellenwand." *Bot. Z.* 18:601–617.

Dalton, A. J. (1961) "Golgi apparatus and secretion granules." In *The Cell* (J. Brachet and Alfred E. Mirsky, ed.), Vol. 2. Academic Press, N. Y.

Dippel, L. (1868) *Das Mikroskop und seine Anwendung,* Braunschweig, Druck und Verlag von Friedrich Vieweg und Sohn, 2, 1898, (First Edition, 1867–1869).

Esau, K., Cheadle, V. I., and Risley, E. B. (1963) "A view of ultrastructure of *Cucurbita* xylem." *Botan. Gaz.* 124:311–316.

Frei, E., and Preston, R. D. (1961) "Cell wall organization and wall growth in the filamentous green algae *Cladophora* and *Chaetomorpha.* I. The basic structure and its formation." *Proc. Roy. Soc. (London), Ser. B* 154:70–94.

Hepler, P. K., and Newcomb, E. H. (1963) "The fine structure of tracheary xylem elements arising by redifferentiation of parenchyma in wounded *Coleus* stem." *J. Exp. Botany* 14:496–503.

———— and ———— (1964) "Microtubules and fibrils in the cytoplasm of *Coleus* cells undergoing secondary wall deposition." *J. Cell Biol.* 20:529–533.

Honda, S. I. (1955) "Ascorbic acid oxidase in barley roots." *Plant Physiol.* 30:174–181.

Kivilaan, A., Beaman, T. C., and Bandurski, R. S. (1961) "Enzymatic activities associated with cell wall preparations from corn coleoptiles." *Plant Physiol.* 36:605–610.

Lamport, D. T. A., and Northcote, D. H. (1960) "Hydroxyproline in primary cell walls of higher plants." *Nature* 188:665–666.

Ledbetter, M. C., and Porter, K. R. (1963) "A 'microtubule' in plant cell fine structure." *J. Cell Biol.* 19:239–250.

———— and ———— (1964) "Morphology of microtubules of plant cells." *Science* 144: 872–874.

Manton, I. (In press) *J. Microscope Soc.*

Mertz, D. (1961) "Distribution and cellular localization of ascorbic acid. Oxidase in the maize root tip." *Am. J. Botany* 48:405–413.

Mollenhauer, H. H., and Whaley, W. G. (1962) "A secretory function of the golgi-apparatus in certain plant cells." In *Fifth International Congress for Electron Microscopy,"* Vol. 2, pp. YY-3. Academic Press, N. Y.

———— and ———— (1963) "An observation on the functioning of the golgi-apparatus." *J. Cell Biol.* 17:222–225.

Myers, A., Preston, R. D., and Ripley, G. W. (1956) "Fine structure in the red algae. I. X-ray and electron microscope investigation of *Griffithsia flosculosa.*" *Proc. Roy. Soc. (London), Ser. B* 144:450.

Porter, K. R. (1961a) "The ground substance; observations from electron microscopy." In *The cell* (J. Brachet and Alfred E. Mirsky, ed.), Vol. 2. Academic Press, N. Y.

—— (1961b) "The endoplasmic reticulum: some current interpretations of its form and functions." In *Biological Structure and Function* (Goodwin and Lindberg, ed.), Vol. 2, pp. 127–155. Academic Press, N. Y.

——, and Machado, R. D. (1960a) "The endoplasmic reticulum and the formation of plant cell walls." *Proc. European Regional Conf. Electron Microscopy, Delft, 1960* 2:754–758.

—— and —— (1960b) "Studies on the endoplasmic reticulum. IV. Its form and distribution during mitosis in cells of onion root tip." *J. Biophys. Biochem. Cytol.* 7:167–180.

Roelofson, P. A. (1959) *Encyclopedia of Plant Anatomy. Part 4. The Plant Cell Wall* (W. Zimmerman and P. G. Ozenda, ed.). Gebruder Borntraeger, Berlin-Nikolassee, Germany. 335 pp.

Schmitz, F. (1880) "Über Bildung und Wachstum der pflanzlichen Zellmembran" *Sitzber. Bes. Natur. u. Heilk.* (Bonn) 159:250.

Sinnott, E. W., and Bloch, R. (1945) "The cytoplasmic basis of intercellular patterns in vascular differentiation." *Am. J. Botany* 32:151.

Strasburger, E. (1882) *Über den Bau u. das Wachstum der Zellhäute.* Verlag von Gustav Fischer, Jena.

Thornton, R. M., and Thimann, K. V. (1964) "On a crystal-containing body in the oat coleoptile." *J. Cell Biol.* 20:345–349.

Wardrop, A. B. (1957) "The phase of lignification in the differentiation of wood fibres." *Tappi* 40:225–243.

Whaley, W. G., and Mollenhauer, H. H. (1963) "The golgi-apparatus and cell plate formation—A postulate." *J. Cell Biol.* 17:216–225.

——, ——, and Leech, J. H. (1960) "The ultrastructure of the meristematic cell." *Am. J. Botany* 47:401–419.

PART II

Wood Constituents—*Their Chemistry, Biosynthesis, Ultrastructure, and Physical Characteristics*

Wood and Bark Polysaccharides

T. E. TIMELL

State University College of Forestry
at Syracuse University

Wood consists of three main constituents, namely cellulose, hemicelluloses, and lignin. Other polymeric components, usually present in lesser and often varying amounts, are starch, pectin, and polyphenols. The middle lamella and the primary wall, the portions first formed in the new cell, at this stage consist mostly of pectic material. During the subsequent cell wall thickening, cellulose and hemicelluloses are deposited, forming the secondary wall. At the end of this phase, deposition of lignin is initiated, beginning at the cell corners and spreading from there into the middle lamella and the secondary wall. When lignification is complete, the cell dies. In softwoods (wood from gymnosperms) approximately 70% of the lignin is located in the middle lamella, the corresponding figure for hardwoods (wood from angiosperms) being 90%.

Cellulose always occurs in nature in the form of microfibrils. In wood these are surrounded (encrusted) by the three-dimensional amorphous lignin. The exact state of the hemicelluloses in wood is not known at present. Most likely they are amorphous and closely associated with the cellulose.

The organization of a typical softwood tracheid or hardwood fiber is shown in Figure 1. The primary wall, which is 0.1 to 0.2 μ thick, contains a loose, random network of cellulose microfibrils, while the outer layer of the secondary wall (0.1 to 0.3 μ) has a crossed fibrillar structure. In the S_2 layer (1 to 5 μ) the microfibrils are oriented almost parallel to the fiber axis. In the S_3 layer (0.1 μ), finally, the microfibrils form a flat helix.

In reaction wood, the pattern of cell wall organization is somewhat different. Compression wood, formed on the lower side of a leaning softwood stem, is characterized by the presence of an extra layer of lignin, located between S_1 and S_2 and by the absence of S_3. Tension wood, which is located on the upper side of a leaning hardwood stem, lacks one or several of the secondary wall layers. Instead, tension wood fibers contain a typical, so-called gelatinous layer (G-layer), which is deposited next to the lumen. It is not lignified and consists largely of highly crystalline cellulose microfibrils which are oriented parallel to the fiber axis.

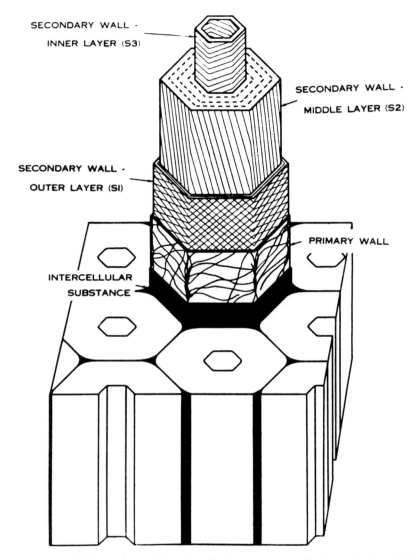

FIG. 1. Simplified structure of the cell wall of a softwood tracheid or a hardwood fiber (Wardrop and Bland, 1959).

The chemistry and biochemistry of wood have been summarized in excellent monographs by Hägglund (1951), Wise and Jahn (1952), Treiber (1957), Kratzl and Billek (1959), and Browning (1963). Comprehensive reviews of the chemistry of lignin have been presented by Brauns (1952) and by Brauns and Brauns (1960). Wood extractives have been dealt with in a recent monograph by Hillis (1962). The chemistry of cellulose has been treated in the classical monograph of Ott *et al.* (1954). A later contribution is that by Honeyman (1959). The chemistry of wood hemicelluloses has recently been discussed in detail by Timell (1964a).

General Chemical Composition of Wood

The average cellulose content of both hardwoods and softwoods is $43 \pm 2\%$. Higher or lower values indicate the presence of reaction wood. In hardwoods (Table I) the lignin content varies between 18 and 25%. The dominating hemicellulose here is a partially acetylated, acidic xylan. White birch (*Betula papyrifera* Marsh.) and silver birch (*Betula verrucosa* Ehrh.) are unusually rich in this polysaccharide (35%), while American elm (*Ulmus americana* L.) represents the other extreme (15%). The second hemicellulose, which is a glucomannan, occurs in only limited amounts.

TABLE I. Chemical Composition of Wood from Three Angiosperms

All values in per cent of extractive-free wood.

Component	Red maple (Acer rubrum L.)	White birch (Betula papyrifera Marsh.)	Trembling aspen (Populus tremuloides Michx.)
Cellulose	45	42	48
Lignin	24	19	21
Glucuronoxylan	25	35	24
Glucomannan	4	3	3
Pectin, starch	2	1	4

The lignin content of softwoods (Table II) is higher and normally varies between 25 and 35%. A series of closely related, partly acetylated galactoglucomannans are the predominant hemicelluloses here, comprising about 20% of the wood. A xylan, somewhat different from that in the hardwoods, is also present. In addition to these two types of hemicelluloses, members of the genus *Larix* contain large quantities (10 to 20% of the wood) of an arabinogalactan which in other conifers is present in only trace amounts.

As can be seen from Tables III and IV, tension wood contains less lignin and xylan but more cellulose and galactan than normal wood. Compression wood (Table V), on the other hand, is characterized by the presence of more lignin and less cellulose and galactoglucomannan. Like tension wood, it contains more galactan than normal wood.

TABLE II. Chemical Composition of Wood from Three Conifers

All values in per cent of extractive-free wood.

Component	Balsam fir (Abies balsamea [L.] Mill)	White spruce (Picea glauca [Moench] Voss)	Eastern white pine (Pinus strobus L.)
Cellulose	42	41	41
Lignin	29	27	29
Arabinoglucuronoxylan	9	13	9
Galactoglucomannan	18	18	18
Pectin, starch	2	1	3

TABLE III. Analytical Data for Normal (Side) Wood and Tension Wood from Eucalyptus goniocalyx F. Muell.

All values in per cent of extractive-free wood.

Component	Side wood	Tension wood
Cellulose	44	57
Lignin	23	14
Pentosan	19	11
Uronic anhydride	4.2	4.0
Acetyl	3.0	2.0
Galactose residues	1.5	7.4

Source: Schwerin (1958).

TABLE IV. Relative Sugar Composition of Normal and Tension Wood from Betula pubescens Ehrh.

All values in per cent of total neutral carbohydrates.

Sugar residue	Normal wood	Tension wood
Galactose	2.4	12
Glucose	58	74
Mannose	0.8	0.4
Arabinose	1.0	Traces
Xylose	38	14

Source: Gustafsson et al. (1952).

CELLULOSE

Cellulose is the main structural component of all plant cell walls and is always the same throughout nature, even if the morphology and the arrangement of the microfibrils can vary. It consists of β-D-glucose residues, linked together to straight chains by (1 → 4)-glycosidic bonds.

TABLE V. Lignin Content and Relative Sugar Composition of Normal and Compression Wood from Sapwood Portion of *Larix Laricina* (Du Roi) K. Koch

Lignin values in per cent of extractive-free wood. Other values in per cent of total neutral carbohydrates.

Component	Normal wood	Compression wood
Lignin	27	38
Residues of:		
Galactose	3	18
Glucose	69	59
Mannose	18	9
Arabinose	2	2
Xylose	8	12

Source: Timell (1964b).

The presence of other sugar residues or other glycosidic bonds is no longer considered likely. The glucose residues are present in the C1-chair conformation, rendering all three hydroxyl groups equatorial (Fig. 2).

Celluloses have recently been isolated from various plants, including trees, in quantitative yields and with a minimum of degradation by a direct nitration method (Goring and Timell, 1962). Light scattering

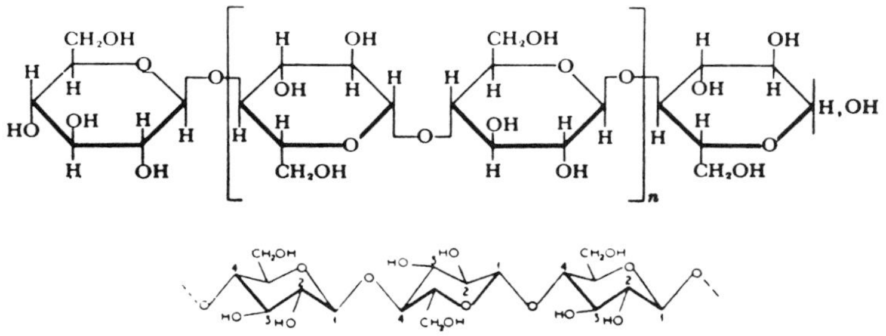

FIG. 2. Structure of cellulose.

measurements gave the weight-average degrees of polymerization presented in Table VI. Wood celluloses evidently have the same average degree of polymerization, 8,000 to 10,000, as cellulose from other plants. A value as high as 15,000 was found for celluloses from unopened cotton bolls. These results have later been confirmed by Marx-Figini and Schulz (1963).

The same authors have also studied the molecular-weight distribution of native celluloses. A cotton cellulose contained three distinct maxima, as can be seen from Figure 3, namely at 1,500, 5,500 and 11,500, respec-

TABLE VI. Weight-Average Degrees of Polymerization of Celluloses
from Various Sources

Source	$\overline{P}_w$
Seed hairs	
Unopened cotton bolls	15,000
Cotton, kapok, milkweed floss (opened)	10,000
Bast fibers	
Flax, hemp, jute, ramie	9,900
Wood	
Red maple (*Acer rubrum* L.)	8,300
White birch (*Betula papyrifera* Marsh.)	10,000
Trembling aspen (*Populus tremuloides* Michx.)	10,300
Amabilis fir (*Abies amabilis* [Dougl.] Forbes)	7,500
Engelmann spruce (*Picea engelmannii* Parry)	8,000
Jack pine (*Pinus banksiana* Lamb)	7,900
Bark Celluloses	10,000
Fern Celluloses	8,000

Source: Goring and Timell (1962).

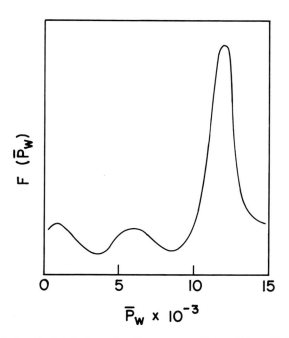

FIG. 3. Chain-length distribution of native cotton cellulose (Marx-Figini and Schulz, 1963).

tively. The first maximum at 1,500 evidently represents the cellulose present in the primary wall (Marx-Figini, 1963), while the third maximum, which represents 65% of the total, is considered to correspond to cellulose deposited in the secondary wall. It is difficult to explain the presence of the second maximum, which could possibly have been formed by a random depolymerization. It is clear that the polymolecularity of the cellulose present in the third maximum is extremely low, and it has been suggested that the polysaccharide might have been formed by a template mechanism (Marx-Figini, 1963).

The actual size of the highly crystalline cellulose microfibrils present in the cell wall is still a moot question. According to earlier views, the width of the cellulose microfibrils is 150 to 200 Å (Colvin, 1963). Frey-Wyssling and Mühlethaler (1963; Mühlethaler, 1960), however, believe that the ultimate biological unit is the so-called *elementary fibril* with a diameter of about 35 Å. These elementary fibrils, which are highly crystalline, can associate, thus forming microfibrils with diameters varying between 100 and 300 Å. It is still not known with certainty whether the cellulose chains in the fibrils are parallel or antiparallel.

HARDWOOD HEMICELLULOSES

O-*Acetyl-4-O-methylglucurono-xylan.* Hardwood xylans can be isolated in yields of 80 to 90% by direct extraction of the wood with aqueous potassium hydroxide. With certain species, such as trembling aspen (*Populus tremuloides* Michx.) (Jones *et al.*, 1961), the yield is almost quantitative. Xylan has a good stability towards alkali, and the product obtained is therefore close in properties to that of the native polymer, except, of course, that all acetyl groups have been eliminated. For isolation of the acetylated polysaccharide, wood is first delignified either by the chlorine (Timell and Jahn, 1951) or by the chlorite (Wise *et al.*, 1946) procedure, after which the resulting holocellulose is extracted in succession with dimethyl sulfoxide and water (Hägglund *et al.*, 1956). The yield in this case is only 50%.

Every hardwood so far investigated has been found to contain the same type of xylan. The repeating unit of the deacetylated polymer is given in Figure 4, while Figure 5 is a simplified but complete structure. The framework consists of $(1 \rightarrow 4)$-linked β-D-xylopyranose residues, some of which carry a 4-*O*-methyl-α-D-glucuronic acid residue linked directly to the 2-position. Seven out of ten xylose units are also acetylated, mostly at C-3, but to a certain extent also at C-2. Earlier evidence indicated a linear nature of the xylan backbone. More recent results, however, clearly show

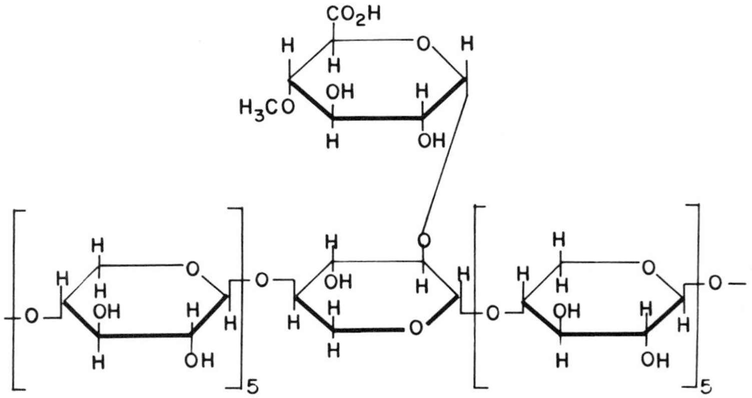

FIG. 4. Structure of 4-*O*-methylglucuronoxylan.

that two branches are present per average molecule (Dutton and Unrau, 1962; Zinbo and Timell, 1964). The branches must be very short, since the xylan can form quite strong films and is similar to cellulose in its hydrodynamic behavior (LeBel and Goring, 1963).

The great majority of the hardwoods in the temperate zone contain a xylan with ten xylose residues per acid side chain. So far, only three exceptions have been found, namely apple (*Malus pumila* Mill.), sweet cherry (*Prunus avium* [L] L.), and American elm (*Ulmus americana* L.), which possess one acid group per 6 to 7 xylose residues. The acid side chains are probably distributed at random along the xylan framework (Timell, 1962a).

Native hardwood xylans contain at least 150 and probably closer to 200 xylose residues per average molecule (LeBel *et al.*, 1963; Koshijima and Timell, 1964). Measurements of the number- and weight-average molecular weights, as well as direct fractionation experiments, indicate that the polymolecularity, like that of cellulose, is very low (LeBel *et al.*, 1963; LeBel and Goring, 1963).

$$\left[\begin{array}{c}\beta\text{-D-Xyl}p\text{-1} \\ 3\,(2) \\ | \\ \text{Acetyl}\end{array}\right]_7 \rightarrow 4\text{-}\beta\text{-D-Xyl}p\text{-1} \rightarrow \begin{array}{c}4\text{-}\beta\text{-D-Xyl}p\text{-1} \\ 2 \\ \uparrow \\ 1 \\ 4\text{-}O\text{-Me-}\alpha\text{-D-Glu}p\text{A}\end{array} \rightarrow 4\text{-}\beta\text{-D-Xyl}p\text{-1}$$

FIG. 5. Repeating unit of *O*-Acetyl-4-*O*-methylglucurono-xylan.

The xylan chains possess a threefold screw axis (Marchessault and Liang, 1962) and are capable of crystallizing. After removal of some of the acid and all of the acetyl groups, the xylan can be induced to form single crystals (Yundt, 1951). Single crystals of a neutral esparto xylan are seen in Figure 6. In its native state, the xylan is soluble in water, a property which is lost when the acetyl groups are removed.

FIG. 6. Single crystals of esparto xylan (Marchessault *et al.*, 1961).

Glucomannan. After removal of all xylan from a hardwood holocellulose, the remaining glucomannan can be obtained by extraction with sodium hydroxide containing borate (Timell, 1960a). The polysaccharide (Figure 7) consists of β-D-glucopyranose and β-D-mannopyranose residues, linked together by (1 → 4)-glycosidic bonds. The molar ratio of glucose to mannose is usually 1:2, except for the genus *Betula*, where it is 1:1. It is not known whether these polysaccharides are branched or not,

→ 4-β-D-Glu$p$-1 → 4-β-D-Man$p$-1 → 4-β-D-Glu$p$-1 → 4-β-D-Man$p$-1 → 4-β-D-Man$p$-1 →

FIG. 7. Repeating unit of glucomannan.

or if they contain acetyl groups. The molecular properties of the native polymer are also unknown.

Tension Wood Galactan. As can be seen from Table IV, tension wood contains more galactose residues than normal wood. These residues originate from a galactan, as recently shown by Meier (1962). This new type of wood hemicellulose contains both β-(1 → 4)- and β-(1 → 6)-linkages. Its constitution has not been fully elucidated, and galacturonic, glucuronic, and rhamnose residues might be integral parts of the polymer.

SOFTWOOD HEMICELLULOSES

Arabino-4-O-methylglucurono-xylan. Only little carbohydrate material can be directly extracted with alkali from softwoods, probably because of the relatively high concentration of lignin in the secondary wall. After delignification, which is usually effected with chlorous acid, potassium hydroxide will remove a mixture of an acidic arabinoxylan and a galacto-glucomannan (Timell, 1961e), as can be seen from Figure 8. The latter polysaccharide is capable of forming an insoluble complex with barium hydroxide (Meier, 1958a) and can thus be separated from the former.

The constitution of the xylan, seen in Figure 9, shows that it is an arabino-4-O-methylglucuronoxylan, similar to the hardwood xylans. Unlike the latter, however, the softwood moiety also contains α-L-arabino-

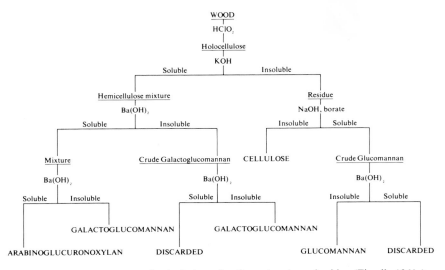

Fig. 8. Extraction sequence for isolation of softwood polysaccharides (Timell, 1961e).

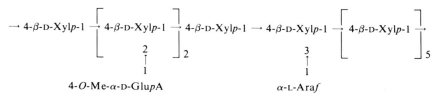

FIG. 9. Repeating unit of arabino-4-*O*-methylglucurono-xylan.

furanose residues, directly attached to C-3 of the xylose. The softwood xylans are more acidic than those normally found in hardwoods and contain 5 to 6 xylose residues per acid side chain, while one arabinose occurs per 7 to 8 xylose. Acetyl groups are not present. The degree of polymerization of the native polysaccharide has not been established, the products so far isolated being depolymerized by the chlorous acid used for removing the lignin, nor is it known whether the xylan backbone is branched or linear.

O-Acetyl-galacto-glucomannans. In the softwoods, the predominant hemicelluloses are the galactoglucomannans, a family of closely related polysaccharides, differing mainly in their relative sugar composition. Their presence in wood was discovered only a few years ago by Hamilton and his co-workers (1956, 1960). The major portion of the hexosans extracted with potassium hydroxide together with the xylan consists of a water-soluble galactoglucomannan containing galactose, glucose, and mannose residues in a ratio of 1:1:3. Extraction of the residual holocellulose with sodium hydroxide-borate (Fig. 8) gives a second polysaccharide (often referred to as a "glucomannan"), where the ratio between the three hexose residues is 0.1:1:3. This polymer is soluble in aqueous sodium hydroxide but not in water. Other galactoglucommans with slightly different sugar compositions are also present. All of them are probably partly acetylated (Meier, 1961a).

A general structural formula is presented in Figure 10. The molecular framework consists of β-D-glucopyranose and β-D-mannopyranose residues, (1 → 4)-linked, and probably distributed at random. Some units carry an α-D-galactopyranose residue, directly attached to C-6. The

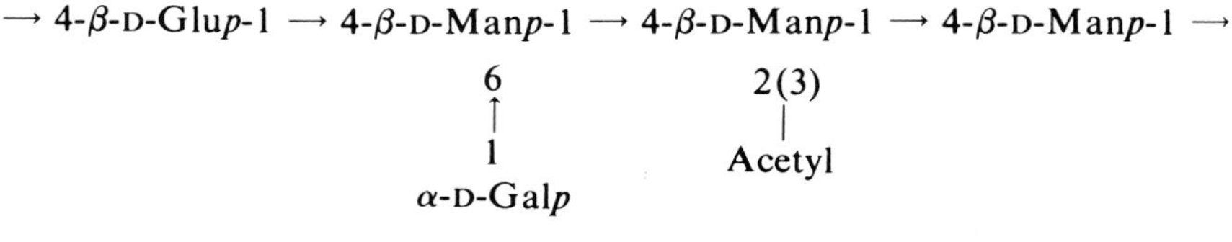

→ 4-β-D-Glup-1 → 4-β-D-Manp-1 → 4-β-D-Manp-1 → 4-β-D-Manp-1 →

    6   2(3)
    ↑ |
    1   Acetyl
α-D-Galp

FIG. 10. Repeating unit of *O*-acetyl-galacto-glucomannans.

acetyl groups are located at the mannose residues. Although conclusive evidence is still lacking, it is probable that the glucomannan backbone is slightly branched, and that it contains at least 150 hexose residues. After deacetylation, the alkali-soluble galactoglucomannan can be induced to crystallize. After further degradation, the glucomannan can form single crystals.

Compression Wood Galactan. Recently, Bouveng and Meier (1959) have been able to isolate a galactan from spruce compression wood. Unlike the tension wood galactan, this polymer consists of only $(1 \rightarrow 4)$-linked β-D-galactopyranose residues. It is not yet certain whether uronic acid residues are integral parts of the polymer or not.

Larch Arabinogalactan. On direct extraction with water, wood from conifers other than larches yields small amounts of a galactoglucomannan and an acidic arabinogalactan (Roudier, 1962; Aspinall and Wood, 1963). Wood from members of the genus *Larix*, on similar treatment, gives considerable quantities of a similar arabinogalactan. Especially large amounts of this polysaccharide, 20 to 25% of the wood, seem to be present in western larch (*Larix occidentalis* Nutt.) and in *Larix dahurica*.

Larch arabinogalactan has an unusually complicated structure. It also seems to be composed of two polymers of similar chemical composition but with different molecular weights (Bouveng and Lindberg, 1958). It is now evident that all species of larch contain the same type of slightly acidic arabinogalactan, the structure of which is seen in Figure 11. In most cases the molar ratio of galactose to arabinose is 6:1. The backbone is composed of $(1 \rightarrow 3)$-linked β-D-galactopyranose residues, each of which carries a side chain attached to its 6-position. Most of these side chains consist of $(1 \rightarrow 6)$-linked β-D-galactopyranose residues, the average chain containing two such units. Some galactose units in the main chain carry a residue of 3-*O*-β-L-arabinopyranosyl-L-arabinofuranose. A

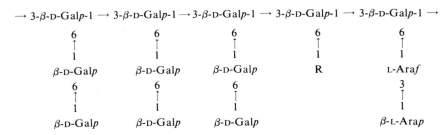

R = β-D-Galactopyranose or, less frequently, L-Arabinofuranose or D-Glucopyranosyluronic acid

FIG. 11. Repeating unit of larch arabinogalactan.

Polysaccharide	Occurrence	Per cent of extractive-free wood	Composition	Parts	Linkages
O-Acetyl-4-O-methylglucuronoxylan	Hardwoods	20–35	β-D-Xylp 4-O-Me-α-D-GlupA O-Acetyl	10 1 7	1 → 4 1 → 2
Glucomannan	Hardwoods	3–5	β-D-Manp β-D-Glup	1–2 1	1 → 4 1 → 4
Arabino-4-O-methylglucuronoxylan	Softwoods	10–15	β-D-Xylp 4-O-Me-α-D-GlupA L-Araf	10 2 1.3	1 → 4 1 → 2 1 → 3
Galactoglucomannan (water-soluble)	Softwoods	5–10	β-D-Manp β-D-Glup α-D-Galp O-Acetyl	3 1 0.24	1 → 4 1 → 4 1 → 6
Galactoglucomannan (alkali-soluble)	Softwoods	10–15	β-D-Manp β-D-Glup α-D-Galp O-Acetyl	3 1 0.1 0.24	1 → 4 1 → 4 1 → 6
Arabinogalactan	Larch wood	10–20	β-D-Galp L-Araf β-L-Arap β-D-GlupA	6 2/3 1/3 Few	1 → 3, 1 → 6 1 → 6 1 → 3 1 → 6

Polysaccharide	Linear or branched	Specific rotation (degrees)	Solvent	$\bar{P}_n$	$\bar{P}_w$
O-Acetyl-4-O-methylglucuronoxylan	Probably branched	−80 ± 5	Water, alkali	150–200	180–250
Glucomannan	Undecided	−30 ± 2	Alkali	70	120
Arabino-4-O-methylglucuronoxylan	Undecided	−37 ± 2	Water	120	
Galactoglucomannan (water-soluble)	Probably branched	−7 to −8	Water	100	150
Galactoglucomannan (alkali-soluble)	Probably branched	−35 ± 5	Alkali	100	150
Arabinogalactan	Heavily branched	+10 ± 2	Water	220	100 and 600

few terminal residues of L-arabinofuranose and D-glucuronic acid are also present. This heavily branched polymer, so unlike other wood polysaccharides, is easily soluble in water, forming solutions of very low viscosity. A review of the occurrence, isolation, properties, and utilization of larch arabinogalactans has recently appeared (Adams and Douglas, 1963).

A summary of the relative amounts and properties of the principal wood hemicelluloses is found in Table VII.

THE POSSIBLE EXISTENCE OF A
LIGNIN-CARBOHYDRATE COMPLEX IN WOOD

The possibility of a chemical (covalent) link between polysaccharides and lignin in wood has been the subject of much controversy, and still remains so. The experimental data available have been critically reviewed by Merewether (1957, 1960). Most of the evidence adduced for the presence of a lignin-carbohydrate bond can actually equally well be explained by the fact that both cellulose and hemicelluloses are completely encrusted in the cell wall by the three-dimensional lignin. Pew and Weyna (1962), in an interesting experiment, replaced the lignin with a three-dimensional phenolic resin by first soaking wood holocellulose in an aqueous solution of the resin and then curing the latter. The product thus obtained behaved very much like the original, fully lignified wood, both on mechanical, chemical, and biochemical treatments.

Even in those cases where a so-called lignin-carbohydrate complex has been brought into solution and been shown to be homogeneous by paper chromatography (Kawamura and Higuchi, 1952, 1953) or by paper electrophoresis (Lindgren, 1958), doubt still exists as to the validity of this seemingly irrefutable evidence for the existence of a lignin-carbohydrate bond. The reason for this is that the essentially linear polysaccharide chains in solution could very well be trapped within the three-dimensional lignin network, which would thus act as a sort of cage.

While this entire question thus has to be regarded as still unsettled, evidence has recently been adduced by Freudenberg (Freudenberg and Harkin, 1960; Freudenberg, 1960) to show how such a complex *could* possibly arise. As can be seen from Figure 12, the p-quinone-methide structure, which is known to be an important intermediate in the biosynthesis of lignin, is capable of adding not only water or an alcohol group from another lignin fragment, but also a carbohydrate hydroxyl group. This has actually been demonstrated in the case of sucrose, with which an ether link was formed, and it is not impossible that a polysaccharide could be added in the same way, even if the addition of water seems to predominate.

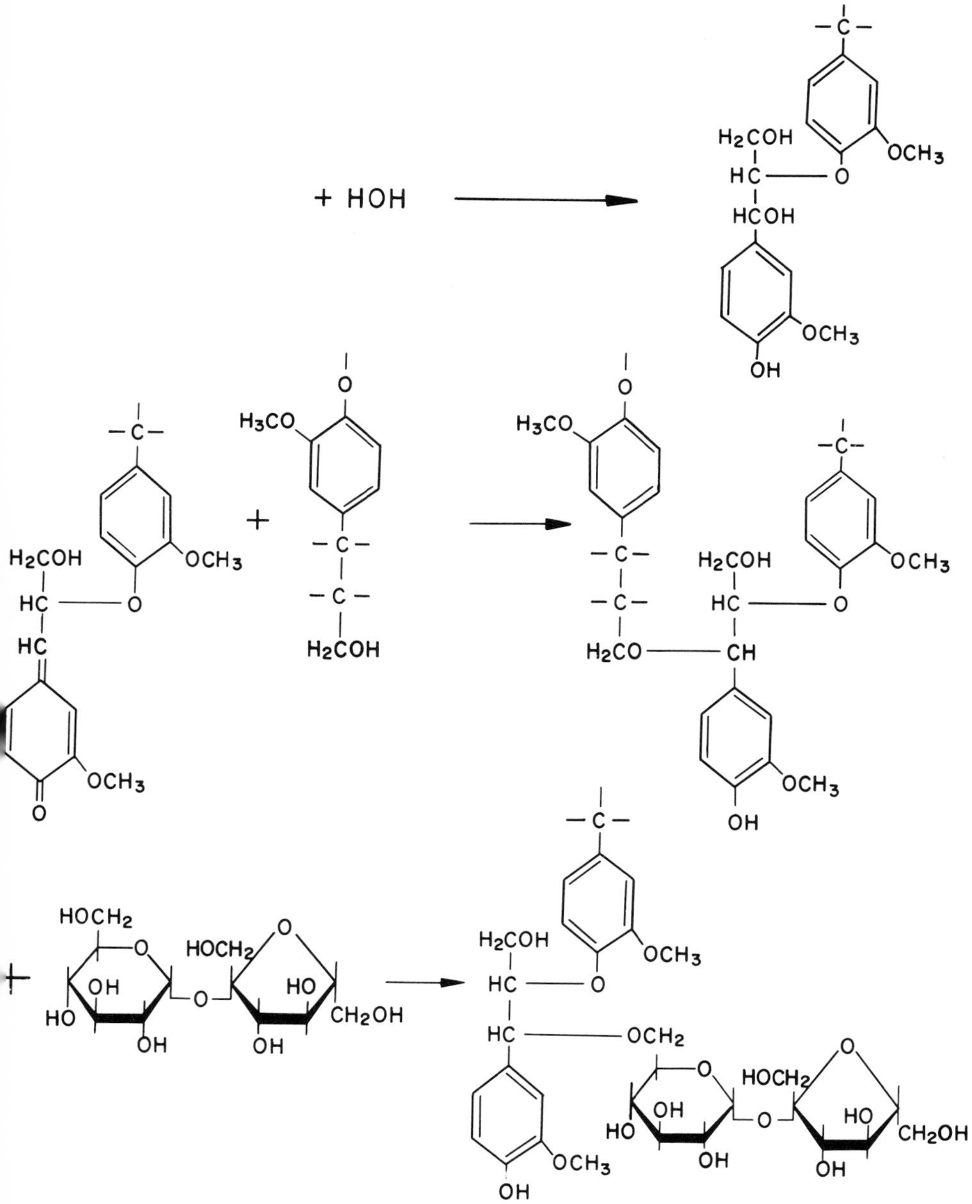

Fig. 12. Possible addition reactions of quinone methide intermediate in lignin bio-synthesis.

BARK POLYSACCHARIDES

The polysaccharides present in bark have been studied in far less detail than those in wood, most likely because of the lesser economic importance of bark, but probably also because bark polysaccharides are difficult to obtain in a pure state. Bast fiber celluloses, such as flax, hemp, jute, and ramie, have, of course, long been known. Callose is another well-known bark polysaccharide which is deposited on the sieve tubes in the phloem. In grape vine (*Vitis vinifera* Marsh.) it is formed every fall, only to be eliminated again in the spring (Eschrich, 1961). Callose has been shown to be a $(1 \rightarrow 3)$-linked β-D-glucan (Aspinall and Kessler, 1957).

A general·method for isolation of bark polysaccharides, similar to that used for softwoods (Fig. 8), has been developed by Timell (1961a), who has also subjected several of the polymers to a detailed structural analysis. Celluloses, identical in chemical and physical properties with wood celluloses, were obtained from four trees (Timell, 1961b). A xylan was isolated from the inner bark of white birch (*Betula papyrifera* Marsh.) (Jabbar Mian and Timell, 1960a), and two galactoglucomannans and one xylan were recovered from the bark of amabilis fir (*Abies amabilis* [Dougl.] Forbes) (Timell, 1961c, 1961d, 1962c) and from Engelmann spruce (*Picea engelmannii* Parry) (Ramalingam and Timell, 1964). All these polysaccharides were identical with the corresponding hemicelluloses occurring in the wood of the same species.

Recently, a pectin has been isolated from the same fir bark (Bhattacharjee and Timell, 1964). This material could be resolved into two fractions. One was a galacturonan (polygalacturonic acid), composed solely of $(1 \rightarrow 4)$-linked α-D-galacturonic acid residues. The second component, like most pectins, in addition to the predominant D-galacturonic acid units also contained residues of D-galactose, L-arabinose, and L-rhamnose. A tentative structural formula, which is only one of several possible, is presented in Figure 13. The galacturonan framework might also contain L-rhamnose residues.

The similarity in carbohydrate composition between secondary xylem and phloem is perhaps not surprising considering the fact that both are formed from the same vascular cambium. The anatomy of xylem and phloem is, however, quite different, and differences could accordingly be expected, as has, indeed, been found.

Thornber and Northcote (1961, 1962) have reported that the xylans and glucomannans present in the cambium and in differentiating xylem and phloem of maple and pine are not the same but differ considerably in general sugar composition. On several occasions barks have yielded polysaccharides which do not seem to have their counterpart in wood. The

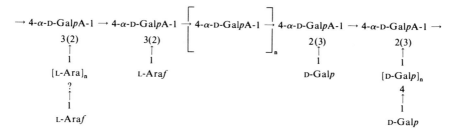

FIG. 13. Repeating unit of bark and pectic acid (Bhattacharjee and Timell, 1964).

callose is one such example. Bark from Engelmann spruce has given a polysaccharide based on galactose, glucose, and xylose residues (Ramalingam and Timell, 1964). Lodgepole pine bark contains unusually large quantities of what is probably an araban (Timell, 1964b). An unknown β-glucan, finally, seems to be present in many barks (Painter and Purves, 1960; Thornber and Northcote, 1961, 1962; Ramalingam and Timell, 1964).

A comparison of the over-all chemical composition of wood and bark of Englemann spruce (*Picea engelmannii* Parry) is seen in Table VIII. The apparent higher lignin content of the bark is entirely due to the additional polyphenols, such as tannins and phlobaphenes which occur abundantly in the bark. The higher value for uronic anhydride is caused by the higher pectin content of the bark. As can be seen from the figures for glucose and mannose, the bark in this particular case contained somewhat less cellulose and much less galactoglucomannan than the wood.

TABLE VIII. Chemical Composition of Wood and Bark
from Engelmann Spruce (*Picea engelmannii* Parry)

All values in per cent of extractive-free material.

Component	Wood	Bark
Lignin	28	40
Ash	0.3	4.0
Acetyl	1.3	0.5
Uronic anhydride	3.3	8.0
Residues of:		
Galactose	1.7	2.4
Glucose	48	36
Mannose	11	2.9
Arabinose	1.0	3.3
Xylose	5.0	3.8

Source: Ramalingsam and Timell (1964).

BIOSYNTHESIS OF WOOD AND BARK POLYSACCHARIDES

In comparison with lignin, present information concerning the bio-synthesis of wood polysaccharides is scanty (Neufeld and Hassid, 1963; Jones, 1961). Previous studies on the biosynthesis of cellulose have mostly been concerned with the cellulose produced by *Acetobacter xylinum* (Colvin, 1964). Quite recently, however, Elbein, Barber, and Hassid (1964) have reported the synthesis of cellulose by an enzyme preparation from mung bean (*Phaseolus aureus*) seedlings, the glucosyl donor being guanosin 5-(α-D-glucopyranosyl pyrophosphate).

The pentosan formation in plants has been extensively studied by Neish (Altermatt and Neish, 1956; Neish, 1959). D-Xylose was found to be a poor precursor of xylan in wheat plants, while both D-glucose and D-glucuronic acid were good precursors. Present evidence indicates strongly that xylan is synthesized from uridine 5-(D-xylopyranosyl pyrophosphate), with the latter compound formed by the following oxidation-decarboxyla-tion sequence:

Uridine 5-(α-D-glucopyranosyl pyrophosphate) $\longrightarrow$ uridine
5-(D-glucopyranosyluronic acid pyrophosphate) $\longrightarrow$ uridine
5-(D-xylopyranosyl pyrophosphate).

In the same way, pectin is probably formed from the uridine derivative of D-galactose, D-galacturonic acid, and L-arabinose, which are chemically interrelated in the same way (Seegmiller *et al.* 1955, 1956).

Feingold, Neufeld, and Hassid (1958) have shown that a (1 $\longrightarrow$ 3)-linked β-D-glucan, similar to the callose occurring in bark, is formed from uridine 5-(α-D-glucopyranosyl pyrophosphate). Little or nothing is pres-ently known about the biosynthesis of the galactoglucomannans.

DISTRIBUTION AND STATE OF THE POLYSACCHARIDES IN WOOD

The distribution of the lignin over the cell wall is now fairly well known from electron microscopic studies on ultrathin sections of wood from which the carbohydrates had previously been removed, either by acid hydrolysis (Jayme and Fengel, 1961a, 1961b; Sachs *et al.*, 1963) or by the use of microorganisms (Meier, 1955).

It has long been known that ray cells contain more pentosans than the entire wood. Recently Perilä and co-workers (Perilä and Heitto, 1959; Perilä and Seppä, 1960; Perilä, 1961, 1962) have studied the carbohydrate composition of parenchyma (ray) and prosenchyma cells in Scots pine (*Pinus sylvestris* L.), Norway spruce (*Picea abies* [L.] Karst.), and silver

birch (*Betula verrucosa* Ehrh.). As can be seen from Table IX, the parenchyma cells in both spruce and birch were richer in hemicellulose than the
prosenchyma. Table X shows a striking difference in hemicellulose composition between the two types of cells. In both pine and spruce the ray
cells contained more xylose than mannose residues, while in the tracheids,
as could be expected, the mannose predominated. The fibers and vessels
in birch wood contained both xylan and glucomannan. The hemicellulose
fraction in the ray cells, on the other hand, consisted almost entirely of
xylan. This polysaccharide accordingly seems to be considerably enriched in the ray parenchyma of both softwoods and hardwoods.

Early attempts by Asunmaa and Lange (1954) to determine the distribution of the polysaccharides over the cell wall by a microspectrographic
method indicated that the relative amount of cellulose increased towards
the lumen. A direct isolation of the various cell wall layers has so far not

TABLE IX. Hemicellulose Content of Various Cells

Cells	Per cent
Pine	
Tracheids	21
Rays	20
Spruce	
Tracheids	18
Rays	30
Birch	
Prosenchyma	22
Parenchyma	39

Source: Perilä (1961).

TABLE X. Composition of Hemicelluloses from Various Cells

Cell	Per cent	
	Mannose	Xylose
Pine		
Tracheids	70	20
Rays	30	50
Spruce		
Tracheids	50	33
Rays	25	30
Birch		
Prosenchyma	7	86
Parenchyma	1	93

Source: Perilä (1961).

been achieved. Long ago, Bailey (1936) succeeded in isolating the middle lamella of Douglas-fir (*Pseudotsuga menziesii* [Mirb.] Franco) and could show that it contained 70% lignin and 14% pentosan. An ingenious summative technique has recently been developed by Meier (Meier and Wilkie, 1959; Meier, 1961b, 1961c). This is based on the fact that in the differentiating wood cell the polysaccharides are deposited in successive layers, and that once a layer has been laid down, it remains unchanged. Tracheids and fibers in various stages of maturation could be distinguished microscopically and were separated by micromanipulation. Four portions were thus obtained, containing the following cell wall layers: (M + P), (M + P + S_1), (M + P + S_1 + S_2 $_{outer}$), and (M + P + S_1 + S_2 + S_3). Each fraction was analyzed for its relative sugar composition. From these data, the relative weight of the different layers in the mature fiber, and from the composition of the major wood polysaccharides, as they were then known, the distribution of the polysaccharides in the cell wall could be calculated. Results obtained with silver birch (*Betula verrucosa* Ehrh.), Norway spruce (*Picea abies* [L.] Karst.), and Scots pine (*Pinus sylvestris* L.) are presented in Table XI.

In all three species, the middle lamella and the primary wall were rich in pectic material, which agrees with previous investigations. In birch, the S_3

TABLE XI. Relative Percentages of Polysaccharides in the Different Layers of the Cell Wall

Polysaccharide	M + P[a]	S_1	$S_{2\,outer}$	$S_{2\,outer}$ + S_3
Scots pine				
Galactan	20.1	5.2	1.6	3.2
Cellulose	35.5	61.5	66.5	47.5
Glucomannan	7.7	16.9	24.6	27.2
Arabinan	29.4	0.6	Nil	2.4
Arabinoglucuronoxylan	7.3	15.7	7.4	19.4
Norway spruce				
Galactan	16.4	8.0	Nil	Nil
Cellulose	33.4	55.2	64.3	63.6
Glucomannan	7.9	18.1	24.4	23.7
Arabinan	29.3	1.1	0.8	Nil
Arabinoglucuronoxylan	13.0	17.6	10.7	12.7
Silver birch				
Galactan	16.9	1.2	0.7	Nil
Cellulose	41.4	49.8	48.0	60.0
Glucomannan	3.1	2.8	2.1	5.1
Arabinan	13.4	1.9	1.5	Nil
Glucuronoxylan	25.2	44.1	47.7	35.1

Source: Meier (1961c).
[a]Contains also a high percentage of pectic acid.

and the inner portion of the S_2 layer had a high cellulose content, while S_1 and the outer part of S_2 contained most of the xylan. Spruce and pine were similar. The tertiary wall was here very rich in xylan, which is in accordance with earlier results (Bucher, 1960). The relative amount of glucomannan increased gradually from the outer to the inner portion of S_2. In summer (late) wood, the S_2 layer is more predominant than in spring (early) wood, and one could therefore expect the former to contain more galactoglucomannan than the latter. The opposite would apply to the arabino-glucurono-xylan. This was indeed found to be the case, as can be seen from Table XII. It should perhaps finally be mentioned that the galactose residues found in the secondary wall of the pine undoubtedly originated from the galactoglucomannan. Their absence in the S_2 layer of the spruce remains to be explained.

TABLE XII. Relative Percentages of Polysaccharides in Spring Wood and Summer Wood from Scots Pine (*Pinus sylvestris* L.)

Polysaccharides	Springwood	Summerwood
Galactan	3.4	3.1
Cellulose	56.7	56.2
Glucomannan	20.3	24.8
Arabinan	1.0	1.8
Arabinoglucuronoxylan	18.6	14.1

Source: Meier (1961c).

While there is abundant evidence for the crystalline, highly oriented, and microfibrillar state of cellulose, as well as for the isotropic, completely amorphous state of lignin in wood, the actual state of the xylans and the glucomannans in the living tree is largely unknown. Neither of these two types of hemicelluloses crystallizes without prior removal of some of the many side chains or without some depolymerization. It would therefore seem likely that they are amorphous in their native state, surrounding the microfibrils as a matrix.

The possibility that the xylan and glucomannan in wood could form microfibrils, albeit unlikely, cannot be entirely excluded at present. A portion of the mannan present in vegetable ivory (*Phytelephas macrocarpa*) has been reported to occur as *amorphous* microfibrils (Meier, 1958b). Frei and Preston (1961) (Preston, 1964) have found that in certain marine algae (*Caulerpales*) the skeletal polysaccharide is not cellulose but a highly crystalline β-$(1 \rightarrow 3)$-linked D-xylan. This polymer is capable of forming microfibrils, although the helical organization of its chains makes it impossible for the latter to be oriented parallel to the microfibrils. In other seaweeds, such as the *Codiales*, the skeletal substance is a β-$(1 \rightarrow 4)$-linked D-mannan, which is also highly crystalline but which does *not* form microfibrils. These examples are sufficient to show that the ability to crystallize or to form microfibrils are not characteristics restricted to cellulose alone among native polysaccharides. It is interesting to note that Liang *et al.* (1960) recently have been able to show with the aid of a polarized infrared technique that the xylan in wood is oriented in the direction of the fiber axis.

The arabinogalactan in larch is obviously not a structural wood polysaccharide. It occurs only in the heartwood portion of the xylem and should be regarded as a heartwood constituent, normal to this genus. It has, actually, several characteristics in common with other heartwood compounds, such as the polyphenols (Côté and Timell, 1964). The exact location in wood of larch arabinogalactan is not known. Zaïtseva (1958), using various staining techniques, has reported that it is largely deposited in the ray parenchyma and in the epithelial cells adjoining the resin canals. As this polysaccharide sometimes constitutes as much as a quarter of the weight of the wood, the possibility that it is also laid down elsewhere obviously has to be considered.

BIOCHEMICAL EVOLUTION OF WOOD POLYSACCHARIDES

Cellulose and hemicelluloses occur in both marine and terrestrial plants. Only the latter, however, contain lignin, which is thus a constituent unique to the vascular plants. The main function of lignin is obviously to confer rigidity to the cell wall, thus making it possible for the plant to increase in height. The appearance of lignin in the course of plant evolution was a decisive event, making possible the entire subsequent evolution of land plants (Barghoorn, 1964). Since the appearance of the first land plants in Silurian time, lignin has undergone an interesting biochemical evolution (Gibbs, 1958; Manskaja, 1959).

Cellulose seems to have remained the same through the ages, but the hemicelluloses have undergone considerable changes. Except for cellulose, almost all polysaccharides occurring in the seaweeds differ conspicuously from those in our present land plants. The $(1 \rightarrow 3)$-glycosidic link, so typical of many seaweed polysaccharides, is replaced by the $(1 \rightarrow 4)$-bond in the land plants. Xylans are rare in marine algae but are present in all and predominate in the later vascular plants. Sulfated polysaccharides are common in seaweeds. Sugar residues frequently found in the latter but absent or extremely rare in terrestrial plants include L-fucose, L-galactose, 3,6-anhydro-D- (or -L-) galactose, D-mannitol, D-mannuronic, and L-guluronic acid. It is evident that the transfer of plant life from an aquatic to a terrestrial surrounding involved the development not only of lignin but also of new types of hemicelluloses.

Wood fossils, even of fairly recent origin, are unsuitable for a study of the biochemical evolution of hemicelluloses in land plants, especially since the polysaccharides in wood have a much lower resistance to decay than lignin. Another, and more fruitful, approach is to make use of the several species which have come down to us through the ages, decandants of plants which once dominated the flora on the earth and which still persist as a sort of living fossils. It seems quite reasonable to assume that such life-essential, and hence "conservative," constituents as lignin, cellulose, and hemicelluloses have remained constant within the major subdivisions of the plant kingdom.

A very generalized picture of the probable evolution of land plants is seen in Figure 14. With the unfortunate exception of the seed ferns

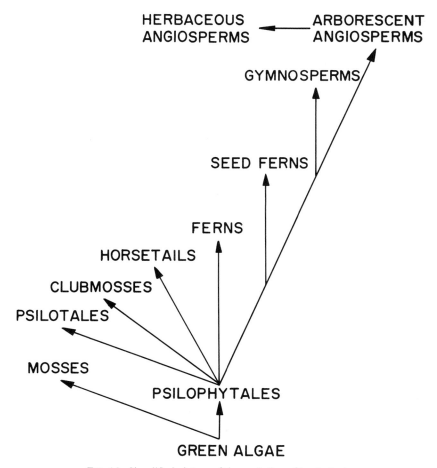

Fig. 14. Simplified picture of the evolution of land plants.

(*Cycadofilicales*), all these plants are extant in the present flora, although in some cases reduction and loss of ability to form secondary xylem has taken place.

The nature of the hemicelluloses occurring in these ancient plants has recently been studied by Timell (1960b, 1962b, 1964c; Jabbar Mian and Timell, 1960b, 1960c). The species investigated included *Psilotum nudum*, 3 species of *Equisetum*, 3 of *Lycopodium*, 15 species of *Filicineae*, and finally the monotypical *Ginkgo biloba* L., probably our botanically oldest, still living tree. The general abundance and composition of each hemicellulose was established in each case. Seven of the polysaccharides were subjected to a complete structural analysis. Some of the results obtained are briefly summarized in Tables XIII and XIV.

The wood of *Ginkgo biloba* had a polysaccharide composition indistinguishable from that of the conifers and was thus from this point of view a typical gymnosperm. All plants older than the gymnosperms contained the same type of hemicelluloses as the latter, namely an arabino-4-*O*-methylglucurono-xylan and galacto-glucomannans. In *Equisetum arvense* the ratio between mannose and glucose was as high as 9:1, instead of the usual 3:1. The glucomannan content of *Psilotum nudum* was much higher than in any of the later plants.

TABLE XIII. Relative Sugar Composition of Some Vascular Plants

All values in per cent of total carbohydrates.

Plant	Galac-turonic acid	Galactose	Glucose	Mannose	Arabinose	Xylose
Psilotum nudum	4	4	46	34	7	5
Equisetum	9	7	56	18	6	4
Lycopodium	2	4	72	8	5	9
Adiantum pedatum	2	4	70	18	1	5
Athyrium filix-femina	5	4	70	5	2	14
Osmunda cinnamomea	8	5	64	10	3	10
Ginkgo biloba L., xylem	4	6	66	15	3	7
Coniferales, xylem	4	2	66	16	3	9
Angiospermae, xylem	4	2	66	3	1	24

Source: Timell (1964c).

TABLE XIV. Predominant Hemicelluloses in Various Plants

Plant	Hemicellulose
Psilotum nudum	Glucomannan
Equisetum	Glucomannan
Lycopodium	Glucomannan and xylan (equal)
Ferns	Glucomannan or xylan or both (equal)
Gymnosperms	Glucomannan
Angiosperms (Arborescent and herbaceous)	Xylan

With the exception of the *Filicineae*, all plants exhibited little or no variation in the ratio between xylan and glucomannan. Among the ferns, members of the ancient *Osmundaceae* contained equal amounts of these two types of hemicellulose. Both polysaccharides were intermediate in chemical composition between the corresponding polymers present in the gymnosperms and in the angiosperms. Other ferns contained three to four times as much glucomannan as xylan, while, in a third type, xylan was by far the predominant hemicellulose. These great variations in hemicellulose composition appear to be typical of ferns only.

The predominance of the xylan in the arborescent angiosperms is conspicuous. This feature has been retained in the herbaceous angiosperms, although the structure of the xylan has been much modified. It would be tempting to suggest that ferns (or seed ferns) rich in glucomannan once might have given rise to the gymnosperms, while the angiosperms might have originated from similar plants containing xylan as the predominant hemicellulose. While this has to remain a conjecture, the chemical evidence certainly indicates a close relationship between the three classes that constitute the *Pteropsida*.

CONCLUSIONS

It can probably be stated with confidence that all major wood polysaccharides have now been discovered, and that their constitution is at least approximately known. The first complete structure of a wood hemicellulose was presented as late as ten years ago (Aspinall *et al.*, 1954). Since then, progress in this field has been extremely rapid. At present, the number of species investigated is also so large that valid generalizations can be made with respect to the amount, nature, and location of all wood hemicelluloses in our more important forest trees. It should be evident, however, even from this brief review, that a vast number of problems still remain to be solved. Structural features of the hemicelluloses, such as their degree of branching, the distribution of their various side chains, and the state of the uronic acid groups in the native polymer, all remain to be established. The molecular properties of all wood polysaccharides except cellulose are still either entirely unknown or not known with certainty. Our knowledge of the location and nature of the special polysaccharides present in reaction wood is still very incomplete. With bark polysaccharides, only a beginning has yet been made.

In the future, more attention will undoubtedly be devoted to the molecular architecture of wood, including the exact physical state of the hemicelluloses in bark and wood, and their relation to other cell wall components. The chemical composition of the various cell types will probably also be established. The chemistry of the cambium has recently attracted more attention (Stewart, 1957), as have also the chemical changes involved in the differentiation of this region into xylem and phloem (Thornber and Northcote, 1961, 1962). Very little is still known about the biochemistry of the wood polysaccharides. Continued progress in the chemistry of wood and bark polysaccharides can therefore be expected also in the coming years.

REFERENCES

Adams, M. F., and Douglas, C. (1963) "Arabinogalactan—a review of the literature." *Tappi* 46:544–548.

Altermatt, H., and Neish, A. C. (1956) "Die Bildung von Cellulose und Xylan aus radio-aktiven Monosacchariden in Weizenpflanzen." *Chimia* 10:157–164.

Aspinall, G. O., Hirst, E. L., and Mahomed, R. S. (1954) "Hemicellulose A of beechwood (*Fagus sylvatica*)." *J. Chem. Soc.* 1734–1738.

————, and Kessler, G. (1957) "The structure of callose from the grape vine." *Chem. Ind.* (London) 1296.

————, and Wood, T. M. (1963) "The structures of two water-soluble polysaccharides from Scots pine (*Pinus sylvestris*)." *J. Chem. Soc.* 1686–1696.

Asunmaa, S., and Lange, P. W. (1954) "The distribution of 'cellulose' and 'hemicellulose' in the cell wall of spruce, birch, and cotton." *Svensk Papperstid.* 57:501–516.

Bailey, A. J. (1936) "Lignin in Douglas-fir. Composition of the middle lamella." *Ind. Eng. Chem. Anal. Ed.* 8:52–55.

Barghoorn, E. S. (1964) "Evolution of cambium in geologic time." In *The Formation of Wood in Forest Trees* (M. H. Zimmermann, ed.), pp. 3–17. Academic Press, N.Y.

Bhattacharjee, S. S., and Timell, T. E. (1964) *Can. J. Chem.* In press.

Bouveng, H. O., and Lindberg, B. (1958) "Studies on arabogalactans. II. Fractionation of the arabogalactan from *Larix occidentalis* Nutt. A methylation study of one of the components." *Acta Chem. Scand.* 12:1977–1984.

————, and Meier, H. (1959) "Studies on a galactan from Norwegian spruce compression wood (*Picea abies* Karst.)." *Acta Chem. Scand.* 13:1844–1889.

Brauns, F. E. (1952) *The Chemistry of Lignin.* Academic Press, N.Y.

——, and Brauns, D. A. (1960) *The Chemistry of Lignin.* Academic Press, N.Y.

Browning, B. L. (1963) *The Chemistry of Wood.* Interscience Publishers, John Wiley and Sons, Inc., N.Y.

Bucher, H. (1960) "Zur Topochemie des Holzaufschlusses." *Papier* 14:542–549.

Colvin, J. R. (1963) "The size of the cellulose microfibril." *J. Cell Biol.* 17:105–109.

—— (1964) "The biosynthesis of cellulose." In *The Formation of Wood in Forest Trees* (M. H. Zimmerman, ed.), pp. 189–201. Academic Press, N.Y.

Côté, W. A., and Timell, T. E. (1964) Unpublished results.

Dutton, G. G. S., and Unrau, A. M. (1962) "The structural analysis of some acidic xylans." *Can. J. Chem.* 42:348–352.

Elbein, A. D., Barber, G. A., and Hassid, W. Z. (1964) "The synthesis of cellulose by an enzyme system from a higher plant." *J. Am. Chem. Soc.* 86:309–310.

Eschrich, W. (1961) "Untersuchungen über den Ab- und Aufbau der Callose." *Z. Botan.* 49:153–218.

Feingold, D. S., Neufeld, E. F., and Hassid, W. Z. (1958) "Synthesis of a β-1,3-linked glucan by extracts of *Phaseolus aureus* seedlings." *J. Biol. Chem.* 233:783–788.

Frei, E., and Preston, R. D. (1961) "Variants in the structural polysaccharides of algal cell walls." *Nature* 192:939–943.

Freudenberg, K. (1960) "Principles of lignin growth." *J. Polymer Sci.* 48:371–377.

——, and Harkin, J. M. (1960) "Model für die Bindung des Lignins an die Kohlenhydrate." *Chem. Ber.* 93:2814–2819.

Frey-Wyssling, A., and Mühlethaler, K. (1963) "Die Elementarfibrillen der Cellulose." *Makromol. Chem.* 62:25–30.

Gibbs, R. D. (1958) "The Mäule reaction, lignins, and the relationships between woody plants." In *The Physiology of Forest Trees* (K. V. Thimann, ed.), pp. 269–312. Ronald Press, N.Y.

Goring, D. A. I., and Timell, T. E. (1962) "Molecular weight of native celluloses." *Tappi* 45:454–460.

Gustafsson, C., Ollinmaa, P. J., and Saarnio, J. (1952) "The carbohydrates in birchwood." *Acta Chem. Scand.* 6:1299–1300.

Hägglund, E. (1951) *Chemistry of Wood.* Academic Press, N.Y.

——, Lindberg, B., and McPherson, J. (1956) "Dimethylsulphoxide, a solvent for hemicelluloses." *Acta Chem. Scand.* 10:1160–1164.

Hamilton, J. K., Kircher, H. W., and Thompson, N. S. (1956) "The nature of the hemicelluloses associated with wood from western hemlock (*Tsuga heterophylla*)." *J. Am. Chem. Soc.* 78:2508–2514.

——, Partlow, E. V., and Thompson, N. S. (1960) "The nature of a galactoglucomannan associated with wood cellulose from southern pine." *J. Am. Chem. Soc.* 82:451–457.

Hillis, W. W. (ed.) (1962) *Wood Extractives.* Academic Press, N.Y.

Honeyman, J. (ed.) (1959) *Recent Advances in the Chemistry of Cellulose and Starch.* Heywood and Company, London.

Jabbar Mian, A., and Timell, T. E. (1960a) "Isolation and properties of a 4-*O*-methylglucuronoxylan from the inner bark of white birch (*Betula papyrifera*)." *Tappi* 43:775–781.

—— and —— (1960b) "Studies on *Ginkgo biloba* L. II. The constitution of an arabino-4-*O*-methylglucuronoxylan from the wood." *Svensk Papperstid.* 64:769–774.

—— and —— (1960c) "Studies on *Ginkgo biloba* L. III. Constitution of a glucomannan from the wood." *Svensk Papperstid.* 63:884–888.

Jayme, G., and Fengel, D. (1961a) "Beitrag zur Kenntnis des Feinbaus der Frühholztracheiden. Beobachtungen an Ultradünnschnitten von Fichtenholz." *Holz Roh-Werkstoff* 19:50–55.

———— and ———— (1961b) "Beitrag zur Kenntnis des Feinbaus der Fichtenholztracheiden. II. Beobachtungen an Ultradünnschnitten von delignifiziertem Holz und Ligningerüsten." *Holzforschung* 15:98–102.

Jones, J. K. N. (1961) "Biogenesis of carbohydrates in wood." *Pure Appl. Chem.* 5:21–35.

————, Purves, C. B., and Timell, T. E. (1961) "Constitution of a 4-*O*-methylglucuronoxylan from the wood of trembling aspen (*Populus tremuloides* Michx.)." *Can. J. Chem.* 39:1059–1066.

Kawamura, I., and Higuchi, T. (1952) "Relation between lignin and carbohydrates in wood. VI. Confirmation of xylobiose combined chemically with lignin in acetylated sawdust." *J. Soc. Textile Cellulose Ind., Japan* 8:442–445. *Chem. Abstracts* (1953) 47:309

———— and ———— (1953) "Relation between lignin and carbohydrates in wood. IX. Residual lignin in chlorite pulp." *J. Soc. Textile Cellulose Ind., Japan* 9:157–159. *Chem. Abstracts* (1954) 48:1675.

Koshijima, T., and Timell, T. E. (1964) Unpublished results.

Kratzl, K., and Billek, G. (ed.) (1959) *Biochemistry of Wood.* Pergamon Press, London.

LeBel, R. G., and Goring, D. A. I. (1963) "Solution properties of birch xylan. II. Fractionation and configuration." *J. Polymer Sci.,* Part C 2:29–48.

————, ————, and Timell, T. E. (1963) "Solution properties of birch xylan. I. Measurement of Molecular Weight." *J. Polymer Sci.,* Part C 2:9–28.

Liang, C. Y., Bassett, K. H., McGinnes, E. A., and Marchessault, R. H. (1960) "Infrared spectra of crystalline polysaccharides. VII. Thin wood sections." *Tappi* 43:1017–1024.

Lindgren, B. O. (1958) "The lignin-carbohydrate linkage." *Acta Chem. Scand.* 12:447–452.

Manskaja, S. M. (1959) "Zur Phylogenese des Lignins." In *Biochemistry of Wood* (K. Kratzl and G. Billek, ed.), pp. 215–226. Pergamon Press, London.

Marchessault, R. H., and Liang, C. Y. (1962) "The infrared spectra of crystalline polysaccharides. VIII. Xylans." *J. Polymer Sci.* 59:357–378.

————, Morehead, F. F., Walter, N. M., Glaudemans, C. P. J., and Timell, T. E. (1961) "Morphology of xylan single crystals." *J. Polymer Sci.* 51:S66–S68.

Marx-Figini, M. (1963) "Kinetische Untersuchungen zur Biosynthese der Cellulose in der Baumwolle." *Makromol. Chem.* 68:227–231.

————, and Schulz, G. V. (1963) "Neuere Untersuchungen über Grösse und Grössenverteilung der β-glukosidischen Ketten nativer Cellulosen." *Makromol. Chem.* 62:49–65.

Meier, H. (1955) "Über den Zellwandabbau durch Holzvermorschungspilze und die submikroskopische Struktur von Fichtentracheiden und Birkenholzfasern." *Holz Roh-Werkstoff* 13:323–338.

———— (1958a) "Barium hydroxide as a selective precipitating agent for hemicellulose." *Acta Chem. Scand.* 12:144–146.

———— (1958b) "On the structure of cell walls and cell wall mannans from ivory nuts and from dates." *Biochim. Biophys. Acta* 28:229–240.

———— (1961a) "Isolation and characterization of an acetylated glucomannan from pine (*Pinus silvestris* L.)." *Acta Chem. Scand.* 15:1381–1385.

———— (1961b) "The distribution of polysaccharides in wood fibers." *J. Polymer Sci.* 51:11–18.

———— (1961c) "Chemical and morphological aspects of the fine structure of wood." *Pure Appl. Chem.* 5:37–52.

———— (1962) "Studies on a galactan from tension wood of beech (*Fagus silvatica* L.)." *Acta Chem. Scand.* 16:2275–2283.

————, and Wilkie, K. C. B. (1959) "The distribution of polysaccharides in the cell-wall of tracheids of pine (*Pinus silvestris* L.)." *Holzforschung* 13:177–182.

Merewether, J. W. T. (1957) "A lignin-carbohydrate complex in wood." *Holzforschung* 11:65–80.

―――― (1960) "The linkage of lignin in the plant." In *The Chemistry of Lignin* (F. E. Brauns and D. A. Brauns), pp. 630–658. Academic Press, N.Y.

Mühlethaler, K. (1960) "Die Feinstruktur der Zellulosemikrofibrillen." *Z. Schweiz. Forstv.* 30:55–65.

Neish, A. C. (1959) "Biosynthesis of hemicelluloses." In *Biochemistry of Wood* (K. Kratzl and G. Billek, ed.), pp. 82–91. Pergamon Press, London.

Neufeld, E. F., and Hassid, W. Z. (1963) *Advan. Carbohydrate Chem.* 18:309–356.

Ott, E., Spurlin, H. M., and Grafflin, M. W. (1954) *Cellulose and Cellulose Derivatives.* Interscience Publishers, N.Y.

Painter, T. J., and Purves, C. B. (1960) "Polysaccharides in the inner bark of white spruce." *Tappi* 43:729–736.

Perilä, O. (1961) "The chemical composition of carbohydrates of wood cells." *J. Polymer Sci.* 51:19–56.

―――― (1962) "The chemical compositions of wood cells. III. Carbohydrates of birch cells." *Suomen Kemistilehti, B* 35:176–178.

――――, and Heitto, P. (1959) "The chemical compositions of wood cells. I. Carbohydrates of pine cells." *Suomen Kemistilehti, B* 32:76–80.

――――, and Seppä, T. (1960) "The chemical compositions of wood cells. II. Carbohydrates of spruce cells." *Suomen Kemistilehti, B* 33:114–116.

Pew, J. C., and Weyna, P. (1962) "Fine grinding, enzyme digestion, and the lignin-carbohydrate bond in wood." *Tappi* 45:247–256.

Preston, R. D. (1964) "Structural plant polysaccharides." *Endeavour* 23:153–159.

Ramalingam, K. V., and Timell, T. E. (1964) "Polysaccharides present in the bark of Engelmann spruce (*Picea engelmannii* Parry)." *Svensk Papperstid.* 67:512–521.

Roudier, A. (1962) "Les galactanes, arabinogalactanes et glucurono-arabinogalactanes des bois." *Assoc. Tech. Ind. Papetiere, Bull.* 16:343–355.

Sachs, I. B., Clark, I. T., and Pew, J. C. (1963) "Investigation of lignin distribution in the cell wall of certain woods." *J. Polymer Sci.,* Part C 2:203–212.

Schwerin, G. (1958) "The chemistry of reaction wood. Part II. The polysaccharides of *Eucalyptus goniocalyx* and *Pinus radiata.*" *Holzforschung* 12:43–48.

Seegmiller, C. G., Axelrod, B., and McCready, R. M. (1955) "Conversion of glucose 1-C[14] to pectin in the boysenberry." *J. Biol. Chem.* 217:765–775.

――――, Jang, R., and Mann, W. (1956) "Conversion of radioactive hexoses to pectin in the strawberry." *Arch. Biochem. Biophys.* 61:422–430.

Stewart, C. M. (1957) "Status of cambial chemistry." *Tappi* 40:244–256.

Thornber, J. P., and Northcote, D. H. (1961) "Changes in the chemical composition of a cambial cell during its differentiation into xylem and phloem tissues in trees. 1. Main components. 2. Carbohydrate constituents of each main component.' *Biochem. J.* 81:449–455; 455–463.

―――― and ―――― (1962) "Changes in the chemical compositions of a cambial cell during its differentiation into xylem and phloem tissues in trees. 3. Xylan, glucomannan and α-cellulose fractions." *Biochem. J.* 82:340–346.

Timell, T. E. (1960a) "Isolation of hardwood glucomannans." *Svensk Papperstid.* 63: 472–476.

―――― (1960b) "Studies on *Ginkgo biloba*. I. General characteristics and chemical comsosition." *Svensk Papperstid.* 63:652–657.

―――― (1961a) "Isolation of polysaccharides from the bark of gymnosperms." *Svensk Papperstid.* 64:651–661.

―――― (1961b) "Characterization of four celluloses from the bark of gymnosperms." *Svensk Papperstid.* 64:685–688.

———— (1961c) "The structure of an arabino-4-O-methyl-glucurono-xylan from the bark of amabilis fir (*Abies amabilis*)." *Svensk Papperstid.* 64:748–750.

———— (1961d) "Constitution of a glucomannan from the bark of amabilis fir (*Abies amabilis*)." *Svensk Papperstid.* 64:744–747.

———— (1961e) "Isolation of galactoglucomannans from the wood of gymnosperms." *Tappi* 44:88–96.

———— (1962a) "Enzymatic hydrolysis of a 4-O-methyl-glucuronoxylan from the wood of white birch (*Betula papyrifera* Marsh.)." *Svensk Papperstid.* 65:435–447.

———— (1962b) "Studies on ferns (*Filicineae*). 3. General chemical characteristics and comparison with gymnosperms and angiosperms." *Svensk Papperstid.* 65:266–272.

———— (1962c) "Constitution of a water-soluble galactoglucomannan from the bark of amabilis fir (*Abies amabilis*)." *Svensk Papperstid.* 65:843–846.

———— (1964a) "Wood Hemicelluloses." *Advan. Carbohydrate Chem.* Vol. 19.

———— (1964b) Unpublished results.

———— (1964c) "Studies on some ancient plants." *Svensk Papperstid.* 67:356–363.

————, and Jahn, E. C. (1951) "A study of the isolation and polymolecularity of paper birch holocellulose." *Svensk Papperstid.* 54:831–845.

Treiber E. (ed.) (1957) *Die Chemie der Pflanzenzellwand.* Springer-Verlag, Berlin.

Wardrop, A. B., and Bland, D. E. (1959) "The process of lignification in woody plants." In *Biochemistry of Wood* (K. Kratzl and G. Billek, ed.). Pergamon Press, London.

Wise, L. E., and Jahn, E. C. (1952) *Wood Chemistry.* Reinhold Publishing Corporation, N. Y.

————, Murphy, M., and D'Addieco, A. A. (1946) "Chlorite holocellulose, its fractionation and bearing on summative wood analysis and on studies on the hemicelluloses." *Paper Trade J.* 122(2):35–43.

Yundt, A. P. (1951) "Crystalline hemicelluloses. I. Crystalline and amorphous xylan from from barley straw. II. Crystalline xylan from paper birch. IV. Crystalline mannan." *Tappi* 34:89–91, 91–92, 94–95.

Zaïtseva, A. F. (1958) "The localization of arabogalactan in the cell walls of *Larix dahurica.*" *Tr. Inst. Lesa, Akad. Nauk SSSR,* Izuchenie Khim. Sostava Drevesiny Daursk. Listvennitsy 45:50–60. *Chem. Abstracts* (1959) 53:4439.

Zinbo, M., and Timell, T. E. (1965) "The degree of branching of hardwood xylans." *Chem. and Ind.* (London), 222.

Lignin—Its Biochemistry and Structure

K. KRATZL

University of Vienna and
Austrian Wood Research Institute

This review deals with biochemical methods used to elucidate the structure of lignin and with chemical reactions for interpreting the chemical behavior of lignin. Applications of radioactive precursors were used to shed light on the biogenesis of lignin in the cell wall. The methods of biogenesis are, therefore, the main facts to be discussed here. Degradation is also a part of the biochemistry of lignin, a very important fact especially in humification and other fields in agricultural chemistry. However, we are only at the beginning (Flaig, 1962; Nord, 1964; Schubert, 1964) and these methods are not so important for structural problems. This paper aims to give an example of the collaboration between organic chemists, biochemists, botanists, and plant physiologists.

Most plant tissues contain, in addition to carbohydrates and extractives, an amorphous polymeric material called lignin. The amount of lignin may vary between 15 and 35%. The biological role of lignin in the living plant is to form, together with the cellulose and other carbohydrates, a tissue of excellent strength and durability. Lignified material may be compared with iron-reinforced concrete, with lignin representing the concrete and cellulose forming the reinforcing iron.

There are many differences between lignin and the other three great classes of natural polymers, namely carbohydrates, proteins, and polyterpenes. Some of them are insolubility, absence of a regular structure, absence of regular weak bonds (e.g., acetal, peptide, and double bonds), and the tendency of condensation reactions of lignin. This makes it easy to understand the extreme difficulties the chemist faces in structural studies, and at present detailed information as to the structure of lignin is lacking. One of the main difficulties is that lignin cannot be isolated from plant materials without undergoing secondary reactions.

157

DETERMINATION OF LIGNIN IN THE CELL WALL

Many chemists and botanists, e.g., Bailey (1936), Lange (1945), Wardrop (1957), and Wardrop and Bland (1959), have tried to detect lignin in the cell wall of plants by physico-chemical methods. These authors mainly made use of ultraviolet absorption. (Lignin shows an absorption in the region of 2800 Å.)

In collaboration with Tschammler, Kisser, Steininger, and Leutner (1953), an infrared method was developed to determine lignin in microscopic sections. This was the first infrared spectrum of a microscopic section (Figs. 1 and 2). The bands found at 6.3 and 6.8 μ, which are characteristic of aromatic carbon–carbon double bonds, confirmed the discovery of Lange (1945) that lignin is aromatic in nature. At that time this method proved important in showing that lignin exists as an aromatic substance in the cell wall, because the theories of Hilpert (1936) and Schütz *et al.*, (1947, 1948) supposed lignin to be "secondary products" of chemical treatments.

The aims of the botanist are to give a macroscopic and microscopic picture of lignin and its distribution in the cell wall. The chemist's aims are,

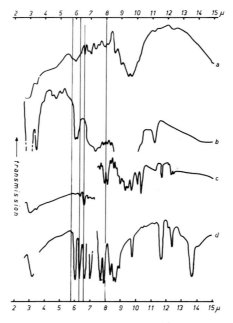

FIG. 1. Infrared absorption spectrum of (a) fir, (b) Celloplan (cellulose), (c) coniferin, (d) vanillin. 6.3 and 6.8 μ (aromatic bonds).

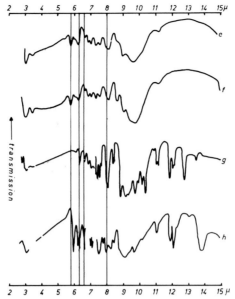

FIG. 2. Infrared absorption spectrum of (e) beech, (f) ash, (g) syringin, (h) syringalde-hyde. 6.3 and 6.8 μ (aromatic bonds).

on the other hand, to show how the atoms and molecules are arranged and bound together. The latter wants to explain the phenomena seen by the botanist, e.g., *the color reaction of wood.*

Lignin, when treated with phloroglucinol-hydrochloric acid, exhibits the well known color reaction of wood. It is used to determine lignifica-tion in plant materials and was discovered by Wiesner (1878). If a plant material pretreated with hypochlorite (bleaching) is used, however, no coloring can be observed. This is due to an oxidation of the coniferyl al-dehyde group, which is the sole reason for the color reaction (Adler *et al.,* 1948), although the main part of the lignin is still present.

According to the history of biochemical evolution of woody plants the botanists distinguish between ontogeny and phylogeny. The latter is con-cerned with the problem of when the evolution of lignin began. Scientists believe that the formation of lignin started with the plants changing from water to the harder conditions of dry soil (gravity, wind). The main prob-lem with which ontogeny deals is: when does lignification start in the growing plant?

We showed with sprouts of potatoes that this process was finished in a few days. Klason (1932) postulated that lignification took place only if the plant assimilated. He considered formaldehyde to be the methylating agent. This was proved to be wrong. To investigate this and to study the problem of biogenesis of lignin we (Kratzl, 1948a) started with a study of the degradation reactions. One of these investigations concerned the determination of lignin with various acids. The reaction was found to be difficult to carry out with living cells. Freudenberg and Plötz (1948) developed a procedure for determination of lignin depending on the concentration of the acid used. By this method a maximum methoxyl content of 15% was found in the potato (Fig. 3).

If this reaction is applied to sprouts, the determination results in only 4% of methoxyl. The insoluble material was shown to contain nitrogen. This proves that fragments of proteins were determined as "acid lignin." Therefore, the usual determination of acid lignin cannot be applied to a living plant. The sprouts also yield vanillin on oxidation with alkaline nitrobenzene. This was one of the reasons why criteria for lignin had to be set up during the last twenty years. These criteria are very helpful, especially for the biochemistry of lignin.

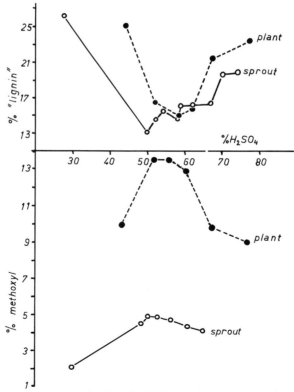

FIG. 3.   Determination of acid lignin. (from Kratzl, 1948a)

LIGNIN CRITERIA

A great variety of reactions have been developed in order to define lignin. The main reactions are as follows:

1. Degradation to vanillin (gymnosperms), vanillin and syringaldehyde (angiosperms), and also to p-hydroxybenzaldehyde (monocotyledons) (Freudenberg *et al.*, 1940; see also Creighton *et al.*, 1944).

2. High pressure hydrogenation resulting in the formation of the corresponding propylcyclohexane derivatives (Harris and Adkins, 1938).

3. Ethanolysis to arylketoles (Brickman *et al.*, 1940).

4. Alkaline degradation of lignosulfonic acid to vanillin-acetaldehyde and acetovanillone-formaldehyde, respectively (Kratzl, 1948b).

5. Isolation of "network acids," which are aromatic polycarboxylic acids originating from condensed aromatic systems of lignin (Freudenberg *et al.*, 1962, 1963).

Besides other analytical data, a quantitative determination of these degradation products allows us to detect lignin, and to assume that lignin is formed during a metabolism.

BIOGENESIS AND STRUCTURE

The best tools available for the elucidation of the structure of lignin are biochemical methods. In the following discussion these useful techniques are presented mainly to show the collaboration of biochemistry, microchemistry, physical chemistry, and botany. The methods were applied *in vivo* to prove the theory of dehydropolymerization which was developed by Freudenberg (1940–1964) in recent years.

Erdtman (1933a,b) was the first to suggest that lignin could be formed by a dehydropolymerization of arylpropane units. Freudenberg (1948–1964) studied the dehydrogenation of coniferyl alcohol by enzymes. He obtained an "artificial" lignin which he called dehydrogenation polymer (DHP). It showed the above-mentioned criteria and analytical data of lignin.

PRECURSORS

We applied precursors labeled with C-14 to establish if this theory was also valid for reactions *in vivo*. Kratzl (1961) used coniferin-2-C-14 and coniferin-3-C-14 to study criteria 1, 3, and 4. Freudenberg (1963) and Freudenberg *et al.*, (1963) applied coniferin-1-C-14 mainly to study criterion 5. He also administered coniferin-2-C-14 to plants. Many other precursors have been used by us and other groups of scientists. Neish, for example (1964), preferred phenylalanine and cinnamic acids. A synthetical group (Billek) and an analytical group (Billek and Silbernagel) have developed the methods used for this purpose in Vienna (Kratzl, 1948–1961). The synthesis of coniferin is shown as an example of the microsynthetical procedures carried out (Figs. 4, 5, and 6).

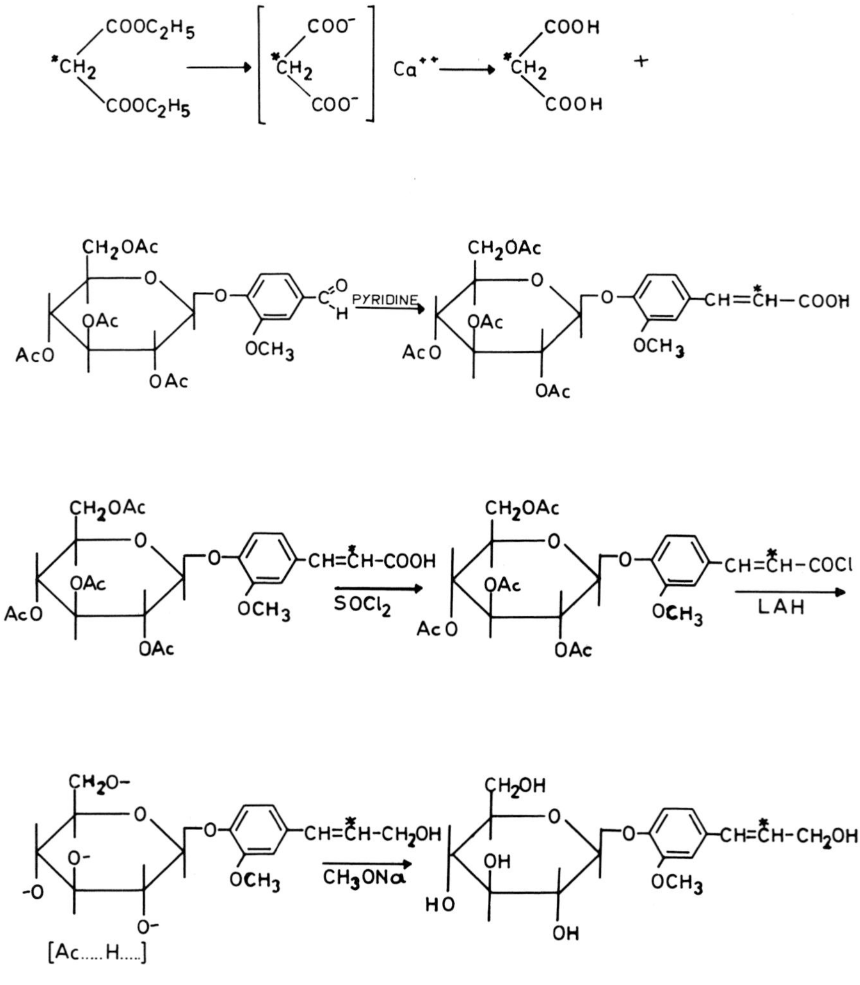

FIGS. 4–5. Synthesis of coniferin-2-C-14, syringin, and p-cumar alcohol glucoside.

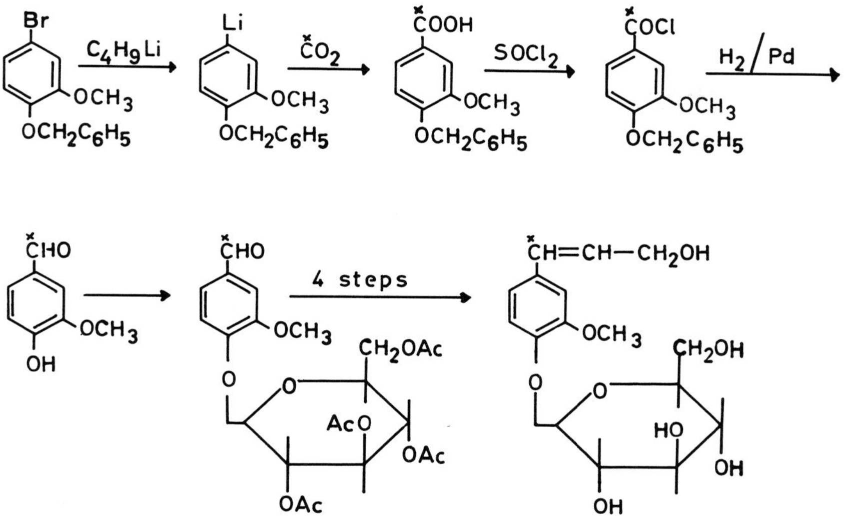

Fig. 6. Synthesis of coniferin-3-C-14.

Methods of Application

There are several methods for feeding plants with the labeled precursors. One of them was developed by Freudenberg (1962), who called it "Tauchtriebverfahren." A solution of the precursors is sucked up through the needles.

The method of feeding may influence the fate of the precursors, as shown by two papers from our laboratory. Coniferin-3-C-14 was administered to spruce branches by *implantation* of crystals into the cambium (Kratzl and Faigle, 1959a). It was found that the vanillin recovered by alkaline nitrobenzene oxidation of the wood residue was about seven times as active as the vanilloyl methyl ketones obtained by ethanolysis. The insoluble polymer was shown to contain 90% of the activity administered. This product, however, proved to differ very much from lignin (Kratzl and Faigle, 1959a).

In a second experiment (Kratzl and Faigle, 1959b) the coniferin was administered through the infusion method, a procedure developed by Neish (1955). It was found that the activity of the vanilloyl methyl ketones recovered was now about the same as that of vanillin. It is probable that a wound reaction was obscuring the results when the implantation reaction was used.

For the present purposes the infusion method is probably the best. One advantage is its economy of time and materials, and the fact that the quick absorption of the precursors minimizes the possibility of their destruction by microorganisms. It is the simplest technique to apply to a wide variety of plants and allows for a rapid and quantitative uptake of the precursors. In studies of biogenesis short-term experiments are also preferable to those requiring a long period of time, because more clearly defined results are usually obtained (Figs. 7 and 8).

The best time for the infusion technique is spring. After the infusion of the precursors the twigs are extracted. The low-molecular substances are found in the extracts. The extracted wood contains about 25% of the administered isotopes. Autoradiographs show that the activity is spread along the cambium. Only substances found in the extracts are active if

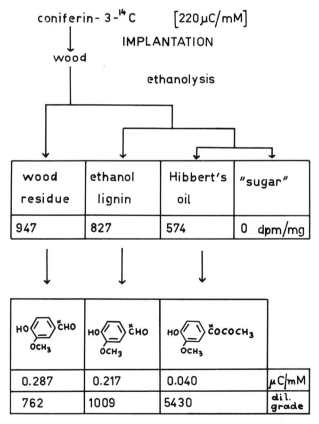

FIG. 7. Distribution of activity. Implantation method.

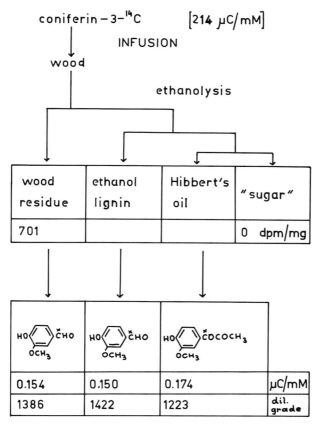

FIG. 8. Distribution of activity. Infusion method.

methylated precursors are used instead of the phenolic ones, the residue containing practically no activity. This is in accordance with the theory of dehydrogenation of phenols.

The infusion of radioactive syringin or syringaldehyde into beech wood resulted in the presence of activity in the cambium. On the other hand, syringin or syringaldehyde, when applied to sprucewood, were also assimilated, showing that a precursor for an angiosperm can be utilized by a gymnosperm. After the feeding with syringin and syringaldehyde and subjecting the lignin formed to a degradation, we isolated labeled vanillin. This was the first proof that a demethoxylation had taken place in a plant organism (Kratzl, 1960) (Tables I and II).

Brown and Neish (1955) carried out a series of experiments to test precursors for their efficiency. They developed a method for this purpose

TABLE I. Spruce (Infusion of Carbonyl-^{14}C-syringaldehyde)

	dpm/mg of substance	dpm/mg of substance
Wood extracted	2,445	—
Mixture of aldehydes	2,609	396,000
Vanillin	272	41,340

TABLE II. Spruce (Infusion of Carbonyl-^{14}C-syringaldehyde) Vanillin

	dpm/mg of substance	dpm/mg of substance
	4,151	631,000
After the first degradation	2,605	396,100
After the second degradation	2,160	328,000
After the third degradation	2,149	326,500

and used the dilution of the radioactivity as a measure of efficiency. A high dilution means that a precursor is used inefficiently. The dilution may also be looked upon as a test for the application technique used. We could thus prove that the method of implantation is not efficient, since the products obtained after a degradation of the lignin showed a high dilution. The infusion, on the other hand, resulted in products of low dilution, and seems to be a valuable biological method.

In another experiment we applied coniferin labeled either at C-2 or C-3 of the side chain. Sulfonation of the biosynthetic "lignin," and alkaline degradation of the lignosulfonic acid formed, resulted in labeled vanillin and labeled acetaldehyde, respectively, demonstrating that the side chain had not been rearranged during the biological process (Fig. 9).

Kratzl and Billek (1959) and Billek (1959) have shown that p-hydroxyphenyl compounds are not converted efficiently to lignin in spruce. We administered p-hydroxybenzaldehyde and p-hydroxyphenylpyruvic acid to spruce, after which the lignin was subjected to a degradation and a mixture of aldehydes could be isolated. After having separated vanillin we assayed a low activity and calculated a high dilution. Thus we could prove that p-hydroxyphenylpyruvic acid is not an efficient precursor for spruce, although biochemists claim this compound to be an intermediate in the biosynthesis of arylpropanes (Fig. 10). Brown et al., (1959) have observed that only monocotyledons are able to utilize p-hydroxyphenylpyruvic acid in lignin biosynthesis.

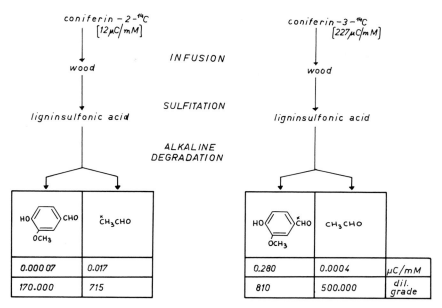

FIG. 9. Characterization of labeled C-atoms. Infusion of coniferin-2-C-14 and coniferin-3-C-14 (spruce), sulfonation, and alkaline hydrolysis of the lignosulfonic acids.

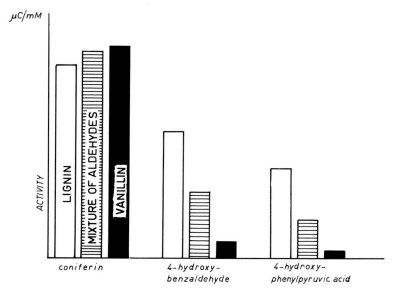

FIG. 10. Infusion of p-hydroxybenzaldehyde and p-hydroxyphenylpyruvic acid (spruce).

An important procedure was developed by Silbernagel (1955) for puri-
fication of vanillin via its m-nitrobenzhydrazone derivative. Repeated
splitting of the hydrazone with Hg-II-chloride in alkaline solution yields
a product of constant radioactivity. The diketones resulting from an
ethanolysis were purified via their Ni-salts. The distribution of the radioactivity in the side chain could be determined as shown in Figure 11.

There is no doubt that the *coniferyl alcohol* grouping acts as an important intermediate in the biosynthesis of gymnosperm and angiosperm lignins. However, some doubts exist as to whether coniferin, the
glucoside of coniferyl alcohol, has the same importance as a precursor.

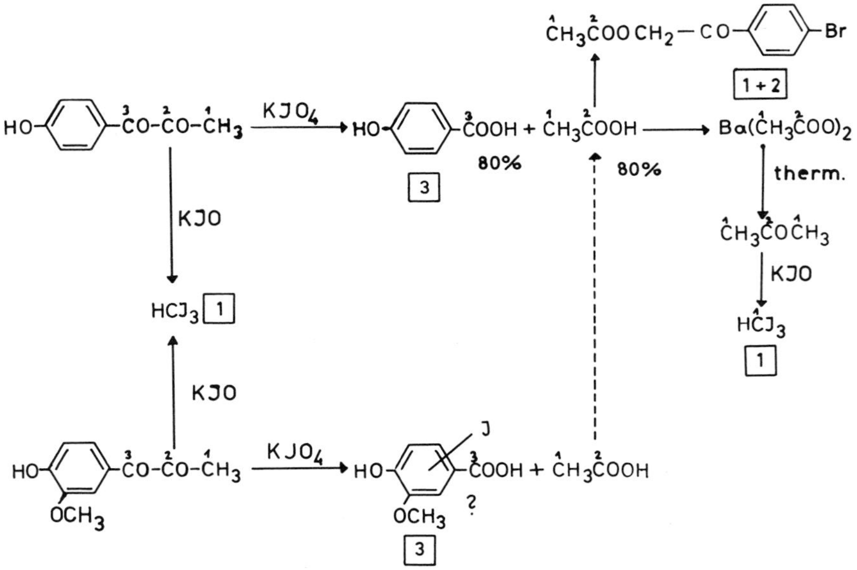

FIG. 11. Characterization of labeled C-atoms in the ketoles of Hibbert and the diketones.

The omnipresence of coniferin has so far not been proven. The β-glucosi-
dase, moreover, which is necessary for the fission of this glucoside, could
not be found in every case where lignification occurs. Nevertheless, the
glucoside coniferin might be important as a real precursor, since it could
be shown that its concentration in the cambial sap decreases during the
period of lignification. We never observed that aromatic compounds
could be degraded completely to aliphatic derivatives within the organism
of plants, for example, that active coniferin could be converted into insoluble lignin to a very great extent. The presence of one or the other in
the cambial sap does not seem to prove its importance as a precursor since

the stationary period of the existence of these compounds depends on too many factors, and one is accordingly not allowed to draw many conclusions from these observations.

In an attempt to solve the problem of how the aromatic precursors are formed, we (Kratzl and Faigle, 1959a, 1960) fed a spruce with glucose-1-C-14. Having subjected the lignin formed to an oxidative degradation, we isolated vanillin and assayed it. A further degradation of vanillin showed the following distribution of the radioactivity in the compound (Fig. 12). The amount of C-14 incorporated in the carbonyl group was high. The methoxyl group and carbon atoms 2 and 6 of the aromatic nucleus contained a somewhat lower percentage of administered isotope.

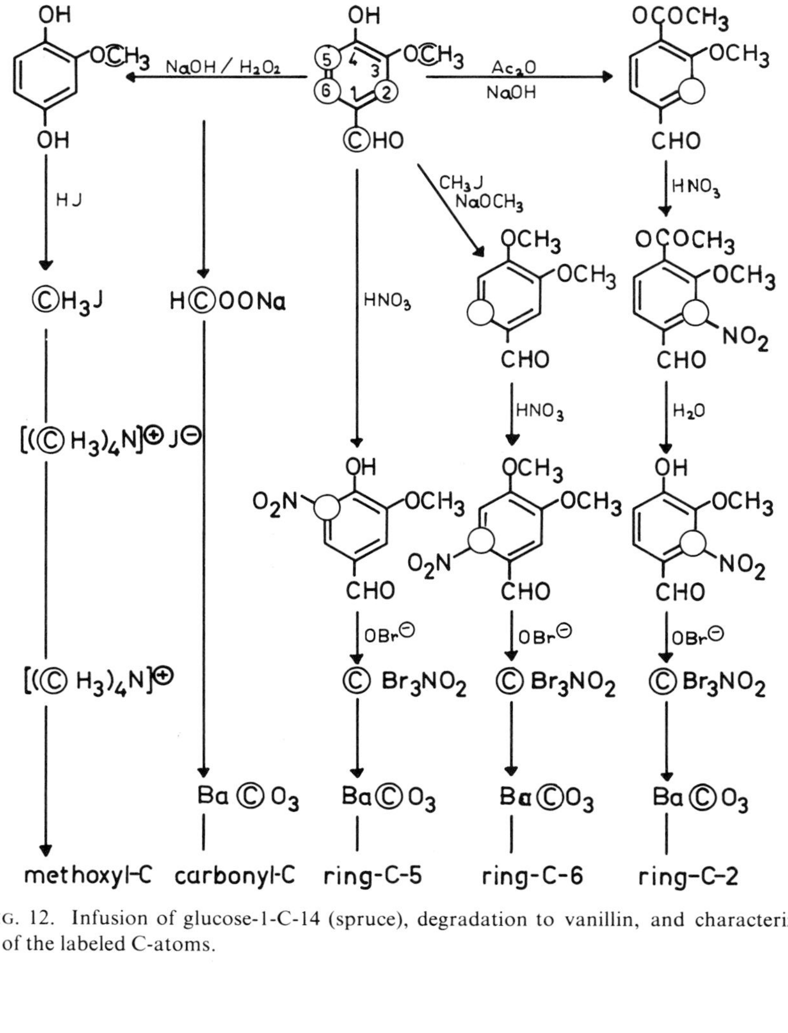

FIG. 12. Infusion of glucose-1-C-14 (spruce), degradation to vanillin, and characterization of the labeled C-atoms.

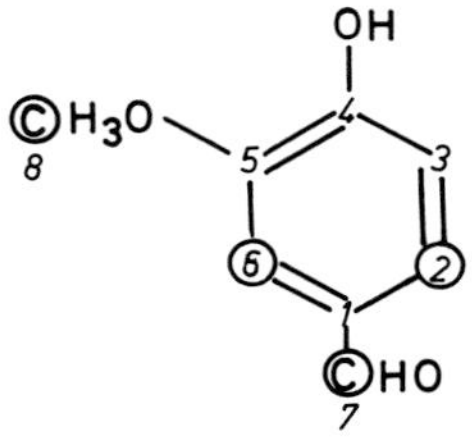

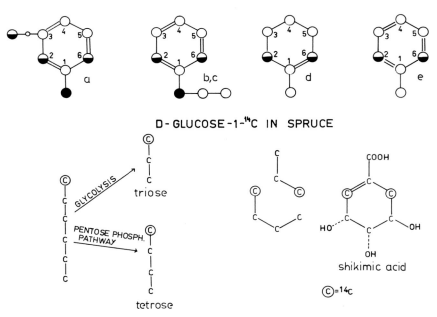

PERCENTAGE ACTIVITY BASED ON VANILLIN

vanillin		100	vanillin	100
○ C-2		18.3		18.2
○ C-5		4.0		3.1
○ C-6		15.1		11.4
○ C-7	carbonyl-C	37.7		28.5
○ C-8	methoxyl-C	21.6		31.1

FIG. 13. Comparison of the experiments with glucose-1-C-14 (spruce). Left: Kratzl and Faigle (1959a). Right: Schubert and Acerbo (1959).

D-GLUCOSE-1-^{14}C IN SPRUCE

shikimic acid

© = ^{14}C

FIG. 14. Infusion of glucose-1-C-14. Distribution of the activity, from left to right: (a) vanillin, (b) tyrosine, (c) phenylalanine, (d) shikimic acid, (e) protocatechuic acid.

Schubert and Acerbo (1959) have carried out the same experiments, also applying glucose-1-C-14 (Fig. 13). The same ratios could be detected in phenylalanine and tyrosine after an infusion of shikimic acid and protocatechuic acid, respectively. This metabolic pathway is well known to the biochemists, and was formulated by Davis and Sprinson (Davis, 1955, 1958) (Fig. 14).

The intermediate steps of the metabolic pathway leading to lignin via glucose, shikimic acid, and prephenic acid proved the validity of the scheme of Davis and Sprinson. The primary aromatic substances obtained can be either phenylpyruvic acid, phenylalanine, or ferulic acid (Fig. 15). The next steps are hydroxylation, methoxylation (by methionine), reduction, and deamination. The coniferyl alcohol formed in the last step represents an important intermediate in the metabolism. It can be considered as an essential metabolite in the formation of lignin.

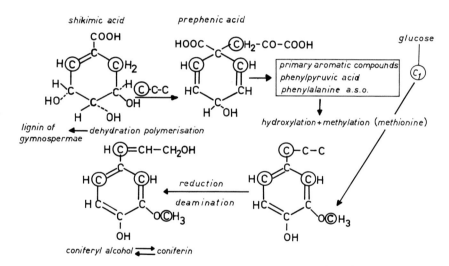

FIG. 15. The metabolic pathway of Davis and Sprinson from shikimic acid to the aromatic precursors of lignin.

Neish (1964) published the pathway mentioned above to show also the connections with other phenolic compounds in wood (Fig. 16). It is supposed that methoxylation occurs at a very early stage and furthermore that only few precursors enter the pool of methoxylation equilibrium. Therefore, lignins of plants show only very little variation as to their substitution at the aromatic nucleus, while the same organism is able to produce a broad spectrum of other phenolic compounds, but of low molecular weight.

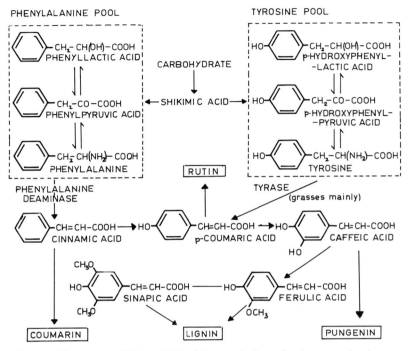

FIG. 16. The scheme of Neish (1964) of the metabolism of arylpropanes in plants.

THE STRUCTURE OF LIGNIN

The experiments with labeled precursors *in vivo* were accompanied by the outstanding experiments of the dehydropolymerization of coniferyl alcohol *in vitro* by Freudenberg and his group (1940–1964). It was found that coniferyl alcohol is dehydrogenated in a radical reaction, this being the only enzymatic step in a series of reactions. The radicals thus formed resemble a mesomeric system and undergo secondary reactions according to their mesomeric structures (Fig. 17). Freudenberg (1964a) has succeeded in isolating many intermediates (lignols) produced by this reaction. The stability of the radicals formed is important for their recombination. In this way oligomers are formed via dimeric intermediates. One of the most important products of all formed by radical coupling is the β-ether structure, amounting to more than 30% in lignin. Besides this, pinoresinol and dehydrodiconiferyl alcohol may be formed (Fig. 18). Freudenberg has also been able to isolate tri-, tetra-, penta-, and hexamers during the dehydropolymerization (Fig. 19 and Table III).

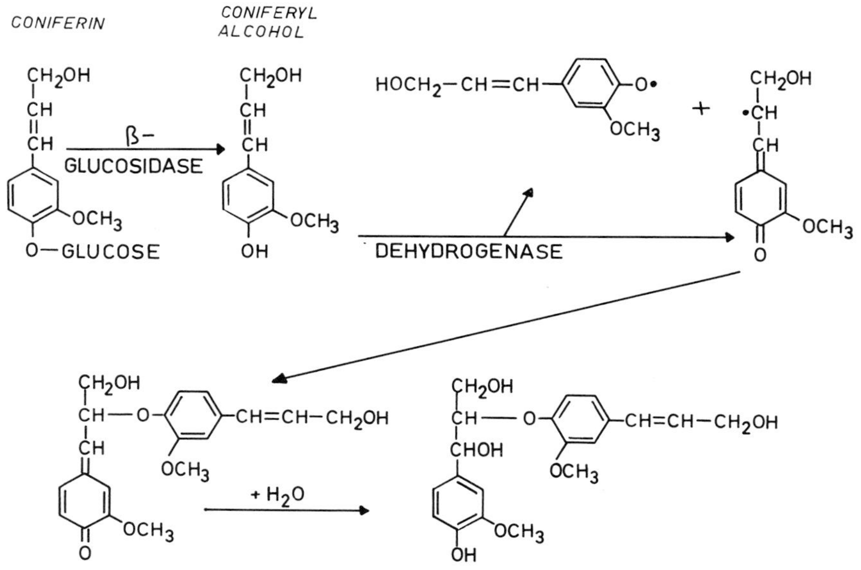

FIG. 17. Freudenberg's theory on the formation of lignin. The primary steps (radical formation and one example of a coupling leading to β-aryl ether bonds).

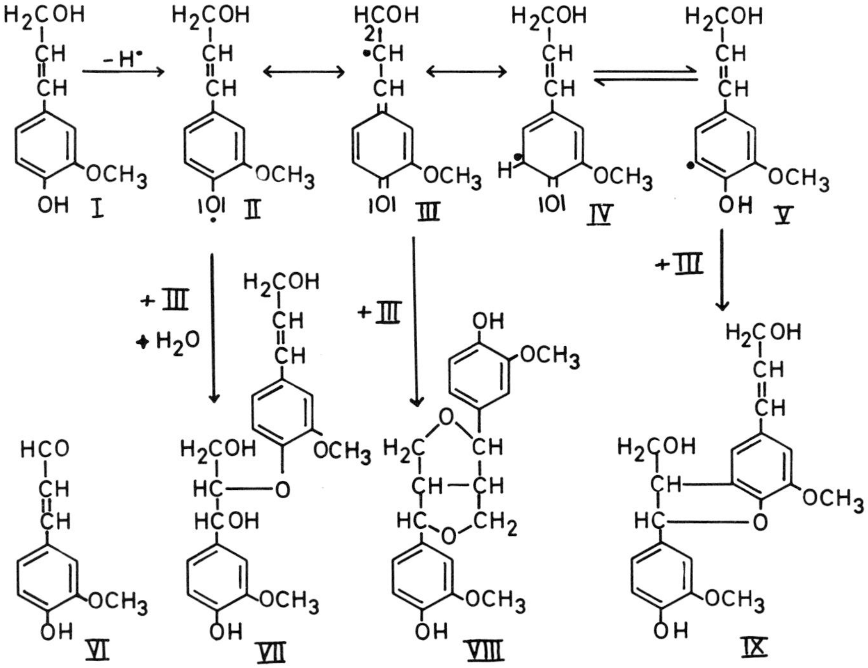

FIG. 18. Mesomeric structures of the radicals of coniferyl alcohol and the possibility for their dimerization. VII: β-aryl ether. VIII: pinoresinol. IX: dehydrodiconiferyl alcohol.

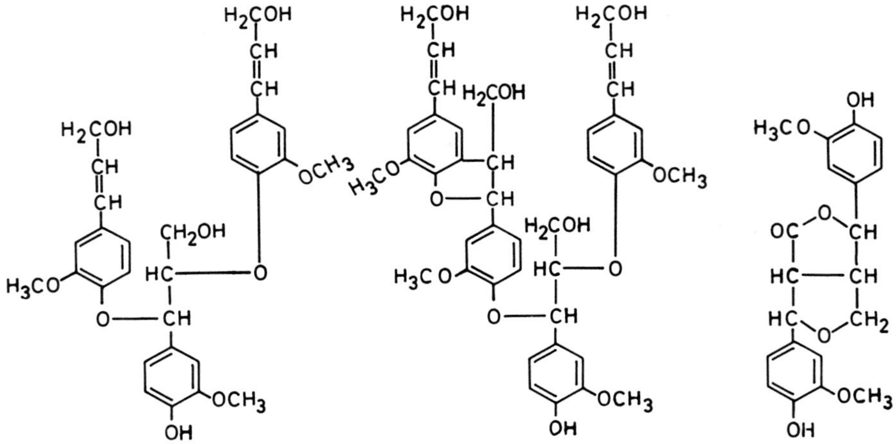

FIG. 19. Dimers, trimers, and tetramers (lignols) isolated by Freudenberg (1964a) by dehydrogenation of coniferyl alcohol.

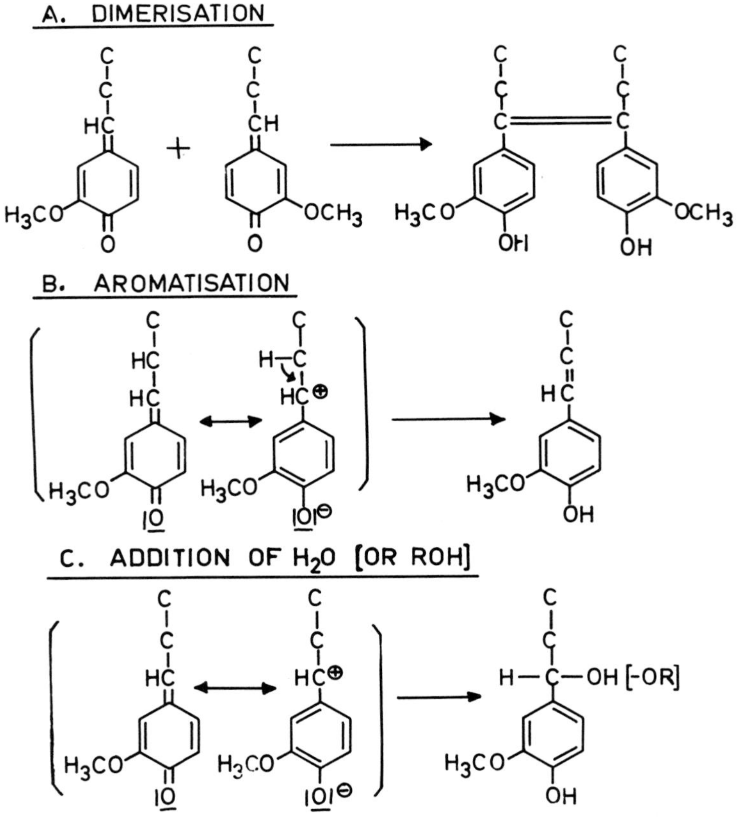

A. DIMERISATION

B. AROMATISATION

C. ADDITION OF H₂O [OR ROH]

FIG. 20. Reaction of the quinone methide according to Adler (1959).

Another important reaction is the one leading to quinone methides. Adler (1959) was the first to show the importance of this highly reactive system for the chemistry of lignin (Fig. 20). The condensation reactions of these quinone methides are not only a means to understand the combination of the lignol fragments, but Freudenberg assumes that the polysaccharides of the cell wall could combine on the same principle (Fig. 21).

By means of these biochemical experiments, and by analytical data (Adler, 1961), Freudenberg (1964a) has constructed a "formula" (scheme) which should be looked upon only as one way the different systems could be bound together (Fig. 22). The agreement between the calculated data

TABLE III. Intermediates (Lignols) Isolated by Freudenberg (1964) during the Dehydrogenation of Coniferyl Alcohol

6 monolignols:
  1. coniferyl alcohol and its 3 monomeric dehydration products formulae II, III, IV (fig. 18)
  5. coniferyl aldehyde
  6. ferulic acid

11 dilignols:
  1. dehydro-diconiferyl alcohol
  2. aldehyde of dehydro-diconiferyl alcohol
  3. pinoresinol
  4. epipinoresinol
  5. quinone methide (precursor of 6)
  6. guaiacyl-glycerol-β-coniferyl ether
  7. aldehyde of guaiacyl-glycerol-β-coniferyl ether
  8. bis-dehydro-coniferyl alcohol
  9. di-coniferyl ether
  10. pinoresinolid
  11. lignenolid

6 trilignols:
  1. guaiacyl-glycerol-β-dehydro-diconiferyl ether
  2. guaiacyl-glycerol-β-pinoresinol ether
  3. guaiacyl-glycerol-β-epipinoresinol ether
  4. bis-guaiacyl-glycerol-β-coniferyl ether
  5. dehydro-triconiferyl alcohol
  6. guaiacyl-glycerol-γ-β-bis-coniferyl ether

2 tetralignols:
  1. dehydro-bis-pinoresinol
  2. guaiacyl-glycerol-γ-dehydro-diconiferyl-β-coniferyl ether

1 pentalignol
  perhaps guaiacyl-glycerol-β-coniferyl ether (dilignol 6), etherified with trilignol 1 in γ position.

1 hexalignol
  probably guaiacyl-glycerol-β-coniferyl ether etherified with tetralignol 2 in γ position

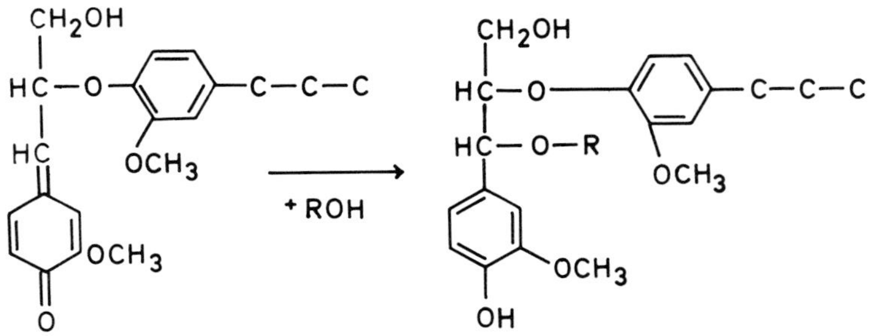

FIG. 21. Reactions of quinone methide with hydroxyl compounds (R can be either sugars or polysaccharides).

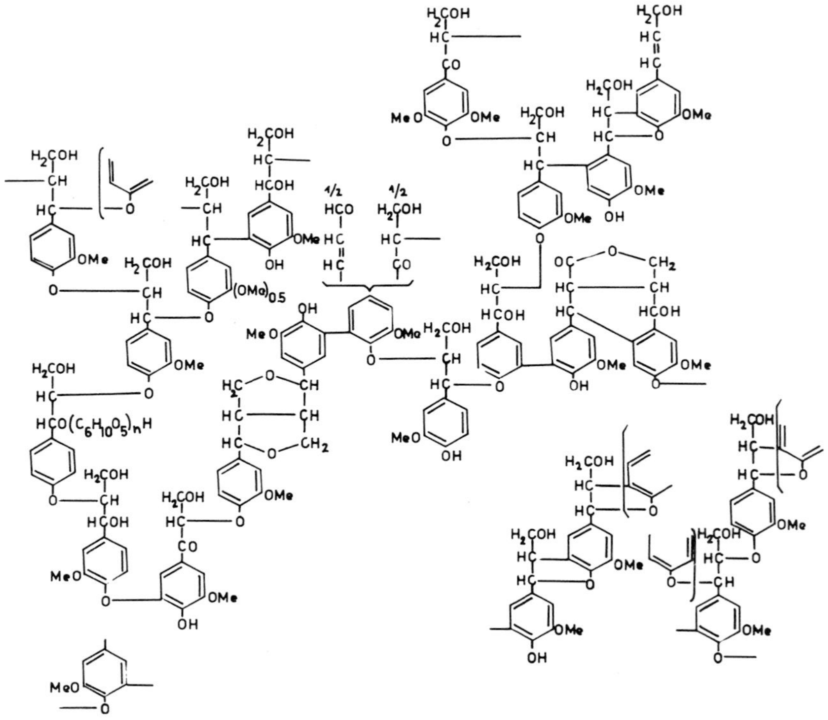

FIG. 22. Freudenberg's (1964a) "formula" (scheme) of lignin.

and observed data is surprising and was proved by an example (Freudenberg, 1964a). The results are based on kinetic data for the sulfonation of lignin. The existence of certain groups and a combination of them (e.g., X, Z, B groups) which had earlier been established were now, for the purpose of comparison, calculated from the scheme. The amount of uptake of methanol at 20°C and the reaction of methanol after a reduction of the carbonyl groups with sodium borohydride, the β-aryl ether bonds, and the precursors of Hibbert's ketoles were also calculated from the scheme and compared with the experimental data, as seen in Table IV.

TABLE IV. Calculated and Found Lignin Data

Characteristic group	Calculated	Found
X	0.17	0.15
Z	0.16	0.15
B	0.24	0.30
Total	0.57	0.60
Uptake of methanol	0.69	0.62
Uptake of methanol after reduction with $NaBH_4$	0.38	0.42
β-Aryl ether	0.41 to 0.47	—
Precursors of Hibbert ketoles	0.17	0.10

The most important result is that new systems of bonds could be predicted (e.g., aryl–aryl ether bonds) which were actually discovered quite recently.

One of the most important new experiments of Adler (1964) and Freudenberg (1964b) resulted in the isolation of definite dimers from lignin, e.g., derivatives of coumarone (Fig. 23), pinoresinol, and dehydrodiconiferyl alcohol (Freudenberg, 1964).

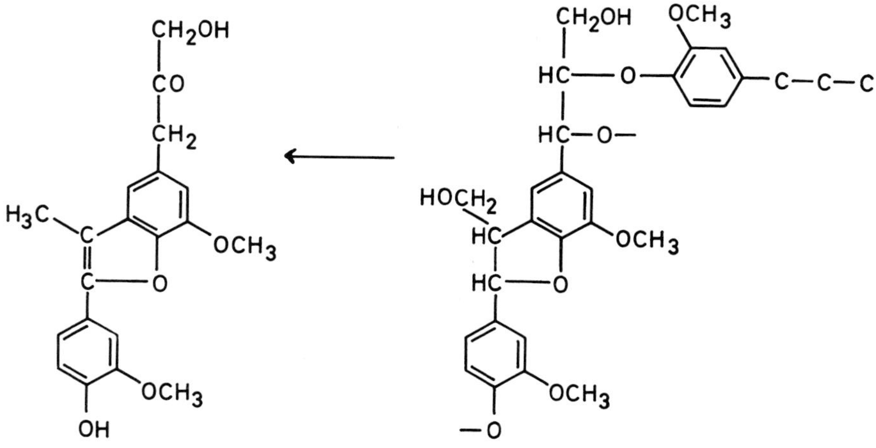

FIG. 23. Dimer isolated by Adler (1964) from lignin

The chemistry of lignin has developed along new and interesting ways in the last twenty years. In my opinion, the main structural problems have been solved, and the most important facts of the biogenesis are also known, whereas details concerning the reactivity of lignin—an important problem for industrial purposes—are still unknown. This will be a task for the future. The greater knowledge which we command nowadays entitles us, however, to hope for a quick and efficient solution to the problems outlined in this paper.

REFERENCES

Adler, E. (1959) "Chinoide Strukturen und Benzylalkoholgruppierungen in der Chemie und Biochemie des Lignins." In *Biochemistry of Wood* (K. Kratzl and G. Billek, ed.), pp. 137–153. Pergamon Press, London.

——— (1961) "Ueber den Stand der Ligninforschung." *Papier* 15:604–609.

——— (1964) "Recent studies on the structure and reactions of lignin." *Symposium international sur la chimie et la biochimie de la lignine, de la cellulose et des hemicelluloses.* Grenoble, 1964. Abstracts:6–7

———, Björkvist, K. J., and Häggroth, S. (1948) "Ueber die Ursache der Farbreaktionen des Holzes." *Acta Chem. Scand.* 2:93–94.

Bailey, A. J. (1936) "Lignin in Douglas-fir. The pentosan content of the middle lamella." *Ind. Eng. Chem. Anal. Ed.* 52:389–391.

Billek, G. (1959) "Zur Isolierung und Bestimmung aktiver Bruckstücke (Phenylpropane) des Lignins nach der Aufnahme markierter Verbindungen." In *Biochemistry of Wood* (K. Kratzl and G. Billek, ed.), pp. 207–214. Pergamon Press, London.

Brickman, L., Hawkins, W. L., and Hibbert, H. (1940) "Studies on lignin and related compounds XLVIII. Identification of vanillin and vanniloyl ketone as ethanolysis products from wood." *J. Am. Chem. Soc.* 62:2149–2154.

Brown, S. A., and Neish, A. C. (1955) "Studies of lignin biosynthesis using isotopic carbon. IV. Formation from some aromatic monomers." *Can. J. Biochem. Physiol.* 33:948–962.

———, Wright, D., and Neish, A. C. (1959) "Studies of lignin biosynthesis using isotopic carbon. VII. The role of p-Hydroxyphenylpyruvic acid." *Can. J. Biochem. Physiol.* 37:25–34.

Creighton, R. H. J., Gibbs, R. D., and Hibbert, H. (1944) "Studies on lignin and related compounds LXXV. Alkaline nitrobenzene oxidation of plant materials and application to taxonomic classification." *J. Am. Chem. Soc.* 66:32–37.

Davis, B. D. (1955) "Intermediates in amino acid biosynthesis." *Advan. Enzymol.* 16:247–312.

——— (1958) "On the importance of being ionized." *Arch. Biochem. Biophys.* 78:497–509.

Erdtman, H. (1933a) "Dehydrierung in der Coniferylreihe I." *Biochem. Z.* 258:172–180.

——— (1933b) "Dehydrierung in der Coniferylreihe II." *Liebigs Ann. Chem.* 503:283–294.

Flaig, W. (1962) "Zur Umwandlung von Lignin in Humusstoffe." *Freiberger Forschungsh.*, A 254:39–56.

Freudenberg, K. (1962) "Forschungen am Lignin." *Fortschr. Chem. Org. Naturstoffe* 20:41–72.

———— (1963) "Biochemische Vorgänge bei der Holzbildung." In *Biochemistry of Wood* (K. Kratzl and G. Billek, ed.), pp. 121–136. Pergamon Press, London.

———— (1964a) "Entwurf eines Konstitutionsschemas für das Lignin der Fichte.' *Holzforschung* 18:3–9.

———— (1964b) *Symposium international sur la chimie et la biochimie de la lignine, de la cellulose et des hemicelluloses.* Grenoble, 1964. Abstracts: 3–4.

————, Jones, K., and Remen, H. (1963) "Künstliches Lignin aus markiertem Coniferylalkohol." *Chem. Ber.* 96:1844–1849.

————, Lautsch, W., and Engler, K. (1940) "Die Bildung von Vanillin aus Fichtenlignin." *Chem. Ber.* 73:167–171.

————, and Plötz, Th. (1948) "Quantitative Bestimmung des Lignins." *Chem. Ber.* 73: 754–757.

Harris, E. E., and Adkins, H. (1938) "Reactions of lignin with hydrogen." *Paper Trade J.* 107(20):38–40.

Hilpert, R. S. (1936) "Ueber die Zusammensetzung der pflanzlichen Zellwand." *Chem. Ber.* 69:1509–1514.

Klason, P. (1932) "Summary of investigations of the chemistry of conifers." *Cellulose Chemie* 10:113–119.

Kratzl, K. (1948a) "Zur Biogenese des Lignins." *Experientia* 4:100–110.

———— (1948b) "Ueber die Konstitution der Lignosulfosäure." *Monatsh. Chem.* 78: 173–174.

———— (1960) "On the biosynthesis of gymnospermae and angiospermae lignins." *Tappi* 43:650–653.

———— (1961) "Zur Biogenese des Lignins." *Holz Roh- Werkstoff* 19:219–232.

————, and Billek, G. (1959) "Ueber das Verhalten der 4-Hydroxyphenylbrenztraubensäure im verholzenden Gewebe der Fichte." *Monatsh. Chem.* 90:536–543.

————, and Faigle, H. (1959a) "Einbau von D-Glucose-1-^{14}C in das Phenylpropangerüst des Fichtenlignins." *Monatsh. Chem.* 90:768–770.

———— and ———— (1959b) "Ueber das Verhalten von Coniferin in der verholzenden Pflanze." *Monatsh. Chem.* 89:708–715.

———— and ———— (1960) "Die Biogenese der Phenylpropan—Einheit des Fichtenlignins." *Z. Naturforsch.* 4:156–167.

Lange, P. W. (1945) "Ultraviolet absorption of solid lignin." *Svensk Papperstid.* 48: 241–245.

———— (1958) "The distribution of chemical constituents through the cell wall." In *Fundamentals Papermaking Fibres, Trans. Symp. Cambridge, England, 1957* (F. Bolam, ed), pp. 147–186.

Neish, A. C. (1955) "Biosynthesis of cell wall carbohydrates." *Can. J. Biochem. Physiol.* 33:658–666.

———— (1964) "Cinnamic acid derivates as intermediates in the biosynthesis of lignin and related compounds." In *Formation of Wood in Forest Trees* (M. Zimmermann, ed.), pp. 219–239. Academic Press, N. Y.

Nord, F. F. (1964) "Formation of lignin and its biochemical degradation." *Symposium international sur la chimie et la biochimie de la lignine, de la cellulose et des hemicelluloses.* Grenoble, 1964. Abstracts:18–19.

Schubert, W. J. (1964) "The fungal degradation of softwood lignin." *Symposium international sur la chimie et la biochimie de la lignine, de la cellulose et des hemicelluloses.* Grenoble, 1964. Abstracts:41.

————, and Acerbo, S. N. (1959) "Conversion of D-glucose into lignin in Norwegian spruce." *Ann. of Biochem. and Biophys.* 83:178–182.

Schütz, F., Sarten, P., and Meyer, H. (1947) "Lignin problem and complete solution of wood." *Holzforschung* 1:2–20.

———, ———, and ——— (1948) "Wood chemistry III." *Angew Chem.* 60:115–125.

Silbernagel, H. (1955) "Ueber die Spaltbarkeit von m-Nitrobenzhydrazonen." *Monatsh. Chem.* 86:256–258.

Tschammler, H., Kratzl, K., Leutner, R., Steininger, A., and Kisser, J. (1953) "Infrared spectra of microscopic wood sections and certain model compounds." *Mikroskopie* 8:238–246.

Wardrop, A. B. (1957) "Phase of lignification in the differentiation of wood fibres." *Tappi* 40:225–243.

———, and Bland, D. E. (1959) "Process of lignification in woody plants." In *Biochemistry of Wood* (K. Kratzl and G. Billek, ed.), pp. 92–116. Pergamon Press, London.

Wiesner, J. (1878) "Das Verhalten des Phloroglucins und einiger verwandter Körper zur verholzten Zellmembran." *Sitzber. Akad. Wiss., Wien Abtlg. I* 77:60–66.

Inorganic Elements in Wood

EVERETT L. ELLIS

School of Natural Resources
The University of Michigan

INTRODUCTION AND FUNCTION

Constituting a very minor portion of the constituents of wood, probably less than one fourth of one per cent of the total wood mass, the principally metallic elements play a role in determining wood properties seldom realized. Despite their low-level occurrence, a number of these elements have proved to be essential for plant growth (Stiles, 1946; Kramer and Kozlowski, 1960). Others, when readily available in the soil, are frequently absorbed by plant roots and end up in secondary wood, although they may not be necessary for growth (Wherry, 1932). The current concept of nutritional status of a majority of these elements is given in Table I.

Examples of "trace" element deficiencies and growth are quite common in cultivated plants of many types grown in orchards, plantations, or as crops (Goodall and Gregory, 1947; Lundegårdh, 1951). The occurrence of limiting quantities of particular elements in forest tree growth is, however, rarely proved, although mineral deficiencies are occasionally suggested as a causative factor in poor growth (Kramer and Kozlowski, 1960). Outstanding examples of the essential nature of certain elements for tree growth are found in the cases of zinc and phosphorous deficiencies in pine plantations in western Australia (Stoate, 1950), and molybdenum deficiencies in citrus orchards in California (Vanselow and Bradford, 1957).

The presence of anomalously high amounts of several elements such as gold, silver, manganese, iron, selenium, zinc, copper, vanadium, and cobalt in woody tissues has long been associated with the presence of these elements at higher than normal levels in underlying soils and substrata, and forms the basis for prospecting for metals through the use of biological tissues, including wood, the field of biogeochemistry (Warren, *et al.*, 1948–1952; Cannon and Starrett, 1956).

Proof of essentiality of an element for growth is complicated by problems of purity of media, contamination, and the likelihood of substitu-

TABLE I.　Classification, Function, and Approximate Level of Occurrence of Elements Found in Wood of Grand Fir

(ppm of dry weight)

Constituent	Essential		Other	
	Major	Minor	Common	Uncommon[b]
C	Ca 754	B 0.9	Ag 0.23	Au 0.04
O	K 865	Mn 19.3	Al 5.4	Ga 0.02
H	Mg 171	Fe 2.6	Ba 20.2	In 0.03
N	Na[a] 23	Mo 0.005	Co 0.01	La 0.04
P	Si[a] —	Cu 2.5	Cr 0.05	Li 0.13
S		Zn 0.9	Ni 0.11	Sn 0.003
Cl[a]			Pb 0.12	V 0.001
			Rb 2.0	Zr 0.002
			Sr 10.2	
			Ti 0.11	

Source: Adapted from Ellis (1959; 1962); and Altman and Dittmer (1964); analytic results largely from spectrographic procedures.
[a] Essentiality questionable; always present.
[b] Also reported were Bi and Cd, infrequently.

tion of one element for another (Murphey, 1964). Both essential and non-essential elements may show stimulatory effects upon growth when present in small quantities, and toxic effects in higher concentrations. Furthermore, there are probably major differences in inorganic require-ments exhibited by different types of plants, such as fungi and seed plants, or even within smaller groups of plants. A broad coverage in the litera-ture discusses many aspects of metallic elements in plant tissues, but with very little reference to wood. Wood does, however, play a unique role among plant tissues, serving as a partial record of past mineral uptake and distribution; a long-lived repository for much of the inorganic ma-terial taken up by woody plants.

PATHWAYS INTO WOOD

The precise pathway of inorganic ions present in the soil to their even-tual position in wood has never been charted. Presumably, the major en-try is through root hairs and root systems (Kramer and Kozlowski, 1960), through mechanisms which may be selective and capable of operating against steep concentration gradients (Hendricks, 1964). Both passive (diffusion) and active (transport) systems may be involved in the original transfer from soil to and through prosenchymatous elements of roots and stems. Once in the leaves, a large share of these elements enter growth and regulatory processes, while some are translocated downward and laterally through phloem and parenchymatous tissues. The recycling of elements to the soil surface through leaf fall and bark sloughing will account for much of the total uptake, but the relative mobility appears to differ among elements (Foulger, 1964; Galligan, 1964). Certainly the soil is the major contributor of metallic constituents in woody plant growth, but the possibilities of air- and precipitation-borne contributions cannot be discounted. Aerial application of fertilizer and other treatments are as effective as soil additions in most cases.

The deposition or arresting of metallic components in wood through low-order molecular and ionic forces is the most likely explanation of their location at any given time. Resorption into actively functioning tissues in response to an active demand for individual elements is possible but questionable. The frequent occurrence of crystals and concretions in wood may be evidence of the former possibility—substantiated by the general location of crystals in or near parenchymatous cells, suggesting active transport mechanisms and deposition at interfaces of parenchyma and prosenchyma.

Methods of Analysis

Previous reference to the generally low-level occurrence of inorganic elements in wood suggests some of the difficulties encountered in their determination. The inorganic components of wood are generally expressed as percentage of ash, based on dry weight of the sample. With the exceptions of mineral streak and areas of decay and stain due to fungi, the normal levels of occurrence appear to be from approximately 0.1% to about 0.5% ash, for most domestic timbers. The alkaline earths calcium, potassium, and magnesium generally comprise the bulk of inorganic elements present and may account for 70% or more of the total. As can be seen from Table I, most other elements occur in relatively small amounts and in an unknown pattern of distribution. Methods of analysis and preparation for rather precise determinations must then be geared to the elements of interest, the level of their occurrence, standards of accuracy, and problems of contamination.

Details with respect to collection and handling of wood samples may be found in the literature. The most commonly employed preparatory step is "dry" ashing of material in a muffle furnace or "wet" ashing with suitable acids. Since either of these processes results in the volatilization of organic material, ashing performs a very valuable separatory and concentrative function with respect to inorganic elements. Ashing conditions, particularly temperatures, are generally held to a minimum to prevent loss of the more volatile elements. Naturally, the "ash" or solution obtained by such methods will consist primarily of appropriate salts of the elements present—largely carbonates and oxides in the case of dry ashing, and the corresponding acid salt for the "wet" method. One additional complication is the occurrence of a relatively great number of elements in one sample, which makes it impossible to design simple and specific methods for individual elements, in most cases.

Destructive Methods

Spot Tests. Due to complex makeup of the inorganic residue from woody tissues, specific spot tests and similar microanalytical methods have been rarely used.

Arc Spectrography. This classical, but tedious, method will provide excellent results for probably forty or more elements when used on dry ash, without any special treatment. General descriptions of methods are given in Brode (1939) and Ahrens (1950); detailed description of suitable methods for plant materials will also be found in Vanselow and Liebig (undated). Detection limits for most elements are very low and the use of refined methods will lead to highly satisfactory results. The method is time consuming, particularly in establishing standards, and demands quite expensive instrumentation.

Spark Spectrography. A special adaptation of the arc method, the use of spark excitation, provides a method suitable for solutions obtained by acid digestion of wood or of ash. This method is not as suitable for as great a number of elements as direct arcing, but newer apparatus is available which provides printed cards suitable for handling by a computer. An advantage of the method is the use of relatively small quantities of solution, making possible the use of wood samples with a magnitude of individual annual rings, or portions thereof, for perhaps ten to fifteen elements (Foulger, 1964).

Flame Emission Spectrophotometry. In many ways the simplest and most readily available method of analysis, the use of flame for excitation has been highly developed and widely applied in many fields. Applicable to solutions containing the elements, it is particularly suitable for determining alkali earths. Flame analysis is more rapid and accurate than most other analytical methods for this group. By special procedures other elements can be investigated, but the complexity of wood ash components presents many problems. Methods are described in Dean (1960) and Lundegårdh (1951).

Flame Atomic Absorption Spectrophotometry. Recently developed apparatus makes possible the use of absorption techniques with special phototubes operating at specific wave lengths. The methods are said to be highly accurate with low detection limits, suitable for solutions, and available for about thirty elements, each element requiring special phototube.

Nondestructive Methods

Radioactivation Analysis. Unique among analytic methods, because it permits nondestructive testing for metals and certain other elements present in small quantities in wood, is the newly developed area of activation analysis. As employed by the author, sample preparation involves making a small plug of the wood in question weighing, at most, about 0.3 grams. This sample, placed in a small polyethylene vial and this in turn in a larger carrier, is transported to the reactor face by means of a pneumatic tube system. The sample is subjected to thermal neutron bombardment for a suitable period of time depending upon the element to be analyzed and its abundance. The activated sample is returned via the pneumatic tube and placed on a gamma scintillation crystal. The scintillation counts are stored in a 400-channel memory unit and are then used to reproduce the energy spectrum. Methods are described by Bowen and Gibbons (1963). Galligan (1964) gives results for manganese determined by this method for individual annual rings in Douglas-fir.

According to early results obtained by the author, using the facilities of the Phoenix Memorial Laboratory and the Ford Nuclear Reactor at the University of Michigan, neutron activation holds promise for analysis of the following elements in wood: manganese, potassium, copper, calcium, sodium, aluminum, and magnesium. With the development of suitable separatory techniques, it is hoped that the following elements can also be determined by a modification of this method involving solubilization of the wood sample: chlorine, molybdenum, zinc, silver, barium, cobalt, strontium, gold, and vanadium.

There are two other nondestructive test methods probably suitable in analyses of wood where appreciable quantities of certain elements are present. They are *Neutron Absorption Analysis* (a method which has been employed to determine boron in treated wood), and *X-ray Fluorescence Microscopy and Diffraction.* The latter methods are apparently suitable in special cases where a metal occurs in a concentration of about 1% or higher for elements heavier than the molecular weight of sodium.

TYPICAL RESULTS

Tables II and III present some data obtained by the methods described for arc spectrography and flame spectrophotometry. Average values in ppm for sixty sound grand fir samples from the northwestern United States are given in Table I. Not shown is the degree of variability illustrated by data of this type.

Table II compares differences in amounts and types of elements found in grand fir: (a) By geographical regions west and east of the Cascade Mountains. All samples are of wood collected in the lower portion of the stem and statistical significance of the difference in mean values between the two areas is given. (b) As a function of decay by the Indian paint fungus of samples collected largely in Idaho (all east of the Cascades). It is noteable that a highly significant difference is found in most cases.

Table III presents limited data on major essential element content of several species and different tissues within a species. Of particular interest are the high levels of these elements in decayed or stained wood, implying a strong mechanism for the translocation of elements through fungal activity. The higher levels of occurrence of these elements in bark is also apparent.

APPLICATION AND IMPORTANCE OF RESULTS

Knowledge of inorganic element content in wood can be used to explain certain factors of variability of growth of trees both within and between species and sites. Refined methods of analysis can also be employed to determine the eventual disposition of inorganic materials entering wood from the soil or air. Of particular consequence is the location of these materials in cell walls or on the inner lumen of cells. Such information obtainable by these means may also assist in clarifying the mechanisms of ion transport and such phenomena as heartwood formation. These methods may also be employed to assist in quantitative determination of levels of retention of preservatives and treating chemicals or in the penetration of cooking liquors into pulp chips.

Other factors with which inorganic composition may play an important part include the following: pulp brightness and the effects of pulpwood storage; processing difficulties in viscose due to the manganese content of pulp; color stability in wood and paper; pitch and extractive difficulties; carbonization and combustion; biochemistry of decay; decay resistance and development; and the presence of silicon as a contributor to marine borer resistance (Tsoumis, 1956; Wise *et al.,* 1952).

TABLE II. Differences in Inorganic Elements in Grand Fir Wood by Geographical Area and Decay

Essential elements:	Buttwood west and east of Cascades			Sound and rotten wood east of Cascades		
	West	East	Signif. level, %[a]	Sound	Rotten[b]	Signif. level, %[a]
Major						
No. samples	26	34	—	8	9	—
Ash, % dry wt.	0.40	0.40	c	0.77	3.40	99
Ca, ppm	549	872	99	914	7747	95
K, ppm	1092	468	99	790	3990	95
Mg, ppm	200	154	80	254	1704	99
Na, ppm	40	14	95	10	51	95
Minor						
Ash, % dry wt.	0.33	0.45	90	0.77	3.40	99
B, ppm	0.9	0.9	20	0.6	c	—
Mn, ppm	21.1	17.9	50	22.4	100.5	95
Fe, ppm	2.3	2.9	95	3.3	11.0	99
Mo, ppm	0.01	0.01	99	0.33	0.10	c
Cu, ppm	2.8	2.3	80	2.4	4.9	50 c
Zn, ppm	0.24	1.44	99	0.12	4.70	50 c
Other elements:						
Ash, % dry wt.	0.33	0.45	90	0.77	3.40	99
Ag, ppm	0.03	0.38	90	0.7	1.7	70
Al, ppm	5.0	5.7	50	12.8	43.2	95
Ba, ppm	10.2	27.8	99	45.8	254.3	95
Co, ppm	0.01	0.02	99	0.02	0.07	80
Cr, ppm	0.04	0.06	80	0.07	0.14	80
Ni, ppm	0.15	0.08	90	0.06	0.18	95
Pb, ppm	0.06	0.17	70	0.02	0.08	70
Rb, ppm	1.7	2.2	50	2.5	9.2	99
Sr, ppm	3.2	15.6	99	25.4	101.2	95
Ti, ppm	0.14	0.08	95	0.13	2.82	70

[a] Probability that differences are real and not due alone to chance.
[b] All decay by Echinodontium tinctorium.
[c] Value not computed because of too few samples or identical measure.

TABLE III. Major Essential Element Content of Various Tissues

(in ppm dry weight)

Sample	Ash %	Ca	K	Na	Mg
Grand Fir:					
60 sound wood	0.40	731	739	25	176
8 matched sound wood	0.77	914	790	10	254
9 matched rotten wood	3.40	7747	3990	51	1704
5 fungus fruiting bodies	2.03	980	3062	28	1404
6 bark	3.72	9360	1171	48	1052
6 needle	7.90	18428	3423	95	3982
Shagbark Hickory:					
1 sapwood	0.60	688	1238	10	
1 heartwood	0.76	1312	1480	4	
1 mineral streak	5.06	18008	344	87	
Sweetgum:					
1 white rotted 24% loss	0.609	1020	824	39	
1 white rotted 47% loss	0.836	1698	594	35	
1 white rotted 65% loss	1.124	2380	754	40	
1 brown rotted 23% loss	0.799	692	120	46	
1 brown rotted 39% loss	1.735	1557	166	56	
1 brown rotted 32% loss	2.334	2664	133	62	
Sitka spruce:					
1 brown rotted 32% loss	0.802	361	164	30	
1 brown rotted 47% loss	1.150	642	120	30	
1 brown rotted 64% loss	2.160	2016	201	40	
Sugar maple:					
1 sapwood	0.37	878	274	170	
1 mineral streak	2.18	7621	120	152	
Aspen:					
7 sound sapwood	0.41	833	628	46	
12 fungal stained wood	1.08	2460	1751	43	
10 bark	5.24	16559	4353	65	

REFERENCES

Ahrens, L. H. (1950) *Spectrochemical Analysis*. Addison-Wesley Press, Cambridge, Mass. 340pp.

Altman, P. L., and Dittmer, D. S. (1964) *Biology Data Book*. Fed. of Amer. Soc. for Experimental Biology. 633pp.

Bowen, H. J. M., and Gibbons, D. (1963) *Radioactivation Analysis*. Clarendon Press, Oxford. 295pp.

Brode, W. R. (1939) *Chemical Spectroscopy*. John Wiley and Sons, N. Y. 677pp.

Cannon, H. L., and Starrett, W. H. (1956) "Botanical prospecting for uranium on La Ventana Mesa, Sandoval County, New Mexico." *Geol. Surv. Wyoming, Bull.* 1009-M: 391–407.

Dean, H. L. (1960) *Flame Photometry.* McGraw-Hill, N. Y. 354pp.

Ellis, E. L. (1959) "The effects of environment and decay on the mineral components of grand fir wood." In *Marine Boring and Fouling Organisms* (D. L. Ray, Ed.). Friday Harbor Symposia. Univ. of Wash. Press, Seattle.

——— (1962) "Inorganic constituents of wood." *Forest Prod. J.* 12:271–274.

Foulger, A. N. (1964) Private communication.

Galligan, W. T. (1964) "Study of trace element distribution in wood by neutron activation." Unpubld. MS in Chem. Engr. Thesis, Wash. State University.

Goodall, D. W., and Gregory, F. G. (1947) "Chemical composition of plants as an index of their nutritional status." Imper. Bur. of Hort. and Plant. Crops. Tech. Comm. 17. 167pp.

Hendricks, S. B. (1964) "Salt transport across cell membranes." *Am. Scientist* 52:306–333.

Kramer, P. J., and Kozlowski, T. T. (1960) *Physiology of Trees.* McGraw-Hill, N. Y. 642pp.

Lundegårdh, H. (1951) (Translated by R. L. Mitchell) *Leaf Analysis.* Hilger and Watts, London. 176pp.

Murphey, W. K. (1964) Private communication.

Stiles, W. (1946) *Trace Elements in Plants and Animals.* Cambridge University Press. 109pp.

Stoate, T. N. (1950) "Nutrition of the pine." For. and Tmbr. Bur. Bull. 30. Canberra. 61pp.

Tsoumis, G. (1956) "Une étude sur la résistance des bois aux attaques des xylophages *Marius* en rapport avec le teneux en silice." *Rev. du Bois et de ses App.* 10(12):23–25.

Vanselow, A. P., and Bradford, G. R. (1957) "Techniques and applications of spectroscopy in plant nutrition studies." *Soil Sci.,* 75–83.

———, and Liebig, G. F., Jr. (undated) "Spectrochemical methods for the determination of minor elements in plants, waters, chemicals, and culture media." Univ. of Calif. Agr. Expt. Sta. Berkeley. 45pp.

Warren, H. V., and Delavault, R. E. (1948) "Biochemical investigations in British Columbia." *Geophysics* 13(4):609–624.

——— and ——— (1949) "Further studies in biogeochemistry." *Bull. Geol. Soc. Am.* 60:531–559.

———, and Matheson, C. R. (1949) "Some relationships between geology and forest growth." *West. Miner.* June, 1949.

———, ———, and Irish, Ruth (1952) "Biogeochemical investigations in the Pacific Northwest." *Bull. Geol. Soc. Am.* 63:435–484.

Wherry, Edgar T. (1932) "Ecological studies of serpentine barren plants. I. Ash composition." *Proc. Penn. Acad. Sci.* 6:32–38.

Wise, L. E., Rittenhouse, Ruth C., Dickey, E. E., Olson, O. H., and Garcia, C. (1952) "The chemical composition of tropical woods." *Forest Prod. J.* 2:227–249.

The Fine Structure of the Cellulose Microfibril

KURT MÜHLETHALER

Electron Microscopy Laboratory
Swiss Federal Institute of
Technology, Zürich

It is now well established that the cellulose in plant cell walls is deposited in fibrillar form. If walls of different origin are extracted with dilute acid and alkali, random or parallel textures become visible, indicating that the noncellulosic components such as pectin, hemicellulose, and lignin are deposited between the cellulose fibrils (Mühlethaler, 1949). In the early days of electron microscopy, the widths of these fibrils, called microfibrils, were believed to be uniform. But later, it was found that they varied considerably even in the same cell wall. In *Valonia*, Preston (1951) measured diameters between 83 and 380 Å. For wood cell walls, Hodge and Wardrop (1950) reported widths between 50 and 100 Å. Vogel (1953), measuring Ramie microfibrils, found values between 170 and 200 Å. The cellulose fibrils in *Funaria* spore membranes were shown by Günther (1960) to have widths between 35 and 140 Å. Each of these studies demonstrated the lack of uniformity in width of microfibrils. When the micellar components of microfibrils are measured by X-ray diffraction method, they have widths varying between 30 and 60 Å. Frey-Wyssling (1937) explained the variability in microfibrillar widths by assuming that the cellulose in the microfibrils is not crystalline throughout, but that there are crystalline and paracrystalline or amorphous regions. Such a hypothesis is supported by two observations. First, the specific weight of cellulose when determined in helium or with other media that penetrate into the capillary spaces proves to be lower than that which can be calculated for cellulose crystals based on the results of the model of the unit cell. Second, the behavior of cellulose during water absorption is significant. Since the X-ray diagram of dry and moist cellulose is the same, the water must be stored in the paracrystalline region. In addition to these observations there are also several chemical indications of the presence of amorphous cellulose. According to Hermans (1949) and Preston *et al.*, (1950), two thirds of the substance must be more or less crystalline and one third amorphous. As Frey-Wyssling (1959) has pointed out in his model, the transition between the crystalline and amorphous states is undoubtedly gradual. Based on these results and concepts, it was thought that the microfibrils would contain a number of crystallites surrounded by amorphous cellulose chains. In Frey-Wyssling's model the crystalline regions are not arranged at regular intervals, but scattered along the axis at random. This is in contradiction to the model proposed by Hess *et al.*, (1957), who postulate an alternation between crystalline and paracrystalline segments. From electron micrographs Vogel (1953) was able to prove that the microfibrils are composed of rectangular smaller units, having a dimension of 30 × 100 Å. These results were confirmed later by Rånby (1958). Several of these flat bands can be joined together to form a microfibril.

As mentioned previously, the width of the microfibril may vary between 30 and 300 Å. This variability can be explained in different ways. If we assume that the strands are formed by a crystallization process, then most probably no uniform fibrils will be produced. Variations would be expected according to the differences in local conditions, the available amounts of precursors, and so on. Another possibility is that the first formed microfibrils may be stretched during growth and thus become thinner. Then the newly deposited fibrils at the inner side of the wall would be thicker than in the lamellae at the outside. The opposite is possible, however, as Günther (1960) showed in the spore walls of *Funaria hygrometrica:*

$$\text{inside}—92 \text{ Å} \pm 4.3 \text{ Å}$$
$$\text{outside}—146 \text{ Å} \pm 3.7 \text{ Å}$$

There are two peaks, one at 70 Å for the inner lamellae and one at 140 Å outside. This shows clearly that the microfibrils are considerably thinner at the beginning of surface growth and subsequently become thicker. During growth of the protonema a linear increase in width was observed. She found that during growth a 10 μ expansion caused an increase of fibrillar width of 13.3 Å. Over their entire length the microfibrils are uniform in diameter. These results led Günther (1960) to assume that the formation of cellulose fibrils begins in the ectoplasm and continues in the loose network of the young wall. If the wall becomes more compact the formation of new fibrils is inhibited and the free glucose molecules are polymerized at the surface of the previously formed microfibrils. As I shall point out later, we explain this increase in thickness by the fasciculation of the existing microfibrils. Our interpretation is based mainly on observations made with the negative staining method introduced by Brenner and Horne (1959). The membrane fragments are suspended first in 1% phospho-tungstic acid and subsequently dried on the grids used for electron microscopy. The cellulose fibrils containing elements of low atomic weight appear as while threads (due to the small amount of electron scatter) on the dark background (Fig. la-c). This method allows a

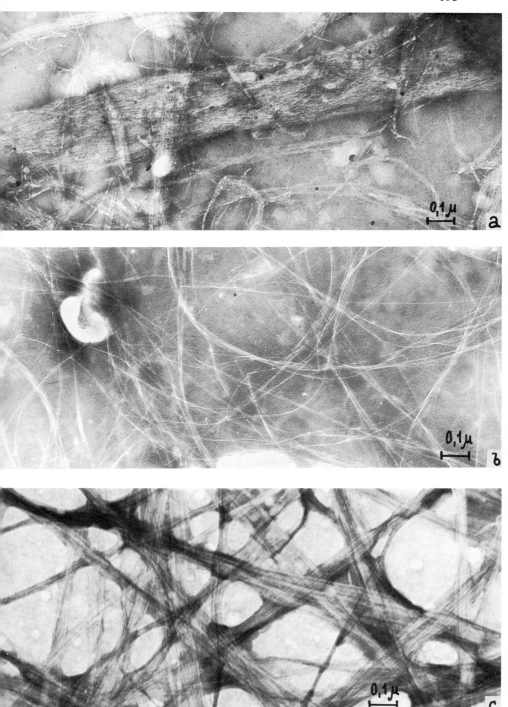

Fig. 1. Negatively stained cellulose fibrils. (a) Ramie cell wall. (b) Onion root cell walls.
(c) Cellulose produced by *Bacterium xylinum*.

much better insight into the internal structure of the microfibrils than the metal evaporation technique used previously, because no additional increase in width occurs. Also, the dried phospho-tungstic acid shows less structure than the metal layer. The contrast medium readily penetrates into the smallest capillary spaces, and regions with loose textures can be detected very easily. Applying this technique to Ramie fibers (Fig. la), meristematic cell walls of onion roots (Fig. 1b), and *Bacterium xylinum* (Fig. lc), we have shown that the microfibrils are always composed of smaller threads. These strands, which have an average width of 35 Å, we call *elementary fibrils* (Mühlethaler, 1960; Frey-Wyssling und Mühlethaler, 1963). Electron micrographs indicated that they must be highly crystalline along their entire length because we have never observed the penetration of the phospho-tungstic acid into these fibrils. If there were an ordered segmentation of crystalline and paracrystalline sections a more or less alternating dark and bright segmentation should occur and this was never observed. There is also another indication of high crystallinity. It can be calculated that an extension of 2% will break the cellulose lattice. This would occur if the microfibrils are bent to a radius smaller than 875 Å. In fact we have never observed loops with a radius smaller than around 700 Å. If the elementary fibrils break, then they must be behaving like thin crystals.

A possible objection is that a similar picture would be obtained if the larger microfibrils were to consist of a crystalline core surrounded by a paracrystalline sheath (Preston, 1962). In this case the phospho-tungstic acid would penetrate the loose sheath and only the central core would be visible. On the other hand the metal evaporation technique should give the same results as the negative staining technique. This was recently shown by Ohad and Danon (1964). In their first publication (Ohad *et al.*, 1963) they reported a new method for the estimation of the true width of fibrillar or rod-like structures. When the measured image widths of several shadowed fibrils are plotted against the sine of the angle (β) between the long axis of the fibril and the direction of the shadow, and extrapolated to $\beta = 0$, the real width can be found. Their results confirm our previous work very well. The measurement of shadow-cast material yields 20 Å for the height (deduced from the length) and 30 Å for the width. In negatively stained material the 30 Å width was predominant and some threads measured up to 40 Å. In view of these results Ohad and Danon (1964) came to the conclusion that the elementary fibrils are rectangular in cross section, about 20 by 30 Å. In our own measurements we used a statistical method which gave us an average of 35 Å. It is not very easy to measure such small units, because the electron microscope has to be calibrated very accurately and the photographic procedure must be controlled with special care.

In the negatively stained preparations it can be seen that two or more elementary fibrils are fasciculated to form larger threads. A comparison of the measurements published by other authors showed that their results are in good agreement with multiples of 35 Å. If we return once more to the results of Günther (1960), who found peaks at 70 Å at the inside of the *Funaria* cell wall and 140 Å in the outer lamella, we can explain this increase in width by fasciculation. In the newly formed lamella only two elementary fibrils are joined. During cell expansion more threads are aggregated, thus increasing the width from 70 to 140 Å. This process is enhanced by the stretching of the cell walls during growth. In order to explain this process of fasciculation which leads to bands having rectangular cross sections with dimensions of 20–30 Å by 100-150 Å, as observed by Vogel (1953) and Rånby (1958), a model based on previous X-ray diffraction work must be built. According to the models, constructed by Meyer and Misch (1937) and Frey-Wyssling (1955), the pyranose rings are in the (002)-plane (Fig. 2a). It is not this plane, however, which corresponds to the surface of the elementary fibrils. Schurz (1955) was able to show that the (101)-plane lies tangential to the cell surface. This orientation is caused by the hydroxyl groups which are concentrated in this plane. The fasciculation of several elementary fibrils must occur in the direction of the (101)-plane (Fig. 2d) because free hydroxyl groups are present at the surface. From the cross section of the elementary fibril and the space occupied by one cellulose molecule we may calculate the number of molecules in such a thread. The calculation shows that an average of 37 molecules are packed into one elementary fibril (Frey-Wyssling and Mühlethaler, 1963). For geometric reasons it seems reasonable to assume that a cross section contains 7 molecules along the (101)-plane and 6 perpendicular to it (Fig. 2b).

There is some controversy about the physical mechanism of fibrillar initiation and growth. According to the original model published by Meyer and Misch (1937), the cellulose molecules are antiparallel. If tip growth is assumed, two enzymes are involved in the final stage of fibril formation. Such a mechanism does not seem impossible. It would mean that two glucose residues must always be added to the antiparallel pair. In this case the elementary fibril would contain 18 antiparallel pairs, of which 16 are at the surface (Fig. 2c). There are also some good arguments, however, in favor of a parallel orientation of all cellulose molecules (Colvin, 1964). In this case the two ends would show different chemical behavior.

As shown in Figure 1 the negatively stained fibrils do not show any periodic changes in their electron scattering power. This indicates that the spaces in the paracrystalline regions are so small that not enough PTA can be stored to become visible. For this reason a regular segmentation of

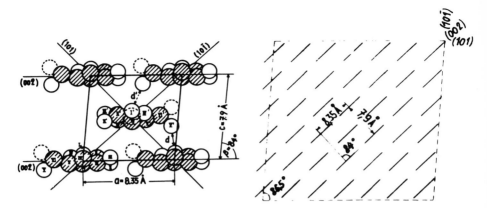

FIG. 2. Lattice structure of cellulose. (a) Projection of a crystal lattice of cellulose I (according to Frey-Wyssling, 1959). (b) Cross section of an elementary fibril with 42 cellulose molecules.

FIG. 2(c).   Elementary fibril with 18 pairs of antiparallel cellulose molecules.

FIG. 2(d).   Fasciculation of three elementary fibrils.

crystalline and amorphous regions does not seem to exist. It is more likely that the cellulose molecules are regularly arranged in bundles, as previously suggested by Meyer and van der Wyk (1941). In such a bundle the paracrystalline parts are small and arranged at random.

For many years it was taken for granted that the cellulose molecules in natural fibers are straight and not folded. Recently, however, doubts have been expressed by several authors (see Dolmetsch and Dolmetsch, 1962) as to whether this is always correct. It is very likely that the straight molecules are folded as soon as they are in solution. Manley (1961) was able to obtain crystals from cellulose triacetate solutions. In these 100 Å-thick lamellae, the chains of molecules are oriented perpendicular to the plane of the layer and are sharply folded. Based on these results Dolmetsch and Dolmetsch (1962) postulated a model for fibrils with folded cellulose chains. It is, however, unlikely that all cellulose molecules are folded in the native state because many of the physical properties (for example, tensile strength) can only be explained if straight molecules are present. It is possible that in the native state a few molecules are folded in a manner similar to the one recently postulated for synthetic fibers by Bonart and Hoseman (1960), but the majority of them are certainly straight. The folding of the long cellulose molecule, which is thermodynamically likely to occur, is prevented by growing cells; how, is another secret of life. -

REFERENCES

Bonart, R., and Hosemann, R. (1960) "Modellversuche zur Deutung der Röntgen-Langperiodeninterferenzen." *Makromol. Chem.* 39:105–118.

Brenner, S., and Horne, R. W. (1959) "A negative staining method for high resolution electron microscopy of viruses." *Biochem. Biophys. Acta* 34:103–110.

Colvin, J. R. (1964) "The biosynthesis of cellulose." In *The Formation of Wood in Forest Trees* (M. H. Zimmermann, ed.), pp. 189-201. Academic Press, N. Y.

Dolmetsch, H., and Dolmetsch, H. (1962) "Anzeichen für eine Kettenfaltung des Cellulosemoleküls." *Kolloid-Z.* 185:106–119.

Frey-Wyssling, A. (1937) "Ueber die submikroskopische Morphologie der Zellwände." *Ber. Deut. Botan. Ges.* 55:119–132

————(1955) "On the crystal structure of cellulose I." *Biochim. Biophys. Acta* 18:166–168.

————(1959) *Die pflanzliche Zellwand.* Springer-Verlag, Berlin, Göttingen, Heidelberg.

————, and Mühlethaler, K. (1963) "Die Elementarfibrillen der Cellulose." *Makromol. Chem.* 62:25–30.

Günther, I. (1960) "Elektronenmikroskopische Untersuchungen an der keimenden Spore von *Funaria hygrometrica.*" *J. Ultrastruct. Res.* 4:304–331.

Hermans, P. H. (1949) *Physics and Chemistry of Cellulose Fibres.* Elsevier Publishing Company, Inc., New York, Amsterdam, London, Brussels.

Hess, K., Mahl, H., and Gütter, E. (1957) "Elektronenmikroskopische Darstellung grosser Längsperioden in Zellulosefasern und ihr Vergleich mit den Perioden anderer Faserarten." *Kolloid-Z.* 155:1–19.

Hodge, A. J., and Wardrop, A. B. (1950) "An electron microscopic investigation on the cell wall organisation of conifer tracheids." *Nature* 165:272–275.

Manley, J. (1961) "Crystals of cellulose." *Nature* 189:390–391.

Meyer, K., and Misch, L. (1937) "Positions des atomes dans le nouveau modèle spatial de la cellulose." *Helv. Chim. Acta* 20:232–244.

————, and van der Wyk, A. J. A. (1941) "Ueber den Feinbau der Cellulosefaser." *Z. Elektrochem.* 47:353–360.

Mühlethaler, K. (1949) "Electron micrographs of plant fibers." *Biochim. Biophys. Acta* 3:15–25.

———— (1960) "Die Feinstruktur der Zellulosemikrofibrillen." *Z. Schweiz. Forstv.* 30: 55–65.

Ohad, I., and Danon, D. (1964) "On the dimensions of cellulose microfibrils." *J. Cell Biol.* 22: 302–305

————, ————, and Hestrin, S. (1963) "The use of shadow-casting technique for measurement of the width of elongated particles." *J. Cell Biol.* 17: 321–326.

Preston, R. D. (1951) "Fibrillar units in the structure of native cellulose." *Faraday Soc. Disc.* 11: 165–170.

———— (1962) "The sub-microscopic morphology of cellulose." *Polymer* pp. 511–528.

————, Hermans, P. H., and Weidinger, A. (1950) "The crystalline-non-crystalline ratio in celluloses of biological interest." *J. Exp. Botany* 1: 344–352.

Rånby, B. G. (1958) "The fine structure of cellulose fibrils." In *Fundamentals Papermaking Fibres, Trans. Symp. Cambridge, Engl., 1957* (F. Bolam, ed.), pp. 1–27.

Schurz, J. (1955) "Textures of native celluloses as revealed by X-rays." *Phyton* 5: 53–66.

Vogel, A. (1953) "Zur Feinstruktur von Ramie." *Makromol. Chem.* 11: 111–130.

The Relation between Cellulose Biosynthesis and the Structure of the Cell Envelope in *Acetobacter xylinum*

D. T. DENNIS

Division of Biosciences, National Research Council, Ottawa, Canada

Present address: Department of Chemistry, University of California, Los Angeles

J. ROSS COLVIN

Division of Biosciences, National Research Council, Ottawa, Canada

In spite of much work and speculation, our understanding of the mechanism(s) of biosynthesis of the cellulose microfibril is still rudimentary (Colvin, 1964). Study of greenplant material is difficult and most investigators have employed the cellulose forming bacteria, *Acetobacter xylinum* or *Acetobacter acetigenum*. Even with these bacteria a major difficulty has been to find methods of disrupting the cells which leave the cellulose synthesizing capacity undamaged, and so far only partial success has been reported. Using a particulate fraction from broken cells of *A. xylinum* supplemented with uridine diphosphate glucose (UDPG), two laboratories have demonstrated the incorporation of glucose residues into cellulose (Glaser, 1958; Klungsöyr, 1960). It has also been shown that adenosine triphosphate (ATP) may stimulate cellulose synthesis in cell homogenates (Colvin, 1957; Greathouse, 1957). However, in all cases the amount of cellulose synthesized was small and possibly it was through a minor pathway. Recently, a method of lysing the cells of *A. xylinum* by lysozyme was described (Webb and Colvin, 1962), in which the broken cells retained most of their initial capacity to synthesize cellulose. After centrifugation of the lysed cell preparations, all the activity for synthesizing cellulose was shown to be in the pellet, indicating that the site of synthesis of the precursor of bacterial cellulose was associated with the cell envelope, not in the cytoplasm. This paper reports the results of an investigation which was designed to identify the component of the cell envelope of *A. xylinum* responsible for the synthesis of cellulose. The effects

This paper was issued as N.R.C. No. 8277.

of certain substrates and co-factors upon cellulose synthesis by this component were also studied.

Materials and Methods

Preparation of Whole and Lysed Cells. Suspensions of whole cells free from cellulose and containing approximately 10^9 viable cells per milliliter in 0.01 M phosphate–0.003 M citrate buffer, pH 6.0, were prepared as described previously (Colvin, 1957). When required, portions of the pellicle containing whole cells were cut away and fixed directly without further treatment.

Suspensions of lysed cells were prepared according to the method of Webb and Colvin (1962). Twenty milliliters of the whole cell suspension were diluted with 70 ml of glass-distilled water and 0.6 ml of 1 M sodium monohydrogen phosphate added to the mixture. The pH of the suspension was then adjusted carefully to 8.1 with sodium hydroxide and 0.6 milliliters of 0.5% lysozyme solution (Armour) added. After incubation of the solution for 15 minutes at 22°C, a trace of deoxyribonuclease (Worthington) was added to decrease the viscosity. For some experiments the lysed preparation was used without further treatment. For other experiments, the envelopes were collected by centrifugation (15,000 g for 15 minutes), washed three times in phosphate-citrate buffer, pH 6.0, and then resuspended in 20 ml of the same buffer.

Digestion of lysed cell envelopes with trypsin (Nutritional Biochemicals Corp.) was carried out at room temperature, pH 8.0, for 24 hours.

Methods for Electron Microscopy. Whole cells and lysed cells were prepared for electron microscopy by fixing a pellet of the cells (or cell envelopes) obtained by centrifugation, in 10% neutral formalin. After fixation the cells or cell envelopes were washed in veronal buffer, pH 7.4, and stained with 2% osmium tetroxide. The fixed, stained cells were dehydrated and embedded in butyl-methyl methocrylate (8:1) by standard methods (Sorvall, I., Inc., 1959) and then sectioned with a Porter-Blum ultramicrotome. After sectioning, the specimens were further stained with lead hydroxide by Millonig's method (1961).

Methods for Cell or Cell Envelope Incubation. For most experiments, 2 ml of the washed, resuspended lysed cell preparation were incubated with 6 ml of 2% substrate dissolved in 0.01 M phosphate–0.003 M citrate buffer, pH 6.0, for 2 hours at 35°C. Cellulose synthesis was stopped by adding 0.5 ml glacial acetic acid. For other experiments, 6 ml of the lysed cell preparation (without centrifugation) were incubated with 2 ml of 6% substrate solution under the same conditions as above. The source of uridine diphosphate glucose (UDPG), uridine triphosphate (UTP), and adenosine triphosphate (ATP) was Pabst Laboratories, Milwaukee, Wisconsin.

Method for Estimation of Cellulose. The method employed for the estimation of cellulose was a modification of that discovered by Mendel for glucose (Mendel *et al.,* 1954) and adapted by Dearing (1957) to cellulose. It depends upon the color produced when sugars are heated with particular commercial lots of sulphuric acid. Since many compounds will produce a color when heated with sulphuric acid, it was essential to remove all substances except cellulose from the products of incubation. Cells, cell envelopes, and cellulose were centrifuged from the suspension and resuspended in 2 ml of water. After heating the samples for 10 minutes in boiling water, three ml of 6% sodium dodecyl sulphate (SDS) were added to each tube and the heating continued for another 10 minutes. At the end of this interval 0.5 ml of sodium hypochlorite (NaOCl) (5% available chlorine) were added. After the reaction had subsided a further 0.5 ml of sodium hypochlorite was introduced and heating at 100°C continued for 15 minutes. This method was found to eliminate everything that produced a color with H_2SO_4 except cellulose. After cooling, the cellulose was separated by centrifugation, washed in hot and cold water (it is essential to remove all traces of the hypochlorite), dried and estimated (Dearing, 1957). Absorption at 520 mμ was measured in a Coleman junior spectrophotometer. In all cases, a sample of cell envelopes which had been incubated with buffer only and then extracted was used as a blank.

RESULTS

Fine structure of Cells and Cell Envelopes. Photographs of cross sections of intact cells of *A. xylinum* which were fixed and stained from suspensions are shown in Figure 1. In general, the structure of the cell envelope and its contents are similar to those found in gram-negative bacteria (Kellenberger and Ryter, 1958) and in particular to that recently described for *Acetobacter suboxydans* by Claus and Roth (1964). The close association of the cell walls of adjacent organisms show that there is no capsular layer outside the wall of *A. xylinum.* Brown and Gascoigne (1960) have found earlier that *A. acetigenum* also lacks a capsule. The cell wall consists of three layers, the outer and inner staining more deeply than the middle layer. The dimensions of these layers vary somewhat but correspond in general to those observed for *A. suboxydans* (Claus and Roth, 1964). Immediately within the cell wall is the double-layered cyto-

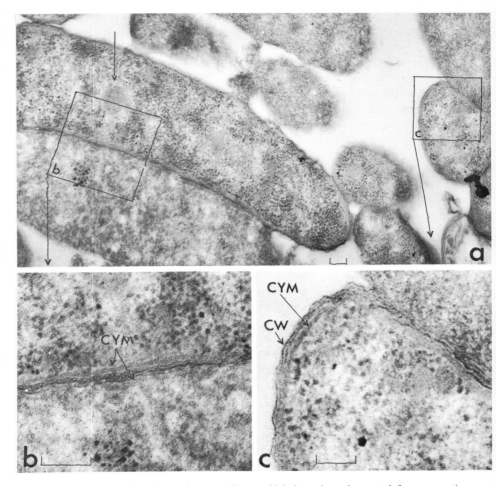

Fig. 1. Intact cells of *Acetobacter xylinum* which have been harvested from an active suspension, showing the multi-layered structure of the cell envelope. CW—cell wall, CYM —cytoplasmic membrane. Figs. 1b and 1c are enlargements of the indicated areas in Fig. 1a. In all micrographs the scale represents 0.1 micron. The arrow indicates membranous or filamentous material (from Dennis and Colvin, 1964).

plasmic membrane, usually closely attached to the wall but occasionally detached. As with *A. suboxydans,* in *A. xylinum* these two layers are much less distinct than those of the cell wall. In the cytoplasm of some cells (but not all) are deeply staining ribosome-like particles (Claus and Roth, 1964). These particles are apparent in only about half of the cells of the same preparation, for reasons which are not known. Within the cells which do display these ribosome-like particles may be seen local areas of undifferentiated material. On the edges of some of these areas are hints of membraneous or filamentous substance (Fig. 1).

A photograph of a cross section of an intact cell harvested in the cellulose pellicle formed by this organism is shown in Figure 2. The structure

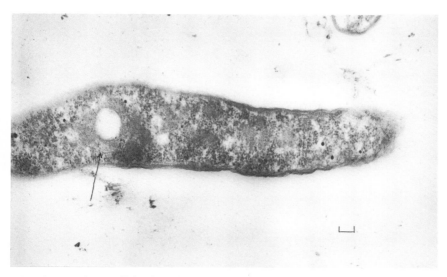

FIG. 2. *A. xylinum* cell fixed, sectioned, and stained while in the cellulose pellicle. The arrow indicates membraneous or filamentous material (from Dennis and Colvin, 1964).

of this cell was the same as that of isolated, washed cells in all respects except one. Cells from the pellicle, which were presumably engaged in active cellulose synthesis at the time of fixation, showed more of the aggregation of the particles which was referred to above. It may be that the cell contents become disorganized to varying degrees when the cells are washed.

Incubation of isolated, washed cells with lysozyme at pH 8.1 in phosphate buffer causes a disruption of parts of the wall (Fig. 3). This disruption usually (but not always) occurs at the ends of the cell, suggesting that the attack may take place preferentially where the last cell division was completed or where the cell wall is growing. Where the cell wall is not ruptured its appearance in the sections remains unchanged. At the point of rupture of the cell, the contents flow out into the medium, allowing the cytoplasmic membrane to withdraw or separate from the wall as was observed with *E. coli* (Kellenberger and Ryter, 1958). In a few of the lysed cells examined, the entire cytoplasmic membrane appeared to have

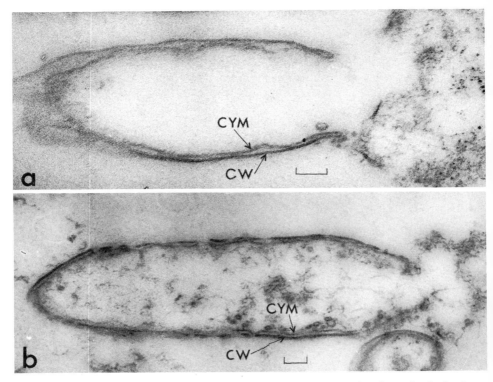

Fig. 3. *A. xylinum* cells treated for one minute with lysozyme, then immediately fixed in 10% formalin (from Dennis and Colvin, 1964).

flowed out of the cell wall on standing and washing. During lysis and dispersion of the cell contents the ribosome-like particles maintain their identity and filaments were seen in the cytoplasm (Fig. 3).

Centrifugation of the lysed cell preparation at 7,000 g for 10 minutes produced a pellet of three layers. At the bottom of the pellet was a small layer of unlysed resistant cells which always remain in these preparations (Webb and Colvin, 1962). Above the whole cells was a layer of dense material, which in turn was covered with a fluffy layer. Examination of the two upper layers by the electron microscope showed them to consist of essentially the same components; namely, the cell walls and an amorphous ground material, in different proportions. The denser lower layer had a greater fraction of ground material (Fig. 4) than the upper fluffy layer, which contained a larger fraction of cell walls only. Probably the ground material in this preparation is derived principally from the cytoplasm which has flowed out of the cell on lysis. Treatment of the resus-

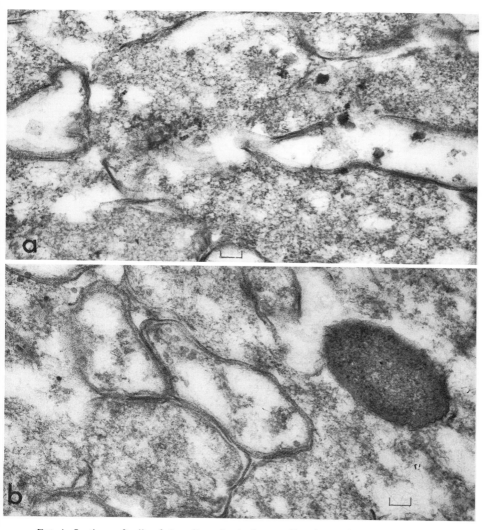

FIG. 4. Sections of cells of *A. xylinum* in the intermediate layer of pellet from lysed cell preparation.

pended pellet with magnesium ions caused a precipitation of the cytoplasm and cytoplasmic membrane (Fig. 5) without any discernible effect upon the cell wall. As will be described below, an additional effect of magnesium ions is to stimulate cellulose synthesis markedly in lysed cell preparations, so the precipitated material visible in Figure 5 would have

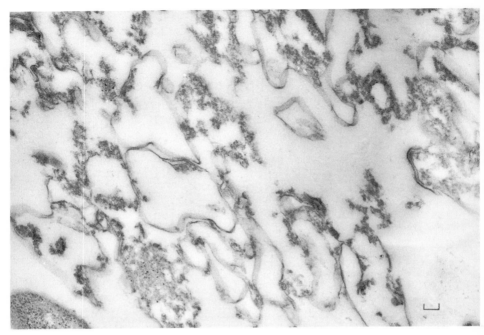

FIG 5. Lysed cell preparation which has been washed twice with phosphate-citrate buffer, pH 6.0, then magnesium chloride added and the precipitate sedimented. The pellet was fixed in 10% formalin (from Dennis and Colvin, 1964).

synthesized cellulose prior to fixation in spite of its obvious separation from the cell walls.

Incubation of the lysed cell preparations with trypsin completely removed the cytoplasmic membrane and associated material, leaving the cell walls apparently untouched (Fig. 6). This treatment completely stopped cellulose synthesis.

Effect of Co-factors upon Cellulose Synthesis by Lysed Cell Envelopes. The effect of some presumed co-factors and/or substrates on cellulose synthesis by the lysed cell preparations is shown in Table I. Since fructose is a better substrate for cellulose synthesis than glucose (at the concentration employed) it was used for this experiment.

Magnesium ions and both ATP and UTP stimulate cellulose synthesis by lysed cell envelopes. Both nucleotides appear to have an equal action and the effects are not cumulative. They may be acting primarily as energy sources. Washing the lysed cell preparations with buffer at pH 6.0 sharply reduces cellulose synthesis but enhances the effect of the co-factors, as shown in Table II. Magnesium ions now increased cellulose

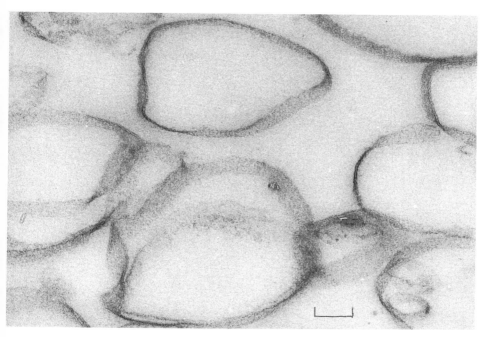

FIG. 6. Washed, lysed cell preparation treated with trypsin for 24 hours (from Dennis and Colvin, 1964).

synthesis by 70%. ATP or UTP added to the mixture increased cellulose synthesis by a further 27% but once again the effects of the two nucleotides are not cumulative. When the above experiment was repeated using glucose as substrate, much less cellulose was synthesized than when fructose was used and the only substance which could be clearly demonstrated to increase cellulose synthesis was UTP.

Because ATP and UTP stimulated cellulose synthesis in lysed cells with either fructose or glucose as a substrate, it was hoped that various hexose phosphates might also serve as substrates. In this system the usual permeability barriers (Schramm *et al.,* 1957) have been circumvented by disruption of the cells. Unfortunately, no cellulose synthesis could be demonstrated under a variety of conditions from glucose-1-phosphate, glucose-6-phosphate, or fructose-1:6-diphosphate. Glucose-1-phosphate in particular was studied over a range of pH values from 4.5 to 6.0, in the presence of varying amounts of glucose, fructose, and magnesium ion without any cellulose being produced. Similarly, because of the lack of a permeability barrier with these lysed cell envelopes, it was hoped to confirm and perhaps extend the conclusions of Glaser (1958) concerning

TABLE I. Cellulose Synthesis by Unwashed Lysed Cell
Envelope Preparations

	μg of cellulose synthesized in two incubations[a]		Average	% of fructose alone
	I	II		
Fructose	185	203	194	100
Fructose + Mg	230	212	221	114
Fructose + ATP	228	203	215	111
Fructose + ATP + Mg	253	249	251	130
Fructose + UTP + Mg	264	253	258	133
Fructose + ATP + UTP + Mg	258	261	259	134

[a]The incubation mixture contained 6 ml of unwashed lysed cell preparation, 2 ml of 6% fructose, and, if appropriate, 12 mg $MgCl_2 \cdot 6H_2O$, 10 mg ATP and 3.7 mg UTP. The solutions were incubated at 35°C for 80 minutes.

TABLE II. Cellulose Synthesis by Washed Lysed Cell
Envelope Preparation

	μg cellulose synthesized in three incubations[a]			Average	% of fructose alone
	I	II	III		
Fructose	55	59	65	59	100
Fructose + Mg^{++}	99	98	102	100	170
Fructose + Mg^{++} + ATP	121	115	103	116	197
Fructose + Mg^{++} + UTP	125	98	125	116	197
Fructose + Mg^{++} + ATP + UTP	122	121	123	122	206

[a]The incubation mixture contained 6 ml of 2% fructose in 0.01 M phosphate-citrate buffer at pH 6.0 and 2 ml of the cell envelope preparation which had been washed twice in buffer, pH 6.0, and resuspended in the same buffer. Where appropriate, 12 mg $MgCl_2 \cdot 6H_2O$, 10 mg ATP or 4.4 mg UTP was added per incubation. Solutions were incubated at 35°C for 2 hours.

the role of UDPG in bacterial cellulose synthesis. However, in only one experiment among many was cellulose formed from UDPG in greater amounts than from glucose.

Investigation of the effects of various co-factors led to the demonstration of at least one difference between whole cells and cell envelopes for cellulose synthesis. In whole cells both dihydroxyacetone and calcium gluconate are good substrates for cellulose synthesis (Schramm *et al.*, 1957) but for lysed cell envelopes only gluconate can serve as a substrate (see Table III). Calcium ion also causes some stimulation of cellulose synthesis by lysed cell envelopes but is not as effective as magnesium ion. Ribose was not utilized by either whole cells or lysed cell envelopes.

TABLE III. Cellulose Synthesis from Lysed Cell Preparations with Various Substrates

	μg cellulose synthesized in two incubations[a]			% of fructose alone
	I	II	Average	
Fructose	114	124	119	100
Fructose + Mg	171	159	165	139
Fructose + Ca	134	127	130	109
Calcium gluconate	92	96	94	79
Calcium gluconate + Mg^{++}	124	158	141	118
Dihydroxyacetone	0	0	0	—
Dihydroxyacetone + Mg^{++}	0	0	0	—
Ribose + Mg^{++}	0	0	0	—

[a]The incubation mixture contained 6 ml of the substrate solution (all at 1% concentration) and 2 ml of washed lysed cell preparation. When appropriate, 12 mg of $MgCl_2 \cdot 6 H_2O$ and 6.6 mg of $CaCl_2$ were added per incubation. All solutions were incubated at 35° C for 2 hours.

DISCUSSION

In most respects, the structure of the cell and cell envelope described above for *A. xylinum* closely resembles that of *A. suboxydans*. *A. suboxydans* has a diffuse capsule while *A. xylinum* has none but both apparently possess the same type of multi-layered wall outside a double cytoplasmic membrane. Both the inner and outer layers of this wall, separated by a space, stain heavily with osmium, indicating a high lipid content, and this is consistent with the resistance to digestion by trypsin of the *A. xylinum* wall. However, one point of interpretation remains unsettled. Claus and Roth (1964) have interpreted their photographs of *A. suboxydans* as indicating the presence of a weakly staining layer, 5–10 mμ thick, between the densely staining layers and the cytoplasmic membrane. For *A. xylinum*, tentatively, we prefer to interpret this layer as simply an open space.

Within the cell body of both *A. xylinum* and *A. suboxydans*, many ribosome-like particles are easily seen in a fraction of the sections. The identity of these particles is not yet known, however, because their number and appearance vary so much from cell to cell.

A. xylinum has compact regions of amorphous nonparticulate material on the edges of which are indications of filaments or membraneous substance. No function is as yet apparent for these areas, and they are lacking from *A. suboxydans*.

A major difference in the functions of the components of *A. xylinum* and *A. suboxydans* is the apparent capacity of the cytoplasmic membrane of *A. xylinum* to synthesize the precursor of bacterial cellulose. Although previous work has indicated that this capacity was limited to the cell envelope (Webb and Colvin, 1962) the present results suggest strongly that the site of synthesis may be the cytoplasmic membrane and not the other components of the cell envelope. Preparations of lysed cells in which the cytoplasmic membranes have flowed out of the outer cell wall layers and have been reprecipitated by Mg^{++} are still active in cellulose synthesis, indicating that there is no necessary close spatial relationship between these components for cellulose synthesis. If the membrances are destroyed by trypsin, without noticeable damage to the other layers, cellulose synthesis is abolished. Since cellulose synthesizing capacity is not in the cytoplasm (Webb and Colvin, 1962), the conclusion requiring the least number of assumptions is that the cytoplasmic membrane is the site of synthesis of the precursor of bacterial cellulose and its structural integrity is necessary for formation of this compound.

The conclusion that the cytoplasmic membrane is the structure in which the precursor of bacterial cellulose is formed is in accord with the observations of the effect of co-factors upon cellulose synthesis by lysed cell envelopes, provided that certain assumptions are fulfilled. Magnesium ion has a pronounced stimulatory effect upon cellulose synthesis by cell envelopes under certain conditions, and since it precipitates the membraneous material of the cell, this effect may be attributed both to a maintenance of the structure of portions of the membrane, perhaps by crosslinking, and to its effect upon essential enzymes. Furthermore, the stimulation of cellulose synthesis by ATP and UTP in lysed cell systems but not with whole cells may be explained by assuming nonpermeability of the bacterial cell wall to these nucleotides. However, the utilization of UTP by lysed cell systems would certainly imply that, under proper conditions, a comparable effect might be observed for UDPG, G-1-P, or related hexose phosphates. No explanation is available yet for the quite definite lack of effect of these compounds under conditions where they should stimulate. The recent observations of Elbein and co-workers (1964) whick link guanosine-diphosphate-D-glucose to cellulose synthesis in preparations from mung beans suggest that the same glycosyl donor might be involved for bacterial cellulose. However, neither guanosine, guanosine monophosphate, guanosine diphosphate, nor guanosine triphosphate had any effect on synthesis in the system used here.

The observation that dihydroxyacetone may not be used by lysed cell preparations as a substrate for cellulose synthesis, while it can be used by whole cells (Schramm *et al.,* 1957), suggests that the cytoplasmic membranes do not have enzyme systems capable of condensing these three carbon fragments to hexoses. However, they do possess systems capable of reducing gluconate to glucose prior to cellulose formation. Incidentally, the difference between lysed and whole cell preparations in their capacity to use dihydroxyacetone also confirms that the cellulose synthesized in these lysed cell preparations is not from the small fraction of whole cells.

On the basis of our present knowledge, the course of cellulose synthesis in *A. xylinum* may be sketched as follows. Glucose (or glucose precursors such as dihydroxyacetone, gluconate, or related compounds) enters the cytoplasmic membrane where it is activated. This mechanism may be the usual route by means of glucose-1-phosphate and UTP to UDPG but we could find no evidence for it here. The glucose residue is then transferred to a lipid carrier (Khan and Colvin, 1960) which diffuses across the cell wall. The point of transfer of the glucose residue to a poly 1 $\rightarrow$ 4 α-glucosan chain and the detailed mechanism of formation of the microfibril are still matters of dispute (Colvin, 1964). However, the final disposition of the insoluble microfibril is completely outside the bacterial cell wall, deep in the medium.

The concept of the synthesis of the precursor of bacterial cellulose in the cytoplasmic membrane removes an apparent dilemma of long standing. The notion that the precursor was formed throughout the cytoplasm implied the existence of an intracellular inhibitor of cellulose formation, otherwise the cells would soon be filled with polymerized glucose. All efforts to find evidence for such an inhibitor have been unsuccessful. If the compound is formed only in the cytoplasmic membrane the apparent necessity for such an inhibitor is removed.

If the main conclusion from this study of bacterial cellulose may be extended to green plants, then the site of synthesis of the precursor of cellulose of the cell wall is in the plasmalemma. Although it has often been suggested that fine threads of cytoplasm may penetrate plant cell walls and synthesize cellulose (Frey-Wyssling, 1962), so far as we are aware this is the first evidence that the site is confined to the cytoplasmic membrane *per se*. The extrapolation would be fully consistent with all previously suggested schemes for cellulose formation in green plants (Setterfield and Bayley, 1961) but no experimental evidence is yet available. A definitive investigation will probably have to wait upon the development of a method for isolating undamaged green plant cytoplasmic membranes in reasonable quantities. If the plasmalemma is the site of synthesis in green plants, it may be that only the outer surface of the double membrane is the active component, since cellulose is synthesized only outside the membranes. If this conjecture is correct, it implies a difference in function (and perhaps fine structure) of these layers but, once again, the speculation requires experimental confirmation.

Acknowledgments

The authors would like to thank Dr. C. M. S. Dass for advice in preparing the sections and taking the electron micrographs. They are also grateful to Mr. L. Sowden for expert technical assistance.

REFERENCES

Brown, A. M., and Gascoigne, J. A. (1960) "Biosynthesis of cellulose by *Acetobacter acetigenum.*" *Nature* 187:1010–1012.

Claus, G. W., and Roth, L. E. (1964) "Fine structure of the gram-negative bacterium *Acetobacter suboxydans.*" *J. Cell Biol.* 20:217.

Colvin, J. R. (1957) "Formation of cellulose microfibrils in a homogenate of *Acetobacter xylinum.*" *Arch. Biochem. Biophys.* 70:294–295.

―――― (1964) "The biosynthesis of cellulose." In *The Formation of Wood in Forest Trees* (M. Zimmermann, ed.). Academic Press, N. Y.

Dearing, G. G. (1957) "A new micromethod for the estimation of cellulose." *Nature* 179:579.

Dennis, D. T., and Colvin, J. R. (1964) "Biosynthesis of cellulose." *Pulp Paper Mag. Can.* 65: T395–T399.

Elbein, A. D., Barber, G. A., and Hassid, W. Z. (1964) "The synthesis of cellulose by an enzyme system from a higher plant." *J. Am. Chem. Soc.* 86:309–310.

Frey-Wyssling, A. (1962) In *The Interpretation of Ultrastructure* (R. J. C. Harris, ed.). Academic Press, N. Y.

Glaser, L. (1958) "The synthesis of cellulose in cell-free extracts of *Acetobacter xylinum.*" *J. Biol. Chem.* 232:627–636.

Greathouse, G. A. (1957) "Isolation of a cell-free enzyme system from *Acetobacter xylinum* capable of cellulose synthesis." *J. Am. Chem. Soc.* 79:4503–4504.

Kellenberger, E., and Ryter, A. (1958) "Cell wall and cytoplasmic membrane of *Escherichia coli,*" *J. Biophys. Biochem. Cytol.* 4:323–325.

Khan, A. W., and Colvin, J. R. (1960) "Isolation of the precursor of bacterial cellulose." *J. Polymer Sci.* 51:1–9.

Klungsöyr, S. (1960) "Transglucosidase activity in *Acetobacter xylinum.*" *Nature* 185:104–105.

Mendel, B., Kemp, A., and Myers, D. K. (1954) "A colorimetric micro-method for the determination of glucose." *Biochem. J.* 56:639–646.

Millonig, G. (1961) "A modified procedure for lead staining of thin sections." *J. Biophys. Biochem. Cytol.* 11:736–739.

Schramm, M., Gromet, Z., and Hestrin, S. (1957) "Synthesis of cellulose by *Acetobacter xylinum.* E. substrates and inhibitors." *Biochem. J.* 67:669–679.

Setterfield, G., and Bayley, S. T. (1961) "Structure and physiology of cell walls." *Ann. Rev. Plant Physiol.* 12:35–62.

Sorvall, I., Inc., Norwalk, Conn. (1959) *Thin Sectioning and Associated Technics for Electron Microscopy.*

Webb, T. E., and Colvin, J. R. (1962) "The lysis of *Acetobacter xylinum.*" *Can. J. Microbiol.* 8:841–846.

PART III

The Wood Cell Wall—*Its Ultrastructure*

Ultrastructure and Organization of Gymnosperm Cell Walls

H. HARADA

Wood Technology Institute, University of Kyoto

The three important areas of investigation concerning the mature cell wall of gymnosperms are as follows: (1) the distribution of the principal chemical components in cell walls; (2) the physical nature of the structural units—cellulose micelles or microfibrils—also one of the most important chemical components of cell wall; and (3) the orientation of structural units (microfibrils) in the primary and secondary cell walls, with respect to the morphological cell axis. The first two areas will be treated by other authors in this volume. This paper is concerned with the third, namely, the physical organization of the cell wall structural units, and is based on the results of electron microscopic observations.

MICROFIBRILS AS STRUCTURAL UNITS

It is well known that the framework substance of wood cell walls consists of cellulose, while their matrix and incrusting substances consist of hemicellulose and noncellulosic substances such as lignin. It was discovered by applying electron microscopy that the cellulose molecules, which are the main constituents of the cell walls of native fibers, including wood cells, are aggregated in the form of microfibrils, thus forming independent structural units (Williams and Wyckoff, 1946). The width of microfibrils is 100 to 300 Å, varying with the kind of native fiber, and their length is indefinite (Mühlethaler, 1960). These results were obtained not only from the examination of samples of disintegrated wood cells, but also from the observations of replicas and ultrathin sections of the secondary wall of untreated tracheids and fibers (Hodge and Wardrop, 1950; Kobayashi and Utsumi, 1955; Jayme and Koburg, 1959; Côté and Day, 1962). The reason why the width of microfibrils is not agreed upon, but is subject to various opinions, is that the measurements by means of electron microscopy have been compared with the results of X-ray diffraction, which is the case for ramie. The width of the micelles (the crystalline region) of ramie, obtained by the X-ray diffraction method, is 50 to 70 Å, and their length 600 Å (Hengstenberg and Mark, 1928). According to one opinion, the width of microfibrils is 50 to 100 Å, being equal to that of the micelle dimensions obtained by X-ray diffraction (Hodge and Wardrop, 1950; Rånby, 1958; Kobayashi and Utsumi, 1955). According to another, a microfibril is composed of 2 to 4 aggregated micellar strands forming an independent unit (Frey-Wyssling *et al.*, 1948). It is also said that the size of microfibrils is variable depending on the source of native fiber specimens (Wardrop, 1954; Mühlethaler, 1960). At present, however, it is generally supposed that in their natural state the structural units observed by electron microscopy occur as shown in the models proposed by Frey-Wyssling (1954, 1955). According to this concept, the microfibrils are about 200 Å in width and are further divided into smaller, elementary fibrils or micellar strands. Whether the structural units of wood cells are microfibrils or micellar strands, independent units in the form of fibrils can be observed with the aid of the electron microscope. Therefore, in this paper these units are called microfibrils.

Cell Wall Organization of Tracheids

What is the nature and composition of the cell wall? How are the microfibrils in the walls and layers oriented with respect to the tracheid axis? These problems will be dealt with in relation to the results of investigation by optical microscopy and X-ray diffraction, but will be limited to normal, mature gymnosperm tracheids.

The optical microscopic investigations of Kerr and Bailey (1934) first gave an established idea of the cell wall organization of the normal tracheids. They divided a cell wall, according to the order of its formation, into several layers of different nature: into the thin primary wall adjoining the intercellular layer and the thicker secondary wall, the latter being further divided into the outer, the central, and the inner layers, of which the central is thick, and the other two are thin. This division is due to the difference in the optical properties observed by polarizing microscopy in the transverse sections of tracheids. Between crossed nicols of the polarizing microscope the primary wall is slightly birefringent (shimmers dimly), the outer and the inner layers of the secondary wall shine brightly, and the central layer is extinct. This was considered to be due to the difference of the orientation of micelles in the primary wall and in each of the layers of the secondary wall. The organization of cell walls, thus conceived by Kerr and Bailey (1934), is frequently referred to even in electron microscopic investigations. The discussion in the present paper also starts from this conception.

Following Kerr and Bailey, many investigations to clarify the micellar orientation in the cell wall with the optical microscope and X-ray diffraction were reported: Bailey and Kerr, 1935; Preston, 1934; Onaka, 1936; Bailey and Vestal, 1937a, b; Ohara, 1939; Kubo and Go, 1941; Wardrop and Preston, 1947; Preston, 1952; Onaka and Harada, 1951; Harada *et al.*, 1951; and Bucher, 1957.

When electron microscopy was applied to the investigation of the tracheid wall organization, the first intention was to confirm, by direct observations, the conception established by Kerr and Bailey: namely, to distinguish the primary wall and the three layers of the secondary from one another, taking notice of their thickness, and to ascertain the microfibrillar orientation in each of them. It was first expected that this purpose would be accomplished by getting transverse sections of tracheids, as in the case of the optical microscopic investigations, and observing them with the aid of the electron microscope. However, this proved to be impossible because it was very difficult to get ultrathin sections from wood, and because the contrast of the ultrathin sections in the electron micrographs was not adequate. Therefore, instead of ultrathin sections, replicas of transverse sections of tracheids cut with an ordinary microtome were used, but the fine structure of the cell wall was masked by knife marks. Then the disintegration method was employed and the orientation of microfibrils in the primary wall could be observed in the disintegrated specimens of cambial cells, for instance. In addition to this method, the replication method was applied. If the surfaces of macerated tracheids were replicated, the structure of the primary wall could be seen; and because the tracheid wall has, as stated below, a lamellar structure, replicas of the split sections of a cell wall showed the structure of a layer or a lamella of the wall. If in this case several layers or lamellae, different in structure from one another, do appear at the same time, we can, by selecting a layer as a basis for identification, recognize the other layers either as the primary wall or as any of the three layers of the secondary wall. Because the surface of a split section of a cell wall has small intermicrofibrillar spaces, the contrast in the replication images is so emphasized that the orientation of microfibrils in the wall can be seen clearly. Therefore, the specimens obtained by the disintegration or the replication method are very useful for observing the fine structure of cell wall. The replicated specimens are especially excellent, in that they can be free from damage by the electron beam.

However, the disintegration and the replication methods could not serve one important purpose, that is, to distinguish the primary wall and the three layers of the secondary from one another and to indicate their thickness. It was necessary, therefore, to take up again the ultrathin transverse sectioning of tracheids. And fortunately it was possible, owing to the great improvements in ultramicrotomes and knives in recent years, to get excellent ultrathin sections almost continually. Thin sections of a high polymer substance such as a wood cell wall are, in electron microscopy, subject to insufficiency of image contrast and to damage by the electron beam. However, these inconveniences can be overcome by removing embedding materials from the sections and by shadowing procedures. The structure of the primary wall and of the layers of the secondary wall can be clarified by comparing the micrographs of sections of tracheids having incrusting substances removed by delignification with those of untreated tracheids.

One result of the above-mentioned electron microscopic observations, based primarily on the disintegration, replication and ultrathin sectioning methods, is that the physical organization of tracheid walls, already suggested in the investigations by optical microscopy and X-ray diffraction, was confirmed. Another is that we could discover hitherto unknown structures, such as a crossed and an intermediate structure in the secondary wall, and a wart structure in tracheids of some species.

Some representative electron micrographs will be referred to in the following discussion. (The abbreviations P, S_1, S_2, and S_3 stand, respectively, for the primary wall and the outer, the central, and the inner layer of the secondary wall.)

Distinction of the Primary Wall and the Three Layers of the Secondary Wall. In the electron micrographs of the transverse sections of tracheids we can, owing to the difference of penetrating power of the electron beam and to surface contrast, distinguish three different layers inside the intercellular layer (Fig. 1) (Yamamoto *et al.*, 1956; Frei *et al.*, 1957; Harada, 1958; Jayme and Fengel, 1961a, b; Wardrop, 1963, 1964). By comparing the micrographs of untreated with delignified sections, these three layers can be identified as the P + S_1, the S_2, and the S_3, and the existence of a wart structure (W) inside them can also be observed. The wall P can be distinguished clearly from the layer S_1 in the delignified section (Fig. 2), though not in the untreated section. This is probably because the microfibrils in the wall P are filled with incrusting substances, such as lignin. We cannot measure the thickness of the Wall P and the layers S_1, S_2, and S_3 because a delignified tracheid, when embedded in methacrylate, swells markedly, though we can measure their thickness in the enlarged micrographs of the untreated section (Fig. 3). According to measurements of an earlywood tracheid of *Pinus densiflora*, the wall P is 0.06 μ in thickness; the layer S_1, 0.31 μ; the layer S_2, 1.93 μ; and the layer S_3, 0.17 μ; the layer S_2 occupying about 78% of the whole wall in thickness. This result is almost the same as that obtained by Jayme and Fengel (1961a) for spruce. A lamellar structure in the layers S_1, S_2, and S_3, and a wart layer along

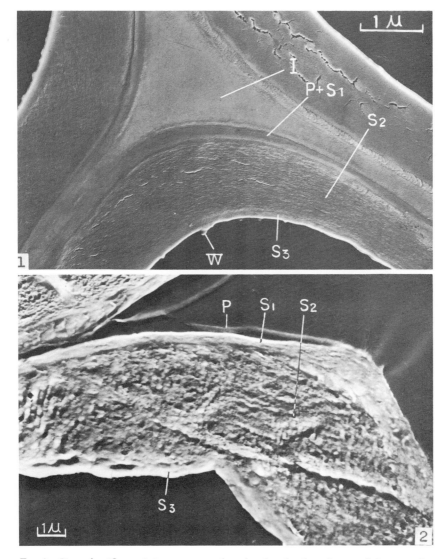

FIG. 1. *Pinus densiflora*. A transverse section showing the three layers of the secondary wall in earlywood tracheids.

FIG. 2. *Pinus densiflora*. A transverse section of delignified tracheids showing the primary wall and the three layers in the secondary wall.

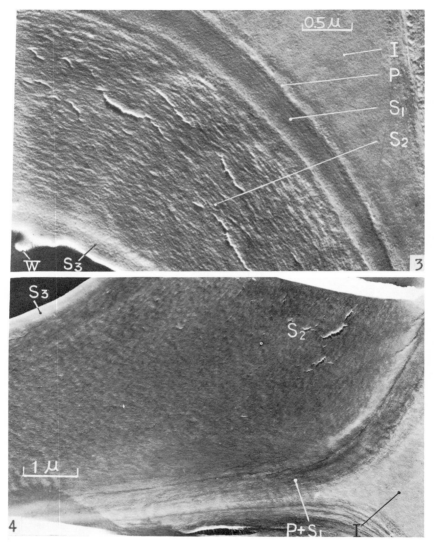

FIG. 3. *Pinus densiflora.* A transverse section of an earlywood tracheid showing the intercellular layer (I), the primary wall (P), the three layers (S_1, S_2, S_3) of the secondary wall and the wart structure (W).

FIG. 4. *Pinus densiflora.* A transverse section of a latewood tracheid showing the individual layers of a cell wall.

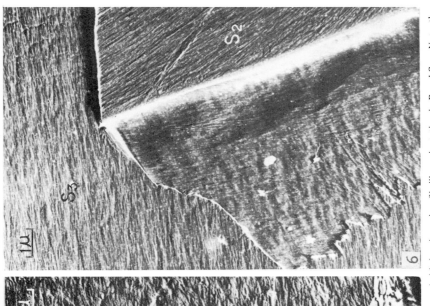

FIG. 5. *Picea jezoensis*. A replica of an earlywood tracheid showing microfibrillar orientation in P and S₁. *Note*: the major cell axis in Figures 5 through 15 is vertical (↕). In Figures 16, 17, and 22, the major cell axis is horizontal (↔). FIG. 6. *Picea jezoensis*. A replica of an earlywood tracheid showing the microfibrillar orientation in S₂ and S₃.

the lumen were also observed. Cell walls of a latewood tracheid are far thicker than those of an earlywood one, probably because the layer S_2 of the former is much thickened (Fig. 4).

Microfibrillar Orientation in the Primary and the Secondary Walls. From the micrographs of replicas of a surface of a chemically macerated tracheid, a net-like orientation of microfibrils in the wall P was confirmed (Kobayashi and Utsumi, 1951). According to the micrographs of disintegrated and replicated specimens of a cambial cell, the wall P is composed of two layers (P_1 and P_2) different from each other in their orientation of microfibrils (Wardrop, 1964). The structure of the wall P is also observed in the micrographs of replicas of an untreated tracheid, and it is assumed that the openings in the wall P are more completely filled with incrusting substances than those in the layer S_1 (Fig. 5). As to the microfibrillar orientation in the layers S_1, S_2, and S_3, many workers have confirmed the earlier findings of polarizing microscopy through the use of electron microscopy (Kobayashi and Utsumi, 1951, 1955; Liese and Fahnenbrock, 1952; Harada and Miyazaki, 1952; Harada et al., 1958; Liese, 1963). The microfibrils in the layer S_1 are oriented almost to a right angle to the tracheid axis, following a flat helical pattern (Fig. 5), while those in the layer S_2 show a steep helical structure (Fig. 6), oriented at an angle of 20 to 30° to the axis in the case of earlywood tracheids of *Cryptomeria japonica* and *Picea jezoensis*, and of 5 to 10° in the case of a latewood tracheids of the same species. In the layer S_3 (Fig. 6), the microfibrils follow a flat helical pattern as in the S_1. It is said that a spruce tracheid sometimes lacks the layer S_3, but at least in *Picea jezoensis* there exists the S_3 with a flat helical structure (Fig. 6).

The assumption by Bailey and Vestal (1937a, b) that the arrangement of microfibrils is, in the places where there are pits, far more deviated than in the places where there are no pits, was also confirmed by electron microscopic observations. In the pit border, the microfibrils are oriented in concentric circles, while around it the microfibrils of the layer S_1, of a flat helical structure, are so oriented as to surround a pit aperture, though they seem to be unconnected with the microfibrils in the pit border. Therefore, there is some doubt that the pit border region belongs to the S_1 (Fig. 7). Also in the S_2 and the S_3, the microfibrils are so oriented as to avoid the pit aperture (Figs. 7 and 8). When a half-bordered pit pair

FIG. 7. *Picea jezoensis*. A replica of an earlywood tracheid showing the microfibrillar orientation of S_1 and S_2 in the pit region.

FIG. 8. *Pinus densiflora*. A replica of an earlywood tracheid showing the microfibrillar orientation of S_2 in the pit region.

FIG. 9. *Picea jezoensis*. A replica of an earlywood tracheid showing S_2 and S_3 in the region of a half-bordered pit.

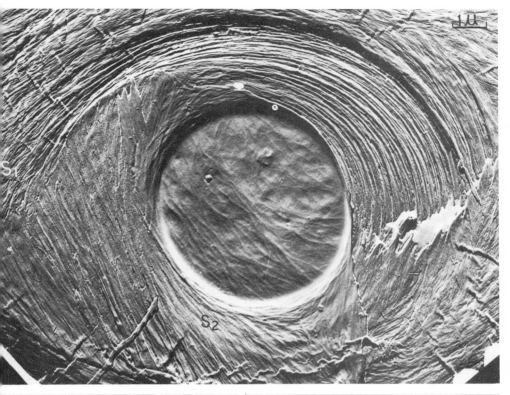

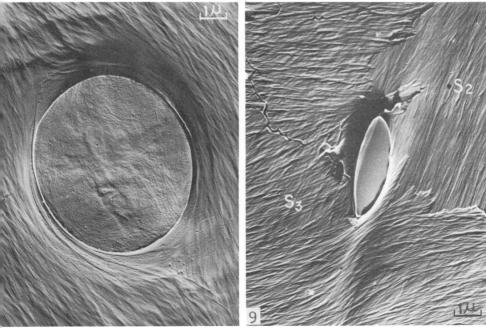

occurs between a tracheid and a ray parenchyma cell, the pit aperture of the tracheid wall takes the form of a convex lens. The long axis of the pit aperture is almost parallel to the microfibrillar orientation in the layer S_2 (Fig. 9).

Parallelism of Microfibrils in the Secondary Wall. Even in a lamella of the secondary wall, the microfibrils are not arranged exactly parallel with one another. The degree of parallelism of microfibrils is the greatest in the layer S_2, and the least in the S_3, being medium in the S_1. The comparison of an earlywood tracheid with a latewood one, as to the S_2, the thickest layer of the secondary wall, shows that the perfection of microfibrillar parallelism is greater in the latter than in the former (Figs. 10 and 11). However, even in the latewood tracheids the microfibrils of the S_2 are not perfectly parallel with one another (Harada *et al.*, 1958; Wardrop, 1964).

Crossed and Intermediate Structures. Optical mocroscopic investigations could not demonstrate the existence, in the layers S_1, S_2, and S_3, of lamellae where the orientation of microfibrils is crossed. Electron microscopy, however, revealed at least two such lamellae in the S_1 (Wardrop, 1954; Meier, 1955; Frei *et al.*, 1957). Wardrop (1957) even suggests that the S_1 of a tracheid of *Pinus radiata* has a structure that consists of three patterns of microfibril orientation: a fine grid pattern, a coarse grid pattern, and a complete. However, such a crossed lamellar structure in the S_1 must be considered in relation to the structures of other layers: namely, a flat structure in the S_1, and an intermediate one between the S_1 and the S_2.

The existence, between the S_1 and the S_2, or between the S_2 and the S_3, of an intermediate structure, in which the angle of microfibrils changes gradually until the direction of their orientation becomes reversed, has been unknown till recently. Kobayashi and Utsumi (1955) suggested, on assuming the existence of microlamellae as wide as microfibrils, that all the layers of the secondary wall are of a minute obliquely crossed structure. Harada *et al.*, (1958), on applying electron microscopy to the replicas of longitudinal sections cut with a microtome, of *Picea jezoensis* and *Pinus densiflora*, examined the intermediate structure in the secondary wall, taking an already known layer as a standard. The layers S_1, S_2, and S_3 are each composed of several lamellae, and the angles and directions of the microfibrillar orientation in these lamellae are almost the same. Between the S_1 and the S_2, however, or between the S_2 and S_3, there can be seen some lamellae where the angle of microfibrils changes gradually, and not, as in the above-mentioned patterns, suddenly, until the direction of their orientation becomes quite reversed (Figs. 12, 13, and 14). Though

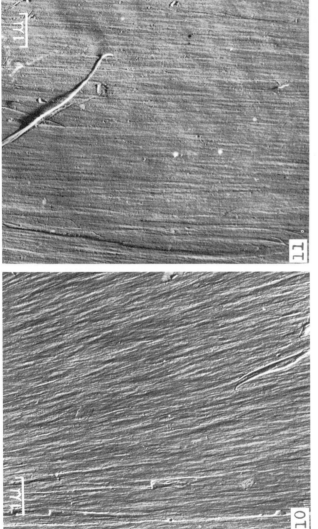

FIG. 10. *Cryptomeria japonica*. A replica of an earlywood tracheid showing the microfibrils in S_2.   FIG. 11. *Cryptomeria japonica*. A replica of a latewood tracheid showing the microfibrils in S_2.

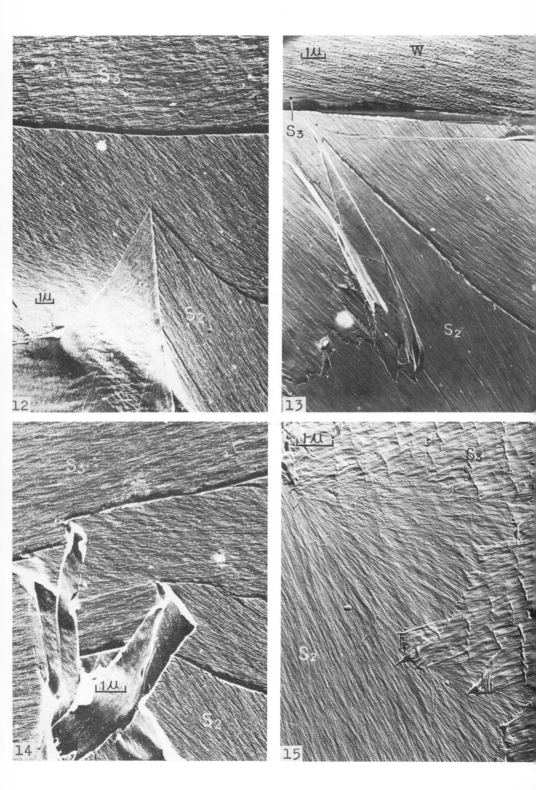

it is possible to regard such a gradual change of the angle of the microfibrillar orientation as attributable to a very few lamellae, at any rate in this case it can be seen that the microfibrils change the direction of their orientation in a form like a spread fan, between the S_2 and S_3 (Fig. 15). Incidentally, it may be that the raised band observed between the S_1 and the S_2, or between the S_2 and the S_3, in the electron micrographs of the transverse sections of a tracheid (cf. Fig. 3), suggests the existence of an intermediate structure there.

ORGANIZATION OF RAY PARENCHYMA CELLS

In softwood, ray parenchyma cells constitute only 2 to 4% of the wood volume, and therefore they have not been investigated as much as tracheid walls. It was found with the aid of the polarizing microscope that the micelles of ray parenchyma cells are oriented spirally, and that the primary wall and the layers of the secondary wall are distinguishable (Wardrop and Dadswell, 1952). Not only the physical organization of parenchyma cells of *Cryptomeria japonica*, but also the distribution of their chemical composition has been minutely examined by Harada and Wardrop (1960). Between crossed nicols of the polarizing microscope it can be observed that ray parenchyma cells are divided into three layers: the thin central layer (S_2), and the comparatively thick outer (S_1) and inner (S_3) layers. By measuring birefringence, it is assumed that the micelles in the layers S_1 and S_3 are oriented in a gentle inclination to the cell axis, while those in the S_2 are almost parallel to it. By applying electron microscopy to the replicas of ray parenchyma cells, much information has been obtained: that in the primary wall the microfibrils show a net-like structure such as in tracheid walls, and that in the secondary wall there can be found a layer in which the microfibrils are oriented quite parallel with the cell axis, and two layers in which they are oriented at an angle of 30 to 60° to the axis, the former being placed between the latter (Fig. 16). In collation with the observations by the polarizing microscope, these three layers are assumed to correspond to the layers S_1, S_2, and S_3. The existence, along the lumen side, of a layer in which the microfibrils are arranged irregularly, was discovered for the first time (Fig. 17). In tracheids of *Cryptomeria japonica*, a wart structure can be found, but not in ray parenchyma cells (Fig. 17).

FIG. 12. *Picea jezoensis*. A replica of an earlywood tracheid showing the intermediate structure between S_2 and S_3.

FIG. 13. *Pinus densiflora*. A replica of an earlywood tracheid showing the same structure as shown in Fig. 12. W—wart layer.

FIG. 14. *Picea jezoensis*. A replica of an earlywood tracheid showing the intermediate structure between S_2 and S_3.

FIG. 15. *Picea jezoensis*. A replica of an earlywood tracheid showing the intermediate structure between S_2 and S_3.

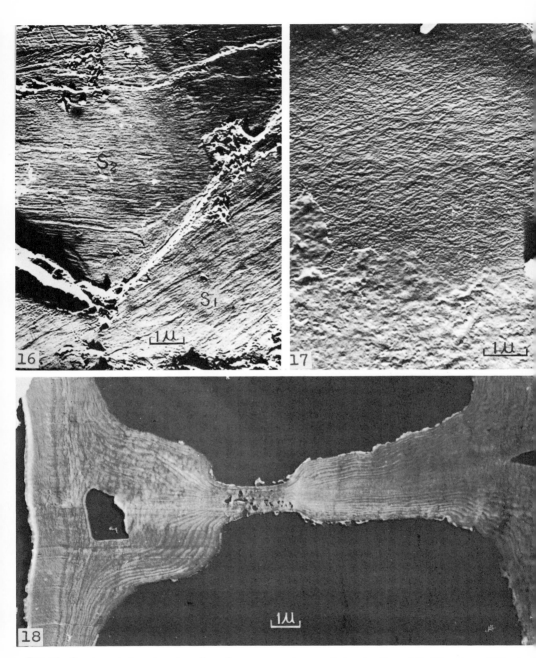

FIG. 16. *Cryptomeria japonica.* A replica of a ray parenchyma cell showing S_1 and S_2 (Harada and Wardrop, 1960). FIG. 17. *Cryptomeria japonica.* A replica of a ray parenchyma cell showing the net-like structure of micro fibrils on the lumen side (Harada and Wardrop, 1960). FIG. 18. *Cryptomeria japonica.* A transverse section of ray parenchyma cells showing the lamellae in the cell wall.

The existence of an intermediate structure in the secondary wall, as in the case of a tracheid, is a matter for further investigation.

In the electron micrographs of the ultrathin sections of ray parenchyma cells, very distinct lamellae can be found (Fig. 18), but the distinction of the layers, such as the P, S_1, S_2, and S_3 in tracheid walls, cannot be observed, nor can any intercellular layer be distinguished between the ray parenchyma cells. This is probably because lignin is equally distributed throughout the whole cell wall (Fig. 19), as was suggested by the results

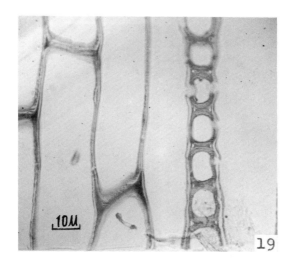

FIG. 19. *Cryptomeria japonica.* An ultraviolet micrograph of a transverse section of ray parenchyma cells showing the distribution of lignin in the cell wall (Harada and Wardrop, 1960).

of the investigation by Asunmaa and Steenberg (1957) on the scattering density of the intercellular layer between tracheids.

It is assumed that the pit membrane in a half-bordered pit pair, formed between a ray parenchyma cells and an axial tracheid, consists of an intercellular layer and the two primary walls. However, as shown in Figure 20, a transverse section of a ray parenchyma cell of *Cryptomeria japonica*, the aperture of a simple pit of a parenchyma cell, which should be open, is completely blocked by the cell wall (Fig. 21) (Harada, 1964).

This feature has been also demonstrated by the replica micrograph taken from the lumen side of the ray parenchyma cell (Fig. 22). Though this has been observed also in the parenchyma cells of *Thuja plicata* (Krahmer and Côté, 1963), it is a matter for further investigation whether this is universal in all softwood species.

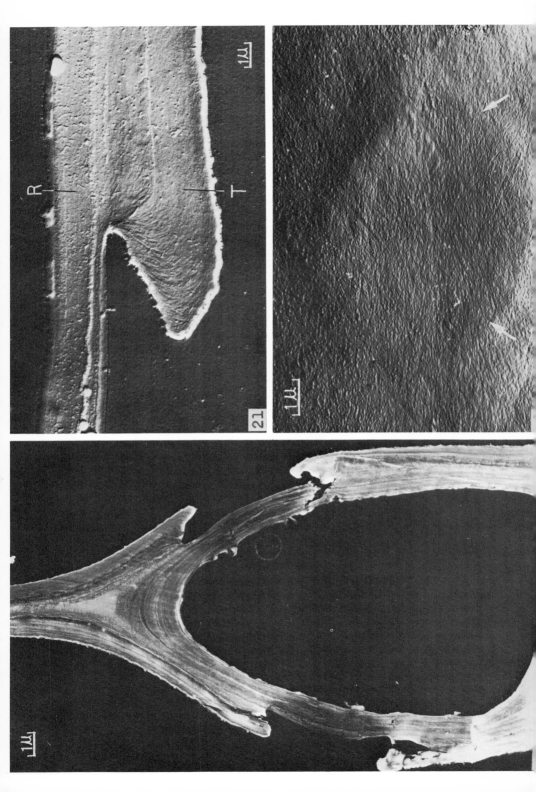

21

REFERENCES

Asunmaa, S., and Steenberg, G. (1957) "Relative scattering densities in pine heartwood, pine sapwood and spruce." *Svensk Papperstid.* 60:751–761.

Bailey, I. W., and Kerr, T. (1935) "The visible structure of the secondary wall and its significance in physical and chemical investigations of tracheary cells and fibers." *J. Arnold Arboretum* 16:273–300.

———, and Vestal, M. R. (1937a) "The orientation of cellulose in the secondary wall of tracheary cells." *J. Arnold Arboretum* 18:185–195.

——— and ——— (1937b) "The significance of certain wood destroying fungi in the study of the enzymatic hydrolysis of cellulose." *J. Arnold Arboretum* 18:196–205.

Bucher, H. (1957) "Die Tertiärwand von Holzfasern und ihre Erscheinungsformen bei Coniferen." Holzforschung 11:1–16.

Côté, W. A., Jr., and Day, A. C. (1962) "The G layer in gelatinous fibers—Electron microscopic studies." *Forest Prod. J.* 12:333–338.

Frei, E., Preston, R. D., and Ripley, G. W. (1957) "The fine structure of the walls of conifer tracheids. VI. Electron microscope investigations of sections." *J. Exp. Botany* 8:139–146.

Frey-Wyssling, A. (1954) "The fine structure of cellulose microfibrils." *Science* 119:80–82.

——— (1955) "On the crystal structure of cellulose." *Biochim. Biophys. Acta* 18:166–169.

———, Mühlethaler, K., and Wyckoff, R. W. G. (1948) "Mikrofibrillenbau der Pflanzlichen Zellwand." *Experientia* 4:475.

Harada, H. (1958) "Electron microscopic structure of wood" (in Japanese). *J. Kobunshi* 7:615–619.

——— (1964) In press.

———, Kishima, T., and Kadita, S. (1951) "The micellar orientation in the secondary wall of coniferous tracheids (II)." Bulletin of the Wood Research Institute, Kyoto Univ., Japan, No. 6, pp. 34–42.

———, and Miyazaki, Y. (1952) "The electron-microscopic observation of the cell wall of conifer tracheids." *J. Japan. Forestry Soc.* 34:350–352.

———, ———, and Wakashima, T. (1958) "Electron microscopic investigation on the cell wall structure of wood." Bulletin of the Govt. Forest Experiment Station, No. 104 (Meguro, Tokyo, Japan).

———, and Wardrop, A. B. (1960) "Cell wall structure of ray parenchyma cells of a softwood (Cryptomeria japonica)." *J. Japan Wood Res. Soc.* 6:34–41.

Hengstenberg, J., and Mark, H. (1928) "Rötgenuntersuchungen über den Bau der C-Ketten in Kohlenwasserstoffen." *Z. Krist.* 67:583–594.

Hodge, A. J., and Wardrop, A. B. (1950) "An electron microscopic investigation of the cell wall organization of conifer tracheids and conifer cambium." *Australian J. Sci. Res.*, B 3:265–269.

Jayme, G., and Fengel, D. (1961a) "Beitrag zur Kenntnis des Feinbaus der Frühholztrache-

FIG. 20. *Cryptomeria japonica.* A section of wood showing the half-bordered pit pair between an axial tracheid and a ray parenchyma cell.

FIG. 21. *Cryptomeria japonica.* A section of a ray parenchyma cell (R) and an axial tracheid (T) showing the same structure as shown in Fig. 20.

FIG. 22. *Cryptomeria japonica.* A replica of a ray parenchyma cell showing the closure of the simple pit aperture with the parenchyma cell wall itself. (Arrows show the outline of the margin of the bordered pit.)

iden. Beobachtung an Ultradünnschnitten von Fichtenholz." *Holz Roh- Werkstoff* 19:50–55.

_____ and _____ (1961b) "Beitrag zur Kenntnis des Feinbaus der Fichtenholztracheiden. II. Beobachtung an Ultradünnschnitten von delignifiziertem Holz und Ligningerüsten." *Holzforschung* 15:97–102.

_____, and Koburg, E. (1959) "Über den elektronenoptisch bestimmten Durchmesser der Mikrofibrillen von Laubholzzellelementen." *Holzforschung* 13:37–43.

Kerr, T., and Bailey, I. W. (1934) "The cambium and its derivative tissues. No. X. Structure, optical properties and chemical composition of the so-called middle lamella." *J. Arnold Arboretum* 15:327–349.

Kobayashi, K., and Utsumi, N. (1951) "Electronmicroscopy of conifer tracheids (in Japanese). Committee Note on Electron Microscopy, No. 56, p. 93.

_____ and _____ (1955) "Reformation of cellulose micell and microfibrils." *Seni Kenkyusho Koenshu*, No. 12, pp. 159–187.

Krahmer, R. L., and Côté, W. A., Jr. (1963) "Changes in coniferous wood cells associated with heartwood formation." *Tappi* 46:42–49.

Kubo, T., and Go, Y. (1941) "Study on the fine structure of wood by X-ray diffraction." *J. Soc. Chem. Ind. (Japan)* 44:651–655.

Liese, W. (1963) "Tertiary wall and warty layer in wood cells." *J. Polymer Sci.*, Part C 2:213–219.

_____, and Fahnenbrock, M. (1952) "Elektronmikroskopische Untersuchungen über den Bau der Hoftüpfel." *Holz Roh- Werkstoff* 10:197–201.

Meier, H. (1955) "Über den Zellwandbau durch Holzvermorschungspilze und die submikroskopische Struktur von Fichtentracheiden und Birkenholzfasern." *Holz Roh-Werkstoff* 13:323–338.

Mühlethaler, K. (1960) "Die Feinstruktur der Zellulosemikrofibrillen. *Z. Schweiz. Forstv.* 30:55–65.

Ohara, K. (1939) "Relation between the species of conifers and the micell angle of their tracheids wall" (in Japanese). *Jinkenkai* 7:635–637.

Onaka, F. (1936) "Identification of olden woods from ancient tombs" (in Japanese). *J. Japan Forestry Soc.* 18:588–602.

_____, and Harada, H. (1951) "The micellar orientation in the secondary wall of coniferous tracheids." *J. Japan Forestry Soc.* 33:60–64.

Preston, R. D. (1934) "The organization of the cell wall of the conifer tracheid." *Phil. Trans. Roy. Soc. London, Ser. B* 224:131–172.

_____ (1952) *The Molecular Architecture in Plant Cell Wall.* Chapman and Hall, London.

Rånby, B. G. (1958) "The fine structure of cellulose fibrils." In *Fundamentals papermaking Fibers, Trans. Symp. Cambridge, Engl., 1957* (F. Bolam, ed.), pp. 1–27.

_____ (1957) "The organization and properties of the outer layer of the secondary wall in Wardrop, A. B. (1954) "The fine structure of the conifer tracheid." *Holzforschung* 8:12–29.

_____ (1957) "The organization and properties of the outer layer of the secondary wall in conifer tracheids." *Holzforschung* 11:102–110.

_____ (1963) "Morphological factors involved in the pulping and beating of wood fibers." *Svensk Papperstid.* 66:231–247.

_____ (1964) "The structure and formation of the cell wall in xylem." In *The Formation of Wood in Forest Trees* (M. H. Zimmerman, ed.), pp. 87–134. Academic Press, N.Y.

_____, and Dadswell, H. E. (1952) "The cell wall structure of xylem parenchyma." *Australian J. Sci. Res., Ser. B*—Bio. Sci. 5:223–236.

————, and Preston, R. D. (1947) "The submicroscopic organization of the cell wall in conifer tracheids and wood fibers." *J. Exp. Botany* 11:20–30.

Williams, R. C., and Wyckoff, R. W. G. (1946) "Applications of metallic shadow casting to microscopy." *J. Appl. Phys.* 17:23–33.

Yamamoto, T., Kadita, S., and Kobayashi, K. (1956) "Electron microscopy of ultrathin sections of softwood" (in Japanese). *Trans. Kansai-Branch Japan. Forestry Soc.*, pp. 161–162.

Ultrastructure of Angiosperm Vessels and Ray Parenchyma

H. HARADA

Wood Technology Institute, University of Kyoto

Angiosperms are said to be more developed than gymnosperms, and they are made up of a variety of elements such as tracheids, vessels, fibers, and parenchyma cells. The cell wall organization of the tracheids and the fibers (fiber tracheids and libriform fibers) has been frequently investigated, because they are somewhat similar to the tracheids of gymnosperms. However, the organization of vessels and parenchyma cells, neither of which is so important from the morphological point of view, has not been investigated so much because it is likely to be quite variable among the individual species.

The present paper is concerned with the electron microscopic investigations of the cell wall organization of vessels and ray parenchyma. However, since the cell walls of fiber tracheids and libriform fibers have features comparable to those of tracheid walls of gymnosperms, and because they seem to show the fundamental structure of vessels and ray parenchyma cells, their organization will first be described.

TRACHEIDS AND WOOD FIBERS

As already stated, the cell wall organization of tracheids and wood fibers has been examined frequently by optical and electron microscopy (Bailey and Kerr, 1935; Meier, 1955; Wardrop and Dadswell, 1957; Meier, 1957; Lange, 1959; Wardrop et al., 1962; Côté and Day, 1962; Côté and Marton, 1962; Sachs et al., 1963; Asunmaa and Marteny, 1963; Wardrop, 1963, 1964). The following are the results of the electron microscopic investigations of *Fagus crenata* by Harada (1962).

The ultrathin transverse sections of tracheids and wood fibers and the replicas of their longitudinal split surfaces were observed. In the electron micrographs of ultrathin sections of tracheids and fibers, there could be distinguished inside the intercellular layer (I) the primary wall (P), the outer (S_1), the central (S_2), and the inner (S_3) layers of secondary wall, and a wart layer (Figs. 1 and 2). The wall P is not always distinguished easily

235

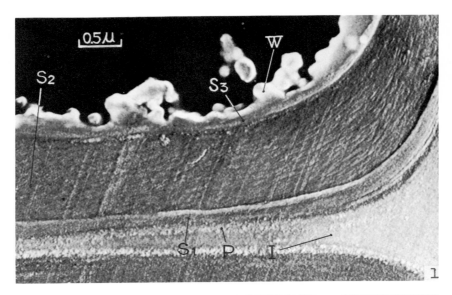

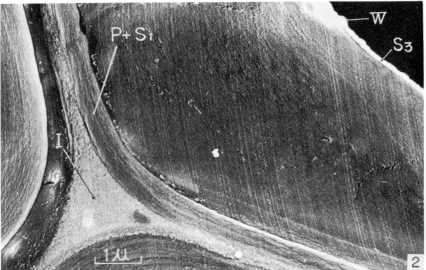

FIG. 1. *Fagus crenata.* A transverse section of a tracheid showing the intercellular layer (I), the primary wall (P), the three layers (S_1, S_2, S_3) of the secondary wall, and the wart layer (W).

FIG. 2. *Fagus crenata.* A transverse section of a fiber tracheid showing I, P + S_1, S_2, S_3 and W.

from the layer I, but the secondary wall clearly shows a typical three-layered structure, and distinct lamellae in the layers S_1 and S_2 can be seen. The layer S_3 and the wart layer cannot be easily distinguished, and the warts are not simple protrusions as in softwood tracheids, but varied in form (Fig. 3). The proportion, in thickness, of the wall P and the layers S_1, S_2, S_3 to the whole wall is, in the case of a tracheid, respectively 5%, 16%, 67%, and 12%, and, in the case of a wood fiber, 1%, 10%, 87%, and 2% (Table I). The high proportion of the layer S_2 in a wood fiber is

TABLE I. An Example of the Thickness of Individual Layers in Various Cells of *Fagus crenata*

Thickness (μ)

Layer	Tracheid	Vessel	Fiber-tracheid	Axial parenchyma	Ray cells
P	0.07	0.25	0.07	0.06	0.50
S_1	0.24		0.51	0.35	
S_2	0.99	0.50	4.32	0.78	0.92
S_3	0.17	0.25	0.10	0.37	0.37
Total	1.47	1.00	5.00	1.56	1.79
Percentage					
P	5	25	1	4	28
S_1	16		10	22	
S_2	67	50	87	50	51
S_3	12	25	2	24	21

worthy of note. As to the organization of the secondary wall, in the areas where there are pits, a diagrammatic representation suggested by Wardrop (1964) was confirmed (Fig. 4). The microfibril orientation in the wall P and the layers S_1, S_2, and S_3 are almost the same as in softwood tracheid walls (Fig. 5), but there can be observed an intermediate structure between the layer S_1 and the S_2, and between the S_2 and the S_3 (Fig. 6).

VESSELS

The organization of vessel walls was investigated by Bailey and Vestal (1937a, b), Preston (1939, 1952), and Wardrop (1964), with the aid of the optical microscope. When a transverse section of a vessel is observed between the crossed nicols of the polarizing microscope, a typical three-layered structure is generally found, as in the case of a cell wall of a tracheid or a wood fiber. This suggests that there are three layers, differ-

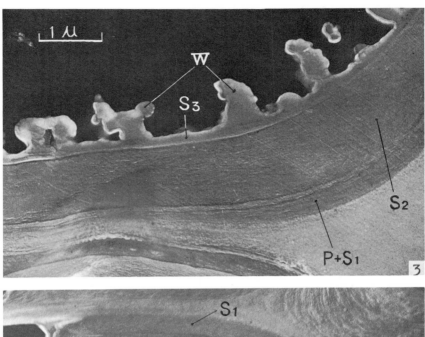

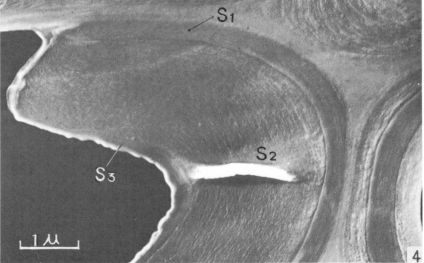

Fig. 3. *Fagus crenata*. A transverse section of a tracheid showing the wart structure (W).
Fig. 4. *Fagus crenata*. A transverse section of fiber tracheid showing S_1, S_2, and S_3 in the region of the bordered pit.

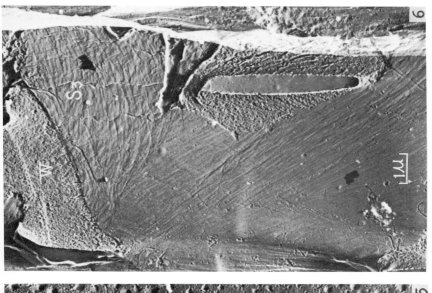

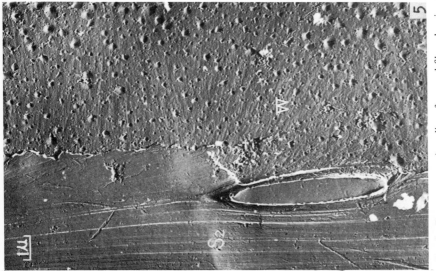

Fig. 5. *Fagus crenata*. A replica of a wood fiber showing the microfibrillar orientation of S_2 and S_3, and the wart layer. *Note:* The major cell axis in Figures 5, 6, 9, 10, 11, 12, 13, and 14 is vertical ($\updownarrow$). In Figure 16, the major cell axis is horizontal ($\rightarrow$). Fig. 6. *Fagus crenata*. A replica of a wood fiber showing the intermediate structure between S_2 and S_3.

ent from one another in their micellar orientation, though sometimes uniform birefringence may be obtained throughout the cell wall. This latter condition suggests that the micellar orientation is the same throughout the cell wall. By measuring the extinction position with the aid of the polarizing microscope, or by applying the X-ray diffraction method, it was found that the main micellar orientation in a vessel wall is almost perpendicular to the longitudinal axis of the vessel. The direction of the orientation can be considered to be parallel with that of slit-like apertures of the bordered pits in the vessel wall. Because there are many pits in a vessel wall, the cell wall organization is very complicated. If, in the observation of a transverse section of a vessel between crossed nicols, uniform birefringence is obtained through the whole cell wall, it is difficult to determine whether this is due to the same micellar orientation in each of the individual layers.

The electron microscopic investigation of vessel walls began with attempts to confirm the results obtained with the polarizing microscope. Wardrop (1964) suggested (for *Eugenia kuranda*) that the uniform appearance of the vessel wall in polarizing micrographs is due to small differences in the microfibrillar orientation of the layers S_1, S_2, and S_3 of the secondary wall. This was based on a comparison of electron micrographs of ultrathin transverse sections and of replicas of longitudinal surfaces of vessel walls with photomicrographs taken with the polarizing microscope. In the polarizing micrographs of transverse sections of a vessel of *Fagus crenata*, three layers could be faintly detected, and, by measuring the extinction angle of a single wall, the average fibrillar angle in a vessel wall was found to be about 50 to 70°. Further, ultrathin sections of a vessel of *Fagus crenata* and replicas of its longitudinal surface were observed with the aid of the electron microscope (Harada, 1962). In the micrographs of sections of vessel cell wall three layers are distinguished. These three layers can be regarded as the layer $P + S_1$, the S_2, and the S_3 (Fig. 7). According to measurements, the proportional thickness of the $P + S_1$, the S_2, and the S_3 to the whole wall is respectively 25%, 50%, and 25%, the S_2 being the thickest (Table I). A wart structure, such as found in a tracheid, sometimes exists in a vessel of the same specimen (Fig. 8) and sometimes does not (Fig. 7). The warts in a vessel are varied in form, as in tracheids. The wart layer cannot be clearly distinguished from the S_3.

Observation of the surface of a macerated vessel showed that the wall P has a net-like structure. In the micrographs of an untreated vessel surface, two layers can be observed, one near the lumen side and the other near the layer I, in which the microfibrils are oriented almost at a right angle to the vessel axis (Fig. 9), and a layer between them in which the microfibrils are oriented at an angle of about 40° to the axis. These three layers can be

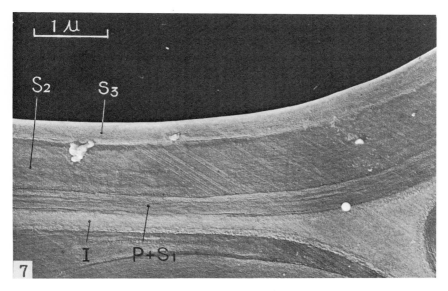

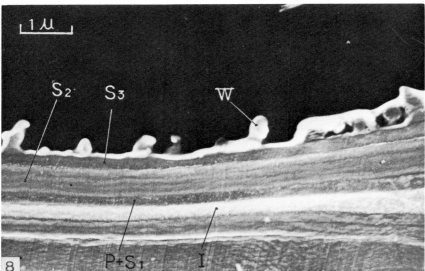

FIG. 7. *Fagus crenata.* A transverse section of a vessel showing P + S_1, S_2, and S_3.

FIG. 8. *Fagus crenata.* A transverse sec ion of a vessel showing the existence of the wart layer.

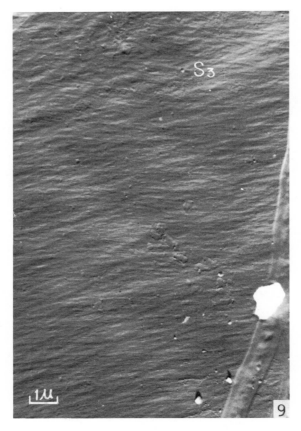

FIG. 9. *Fagus crenata*. A replica of a vessel showing the microfibrillar orientation of S_3.

regarded, from outside, as the layer S_1, the S_2, and the S_3. The direction of the slit-like apertures of the bordered pit is generally almost parallel with the microfibrillar orientation in the layers S_1 and S_3 (Figs. 10 and 11). However, since the orientation of microfibrils in the S_3 is not always perpendicular to the vessel axis, being variable in different parts of a vessel, the direction of the bordered pit apertures is not always in accord with that of the microfibrillar orientation in the S_3 (Fig. 12). This shows that the vessel organization (of *Fagus crenata*) is very complicated. Variety is also demonstrated in the replica micrographs of wart structure on the lumen side of a vessel (Fig. 13). The warts are varied in form, as already revealed in the micrographs of the ultrathin sections. Between the layer S_3 and the S_2 an intermediate structure can sometimes be found (Fig. 14),

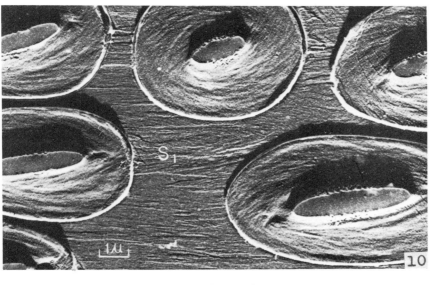

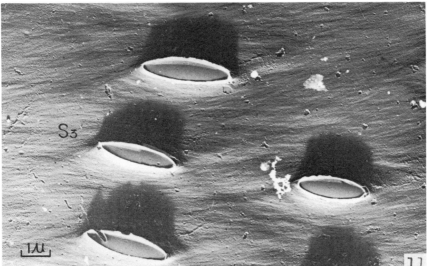

FIG. 10. *Fagus crenata.* A replica of a vessel showing the pit border and the micro-fibrillar orientation of S_1.

FIG. 11. *Fagus crenata.* A replica of a vessel showing the slit-like pit aperture of a bordered pit and S_3.

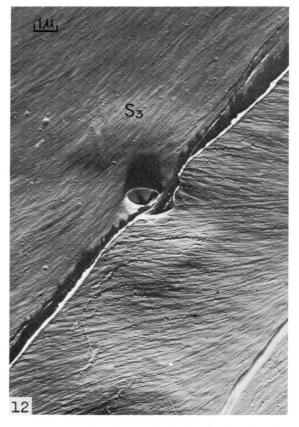

FIG. 12. *Fagus crenata*. A replica of a vessel showing the S_3 and one layer represented by stripping off S_3.

but the existence of this structure in all of the vessel walls is open to question, as is the existence of a crossed structure in the S_1.

In the parts where there are bordered pits, the microfibrillar orientation in the layers S_1, S_2, and S_3 deviates much as in tracheids (cf. Fig. 11).

RAY PARENCHYMA

The organization of ray parenchyma cells of angiosperms was first investigated, as in the case of softwoods, by polarizing microscopy and X-ray diffraction (Ritter and Mitchell, 1936; Gross *et al.*, 1939; Wardrop

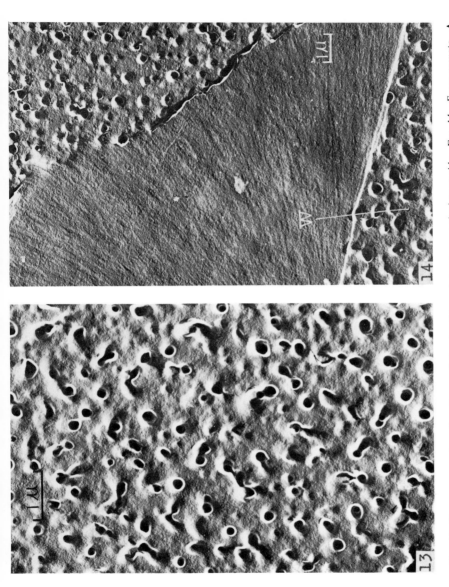

FIG. 13. *Fagus crenata*. A replica of a vessel showing the wart structure on the lumen side. FIG. 14. *Fagus crenata*. A replica of a vessel showing the intermediate structure between S_2 and S_3.

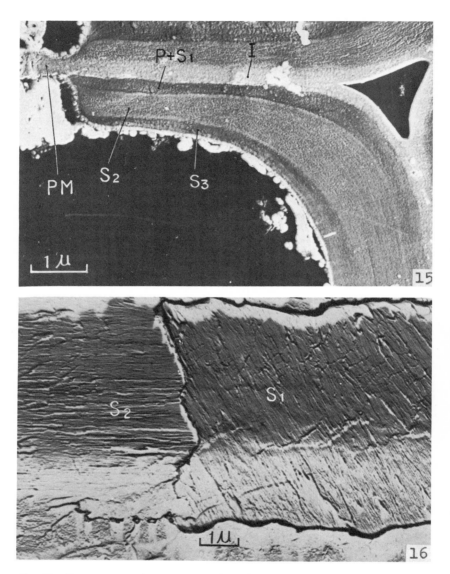

FIG. 15. *Fagus crenata.* A transverse section of a ray parenchyma cell showing P + S_1, S_2, and S_3.

FIG. 16. *Fagus crenata.* A replica of a ray parenchyma cell showing S_1 and S_2.

and Dadswell, 1952). The primary wall and the three layers of the secondary wall were thus distinguished.

The distinction of the primary and the secondary walls and of the layers
of the secondary wall, and the microfibrillar orientation in each of the
layers, were further investigated by electron microscopy of ultrathin
sections or of replicas (Ribi, 1953; Migita and Hosoi, 1956; Harada et al.,
1958; Cronshaw, 1960; Preusser et al., 1961; Harada, 1962).

In the electron micrographs of ultrathin transverse sections of procumbent ray parenchyma cells, there could be distinguished three layers in
a cell wall, the $P + S_1$, the S_2, and the S_3 (Fig. 15), and this result confirmed the polarizing microscopic investigation by Wardrop (1964). The
layer S_4 described previously (Harada, 1962) has not yet been observed in
the replicas of the lumen side, and is therefore to be regarded as a layer of
a cytoplasmic substance. Measurements show that the layer S_2 is, also in
ray parenchyma cells, the thickest of the whole cell wall (Table I). In the
parts where there are pits, the structure suggested by Wardrop (1964) has
been also confirmed (Fig. 15).

In the micrographs of replicas of an untreated and a delignified surface
of a procumbent ray cell, it has been observed that the wall P has a net-
like structure and that the secondary wall is divided into three layers:
the S_1 and the S_3, in which the microfibrils are oriented at an angle of

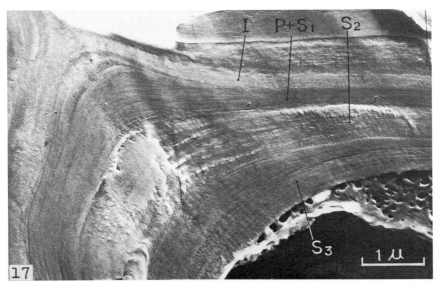

Fig. 17. *Fagus crenata.* A transverse section of an axial parenchyma cell showing
$P + S_1$, S_2, and S_3.

about $60 - 80°$ to the cell axis; and the S_2, between them, in which the microfibrils are oriented parallel with the axis (Fig. 16). The lumen side is covered with a cytoplasmic substance and the net-like structure, seen in the ray parenchyma cells of *Cryptomeria japonica*, has not been found. The existence of a crossed lamellar structure and an intermediate structure has not yet been ascertained.

Axial parenchyma cells have not been fully investigated, but electron micrographs of ultrathin transverse sections of *Fagus crenata* show that they consist, just as ray parenchyma cells, of the wall P and the layers S_1, S_2, and S_3 (Fig. 17 and Table I).

REFERENCES

Asunmaa, S., and Marteny, W. W. (1963) "Morphology of refined pulps of southern pine and black ash." *Tappi* 46:613–622.

Bailey, I. W., and Kerr, T. (1935) "The visible structure of the secondary wall and its significance in physical and chemical investigations of tracheary cells and fibers." *J. Arnold Arboretum* 16:273–300.

———, and Vestal, M. R. (1937a) "The significance of certain wood destroying fungi in the study of the enzymatic hydrolysis of cellulose." *J. Arnold Arboretum* 18:196–205.

——— and ——— (1937b) "The orientation of cellulose in the secondary·wall of tracheary cells." *J. Arnold Arboretum* 18:185–195.

Côté, W. A., Jr., and Day, A. C. (1962) "Vestured pits—Fine structure and apparent relationship with warts." *Tappi* 45:906–910.

———, and Marton, R. (1962) "Brightness of high yield pulps. IV. Electron microscopy of white birch heartwood." *Tappi* 45:46–53.

Cronshaw, J. (1960) "The fine structure of the pits of *Eucalyptus regnans* (F. Muell) and their relation to the movement of liquids into the wood." *Australian J. Botany* 8:51–57.

Gross, S. T., Clark, G. L., and Ritter, G. J. (1939) "Arrangement of the cellulose crystallites in ray cells of white oak as determined by X-rays." *Paper Trade J.* 109:37–38.

Harada, H. (1962) "Electron microscopy of ultrathin sections of beech wood (*Fagus crenata* Blume)." *J. Japan Wood Res. Soc.* 8:252–258.

———, Miyazaki, Y., and Wakashima, T. (1958) "Electron microscopic investigation on the cell wall structure of wood." Bulletin of the Govt. Forest Experiment Station, No. 104 (Meguro, Tokyo, Japan).

Lange, P. W. (1959) "The morphology of hardwood fibers." *Tappi* 42:786–792.

Meier, H. (1955) "Über den Zellwandbau durch Holzvermorschungspilze und die submikroskopische Struktur von Fichtentracheiden und Birekenholzfasern." *Holz Roh-Werkstoff* 13:323–338.

——— (1957) "Discussion of the cell wall organization of tracheids and fibers." *Holzforschung* 11:41–46.

Migita, N., and Hosoi, H. (1956) "Research on the swelling of fibers. II. Relation between the swelling property of hardwood pulp elements and the microstructure of their secondary cell wall." Bull. Tokyo Univ. Forests, No. 52, pp. 119–134.

Preston, R. D. (1939) "Wall structure and growth. I. Spring vessels in some ring-porous Dicotyledons." *Ann. Botany (London)*, New Series 111:507–530.

―――― (1952) *The Molecular Architecture of Plant Cell Walls.* Chapman and Hall, London.

Preusser, H. J., Dietrichs, H. H., and Gottwald, H. (1961) "Elektronmikroskopische Untersuchungen an Ultradünnschnitten des Markstrahlparenchyms der Rotbuche— *Fagus sylvatica* L." *Holzforschung* 15:65–75.

Ribi, E. (1953) "Electron microscopic investigation of the cell wall organization of wood." *Exp. Cell Res.* 5:161–172.

Ritter, G. J., and Mitchell, R. L. (1936) "Crystal arrangement and swelling properties of fibers and ray cells in Basswood holocellulose." *Paper Trade J.* 108:33–37.

Sachs, I. B., Clark, I., and Pew, J. C. (1963) "Investigation of lignin distribution in the cell wall of certain woods." *J. Polymer Sci.* Part C 2:203–212.

Wardrop, A. B. (1963) "Morphological factors involved in the pulping and beating of wood fibers." *Svensk Papperstid.* 65:66–83.

―――― (1964) "The structure and formation of the cell wall in xylem." In *The Formation of Wood in Forest Trees* (M. H. Zimmerman, ed.), pp. 87–134. Academic Press, N.Y.

――――, and Dadswell, H. E. (1952) "The cell wall structure of xylem parenchyma." *Australian J. Sci. Res., Ser. B*—Bio. Sci. 5:223–236.

―――― and ―――― (1957) "Variations in the cell wall organization of tracheids and fibers." *Holzforschung* 11:33–41.

――――, ――――, and Davies, G. W. (1962) "Aspects of wood structure influencing the preparation of semichemical pulps." *APPITA* 14:185–202.

The Warty Layer

WALTER LIESE

University of Hamburg, Germany

The inside of the wood cell wall is lined against the cell lumen mostly by an additional structure, the so-called warty layer. It is one of the very few basic cell wall components, the existence of which has been established only by electron microscopy. In 1951 Kobayashi and Utsumi, as well as Liese, reported small particles on the inside of the pit chamber of *Pinus* species. Systematical investigations by Harada and Miyazaki (1952), Harada (1953, 1955, 1956), Liese and Hartmann-Fahnenbrock (1953), Liese and Johann (1954), Liese (1956a, b, 1957a), and Frey-Wyssling *et al.*, (1955, 1956) revealed the presence of this structure also in other conifers. Later on, it was shown that hardwoods as well as arborescent mono-cotyledons possess an equal structure (Liese, 1957b) and recently its existence could be established also in herbaceous plants (Liese and Led-better, 1963).

Fortunately there has not been much confusion about the terminology. Because of the granular appearance the small particles were at first called "particle-structure" (Harada and Miyazaki, 1952) or "warzenähnlich" (wart-like) (Liese and Hartmann-Fahnenbrock, 1953). Later on the term "Warzenstruktur" (wart-structure) was applied. According to more specific investigations about its origin and nature, the term "warty layer" (Warzenschicht) seems to be more suitable (Liese, 1963).

OCCURRENCE

In normal, differentiated wood cells the warty layer covers the lumen side of the tertiary wall (S_3) (Fig. 1). It is present in tracheids, fibers, and vessels of softwood and hardwood species; in cells with spiral thickenings, the warts cover wall and spirals evenly. The chambers of bordered pits and the canals of simple pits also bear this structure (Fig. 2). The warty layer exists in wood cells throughout the tree, that is, in springwood and summerwood, in sapwood and heartwood, in the stem, in branches, and in the roots. The tracheids of vascular bundles in needles (Fig. 3) and the vascular cells of numerous herbaceous plants also contain this structure.

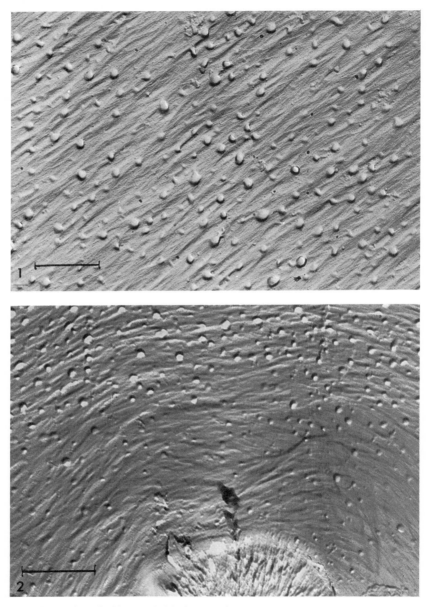

FIG. 1. Warty layer inside a tracheid of *Pinus silvestris*.
FIG. 2. Warty layer inside a pit chamber of *Pinus silvestris* (from Liese and Johann, 1954).

Fig. 3. Cross section through a tracheid from a vascular bundle of a needle of *Pinus silvestris*.

Its presence is not restricted to normal differentiated and lignified cells, since it appears also in cells of compression (Fig. 4) and tension wood, as well as in cotton hair. The warty layer must be distinguished from residual plasmatic substances, which occur in degenerated parenchyma cells, and from extraneous material due to heartwood formation. Because of its usual presence the warty layer can be regarded as a general structural feature in certain plant cells.

MORPHOLOGICAL FEATURES

Light Microscopic. Some light microscopic observations on a "granular structure" inside tracheids and vessels were obtained even before, or independent of, the electron microscopic findings of such structures (Bailey, 1933; Huber and Rouschal, 1954; Greguss, 1955), but not much attention was paid to these observations. With the knowledge obtained by the electron microscope it is now quite simple to recognize the warty layer with an ordinary light microscope (Fig. 5a,b). To improve such observations, the sections should be mounted only in water; air bubbles inside the cell may act as a magnifier, thus giving an improved image.

A thorough investigation of several hundred softwood and hardwood species from about 160 families proved that the warty layer is visible under an ordinary light microscope in most species. In certain families all species examined so far showed a distinct warty layer, for example, the families Cycadaceae, Cupressaceae, Aceraceae, Dipterocarpaceae, Fagaceae, Magnoliaceae, Lauraceae, Myrtaceae, Papilionaceae, and Winteraceae. However, other species show only an obscure granular structure in the light microscope, whereas several do not reveal any signs of it.

Electron Microscopic. In the electron microscope the warty layer can easily be investigated on replicas, but also in sections. Its appearance, however, varies, due to the size and distribution of the warts as well as to the existence of an additional layer. Usually the warts appear as spherical bodies. Their *size* ranges from 0.01 μ to 1 μ (Liese, 1956b, 1957a). The average diameter lies between 0.1 and 0.25 μ. Only some species, such as *Widdringtonia dracomontana* or *Fagus silvatica*, possess warts bigger than 0.5 μ, but then numerous smaller ones are also present (Fig. 6). Since the optical resolution of the light microscope is about 0.2 μ, the warty layer of many species can readily be seen under the light microscope. Though the appearance of the warty layer varies within species, the size range appears to be fairly consistent. Figure 7 contains measurements of their dimensions in species with a different warty layer. Only the frequency of bigger warts in *Widdringtonia* is higher. Warts in pit chambers are generally smaller in size and not as variable as in tracheids.

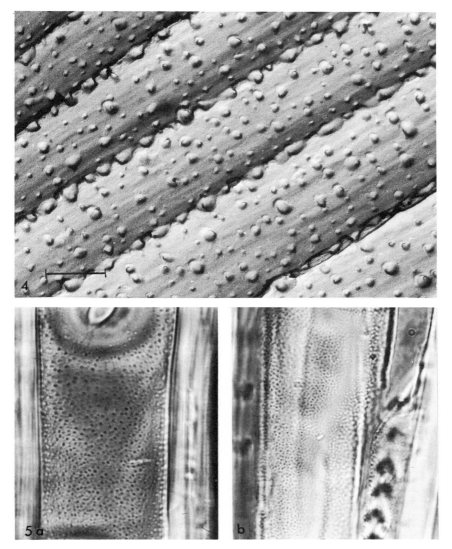

FIG. 4. Compression wood with warty layer (*Callitris calcarata*).

FIG. 5. Light microscopic evidence of the warty layer. a. *Cedrus deodora*. b. *Fagus silvatica*.

Since the warts represent small protuberances into the cell lumen, their height has also been measured. In general, they form only small excrescences; in certain species, however, they can protrude up to 0.5 μ and even nearly 1 μ into the lumen.

The *frequency* of the warts ranges from a densely packed arrangement,

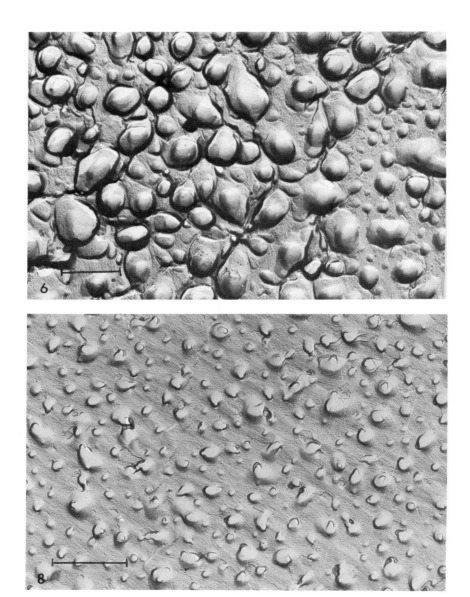

FIG. 6. Warty layer inside a vessel (*Fagus silvatica*).
FIG. 8. Warty layer inside a tracheid of *Abies alba*.

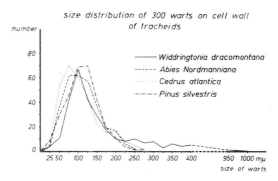

FIG. 7 (from Liese, 1957a)

where one particle is lying beside the next, to such a sparsity that the cell wall seems to be almost without warts. The *distribution* of the warts is mostly regular and independent of the frequency. Local crowding of warts is rare. Within one species the pattern of frequency and distribution varies to some extent and even between neighboring cells remarkable differences can exist. In general, however, a distinction is possible between species or even genera such as *Picea* with almost no, or very few, warts, *Abies* with frequent warts (Fig. 8), and finally species with numerous bigger warts, such as *Callitris*. Table I summarizes the observation on the appearance of the warty layer in the genera of gymnosperms.

The visibility of the actual warts seems to differ with species. In most species they are covered by an additional layer, which forms protuberances into the cell lumen and in which the warts are encased (Fig. 9). This layer seems to be amorphous, yet sometimes it reveals a fibrillar structure. Because of such a covering the tertiary wall is not detectable and the warts also appear hazy. In other cases the warts are not veiled by a layer; they lie directly on the tertiary wall so that its fibrillar texture as well as the warts are clearly visible (Fig. 10).

Cross sections through a cell wall with a warty layer confirm that it is composed of warts and a covering layer which forms excrescences (Fig. 11). The warts appear as globular bodies which lie mostly in the tip of the pouches (arrow in Figure 11). The layer itself seems to be quite thin and transparent whereas the warts are more electron-dense. Sometimes a second layer becomes visible between cell wall and warts. Apparently the warty layer consists of two membranes which include spherical bodies forming the warts.

In some species the granular appearance of the warty layer is attributed to localized thickenings of the cell wall (Wardrop and Davies, 1962; Wardrop, 1964). These are larger in size than the spherical warts and can

TABLE I. Occurrence of a Warty Layer within the Gymnosperms

× = rare;   + = distinct;   ++ = strong

Family	Genera	Species examined	Appearance
Cycadaceae	Cycas	1	×
Ginkgoaceae	Ginkgo	1	×
Pinaceae	Abies	10	+
	Pseudotsuga	1	×
	Tsuga	5	+
	Picea	11	×
	Pseudolarix	1	×
	Larix	4	×
	Cedrus	2	+
	Pinus:		
	Subgenus Haploxylon	19	×
	Diploxylon	62	+
Taxodiaceae	Sequoia	1	+
	Sequoiadendron	1	+
	Metasequoia	1	×
	Taxodium	1	+
	Cryptomeria	1	+
	Cunninghamia	1	+
	Sciadopitys	1	+
	Athrotaxis	1	+
	Taiwania	1	+
Cupressaceae	Cupressus	3	+
	Chamaecyparis	5	+
	Thuja	4	×, +
	Thujopsis	1	×
	Librocedrus	4	+
	Pilgerodendron	1	++
	Callitris	5	++
	Neocallitropsis	1	+
	Tetraclinis	1	++
	Widdringtonia	1	++
	Fitzroya	1	+
	Diselma	1	+
	Juniperus	5	+
Podocarpaceae	Pherosphaera	1	×
	Phyllocladus	3	×
	Saxegothea	1	×
	Microcachrys	1	×
	Dacrydium	10	×, +
	Podocarpus	5	×
Cephalotaxaceae	Cephalotaxus	1	×
Araucariaceae	Agathis	3	×, +
	Araucaria	5	×, +
Taxaceae	Torreya	3	+
	Taxus	3	+
Welwitschiaceae	Welwitschia	1	×
Ephedraceae	Ephedra	1	×
Gnetaceae	Gnetum	1	×

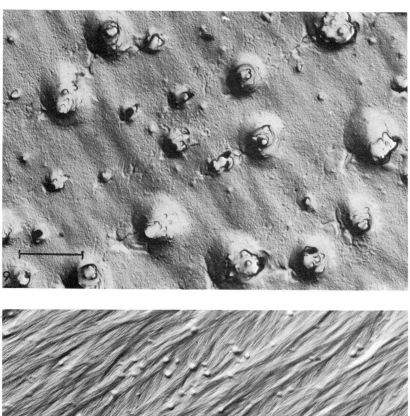

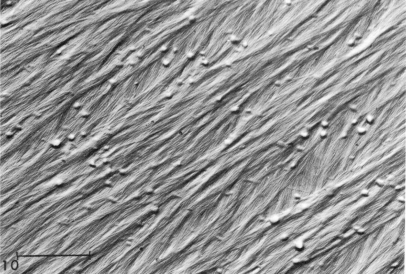

FIG. 9. Layer covering warts and tertiary wall (*Callitris robusta*).
FIG. 10. Warts on top of the tertiary wall without a covering layer.

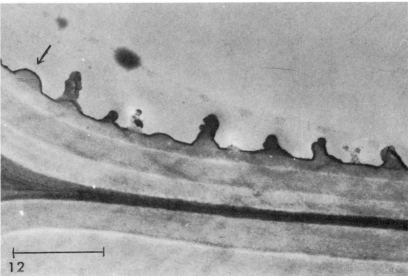

FIG. 11. Warty layer in a cross section through a tracheid of a needle (*Pinus silvestris*). Arrow shows spherical body inside the membrane pouch.

FIG. 12. Local cell wall incrustation on top of the tertiary wall (S_3) (*Juniperus obtusa*)

be recognized best in sections (Fig. 12). They form incrustations on top of the tertiary wall with a different density than the actual cell wall substances. Replicas from cell wall areas from which the warty layer has been stripped do not show a corresponding sculpturing of the cell wall (Fig. 13). The thickenings must have been removed accordingly, and therefore they are not regarded as a part of the cell wall, but rather as incrustations. It appears likely that the larger warts present in some species are formed by such incrustations rather than by the warty layer (Figs. 6, 9).

CHEMICAL FEATURES

Little is known about the chemical composition of the warty layer. Some preliminary findings have been recorded by Wardrop et al., (1959). Ultraviolet examinations on isolated material have shown that its two components, the warts and the membranes, are chemically different, as only the former absorb ultraviolet light. As already mentioned, the warts are quite dense to electrons. The warty layer seems to be isotropic in polarized light. Its refractive index has been calculated as $n = 1.52$. This figure approaches those of embedding materials such as Canada balsam. Consequently the warty layer is, to some extent, extinguished in permanent slides, whereas it can be seen more easily in sections mounted only in water. It can be stained with osmium tetroxide, and a positive reaction with methylene blue indicates the presence of protein.

The warty layer is very difficult to dissolve chemically. Studies concerning its solubility showed a resistance to soaking in 98% sulphuric acid or sodium hypochlorite, and to boiling in 17.5% sodium hydroxide or 100% hydrogen peroxide, but solubility occurred after treatment with sodium hydroxide and chlorine water or hydrogen peroxide and acetic acid. Recent observations by Wardrop (1964) indicate that during maceration the warty material tends to be more easily hydrolyzed than the actual cell wall, which suggests that it contains a different type of polysaccharide.

The remarkable resistance of the warty layer to chemical dissolution made its isolation possible by dissolving the cell wall using the method of Pew (1949). A microchemical analysis of such residues for several species resulted in carbon (47–60%), hydrogen (5.5–6%), oxygen (32–40%), methoxyl (3.6–7.3%), but only a low nitrogen content (0.6–2.1%) (Cronshaw et al., 1961). Further work along this line appears desirable. Bradway (1954), working with cellulose acetates made from wood pulp, analyzed the haze, which might arise from the warty layer during acetylation, and obtained a high proportion of mannan and xylan; Sperling (1963) found mostly xylan with a trace of silica.

The warty layer also exhibits partial resistance to attack by wood-destroying fungi (Liese and Schmid, 1962; Liese, 1964). Fungi of the brown rot group, which hydrolyze only the polysaccharides of the cell wall, do not appear able to digest the warts nor the covering membrane. In wood buried or soaked over long periods, often only the warty layer remains together with the middle lamella. In contrast, white rot and also some soft rot species can dissolve both components (Fig. 14). In this case the warts appear more readily decomposed than the layer, so that small craters occur during the first stages of enzymatic dissolution.

ORIGIN

Observations in the cambium region have shown that the warty layer appears when the protoplast vanishes. The localized incrustations on the cell wall must be formed simultaneous with or prior to the formation of the warty layer (Wardrop and Davies, 1962). They seem to consist of a different material than the lignified cell wall, which might permeate from the cytoplasm through the plasmalemma. The incrustations are not generally present together with a warty layer. Their origin and relationship with other formations is under investigation.

The development of the warty layer occurs as the last stage of cell differentiation. In maturing vascular cells the protoplast forms a thin tube which lines the wall around the large central vacuole. It is bounded by one membrane on each side, the plasmalemma (ectoplast, plasmamembrane) and the tonoplast; the remaining cytoplasm with the various cell organelles is concentrated between these two membranes. With progressive aging of the cell, electron-dense spherical particles occur within the cytoplasm (Fig. 15). Their origin is still unknown; they might be formed by condensation of certain plasma constituents. So far, there is not much evidence that they consist of specific cell organelles, like plastids or mitochondria. Our present knowledge of the degeneration of the protoplast and the simultaneous changes of cell structures is still insufficient for an explanation of the origin of the spherical warts. When, at the last stage of degeneration, the tonoplast collapses on the plasmalemma, these particles are sandwiched between, and pouches are formed in the cell lumen (Fig. 16). Their content corresponds with the warts, whereas the layer covering the warts arises from the tonoplast. Since in maturing cells the cytoplasmic components are sometimes more concentrated at the cell corners, the warts are then also localized predominantly in these parts (Fig. 17). The spherical warts can also be laid down over the cell wall incrustations, so that "double-warts" occur. In certain species the in-

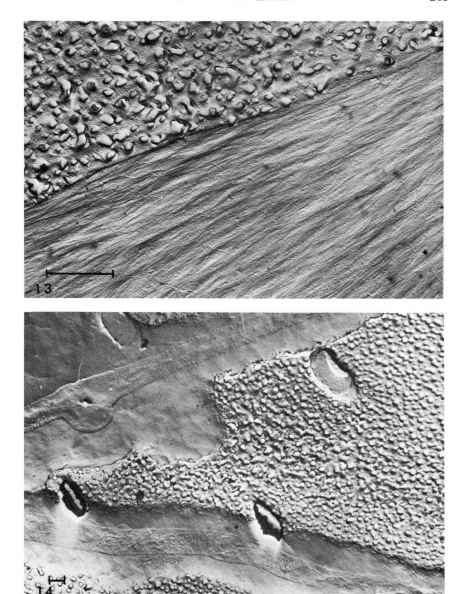

FIG. 13. Warty layer partially stripped off the tertiary wall (*Tsuga heterophylla*).
FIG. 14. Deterioration of the warty layer of a vessel (*Fagus silvatica*) by *Polyporus versicolor*.

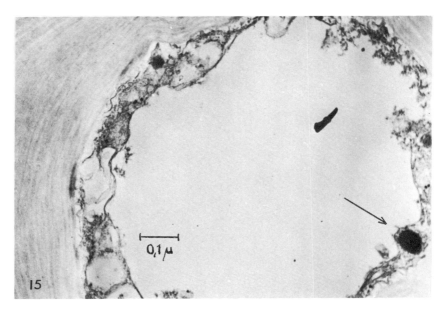

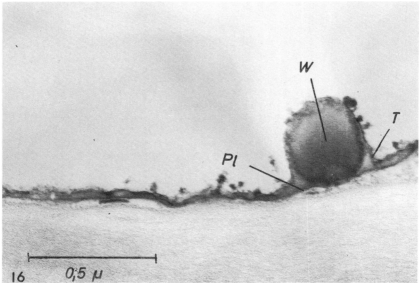

FIG. 15. Fiber of *Plantago major* with an electron-dense particle inside the degenerating cytoplasm.

FIG. 16. Vessel of *Plantago major* with warty layer consisting of plasmalemma (Pl), wart (W), and tonoplast (T) (from Liese and Ledbetter, 1963).

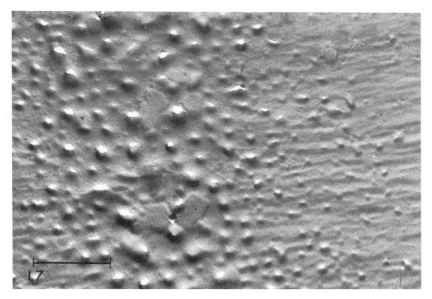

FIG. 17. Warts concentrated at the cell corner (*Pinus silvestris*)(from Liese and Johann, 1954).

crustations contribute considerably to the warty appearance of the inner cell wall, especially to the granular images in the light microscope. Figure 18 is a diagrammatic representation of the warty layer in species with and without additional cell wall incrustations.

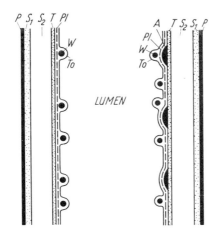

Fig. 18. Diagrammatic representation of the warty layer in species without and with cell wall incrustations; primary wall (P), secondary wall (S₁, S₂), tertiary wall (T), plasmalemma (Pl), wart (W), tonoplast (To), cell wall incrustation (A).

According to the above assumption, the actual warty layer is the remainder of the dying protoplast in cells where death is the precondition for their function. The formation of the warty layer appears in an organized pattern, contrary to the dying of the protoplasm in parenchyma cells. On the basis of this concept, it could be excluded that residual components of the cytoplasm are involved to a greater extent in the formation of the tertiary wall (S_3). Whereas the tertiary wall forms a part of the three-layered cell wall, the warty layer is regarded as an individual structure arising from the dying protoplast.

Further work is needed to explain the variable appearance of the warty layer in different species. It might be recalled that size and frequency, as well as the appearance of a covering membrane, differ according to species. The reasons could be related to a different process of protoplasmic disintegration, to the frequency and enzymatic lysis of cell organelles, or to a different regulation of lignification, which may contribute to a "fixation" of the components. Though at present all explanations are more or less speculative, one can conclude from the varying appearance of the warty layer a different behavior of the protoplasm during its final breakdown.

A striking similarity exists between the warty layer and the sculpturing of the pollen sexine at the outer part of the exine of pollen grains. These excrescences were formed by the degenerating protoplasts of the tapetal cells, and corresponding processes seem to be obvious. The solubility of this material with various procedures showed an even greater resistance than the warty layer, although some of their solubility properties are similar; the chemical composition shows differences (Cronshaw *et al.,* 1961).

Sometimes the warty layer also resembles the pit vestures or sculptures of certain species of angiosperms. These structures also originate at the end of cell differentiation when the protoplast degenerates. More detailed investigations by Schmid and Machado (1964) have proved the individuality of each structure. Whereas the vestures are deposited directly on the cell wall outside the plasmalemma, the warts arise in a later stage.

SIGNIFICANCE

The warty layer acts as a terminal lamella of the cell wall. One can assume that certain properties of cell walls, such as the diffusion of water, preservatives, or pulping liquids may be affected by its presence. Depending on its exact chemical nature, adhesion and fixation of chemicals might also be altered. Excessive drying of wood could change its properties, thus affecting the penetration of solutions into the cell wall, as suggested by Wardrop and Davies (1958). Also the flow of water in the conducting sapwood might be influenced by the sometimes quite rough surface of the cell wall.

The remarkable resistance of the warty layer to chemical dissolution does probably contribute to the difficulties regarding the filtrability of solutions from cellulose acetates and viscoses. Filters are sometimes blocked by material which has not been dissolved during processing. This haze or gel consists of a nearly monodisperse fraction of spherical or potato-shaped particles, as well as membrane fragments (Sperling and Easterwood, 1960). Similar ingredients can be obtained from the warty layer by dissolving the cell wall substances. Also the size of the gel particles is of the same order as the warts. Therefore, it is likely that the above material arises from this layer.

Taxonomic significance of the warty layer deserves special consideration. Its prospects and limitations can be judged on the basis of detailed investigations into its appearance within species, genera, and families. The mentioned variability of frequency and size of the warts reduces its value for purposes of identification. On the other hand, some characters, such as the almost complete absence of warts in certain species and genera, as well as the predominant presence of smaller or larger warts, could be used to some advantage together with other anatomical features. Conifers with resin canals often have a less pronounced warty layer, with the apparent exception of *Pinus*. In most genera studied so far, all species possess a similar pattern of warty layer. *Pinus*, however, reveals a remarkable split between the Haploxylon species and the Diploxylon species (Frey-Wyssling *et al.*, 1955, 1956). While the former rarely displays a distinct warty layer, it is well developed in the latter. A detailed investigation of more than eighty pine species (Liese, 1956b) proved a similarity within the various sections, so that an attempt could be made to compare the appearance of the warty layer in different species with their systematic classification. The close relationship between the presence of warts and the presence of dentate ray tracheids of pine seems worth mentioning. To summarize taxonomic significance, it can be stated that the warty layer is of little value for the systematic classification of families, genera, and species.

ACKNOWLEDGMENTS

The investigations were supported by the Deutsche Forschungsgemeinschaft. Figures 1, 4, 6, 8, 9, 10, 13 were produced at the Institut für Holzforschung und Holztechnik, Universität München, with the assistance of

Miss Baldermann; Figure 14 in cooperation with Dr. R. Schmid; Figures 3, 11, 12, 15, and 16 in cooperation with Dr. Ledbetter, Harvard University.

REFERENCES

Bailey, I. W. (1933) "The cambium and its derivative tissues. 8. Structure, distribution, and diagnostic significance of vestured pits in dicotyledons." *J. Arnold Arboretum* 14:259–273.

Bradway, K. E. (1954) "An investigation of haze in cellulose acetates made from wood pulps." *Tappi* 37:440–446.

Cronshaw, J., Davies, G. W., and Wardrop, A. B. (1961) "A note on the wart structure of conifer tracheids." *Holzforschung* 15:75–78.

Frey-Wyssling, A., Mühlethaler, K., and Bosshard, H. H. (1955, 1956) "Das Elektronenmikroskop im Dienste der Bestimmung von Pinusarten." *Holz Roh- Werkstoff* 13:245–249; 14:161–162.

Greguss, P. (1955) *Xylotomische Bestimmung der heute lebenden Gymnospermen.* Akadémiai Kiadi, Budapest. 308pp.

Harada, H. (1953) "Electron-microscopic investigation on the wart-like (particle) structure of conifer tracheids." *J. Japan. Forestry Soc.* 35:393–396.

⸻(1955) "Electron-microscopic investigation on the wart-like structure of conifer tracheids. II." *J. Japan. Wood Res. Soc.* 1:85–89.

⸻(1956) "The electron-microscopic investigation of wood. On the fine structure of the wart-like structure and of the pit membrane." *Transactions 65th Meet. Japan. Forestry Soc.,* pp. 1–5.

⸻, and Miyazaki, Y. (1952) "The electron-microscopic observation of the cell wall of conifer tracheids." *J. Japan. Forestry Soc.* 34:350–352.

Huber, B., and Rouschal, C. (1954) *Mikrophotographischer Atlas mediterraner Hölzer.* Haller Verlag, Berlin-Grunewald. 105pp.

Kobayashi, K., and Utsumi, N. (1951) "Electron microscopy of conifer tracheids" (in Japanese). Committee Note on Electron Microscopy, No. 56, p. 93.

Liese, W. (1951) "Demonstration elektronenmikroskopischer Aufnahmen von Nadelholztüpfeln." *Ber. Deut. Botan. Ges.* 64:31–32.

⸻(1956a) "Elektronenoptische Beobachtungen über die Warzenstruktur bei den Koniferen." *Electron Microscopy, Proc. Stockholm Conf., 1956,* pp. 276–279.

⸻(1956b) "Zur systematischen Bedeutung der submikroskopischen Warzenstruktur bei der Gattung Pinus L." *Holz Roh- Werkstoff* 14:417–424.

⸻(1957a) "Beitrag zur Warzenstruktur der Koniferentracheiden unter besonderer Berücksichtigung der Cupressaceae." *Ber. Deut. Botan. Ges.* 70:21–30.

⸻(1957b) "Zur Struktur der Tertiärwand bei den Laubhölzern." *Naturwiss.* 44:240–241.

⸻(1963) "Tertiary wall and warty layer in wood cells." *J. Polymer Sci.,* Part C 2:213–229.

⸻(1964) "Über den Abbau verholzter Zellwände durch Moderfäulepilze." *Holz Roh-Werkstoff* 22:289–295.

⸻, and Hartmann-Fahnenbrock, M. (1953) "Elektronenmikroskopische Untersuchungen über die Hoftüpfel der Nadelhölzer." *Biochim. Biophys. Acta* 11:190–198.

————, and Johann, I. (1954) "Elektronenmikroskopische Beobachtungen über eine besondere Feinstruktur der verholzten Zellwand bei einigen Koniferen." *Planta* 44:269–285.

————, and Ledbetter, M. (1963) "On the occurrence of a warty layer in the vascular cells of plants." *Nature* 197:201–202.

————, and Schmid, R. (1962) "Elektronenmikroskopische Untersuchungen über den Abbau des Holzes durch Pilze." *Angew. Botan.* 36:291–297.

Pew, J. C. (1949) "Membranous substances in common heartwoods." *J. Forestry* 47:196–199.

Schmid, R., and Machado, R. D. (1964) "Zur Entstehung und Feinstruktur skulpturierter Hoftüpfel bei Leguminosen." *Planta* 60:612–626.

Sperling, L. H. (1963) "Characterization of small gels in viscose." *J. Appl. Polymer Sci.* 7:1411–1423.

————, and Easterwood, M. (1960) "Chemical and physical nature of insolubles: Acetone solutions of cellulose acetate." *J. Appl. Polymer Sci.* 4:25–33.

Wardrop, A. B. (1964) "The structure and formation of the cell wall in xylem." In *The Formation of Wood in Forest Trees* (M. H. Zimmerman, ed.), pp. 87–134. Academic Press, N. Y.

————, and Davies, G. W. (1958) "Some anatomical factors relating to the penetration of water into xylem of gymnosperms." *Australian J. Botany* 6:96–102.

————and————(1962) "Wart structure of gymnosperm tracheids." *Nature* 194:497–498.

————, Liese, W., and Davies, G. W. (1959) "The nature of the wart structure in conifer tracheids." *Holzforschung* 13:115–120.

The Fine Structure of Bordered Pits in Softwoods

WALTER LIESE

University of Hamburg, Germany

In plant anatomy the structure of pits has received attention for a long time (Sachs, 1879; Russow, 1883; Bailey, 1913, 1915). When the electron microscope became available for investigations of the fine structure of wood, the pits were one of the first features to be studied (Liese, 1951, 1954; Liese and Fahnenbrock, 1952; Harada and Miyazaki, 1952; Eicke, 1954). This interest has continued, and even now new facts about their fine structure are being published. The main reason for such interest is the role which the pits play in the movement of water and other liquids within the wood; however, their influence upon treatability is sometimes overestimated (Liese, 1956). Appearing at a glance to be relatively simple and uniform structures, the pits still bear many secrets which are to be discovered.

BORDERED PITS OF TRACHEIDS

The bordered pits in the secondary xylem of softwoods are formed by an overarching of the pit membrane by the cell wall of the two adjacent tracheids, leaving an opening, the pit aperture. The two pit cavities are limited by the pit membrane, which is the important feature for water movement.

Pit Border

The development of the pit border is already initiated before the secondary thickening of the cell wall begins and the differentiation of the pit membrane starts (Sachs, 1882; Frey-Wyssling *et al.*, 1956a). Concentrically oriented microfibrils are laid down on the primary wall and form the "initial pit border" which lines the pit field. Further growth occurs by centripetal apposition of tangentially oriented microfibrils to the thickened edge of the initial pit border. Whereas Frey-Wyssling *et al.*, (1956a) consider the initial pit border as part of the S_1, Wardrop and Dadswell

271

(1957) emphasize its formation before deposition of the S_1 layer and regard it as structurally distinct from the secondary wall layers. In later stages of differentiation, the lamellae of S_2 are laid down in such a manner that they grow centripetally until the final size of the pit aperture is reached (Fig. 1). The microfibrils form a streamline pattern by following the orientation of the respective lamella, as was supposed from the polarizing microscopy studies of Scarth *et al.*, (1929). Consequently the axis of the pit aperture reflects the main orientation of the S_2 layer.

Recently Jutte and Spit (1963) observed in sections a contrasting zone within the pit border, which they regard as layer S_1. They conclude that this layer is built up in the first phase of border formation as a thin dome with a large central opening. Later on, the S_2 lamellae are added on both sides so that, near the aperture, two different S_2 layers are in contact with each other. Sections through the pit border of tracheids from the xylem of a conifer needle did not show a corresponding zone. Here the pit border appears to be built up of numerous layers of the secondary wall, which are laid down centripetally so that, by apposition, lamellation occurs (see Figure 17). Further observations would be desirable in order to elucidate the formation of the pit border and to explain the contrasting zone within it.

The secondary wall layers of the pit border are covered towards the cell lumen and the pit cavity by the tertiary wall (S_3). A surface view from the lumen exhibits its typical slightly crisscrossed texture (Fig. 2). The presence of the warty layer depends upon the species. The microfibrils are oriented around the aperture in a streamline pattern. At the two areas where the microfibrils separate, the circular orientation of the layer beneath sometimes becomes visible. Jutte and Spit (1963) observed a thin veil within the porus, which they regard as a remnant of the plasma membrane.

At the inner side of the pit border the microfibrils form a circular pattern. This had already been shown with the polarizing microscope (Frey, 1926; Bailey and Vestal, 1937). Actually, the microfibrils have a straighter orientation, and it is mainly their tangential position that leads to a circular appearance (Fig. 3). On two opposite sides of the pit chamber the orientation is disturbed by an overlapping of microfibrils which appear to end here. These areas lie mostly transverse to the cell axis, and they correspond to the microfibrillar orientation of the tertiary wall. This supports the theory that they belong to the inner layer of the tertiary wall, as was also shown by Bucher (1957), by means of staining reactions. A warty layer covers the pit chamber in most species.

Notable differences in the structure of the pit border related to species, genera, or families of gymnosperms have not yet been reported. Thus, this

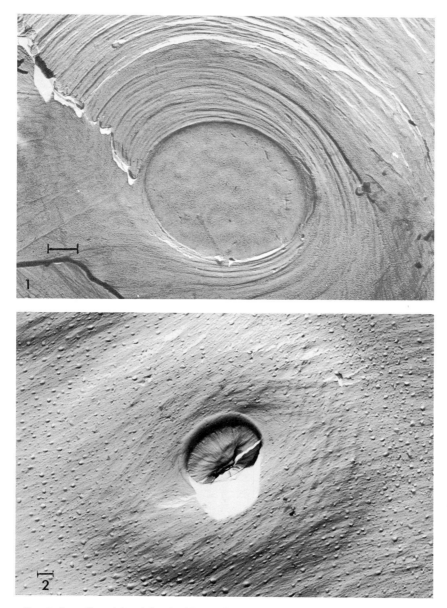

FIG. 1. Lamellae of the pit border (*Pinus silvestris*).
FIG. 2. Pit border from the lumen side (*Pinus silvestris*)(from Liese and Johann, 1954).

part of the pit can be regarded as being quite stable. Even the pit border of hardwoods shows the same structure; only the warty layer appears to be less developed.

Pit Membrane

The structure of the pit membrane has been investigated mostly in species of the Pinaceae. However, findings in recent years have revealed structural differences of the pit membrane within the gymnosperms, which will be discussed later.

The Pit Membrane in Pinaceae. The pit membrane of fully differentiated tracheids is composed mostly of radially oriented microfibrils with an additional central thickening which forms the torus (Fig. 4). The part of the membrane between the edge of the pit border and the torus is called the margo. The development of the pit membrane starts in primary tracheids after completion of surface growth, and in secondary cells after initiation of secondary thickening (Frey-Wyssling *et al.*, 1956a). Microfibrils of the primary wall, delineated by the initial pit border, are partly combined into thicker bundles and reoriented to a preferential radial pattern. Between them, other microfibrils tend to a more or less tangential direction. An addition of new microfibrils seems to be likely. During further differentiation of the margo, the matrix substance is dissolved so that only the cellulosic microfibrils remain, and direct communication between adjacent cells is complete. In the central region of the pit membrane the torus is formed as an additional thickening from both sides. New microfibrils are laid down in a preferentially circular-parallel texture. The matrix substance remains and further material is deposited. In general, the torus is regarded as a secondary structure because of the partly parallel oriented microfibrils.

In differentiated tracheids of water-conducting sapwood the margo consists of numerous microfibrils separated from each other and forming a loose texture. They are oriented preferentially in a radial pattern, though many run in other directions. At two opposite sides they appear more densely arranged. The microfibrils seem to crisscross each other, but this appearance is due more to a superposition than to an actual woven texture. They extend mostly inside the torus, while some can be followed along its surface.

The size of the radial strands differs considerably on replicas (Fig. 5). Many are built up of single microfibrils with a diameter of about 150–200 Å. Others appear to be composed of several microfibrils combined into thick bundles. They may represent, to some extent, fasciculated

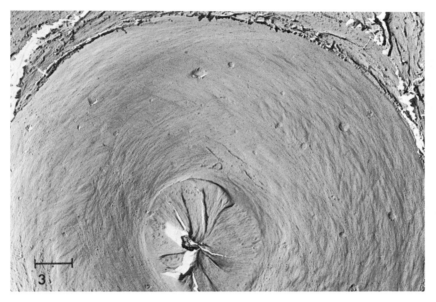

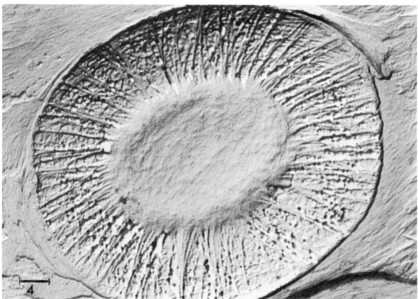

FIG. 3. Inner side of the pit border (*Picea excelsa*).
FIG. 4. Pit membrane with margo and torus (*Pinus silvestris*)(from Liese, 1960).

microfibrils, formed during the differentiation of the pit membrane. More often the joining may have occurred during the withdrawal of the capillary water, which brought single microfibrils together. As many as 500 microfibrils have been counted in the margo of *Pinus silvestris*. The outermost edge of the margo appears more compact and electron-dense. This membrane rim (Jutte and Spit, 1963), or annulus, can be observed in sections (see Figure 16) as well as in replicas (Fig. 5, arrow) and is present in the pit membrane of softwoods and hardwoods. It appears as if the lignified middle lamella with two primary walls extends into the pit chamber somewhat. With the pit membrane in aspirated condition, the inside of the pit border becomes visible between the microfibrils. This indicates that open spaces exist within the margo. Since their size determines greatly the permeability of pits, exact measurements are of special interest. It is doubtful if data on the average distance of the margo fibrils measured on replicas are reliable. In this condition, structural disruption must be considered because of the influence of drying. Furthermore, the microfibrils lie tightly one above another, whereas in their functional position the margo forms a three-dimensional structure with a certain depth, which affects the spacing of the microfibrils. Therefore, the results from filtration experiments with particles appear to be more reliable, a method which was applied for light microscopic studies by Bailey (1913) and Frenzel (1929). Filtrations of a TiO_2 suspension with particles from 10 to 850 mμ through freshly cut sapwood samples from several species of Pinaceae revealed openings up to 200 mμ in the pit membrane (Liese and Johann, 1954). Consequently, water movement from one tracheid to the next occurs as laminar flow. The pit membrane bears, in the central part, *the torus*, which originates from incrustations on both sides of the primary walls. Its form is mostly lens-shaped. The thickening consists of additional microfibrils and of amorphous material which appears lignin-like (Sachs, 1963). Depending on the degree of incrustation, its surface shows a more or less distinct fibrillar structure. The microfibrils are often oriented, at the outer part of the torus, in a circular pattern, while in the center they are more dispersed. In other cases a parallel arrangement of microfibrils over the whole torus or a diffuse texture can be observed (Fig. 6). Investigations of pit structure in different pine species and in other genera of the Pinaceae than *Pinus* did not show any distinct differences between species (Liese and Hartmann-Fahnenbrock, 1953; Harada *et al.*, 1958).

The compact torus is generally regarded as impermeable. However, Stemsrud (1956) found perforations in its central part, whose number and size were said to increase from the outer sapwood to the heartwood boundary. In all of our studies we have never observed such structures, and there is no doubt that these openings are preparation artifacts, as was

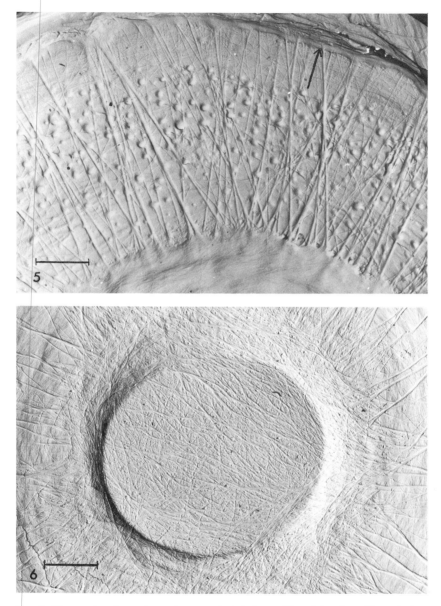

Fig. 5. Margo of a pit membrane in an aspirated stage. The pit border with warty layer becomes visible; arrow shows the membrane rim (*Pinus silvestris*)(from Liese, 1964).

Fig. 6. Microfibrillar texture of the torus; delignified after Wise (*Cedrus deodara*).

also stated by Frey-Wyssling *et al.*, (1956b). Similar perforations of the torus have been found by Jayme and Hunger (1956, 1958) in tracheids from pulp and are regarded as consequences of the drying of the material. The prior delignification and the preparation method may also enhance the formation of such structures.

Some species, such as *Tsuga canadensis* and *Cedrus deodara* (Krahmer and Côté, 1963), possess peculiarly shaped tori, called extended and scalloped, respectively. They result from thick, amorphous strands which extend from the torus into the margo (Fig. 7). The material appears to be the same as in the torus; however, additional microfibrils could also be present in these areas. Replicas of delignified cells have demonstrated an even removal of the torus substances as well as the material of the strands. The microfibrillar texture of the margo is denser in the region of the strands, because the matrix substances resist distorting influences, during drying.

A new theory of the formation of the torus has been proposed by Jayme and Hunger (1956) and Jayme *et al.*, (1960). According to them the pit membrane is of equal thickness throughout in water-conducting bordered pits and does not contain any central thickening (torus). The two primary walls are said to have no preferred orientation, such as a radial pattern. Only by aspiration of the pit membrane does the retreating water contract the loose primary wall texture towards the center like an iris diaphragm, thus forming a thickened layer of microfibrils which makes up the torus. Therefore its existence is regarded as a result of the deformation of the primary walls by distorting influences, during the closing of the pit. However, sections through unaspirated bordered pits already show the existence of a torus (see Figures 16, 17). On the other hand, the absence of a torus in aspirated pit membranes of gymnosperm families other than the Pinaceae also disproves this theory.

The Pit Membrane in Other Families of Gymnosperms. Most of the results concerning the fine structure of bordered pits were obtained from species of the Pinaceae. Bailey (1957) pointed out the variability of the light microscopic appearance of the pit membrane in the conifers. Electron microscopic observations proved that species of other families, such as *Gnetum gnemon* (Eicke, 1957), *Araucaria* spp. (Eicke, 1958; Jutte and Spit, 1963), and *Thuja plicata* (Krahmer and Côté, 1963), possess a different membrane texture. In order to elucidate the structural variability of the pit membrane within the gymnosperms a systematic investigation was undertaken on species from more than forty-five genera. The results indicate that the pit membrane of gymnosperms has a rather variable structure. The differences are due to the number and density of microfibrils within the margo as well as to the presence or absence of a torus.

In general, five main types appear to exist:

1. Pinus-type: microfibrils in a moderately dense radial pattern, with larger spaces; distinct torus by apposition (Fig. 4).

2. Araucaria-type: microfibrils in a radial pattern, more densely packed with narrower spaces; torus not due to apposition, but only as matrix substance at the central region (Fig. 8).

3. Thujopsis-type: microfibrils in a radial pattern, very densely packed with only small spaces; torus absent, no matrix visible at the central region (Fig. 9).

4. Gnetum-type: microfibrils densely arranged in a more dispersed pattern; no spaces visible between; torus absent (Fig. 10).

5. Cycas-type: microfibrils in a dispersed pattern with matrix substance between; torus absent (Fig. 11).

According to these findings a distinct torus as additional thickening is present only in species in which the pit membrane consists of a radial pattern with a loose texture. In many species, a slight thickening of the central part exists, due to the presence of some amorphous material between the microfibrils, but without additional incrustations. In other species, the microfibrils can be seen to lack masking substances. They extend over the whole pit membrane and crisscross at the center. In *Araucaria* species with alternate pitting the microfibrils can be traced from one pit membrane to the next (Jutte and Spit, 1963) (Fig. 12). This proves that the pit membranes arise from the continuous primary walls.

The differences in the structure of the pit membrane seem to be typical for species and, in most cases, also for genera, whereas within families various types can occur. Only the Pinaceae and the Cephalotaxaceae always possess a margo with a distinct torus. In the species of Ginkgoaceae, Taxodiaceae, and Araucariaceae investigated so far, the pit membrane consists only of densely packed microfibrils in a radial orientation without secondary appositions. The central part sometimes appears occluded with incrustations by which the microfibrils are partly covered. Circularly oriented microfibrils as a typical feature of a torus do not exist. In the other families of gymnosperms, various types of membrane structures occur, sometimes even within one genus. Worth mentioning are the differences within the Chlamydospermae. *Welwitschia mirabilis*, as well as *Gnetum gnemon* and *G. scandens*, possesses a pit membrane consisting only of radially oriented microfibrils, whereas in *Ephedra americana* (Eicke, 1957), *E. campylopoda*, and *E. neradensis*, a well developed torus is present, surrounded by a pit membrane with a dense primary wall texture (Fig. 13). This structural distinction of the pit membrane of *Ephedra* supports other observations on its special morphology. The woods of the phylogenetically oldest family among the recent gymno-

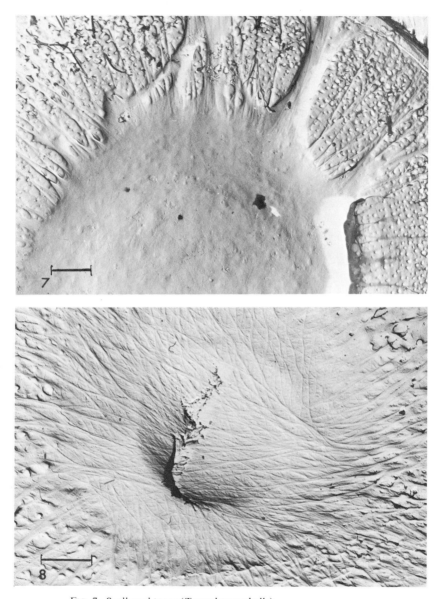

FIG. 7. Scalloped torus (*Tsuga heterophylla*).
FIG. 8. Araucaria-type of pit membrane (*Araucaria angustifolia*).

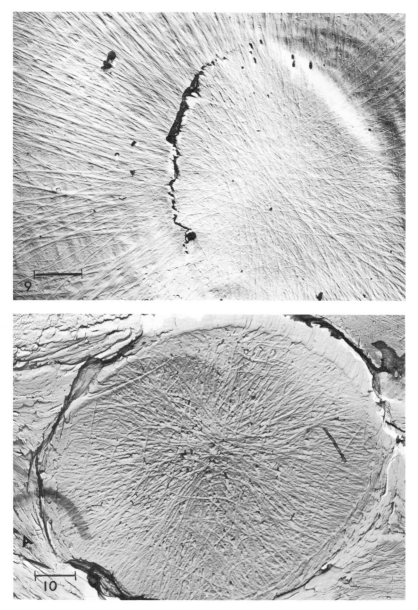

FIG. 9. Thujopsis-type of pit membrane (*Thujopsis dolabrata*).
FIG. 10. Gnetum-type of pit membrane (*Gnetum scandens*)(both from Liese, 1964).

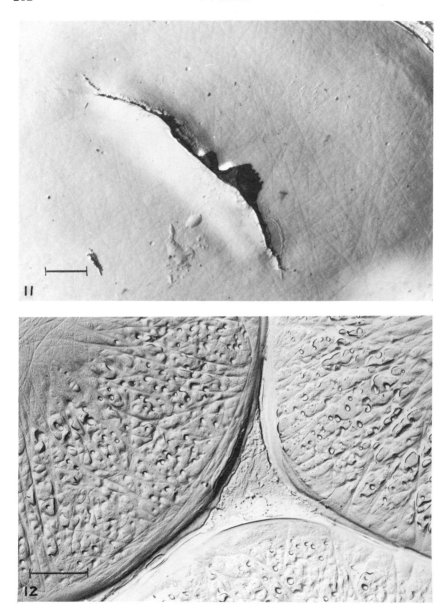

FIG. 11. Cycas-type of pit membrane (*Cycas media*). The slit is due to preparation.
FIG. 12. Margo of three alternate pits with connected strands (*Araucaria angustifolia*).

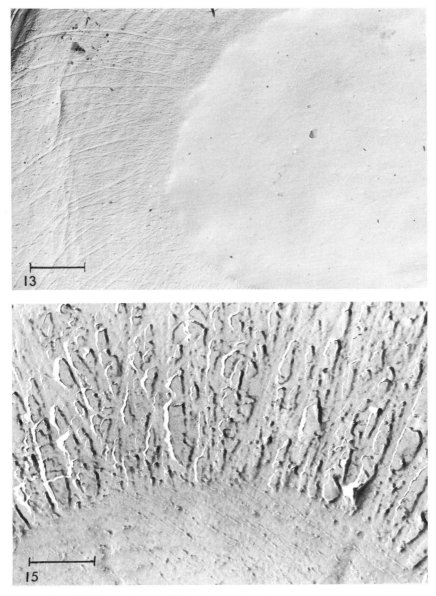

FIG. 13. Pit membrane of *Ephedra campylopoda*.
FIG. 15. Pit membrane in heartwood with incrustations (*Pinus muricata*).

sperms, the Cycadaceae, possess a tight membrane of microfibrils in a dispersed texture embedded in matrix substance (see Figure 11). No openings and no torus are to be seen, just as in the pit membranes of hardwoods (see Schmid, this volume). It seems possible that this type of pit structure represents the most primitive form within the gymnosperms, from which the others originated (Eicke, 1963).

Summarizing the observation on the variability of the pit membrane, it can be stated that the well known structure of Pinaceae species cannot be regarded as representative for the gymnosperms as a whole. In fact, the greater number of genera do not have a torus structure.

These investigations into the structure of the pit membrane have been made with air-dry wood by using the replica technique. Therefore, the possibility must be considered that the texture of the membrane has been influenced by forces during the withdrawal of the capillary water. In order to confirm the results about the different structures in air-dry wood, the behavior of pits in function has been investigated. For this, filtration experiments were made with three species and a suspension of titanium dioxide particles ranging from 40 mμ to 240 mμ in size (Liese and Bauch, 1964). *Abies nordmanniana* has the typical pit membrane of the Pinaceae with radially oriented microfibrils and a torus. *Thuja occidentalis* shows a denser fibrillar texture with slight incrustations at the center, whereas in *Thuja plicata* the microfibrils are clearly visible without any distinct matrix substance between.

The filtrates from these species differ distinctly in the distribution of particle size from the original solution (Fig. 14). In *Thuja occidentalis* only particles up to 1600 Å penetrated the membranes, whereas in *Abies nordmanniana* particles up to 2000 Å passed through. The results confirm the penetrability of the margo for particles up to a certain size. Furthermore, it can be concluded that pit membranes of different species also possess a different structural organization in their functional stage. Permeability and flow will certainly be influenced by these differences. Even more variations can be expected for other species of gymnosperms, such as *Ginkgo*, *Gnetum*, or *Ephedra*.

Alterations of the Pit Membrane.   The microfibrils of the margo show alterations with time. Light and electron microscopic investigations have shown that the structural appearance of the pit membrane can vary even between adjacent tracheids. These differences appear in the light microscope with respect to the discernibility of the radial pattern of the membrane and in the electron microscope with respect to the number and size of the margo fibrils as well as to the structure of the torus. In general, the margo has a denser texture in latewood tracheids than in those of earlywood. In older annual rings of sapwood a coarseness of the micro-

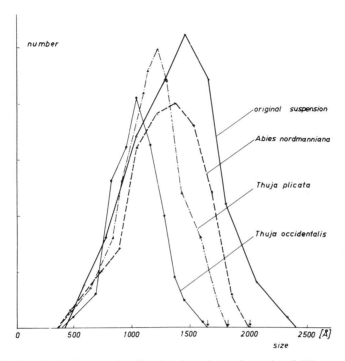

FIG. 14. Particle distribution after filtration through wood samples of different species.

fibrils occurs, so that strands become visible in the light microscope (Frey-
Wyssling *et al.*, 1959). The visibility of a radial texture might be caused
primarily by a kind of fasciculation during the withdrawal of capillary
water from the tracheids, rather than a coarseness increasing with age.

The *aspiration* of the pit membrane on one of the pit borders takes place
by the removal of capillary water during drying (Liese, 1953). Hereby a
tight sealing of the pit aperture by the torus occurs, which is regarded as
irreversible in air-dry wood. Its function is generally seen as limiting the
expansion of gas in order to prevent a disruption of water transport in
adjacent tracheids. Filtration experiments with India ink by Côté and
Krahmer (1962) gave evidence of this sealing effect. The way in which
aspiration takes place in species without a torus thickening needs further
experiments and consideration. Apparently its formation is not essential
for the closing function of a bordered pit.

Aspiration is based on a suction process combined with adhesion forces
between the pit membrane and the water surface. By reducing the surface
tension of the capillary water below a value of 24–25 dynes/cm, the pit

membrane of the Pinus-type remains unaspirated during water withdrawal. For species with a Thujopsis-type of membrane, the critical value
is distinctly higher (Liese and Bauch, 1965).

Transformation from sapwood to *heartwood* also affects pit structure.
The pit membrane becomes heavily incrusted, and the microfibrils are
coated with amorphous material (Fig. 15), which further restricts the
movement of liquids. Investigations by Krahmer and Côté (1963) have
shown that two types of incrustations can be distinguished. Some of the
material consists of extractives which are removable with hot water and
organic solvents, whereas others resemble lignin-like substances which can
increase the sealing effect of pit closure.

Bordered Pits in Needles

Bordered pits are present not only in the tracheids of the secondary
xylem, but also in needles. Here they are located in the xylem tracheids of
the vascular bundle as well as in the transfusion tracheids. Their fine
structure reveals further details which had not been recognized in the
bordered pits investigated so far. The margo is composed of layers of
microfibrils in a parallel orientation, which can be seen, in a cross section,
throughout the whole pit membrane (Fig. 16). At the outer edge, the lig-

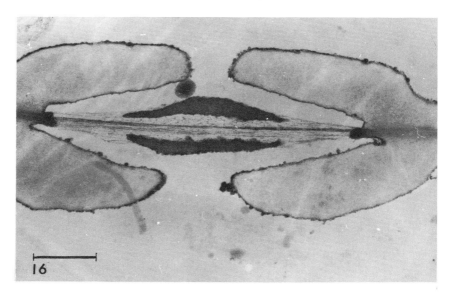

Fig. 16. Cross section through a bordered pit of a transfusion tracheid in a needle (*Pinus silvestris*).

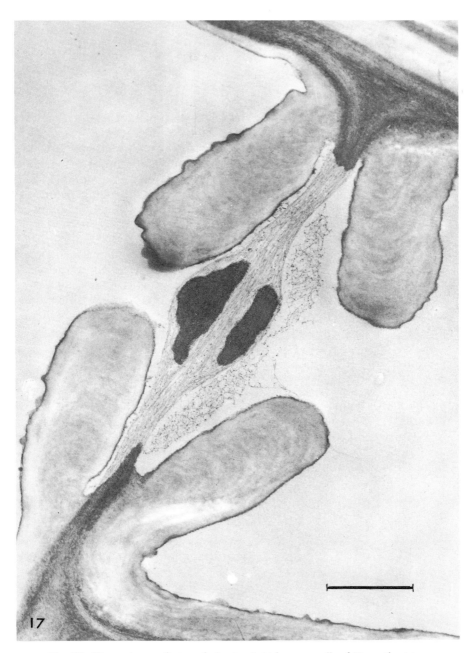

FIG. 17. Pit membrane of a transfusion tracheid from a needle of *Pinus silvestris*.

nified chamber rim (annulus) projects into the pit cavity. The thickness of the margo is sometimes remarkable. At the central region additional microfibrils are present, which can often be seen in a cross section, indicating a dispersed orientation. Consequently the pit membrane shows a distinct layering due to the two primary walls and the apposited microfibrils on both sides. Furthermore, electron-dense material has been deposited, which forms the torus. The intensity and thickness of these incrustations is variable. Sometimes they appear only as small calottes on top of the primary walls, whereas in other cases they penetrate the whole area, and even the margo can appear uniformly dense. The amorphous material of the torus may be covered on both sides by an additional layer of microfibrils which originate from the margo (Fig. 17). Thus the incrustations appear embedded in a receptacle-like structure. Such a concept of torus composition has been proposed by Sachs (1963) for the bordered pit of xylem tracheids.

Further work will be directed to the similarities and differences between the bordered pits in the secondary xylem and in the xylem and transfusion tissue of needles. Preliminary light and electron microscopic investigations of the pit structure in needles of gymnosperm species other than Pinaceae have already revealed differences regarding the presence or absence of a torus as a central thickening of the pit membrane.

ACKNOWLEDGMENTS

These investigations were supported by the Deutsche Forschungsgemeinschaft. Figures 5–13 were produced at the Institut für Holzforschung und Holztechnik, Universität München, and Figure 17 in cooperation with Dr. Ledbetter, Harvard University. The assistance of Miss Baldermann, München, and Miss Schultze, Reinbek, is gratefully acknowledged.

REFERENCES

Bailey, I. W. (1913) "The preservative treatment of wood. II. The structure of the pit membranes in the tracheids of conifers and their relation to the penetration of gases, liquids and finely divided solids into green and seasoned wood." *Forestry Quarterly* 11:12–20.
———— (1915) "The structure of the bordered pits of conifers and its bearing upon the tension hypothesis of the ascent of sap in plants." *Botan. Gaz.* 62:133–142.
———— (1957) "Die Struktur der Tüpfelmembranen bei den Tracheiden der Koniferen." *Holz Roh- Werkstoff* 15:210–213.

———— (1958) "The Structure of tracheids in relation to the movement of liquids, suspensions, and undissolved gases." In *Physiology of Forest Trees*, pp. 71–82. Ronald Press Co., New York.

————, and Vestal, M. R. (1937) "The orientation of cellulose in the secondary wall of tracheary cells." *J. Arnold Arboretum* 18:185–195.

Bucher, H. (1957) "Die Tertiärlamelle von Holzfasern und ihre Erscheinungsformen bei Coniferen." *Holzforschung* 11:1–16.

Côté, W. A., Jr. (1958) "Electron microscope studies of pit membrane structure." *Forest Prod. J.* 8:296–301.

————, and Krahmer, R. L. (1962) "The permeability of coniferous pits demonstrated by electron microscopy." *Tappi* 45:119–122.

Eicke, R. (1954) "Beitrag zur Frage des Hoftüpfelbaues der Koniferen." *Ber. Deut. Botan. Ges.* 67:213–217.

———— (1957) "Elektronenmikroskopische Untersuchungen an Gymnospermenhölzern als Beitrag zur Phylogenie der Gnetales." *Botan. Jahrb.* 77:193–217.

———— (1958) "Beitrag zur Kenntnis der submikroskopischen Struktur der Araucariaceenhölzer." *Ber. Deut. Botan. Ges.* 71:231–240.

———— (1963) "Feinbauuntersuchungen an den Tracheiden von Cycadeen." *Ber. Deut. Botan. Ges.* 76:229–234.

Frenzel, P. (1929) "Über die Porengrösse einiger pflanzlicher Zellmembranen." *Planta* 8:642–665.

Frey, A. (1926) "Die submikroskopische Struktur der Zellmembranen." *Jahrb. wiss. Botan.* 65:195–223.

Frey-Wyssling, A., Bosshard, H. H., and Mühlethaler, K. (1956a) "Die submikroskopische Entwicklung der Hoftüpfel." *Planta* 47:115–126.

————, Mühlethaler, K., and Moor, H. (1956b) "Elektronenmikroskopische Praeparationsartefakte dünner Cellulosemembranen." *Mikroskopie* 11:219.

————, ————, and Bosshard, H. H. (1959) "Über die mikroskopische Auflösung der Haltefäden des Torus in Hoftüpfeln." *Holzforsch. Holzverwert.* 11:107–108.

Harada, H., and Miyazaki, Y. (1952) "The electron-microscopic observation of the cell wall of conifer tracheids." *J. Japan. Forestry Soc.* 11:350–352.

————, ————, and Wakashima, T. (1958) "Electron microscopic investigation on the cell wall structure of wood." Bulletin of the Govt. Forest Experiment Station, No. 104 (Meguro, Tokyo, Japan).

Jayme, G., and Hunger, G. (1956) "Verhornungserscheinungen an Cellulosefaserstrukturen in elektronenoptischer Sicht." *Monatsh. Chem.* 87:8–23.

———— and ———— (1958) "Eine elektronenoptische Studie über das Verhalten der Zellulosemikrofibrillen bei der Trocknung. Ausbildung von Ringnetzstrukturen und Fibrillensträngen." *Mikroskopie* 13:24–38.

————, ————, and Fengel, D. (1960) "Das elektronenmikroskopische Bild des Cellulosefeinbaues verschlossener und unverschlossener Hoftüpfel der Nadelhölzer." *Holzforschung* 14:97–105.

Jutte, S. M., and Spit, B. J. (1963) "The submicroscopic structure of bordered pits on the radial walls of tracheids in Parana Pine, Kauri and European Spruce." *Holzforschung* 17:168–175.

Krahmer, R. L., and Côté, W. A., Jr. (1963) "Changes in coniferous wood cells associated with heartwood formation." *Tappi* 46:42–49.

Liese, W. (1951) "Demonstration elektronenmikroskopischer Aufnahmen von Nadelholztüpfeln." *Ber. Deut. Botan. Ges.* 64:31–32.

———— (1953) "Über die Hoftüpfel der Koniferen." *Ber. Deut. Botan. Ges.* 66:203–211.

—— (1954) "Der Feinbau der Hoftüpfel im Holz der Koniferen." *Proc. Intern. Conf. Electron Microscopy, 3rd, London, 1954,* pp. 550–554.

—— (1956) "Die Feinstruktur des Holzes und ihr Einfluss auf die Imprägnierung." *Holzindustrie* 9:1–6.

—— (1960) "Elektronenmikroskopie des Holzes." *Naturw. Rundschau* 13:389–394.

—— (1964) "Über die Struktur der Hoftüpfel bei den Gymnospermen." In *Proceedings of Third European Regional Conf. on Electron Microscopy,* Prague, pp. 167–168.

——, and Bauch, J. (1964) "Über die Wegsamkeit der Hoftüpfel von Coniferen." *Naturwiss.* 51:516.

—— and —— (1965) "On the mechanism of pit-closure in Pinaceae." In press.

——, and Fahnenbrock, M. (1952) "Elektronenmikroskopische Untersuchungen über den Bau der Hoftüpfel." *Holz Roh- Werkstoff* 10:197–201.

——, and Hartmann-Fahnenbrock, M. (1953) "Elektronenmikroskopische Untersuchungen über die Hoftüpfel der Nadelhölzer." *Biochim. Biophys. Acta* 11:190–198.

——, and Johann, I. (1954) "Experimentelle Untersuchungen über die Feinstruktur der Hoftüpfel bei den Koniferen." *Naturwiss.* 41:579.

Russow, E. (1883) "Zur Kenntnis des Holzes, in Besonderheit des Koniferenholzes." *Botan. Centralbl.* 13:29, 60, 95, 134, 166.

Sachs, I. B. (1963) "Torus of the bordered-pit membrane in conifers." *Nature* 198:906–907.

Sachs, J. (1879) "Über die Porosität des Holzes." *Arb. Bot. Inst. Würzburg* 2:291.

—— (1882) *Textbook of Botany.* Oxford University Press.

Scarth, G. W., Gibbs, R. D., and Spier, J. D. (1929) "The structure of the cell wall and the local distribution of the chemical constituents." *Trans. Roy. Soc. Can.* 5:269–279.

Stemsrud, F. (1956) "Über die Feinstruktur der Hoftüpfel-Schliesshaut von Nadelhölzern." *Holzforschung* 10:69–75.

Wardrop, A. B., and Dadswell, H. E. (1957) "Variations in the cell wall organization of tracheids and fibers." *Holzforschung* 11:33–41.

The Fine Structure of Pits in Hardwoods

ROSWITHA SCHMID

Forest Botany Institute
University of Munich

GENERAL ORGANIZATION OF HARDWOOD PITS

The early electron microscopic studies on the structure of pits were directed primarily to the pits in softwoods. Less attention has been paid to the pits in hardwoods. The principal contributions in this field were made by Bosshard (1952), Mühlethaler (1953), Harada (1954, 1963), Liese (1957), Côté (1958), and Cronshaw (1960). The protraction of the investigation of hardwood pits is attributed mainly to the complex and heterogeneous nature of hardwood tissue. Compared with the relative simplicity of coniferous wood, consisting only of tracheids and parenchyma cells, hardwoods contain vessels, tracheids, dead and living fibers, and various kinds of parenchyma cells. Corresponding with these different cell types, there are many variations in pit structure and in pit-pair combination.

The pits in different wood species and wood cell elements show considerable variation in size, shape, and distribution. This is true particularly of the vessel pits. The pit apertures, e.g., can appear either circular, elliptical, or slit-like (Fig. 1). In a single vessel element, however, they are largely uniform in shape. Size and shape of the pit chamber (Fig. 2) vary in a similar way. Depending on the thickness of the cell wall, an extended opening through the secondary wall, the pit canal, provides communication between the cell lumen and pit chamber. Both the pit canal and the pit chamber are lined by the tertiary wall, which can be covered by the warty layer. The pit membrane (Fig. 3) is composed of the primary walls and the intercellular layer of the adjacent cell elements.

In spite of the variations in size and shape, no basic differences exist in the morphology of the pits of the different cell types in hardwoods and softwoods. Differences, however, occur in the structure of the pit membranes. In softwoods, the typical bordered pit membrane is perforated, whereas in hardwoods, it lacks any visible openings.

The variation of pit membrane structure is closely related to the function of the cell elements involved. Therefore, the pit membranes are better distinguished according to the nature of the cells which form the

FIG. 1. Slit-like inner aperture of vessel pit (*Fagus silvatica*); the vessel wall is covered by the warty layer. X 14,000.

pit pair. This appears more reasonable than the conventional classification of the pits based upon their morphological features (e.g., bordered pits, simple pits, and so on).

THE PIT MEMBRANES

In the following, three main types of pit membranes are distinguished: the intervascular pit membrane (between two vessel pits); the vessel-parenchyma pit membrane (between a vessel pit and a parenchyma cell pit); and the interparenchymatous pit membrane (between two parenchyma cell pits).

The Intervascular Pit Membrane. The intervascular pit membrane generally is described as a simple membrane, consisting of the middle lamella (intercellular layer) and the primary walls of the adjacent vessel elements.

FIG. 2. Chamber of bordered pit of a fiber (*Fagus silvatica*). X 11,000.

Observations of replicas, taken from fully differentiated sapwood samples, usually show the microfibrils loosely packed and lying at random, which is typical of the texture of the primary wall (see Figure 3). The microfibrils are frequently incrusted by amorphous material. No central thickening (torus), and no openings, resolvable by the electron microscope, are visible. Yet various findings, obtained by examination of the cambial region and of sections from fresh, fixed material (Machado and Schmid, 1964), gave evidence of a more complex structure and of distinct development.

In the developing pit membrane between a young vessel and a cambium cell, plasmodesmata are visible. In later stages, the fine canals and cytoplasmic strands are no longer visible. The pit membrane between two young vessels shows a decrease in density and a loosening of the texture, which is initiated in the central region and proceeds inside the pit membrane towards its margins. Several layers can be distinguished inside the pit membrane: a denser one in the middle, with a parallel orientation of the microfibrils, and two less compact layers at both sides, where the microfibrils appear to be distributed more irregularly. In the next stage,

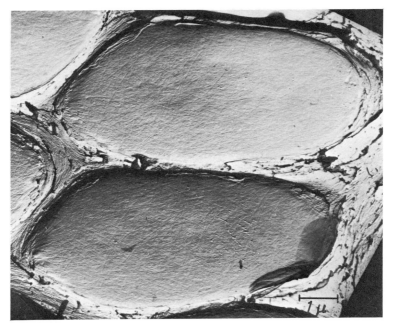

Fig. 3. Membranes of vessel pits (*Amburana acreana*), showing a loose texture of randomly arranged microfibrils. X 10,500.

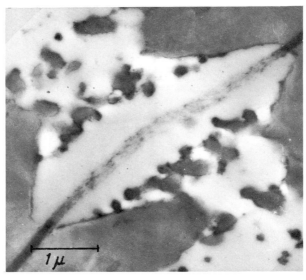

Fig. 4. Membrane between two vessel pits (with vestures); *Amburana acreana*; section. X 17,000.

the entire membrane shows a fairly uniform fibrillar texture, extremely transparent to electrons. Close to the junction with the pit chamber a marked dense region is visible (Fig. 4). This "membrane-rim" also occurs in softwoods and can be regarded as a general feature of pit membranes. In later stages the membrane contains scattered dark regions. These may be due to an alteration of substances already present or to secondary incrustations. Frequently, a lamellation of microfibrillar and amorphous layers can be perceived. This stratified structure, as well as the different orientation of the microfibrils in the various layers, is indicated also on the replicas (Fig. 5). The findings suggest that the fully differentiated

FIG. 5. Part of the intervascular pit membrane (*Goniorrhachis marginata*), showing two layers with different arrangement of microfibrils. X 28,000.

intervascular pit membrane consists of various monofibrillar layers which alternate with amorphous layers of incrusting material.

The Vessel-Parenchyma Pit Membrane. The pit membrane between a vessel pit and a parenchyma cell pit undergoes a development similar to the intervascular pit membrane. In the latter the alterations occur symmetrically inside the pit membrane involving both parts in a corresponding pattern. The changes of the vessel-parenchyma pit membrane, however, occur largely asymmetrically. This is due to the fact that in the first case the membrane belongs to homogeneous cells (two vessels), in the second case to heterogeneous cells (vessel and parenchyma cell).

In early stages the outermost layer of the vessel-parenchyma pit membrane adjoins the plasmalemma of the parenchyma cell. When the vessel cytoplasm dies an additional layer originates between the plasmalemma of the parenchyma cell and the pit membrane. This additional layer is characterized by a loose, vesiculated texture and low electron density (Fig. 6). After complete formation, its thickness corresponds approxi-

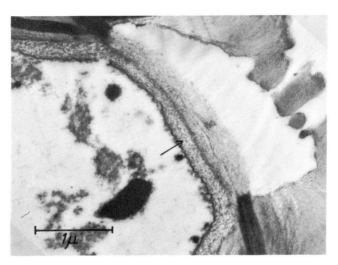

FIG. 6.   Vessel-parenchyma pit membrane (*Amburana acreana*), with additional layer (arrow); the vessel pit is vestured. X 20,000.

mately to the diameter of the pit membrane. Frequently, it also covers part of the parenchyma cell wall around the pit, where it diminishes gradually with distance from the pit membrane. It may be assumed that this layer represents a "protection layer," which is formed by the living cell as a protection against the adjacent dead cell element. A similar layer was observed at the pit membranes of "blind" pits of parenchyma cells, which lead to an intercellular space.

The Interparenchymatous Pit Membrane.   The membrane between the pits of two adjoining parenchyma cells does not show the typical stages of development which were described for the other types of pit membranes. Characteristic for this membrane is the perforation by numerous small openings, the plasmodesmata. In replicas, they appear as small pores (Fig. 7a); in sections, delicate cytoplasmic strands can be observed (Fig. 7b) which cross the pit membrane in small canals, thus connecting the protoplasm of the neighboring parenchyma cells. Similar cytoplasmic

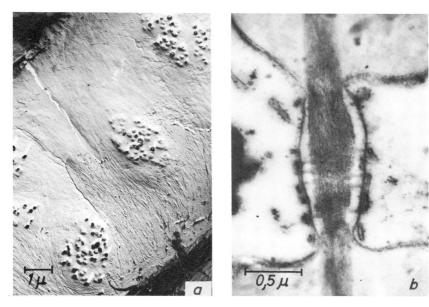

FIG. 7.   a. Replica of a ray parenchyma cell (*Goniorrhachis marginata*) with pores (plasmodesmata) in the pit membranes. X 7,500.   b. Section of membrane between two parenchyma cell pits (*Amburana acreana*) with plasmodesmata. X 40,000.

filaments occur also in the pit membranes of living wood fibers.   Generally, plasmodesmata are present in all pit membranes which separate living cell elements.

VESTURED PITS

Vestured pits are an anatomical feature of certain dicotyledonous woods. They occur in many different families and typify especially the Leguminosae, where all investigated genera and species have vestured pits, with the exception of the genus *Bauhinia*. The first extended studies of these peculiar pits were made by Bailey (1933), who also introduced the term "vestured pits." In the light microscope the vestured pits are recognized by their punctated appearance, which formerly was attributed to a perforation of the pit membrane; therefore these pits were first described as "cribriform" or "sieve-like." Bailey, however, proved that this aspect was due to small outgrowths from the pit wall, which project into the pit cavity (Fig. 8). In recent years vestured pits were investigated by electron microscopy, especially by Côté and Day (1962), Schmid and Machado (1963), and Wardrop *et al.*, (1963). These studies were made with fully differentiated sapwood samples and provided evidence of the occurrence, localization, and shape of the vestures. However, the origin of these out-

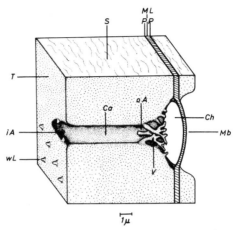

FIG. 8. Schematic representation of vestured pit (*Goniorrhachis marginata*). Ca—pit canal, Ch—pit chamber, iA—inner aperture, Mb—pit membrane, ML—middle lamella, oA—outer aperture, P—primary wall, S—secondary wall, T—tertiary wall, wL—warty layer, V—vestures. (from Schmid and Machado, 1964)

growths, their relationship to the cell wall, and their chemical nature were not yet understood. Some investigators considered the vestures as belonging to the secondary wall, whereas others pointed out the striking similarity to the warty layer, suggesting the analogy of both structures. To elucidate these points, fresh material from the cambial region of living trees was fixed and examined in ultrathin sections (Schmid and Machado, 1964).

In the latest stages of vessel differentiation a concentration of cell organelles in the pit chamber occurs. The surfaces of the vessel wall as well as the pit wall still appear smooth. In the vessel cytoplasm there are numerous small vesicles with homogeneous or slightly flaky contents. The products of these vesicles apparently pass through the plasmalemma and accumulate at the cell wall, preferably at the pit borders. The structures which thereby originate are attached to the cell wall. However, they are clearly distinguished from the latter by their greater density and non-fibrillar content (Fig. 9). The progressive degeneration of the vessel cytoplasm finally leads to the formation of the warty layer, which is deposited

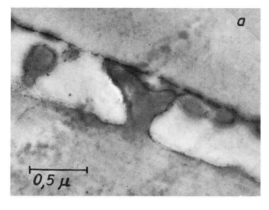

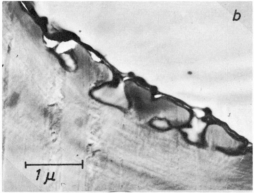

FIG. 9. Formation of vestures. a. Cell wall with attached body, limited by the plasma-lemma (dark line). X 30,000. b. Vestures at cell wall, covered by the warty layer. X 15,000. (from Schmid and Machado, 1964)

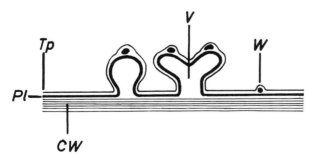

FIG. 10. Cell wall with vestures and warty layer. CW—cell wall, Pl—plasmalemma, Tp—tonoplast, V—vesture, W—wart. (from Schmid and Machado, 1964)

on the cell wall as well as on the attached bodies (Fig. 9b). The fully differentiated structures or "vestures" therefore consist of locally accumulated material at the cell wall, which is covered by the warty layer
(plasmalemma and tonoplast, with enclosed particles). In sections, the
warts are discernable as dense particles on the surface of the vestures
(Figs. 9b and 11). The warty layer can also be observed on replicas, covering the vestures and the cell wall. Thus, the vestures appear as big warts,
which explains why both were considered as analogous structures, but
obviously they represent two different formations (Fig. 10). The vestures
are formed by the living cytoplasm, whereas the warts are remnants of the
dead protoplast. Yet, morphologically, they seem to be closely connected,
which is indicated also by the fact that in all species with vestured pits
investigated, the warty layer is present. The substances for the vestures
apparently are derived from the Golgi vesicles. They are secreted through

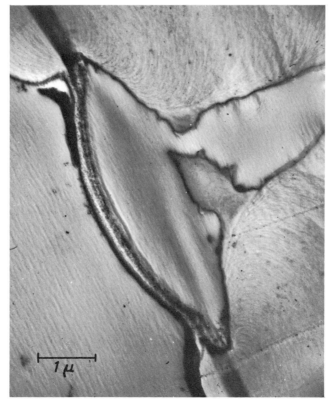

FIG. 11. Vestures with warts at outer pit aperture (*Plathymenia foliolosa*). X 15,000.
(from Schmid and Machado, 1964)

the plasmalemma, as is also known for other types of "rough" or sculp-
tured cell walls (e.g., in the submersed leaves of *Elodea* and in certain
glandular cells of insectivores). The successive deposition of the substances at the cell wall is suggested by a stratification, which can be seen in
the formed vestures (Fig. 11). Their chemical nature is not yet fully clarified. Certain findings indicate that they consist mainly of pectic compounds.

The vestures occur only at vessel pits and, in certain species, also on the
vessel wall. They can be located at the border of the outer pit aperture
(entrance to the pit chamber, Figure 12) and/or also at the inner aperture
(lumen side, Figure 13); they may occur also in the pit canal. The location
of the vestures is characteristic for the genera. Their distribution, size,
and shape varies considerably. A simple division of types can be made:
branched (coralloid of filamentous), and unbranched (simple, papilloid).
As a rule, they show a general uniformity within a single species. In rare
cases, single vestures were also observed at the pit membrane. They are to
be distinguished from the relief-like sculpturing of the pit membrane, ap-

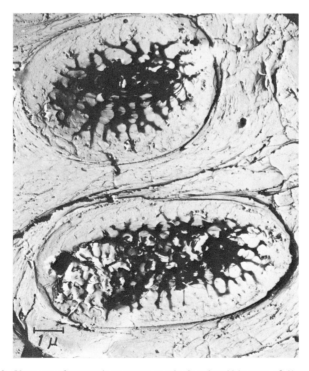

FIG. 12. Vestures of outer pit aperture on pit chamber (*Monotes cf. Kerstingii*).

Fig. 13. Vestured inner apertures (lumen side) of vessel pits (*Monotes cf. Kerstingii*). X 4,200.

pearing frequently on replicas (Fig. 14). These elevations are caused by the vestures situated underneath at the opposite outer aperture against which the membrane was pressed by the replicating material. Also, in the pit membranes of vestured pits, no openings are resolvable with the electron microscope.

The presence or absence of vestured pits, as well as the location and shape of the vestures, are used for the identification and classification of wood species. Yet their diagnostic value has to be considered with certain reservations. Light microscopy, as a tool for identification, in many cases cannot provide correct information on the localization and, furthermore, on the nature of the vestured appearance of the pits. Such aspects can be caused by substances which are deposited on the pit membrane and in the pit chamber, which frequently occurs during heartwood formation.

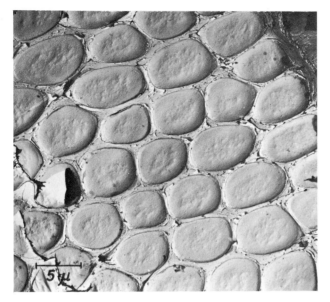

FIG. 14. Pit membranes of vestured pits (*Amburana acreana*). X 2,400.

In conclusion, it should be pointed out that "vestures," in the sense of cell wall sculpturing by locally deposited products of the cytoplasm, occur in different plants and cell types. In the case of living cells, the deposits are limited by the plasmalemma and not by the warty layer, which is found only in dead cells with a degenerated protoplast (see Liese, "The Warty Layer," present volume). Thus, cell wall sculpturing similar to the warty layer (Liese and Ledbetter, 1963) can be regarded as a general structural feature of certain plant cells.

ACKNOWLEDGMENTS

This report is based on investigations which were carried out mainly in collaboration with Dr. R. D. Machado, Jardim Botanico, Rio de Janeiro, supported by the Brazilian Conselho Nacional de Pesquisas and the Deutsche Forschungsgemeinschaft.

Figures 1, 2, 3, 12, 13, and 14 were taken with the Aeg Zeiss Em 8 (Institut fur Holzforschung und Holztechnik, Universität Munchen); Figures 4, 5, 6, 7, 9, and 11 with the Elmiskop I (Jardim Botanico, Rio de Janeiro).

REFERENCES

Bailey, I. W. (1933) "The cambium and its derivative tissues. VIII. Structure, distribution and diagnostic significance of vestured pits in dicotyledons." *J. Arnold Arboretum* 14:259–273.

Bosshard, H. (1952) Elektronenmikroskopische Untersuchungen im Holz von *Fraxinus excelsior. Ber. Schweiz. Botan. Ges.* 62:482–508.

Côté, W. A., Jr. (1958) "Electron microscope studies of pit membrane structure." *Forest Prod. J.* 8:296–301.

————, and Day, A. C. (1962) "Vestured pits—Fine structure and apparent relationship with warts." *Tappi* 45:906–910.

Cronshaw, J. (1960) "The fine structure of the pits of *Eucalyptus regnans* (F. Muell.) and their relation to the movement of liquids into the wood." *Australian J. Botany* 8:51–57.

Harada, H. (1954) "Electron-microscopic investigations on the pit of 'Buna' (*Fagus crenata* Blume) and 'Nara' (*Quercus crispula* Blume) wood." *J. Wood Ind.* **9**:1–3.

————(1963) "Electron microscopy of ultrathin sections of beech wood (*Fagus crenata* Blume)." *J. Japan Wood Res. Soc.* **8**:252–258.

Liese, W. (1957) "Der Feinbau der Hoftüpfel bei den Laubhölzern." *Holz Roh- Werkstoff* 15:449–453.

————, and Ledbetter, M. C. (1963) "Occurrence of a warty layer in cells of plants." *Nature* (London) 197:201–202.

Machado, R. D., and Schmid, R. (1964) "Observations on the structure of pit membranes in hardwood cells." *Proc. 3rd Europ. Conf. Electron Microscopy, Prague*, pp. 163–164.

Mühlethaler, K. (1953) "Elektronenmikroskopische Untersuchungen an pflanzlichen Geweben." *Z. Zellforsch.* 38:299–327.

Schmid, R., and Machado, R. D. (1963) "Über den Feinbau der 'verzierten' Tüpfel bei der Gattung *Plathymenia.*" *Holz Roh- Werkstoff* 21:41–47.

———— and ———— (1964) "Zur Entstehung und Feinstruktur skulpturierter Hoftüpfel bei Leguminosen." *Planta* 60:612–626.

Wardrop, A. P., Ingle, H. D., and Davies, G. W. (1963) "Nature of vestured pits in angiosperms." *Nature* (London) 197:202–203.

Light and Electron Microscopic Evidence on the Structure of the Membrane of Bordered Pits in Tracheids of Conifers

GEORGE TSOUMIS

School of Forestry, The Pennsylvania State University

INTRODUCTION

The electron microscope, with its high resolving power, provides a unique tool for investigation of the ultrastructure of wood cell walls. Among the structural characteristics so far studied, considerable attention was given to the membranes of bordered pits in tracheids of conifers. In addition to expanding our knowledge on this subject, the evidence produced has helped to verify related light microscopic observations, but has also led to dissenting interpretations when used independently.

In view of the fact that another paper, by Liese, on the structure of such membranes is included in this volume, this presentation will be limited mainly to a consideration of the relationship between light and electron microscopic evidence. Specifically, attention will center on a theory that was proposed on the existence of a casual relationship between pit aspiration and formation of the torus. Certain general remarks will precede this discussion to explain the nature of the membranes under consideration and the contribution of pertinent information by light and electron microscopy.

Long before the advent of the electron microscope, it had been well established, on the basis of light microscopy, that membranes of bordered pits in tracheids of conifers are characterized by a central, disc-like thickening, termed "torus." It had also been observed early that the portion of the membrane surrounding the torus is not homogeneous but equipped with radial filaments (Russow, 1883). Bailey (1913) was able to prove, by injecting an aqueous suspension of finely divided particles and by microscopic observation of very thin sections under high magnification, that the membrane is not entire but perforated with "extremely minute openings" which are located in its "thinner radii."

Figure 1 is a diagram of a membrane as pictured by Bailey on the basis of these observations. This concept of 1913 is in admirable agreement

305

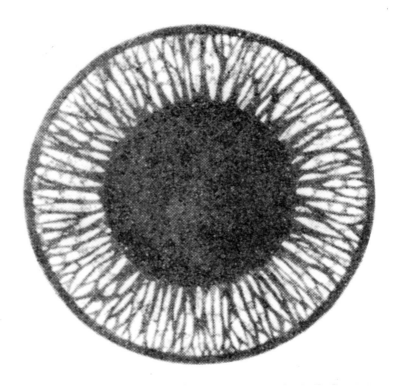

FIG. 1. Diagrammatic representation of a bordered pit membrane, as conceived by Bailey (1913) long before the advent of the electron microscope. (Compare with Figures 2, 6, 7, and 8.)

with the current status of knowledge based on studies with the electron microscope.

It should be noted, however, that during initial electron microscopic investigations there has been some discussion on the interpretation of photomicrographs such as Figure 2. Filaments radiating from the torus and composed of microfibrils may be clearly observed, but there was some disagreement as to whether these define openings (Liese and Fahnenbrock, 1952) or are reinforcements of the membrane, which acts not as a sieve but as an "ultrafilter" (Frey-Wyssling and Bosshard, 1953). Later, it was agreed (Frey-Wyssling et al., 1956) and demonstrated by impregnation with titanium oxide (Liese, 1954) and India ink (Côté and Krahmer, 1962) that the membrane is indeed perforated. Although variations in the structure of membranes may exist not only between different

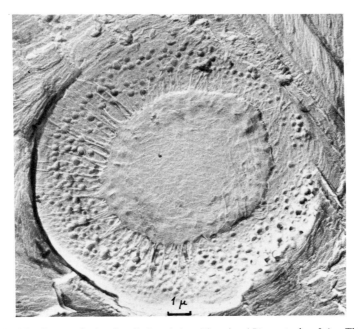

Fig. 2. Membrane of a bordered pit pair in white pine (*Pinus strobus* L.). This membrane is displaced, since the microfibrils supporting the torus are lying against the wall of the pit chamber, which is covered by a warty layer. The microfibrils at the righthand side were broken during sample preparation, and some may be seen lying on the torus. This electron micrograph was taken from a wood sample of a terminal twig cut off in late summer. Note that deposition of incrusting materials and formation of a compact torus disc has already taken place. ×6,000.

coniferous genera but also within a tree and between neighboring tracheids (Bailey, 1957; Frey-Wyssling *et al.*, 1956; Krahmer and Côté, 1963; Jutte and Spit, 1963; Kórán, 1964), the current consensus is that the torus, when present, is suspended by radially oriented microfibrils and microfibrillar bundles forming real openings, the size of which varies from a few Ångstrom units to one micron and over (Liese and Fahnenbrock, 1952; Liese and Johann, 1954; Liese, 1954; Frey-Wyssling *et al.*, 1956; Harada *et al.*, 1958; Liese and Côté, 1960; Krahmer and Côté, 1963).

Differential pressure between adjoining tracheids may cause membranes to become displaced from their normal, central position. Such displacement may extend to aspiration, in which case the torus seals one of the apertures. This phenomenon of "aspirated pit pairs" (IAWA, 1964) is a common occurrence, especially in heartwood and dry wood. According to Hawley's (1931) theory of movement of water in wood, aspiration (at least in drying wood) results from large tension forces set up by the menisci formed in the passages through which water is moving out, particularly in pit apertures and in the minute openings of the membrane. Due to the smallness of these passages, the magnitude of such capillary forces is very high.

Aspirated pit pairs are a common feature under the light microscope, and have also been observed with the electron microscope (Jayme *et al.*, 1960; Côté and Krahmer, 1962; Krahmer and Côté, 1963; Jutte and Spit, 1963).

TORUS AND ASPIRATION—A THEORY ADVOCATING A RELATIONSHIP

Jayme *et al.*, (1960) proposed a causal relationship between aspiration and the presence of a torus. They maintain that the electron microscopic image of the torus suspended by radially oriented microfibrils (Fig. 2) is not a normal occurrence but a result of aspiration. A torus does not exist until a membrane becomes displaced.

This opinion, founded solely on electron microscopic work, may be summarized as follows: Initially, the membrane is centrally located and does not possess a torus. It has a primary wall structure, being composed of the primary walls of the two adjacent tracheids. These walls are not interwoven. Their component microfibrils do not exhibit a preferred orientation in many pits; in others some microfibrils tend to be radially oriented towards the center (Fig. 3-1). Later, sap passing through the pit pair causes dislocation of the membrane. The microfibrils are contracted together at its center (in a manner resembling the movement of the iris diaphragm of a camera) and there become closely packed. At the same time, the microfibrils that lie outwards stretch, tending to attain a radial orientation (Fig. 3-2). In a final stage, the membrane is pushed all the way, sealing one of the apertures. It is at this stage that, according to this interpretation, the torus appears in the electron microscope as a centrally located disc held in position by radially stretched microfibrils. In the process of stretching, some microfibrils combine into bundles and others break (Fig. 3-3).

This theory was based on interpretation of electron micrographs taken mainly from replicas of wood, macerated cells, and pulp of European spurce (*Picea excelsa* Link) and pine (*Pinus silvestris* L.), in which several membranes with primary wall structure were found to be present. However, the "strongest support" was considered to come "from the fact that in all cases when the pit membrane has the appearance of a torus held at the middle of the pit by fine microfibrillar strands, torn microfibrils are

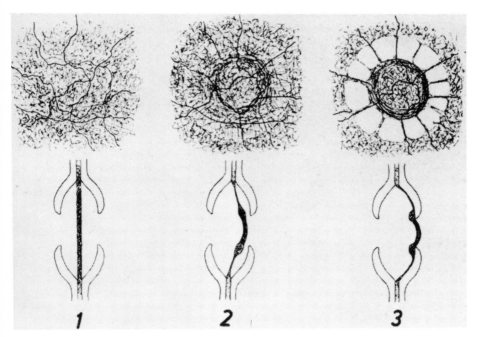

FIG. 3. Diagrammatic representation of the initial condition and consecutive changes of a membrane as a result of displacement, according to a theory by *Jayme et al.*, (1960). Torus is shown to be not a normal feature but to exist only as a result of membrane displacement and pit aspiration. (See text for explanations.)

visible .... These point towards physical and not biological arrangements in cell wall structure" (Hunger, 1964).

DISCUSSION

Is then the presence of a torus limited to aspirated pit pairs? Both light and electron microscopic observations supply ample evidence for disagreement with this point of view.

Examination of tangential (or transverse) microtome sections with a light microscope can detect, sometimes in abundance, presence of tori in undisturbed, i.e., centrally located membranes. Light photomicrographs of this condition were published long ago by Bailey (1913; see also Figure 7 in Record, 1934). In heartwood and dry wood, membranes, as a rule, appear aspirated, but in young sapwood the opposite may be the case. Figures 4 and 5, showing a number of centrally located membranes equipped with tori, were taken from the last growth ring of an increment core of white spruce (*Picea glauca* [Moench.] Voss.) that was placed in fixative immediately after removal from the tree. In the slides prepared,

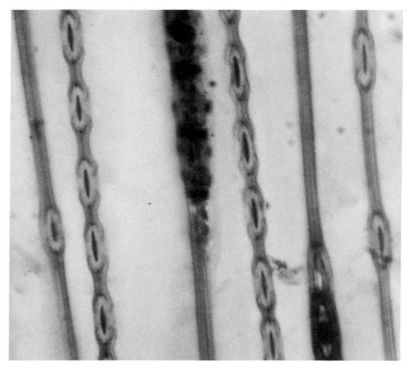

Fig. 4. Tori in nonaspirated pit pairs, as seen with a light microscope in tangential microtome sections taken from near the cambium region of white spruce (*Picea glauca* [Moench.] Voss.), after staining with safranin and Delafield's haematoxylin. ×650.

the majority of membranes were observed to occupy a central position and tori were clearly visible after staining with safranin and Delafield's haematoxylin. In several cases, membranes and tori were displaced, seemingly by tearing (Fig. 5; see also Fig. 6), but altogether few aspirated pit pairs could be found.

Similarly, presence of tori in undisturbed membranes has been demonstrated by electron micrographs of ultrathin sections of wood tissue (Frey-Wyssling *et al.*, 1956; Krahmer and Côté, 1963; Sachs, 1963).

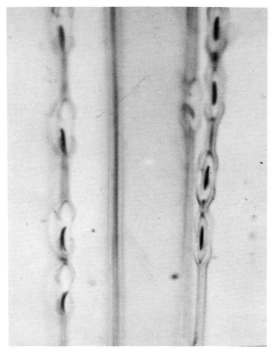

FIG. 5. Centrally located membranes equipped with tori (right), and membranes and tori displaced during microtome sectioning (left). Like Figure 4, this light micrograph was taken from near the cambium region of white spruce. × 650.

The existence of membranes with a primary wall structure, as reported by Jayme *et al.*, (1960), cannot be precisely explained in all cases. It may be noted, however, that in most of such electron micrographs included in the paper by Jayme and his co-workers (Abb. 9, 11, 12, and 13 in that paper), no delineation of the bordered pit chambers are seen, but only what seem to be impressions of pit apertures. It is difficult to visualize how the conditions shown in Figures 2 and 6 (and in Abb. 10 and others by Jayme *et al.*) could derive from the conditions described in the previous paragraph. Similar comments may be made for the electron micrographs taken from wood by a wet replica technique using Sorbit (Abb. 5 and 17 by Jayme *et al.*).   The most probable explanation of these electron micrographs may be that they represent half-bordered or simple pits, the membranes of which are known to possess a primary wall structure (Côté, 1958; Harada *et al.*, 1958).   On the other hand, Abb. 10 in Jayme *et al.*

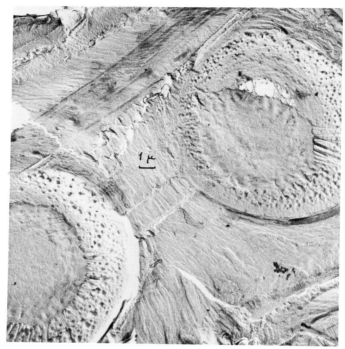

Fig. 6. Electron microscopic appearance of the condition shown in Figure 5. One of the tori was displaced during sample preparation (see knife marks). White pine. ×4,600.

may have come from a bordered pit in summerwood (as may be judged from the oblong impression of its aperture) or from a bordered pit between a ray tracheid and an axial tracheid (see Harada *et al.*, 1958). In electron microscopic work carried out with pulp samples, it is difficult to recognize the origin of the structural characteristics observed.

The observation of "torn microfibrils" (Jayme *et al.*, 1960; Hunger, 1964) also constitutes a weak argument that the torus results from aspiration. Electron micrographs showing such tears were presumably taken from aspirated pit pairs, but tearing may also occur as a result of sample preparation. The extensive tearing and actual missing of parts of microfibrils shown in Figure 8 (as well as in Abb. 8 and 16 by Jayme *et al.*) suggest physical damage during treatment of wood, that is, during delignification or pulping. In untreated wood such extensive tearing is not evident, but some damage may also occur during preparation of wood by splitting or microtoming or during preparation of a replica.

Undoubtedly, the best electron microscopic evidence for existence of tori in undisturbed membranes is provided by micrographs obtained from ultrathin sections and this, together with analogous evidence supplied by the light microscope, cannot be disregarded.   The electron micrograph presented by Jayme *et al.*, and showing a centrally located membrane without a torus (Abb. 18) is based on a not too successful ultrathin section, and seems to depict an area away from the pit apertures and away from the torus.

Occasionally, even replicas, which show the torus in front (radial) view, can furnish pictures of undisturbed membranes.   Although judgement of the condition of a membrane is not as easy in such a view as on the basis of sections, Figure 7 appears to depict a membrane which is not displaced. This electron micrograph, as well as Figures 2 and 6, were taken from a terminal twig of white pine (*Pinus strobus* L.) cut off in late summer. The wood sample was handled in a conventional manner, i.e., not by a wet replica technique but by shadowing with platinum and carbon in an

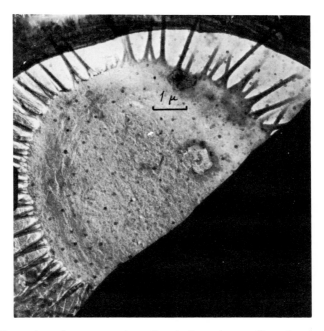

FIG. 7. Front view of an apparently undisturbed membrane. Note that the microfibrils supporting the torus are not lying against the wall of the pit chamber but appear to be free-hanging. Like Figures 2 and 6, this electron micrograph was taken from a terminal twig of white pine. ×8,800.

evaporating unit (Tsoumis, 1964), after gradual air-drying. Unlike similar electron micrographs, the microfibrils that support the torus in Figure 7 are not lying against the wall of the pit chamber but appear to be free-hanging. This wall, which in white pine is covered by a warty

FIG. 8.   A treated (delignified) membrane in cedar of Lebanon (*Cedrus libani* Barr.). This membrane is aspirated, lying against the wall of the pit chamber. The compact torus disc, which is characteristic of this species, was dissolved and disappeared. Note many microfibrils broken and some parts missing as a result of the treatment. × 10,400.

layer (see Figures 2 and 6), is not shown except slightly at the lower left corner of the picture.

Figures 2, 6, and 7 demonstrate also that deposition of incrusting materials on the tori has taken place early, before completion of the first growing season. This early deposition was also observed with the light microscope in transverse microtome sections of white spruce, where tori were clearly visible after staining, in the region near the cambium where lignification was nearly completed. Similar observations were made in tangential sections obtained from the same region.   In fact, Figures 4 and 5 were taken from such tangential sections.

Figures 8 and 9, taken from samples of cedar of Lebanon (*Cedrus libani* Barr.) and white spruce respectively, show membranes after a delignification treatment. This did not involve maceration or pulping, but only removal of the incrusting materials from the replicated surfaces, and was performed in the following manner: Radially split wood samples about

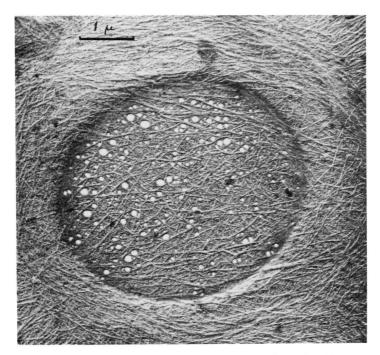

FIG. 9. The central portion of a treated and aspirated membrane in white spruce. The incrusting materials covering the torus were also removed by the treatment. A secondary deposition of circularly arranged microfibrils may be seen at the upper right corner of this electron micrograph. ×14,200.

1 mm × 1 cm in cross section and 1 cm in length were immersed in a mixture of equal parts of glacial acetic acid and 30% hydrogen peroxide and then placed in an oven at 60°C. This treatment resulted in bleaching and softening of the wood tissue, but after air-drying it became again sufficiently rigid to handle through the shadowing and other procedures employed in preparing preshadowed carbon replicas (Tsoumis, 1964).

Figures 8 and 9, which are similar to electron photomicrographs taken from pulp (Jayme *et al.*, 1960) and delignified wood (Harada *et al.*, 1958), show that the compact torus disc which is characteristic of the membranes in these species, was dissolved and disappeared as a result of the treatment, revealing the underlying microfibrils. Both of these micrographs obviously depict displaced membranes lying on the walls of the pit chambers and covering the pit apertures, which may be seen through openings of the uncovered microfibrillar network. In white spruce (Fig. 9) a circular secondary deposition of microfibrils is shown (at the upper right corner), but this is not evident in cedar of Lebanon (Fig. 8).

As a final side note it may be pointed out that, in addition to removal of the incrusting materials from the tori, the treatment applied also dissolved the warty layers, which in untreated wood cover the walls of the pit chambers in both species.

Summary

Light and electron microscopy are complementary tools in investigations of cellular ultrastructure. Early concepts of the structure of membranes of bordered pits in tracheids of conifers, proposed by Bailey (1913) on the basis of his work with the light microscope, have been admirably verified by electron microscopic studies. Independent use of the electron microscope has led to incorrect assumptions regarding a causal relationship between pit aspiration and torus formation. On the basis of both light and electron microscopic evidence, it may be stated that the torus is a normal feature of such membranes and not a result of membrane displacement. Electron microscopic study of wood treated by delignification shows that the torus is composed of a deposition of incrusting materials on an underlying microfibrillar network.

REFERENCES

Bailey, I. W. (1913) "The preservation treatment of wood. II. The structure of the pit membranes in the tracheids of conifers and their relation to the penetration of gases, liquids, and finely divided solids into green and seasoned wood." *Forestry Quarterly*

11:12–20. *In* Bailey, I. W. (1954) *Contributions to Plant Anatomy*, Chapter 19, pp. 207–212. Chronica Botanica Co., Waltham, Mass.

——— (1957) "Die Struktur der Tüpfelmembranen bei den Tracheiden der Koniferen." *Holz Roh- Werkstoff* 15:210–213.

Côté, W. A. (1958) "Electron microscope studies of pit membrane structure—Implications in seasoning and preservation of wood." *Forest Prod. J.* 8:296–301.

———, and Krahmer, R. L. (1962) "The permeability of coniferous pits demonstrated by electron microscopy." *Tappi* 45:119–122.

Frey-Wyssling, A., and Bosshard, H. H. (1953) "Über den Feinbau der Schliesshäute in Hoftüpfeln." *Holz Roh- Werkstoff* 11:417–420.

———, and Mühlethaler, K. (1956) "Die submikroskopische Entwicklung der Hoftüpfel." *Planta* 47:115–126.

Harada, H., Miyazaki, Y., and Wakashima, T. (1958) "Electron microscopic investigation on the cell wall structure of wood." Bulletin of the Govt. Forest Experiment Station, No. 104 (Meguro, Tokyo, Japan). (In Japanese with English summary.)

Hawley, L. F. (1931) "Wood-liquid relations." U.S.D.A. Tech. Bull. No. 248.

Hunger, G. (1964) Private communication.

International Association of Wood Anatomists (Committee on Nomenclature) (1964) *Multilingual Glossary of Terms Used in Wood Anatomy.* Verlagsanstalt Buchdruckerei Konkordia, Winterthur, Switzerland.

Jayme, G., Hunger, G., and Fengel, D. (1960) "Das elektronmikroskopische Bild des Cellulosefeinbaues verschlossener und unverschlossener Hoftüpfel der Nadelhölzer." *Holzforschung* 14:97–105.

Jutte, S. M., and Spit, B. J. (1963) "The submicroscopic structure of bordered pits on the radial walls of tracheids in Parana pine, Kauri and European spruce." *Holzforschung* 17:168–175.

Kórán, Z. (1964) "Air permeability and creosote retention of Douglas-fir." *Forest Prod. J.* 14:159–166.

Krahmer, R. L., and Côté, W. A. (1963) "Changes in coniferous wood cells associated with heartwood formation." *Tappi* 46:42–49.

Liese, W. (1954) "Der Feinbau der Hoftüpfel im Holz der Koniferen." *Proc. Intern. Conf. Electron Microscopy, 3rd, London, 1954*, pp. 550–555.

———, and Côté, W. A. (1960) "Electron microscopy of wood. Results of the first ten years of research." *Proc. Fifth World For. Congress*, vol. 2, pp. 1288–1298.

———, and Fahnenbrock, M. (1952) "Elektronmikroskopische Untersuchungen über den Bau der Hoftüpfel." *Holz Roh- Werkstoff* 10:197–201.

———, and Johann, I. (1954) "Elektronmikroskopische Beobachtungen über eine besondere Feinstruktur der verholzten Zellwand bei einigen Koniferen." *Planta* 44:269–285.

Record, S. J. (1934) *Identification of the Timbers of Temperate North America.* J. Wiley & Sons, Inc., New York.

Russow, E. (1883) "Zur Kenntniss der Holzes, insonderheit des Coniferenholzes." *Bot. Zbl.* 13, 171. (Cited by Frey-Wyssling *et al.*, 1956).

Sachs, I. B. (1963) "Torus of the bordered-pit membranes in conifers." *Nature* 198:906–907.

Tsoumis, G. (1964) "Preparation of preshadowed carbon replicas for electron microscopic investigation of wood." *Holzforschung* 18:177–179.

The Ultrastructure of Tyloses

Z. KÓRÁN

Pulp and Paper Research Institute of Canada

AND

W. A. CÔTÉ, JR.

State University College of Forestry
at Syracuse University

According to the glossary developed by the International Association of Wood Anatomists (1964), a tylosis is "an outgrowth from an adjacent ray or axial parenchyma cell through a pit cavity in a vessel wall, partially or completely blocking the vessel lumen." Tyloses are found as normal structures in many hardwood species. Their occurrence was noted in a drawing of a cross section of chestnut wood by Malphige as early as 1675. However, they were named by a German botanist, believed to be Frl. Hermine von Reichenback, in 1845. Since then the development of tyloses in the vessels of certain hardwood species has been of concern in both basic research and industrial wood utilization.

Over a period of almost 300 years, a remarkable amount of information has been compiled in the literature on different features of tyloses. Included in the topics covered are the cause and mechanism of tyloses formation, their origin, occurrence, shape, gross structure, effect on various properties of wood, and a number of other characteristics. However, there have been but few reports on the fine structure of tyloses. One of these was made by Nečesaný (1955), who studied the tyloses of *Fagus silvatica*.

Although tylosis formation is considered to be a normal physiological process in many families of trees, tylosis growth has also been found to be induced by mechanical injury (Jurášek, 1956, 1958; Klein, 1923; Paclt, 1930), or by different types of tree diseases such as fungus growth (Beckman *et al.,* 1953; Kerling, 1955; Struckmeyer *et al.,* 1954; Van der Meer, 1926), and virus infection (Esau, 1948). In fungus-infected trees, tyloses were found to be most abundant in the outermost annual ring, but in severe cases of wilt, they were apparent also in the second annual ring (Beckman *et al.,* 1953; Struckmeyer *et al.,* 1954).

An intensive study on the occurrence of tyloses in different species of American woods was made by Gerry (1914). Similar work was reported

Fig. 1. Ultrathin cross section of tyloses in a springwood vessel segment of white ash, *Fraxinus americana* L., heartwood. The round structures lying on the inner vessel wall are believed to be tylosic buds which originated in the parenchyma cell at lower center. *Note:* Figures 1 through 15 are all electron micrographs. The magnification of each figure is indicated by the 1-micron mark which appears on the micrographs.

by Itō and Kishima (1951) on the presence or absence of tyloses in heart-wood and sapwood of 109 Japanese species. An unusual occurrence of tyloses in the wood of *Palaquium* species was noted by Ghosh (1957). A special type of tylosis, called "stone tylosis," was observed around the larval chambers of *Laperda populnea* L., in *Populus tremula* L., and in the vessels of a stem of *Bauhinia* species (Weber, 1954). Sclerosed tyloses were reported to develop in live oaks by Williams (1939).

In fungus-infected trees a reduction in sap flow, as a result of plugging the vessels with tyloses caused by fungus infections, has been observed by a number of investigators (Goss and Frink, 1934; Parmeter and Kuntz, 1954; Struckmeyer *et al.,* 1954). Liquid penetration through wood was also reported to be markedly reduced by tyloses (Hunt and Garratt, 1953; Kishima and Hayaschi, 1960; MacLean, 1952). Vodoz (1957) noted a re-duction in heating rate with RF drying of certain hardwood species con-taining tyloses. The presence of tyloses was noted to be a factor in dur-ability by Jorgensen (1962). Gerry (1914) tabulated hardwood species ac-cording to their relative durabilities and concluded that the more durable species, with a few exceptions, contain many or well developed tyloses. The chemical composition of tyloses was investigated by Isenberg (1933).

The mechanism of tylosis formation has been a concern of a number of investigators, including Molisch (1888), Von Alten (1909), Gertz (1916), and Chattaway (1949). Theories on this mechanism were reviewed by Kórán (1964), and another suggested by Kórán and Côté (1964). The present report deals only with the ultrastructure of tyloses.

Electron microscopy was used for the study of the features of tyloses which are too fine to be resolved by the light microscope. Both the ultra-thin sectioning method and the direct carbon replica technique (Côté *et al.,* 1964) were employed in specimen preparation. The features of ty-loses which were investigated included shape, nature of contact between tylosis wall and vessel wall, intertylosic contact and pitting, layering, and chemical composition.

Fully developed tyloses are known to be extremely variable in shape and arrangement, depending on the wood species in which they occur. In white ash, *Fraxinus americana* L., they exhibit highly irregular shapes and a range of sizes. They are often collapsed, wrinkled, and curled (Fig. 1).

At the other extreme, tyloses may be relatively simple in structure, as they are in American beech, *Fagus grandifolia* Ehrh. In this species the tyloses appear as ladder-like partitions oriented horizontally across the vessel cavities. Figure 2 shows the detail at the vessel wall where one of the tylosic partitions projects to the upper left and across the vessel.

In white oak, *Quercus alba* L., tyloses are balloon-shaped when first formed (Fig. 3), but as their numbers increase in a vessel they become

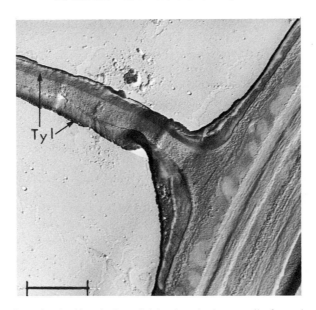

FIG. 2. Portion of a double tylosis wall joined to the inner wall of a springwood vessel segment in American beech, *Fagus grandifolia* Ehrh., heartwood. The tyloses project across the vessel lumen to the left.

crowded and irregular in shape. The vessel is usually completely occluded with a foam-like mass of tyloses in this species.

Tyloses in white ash may lie loosely on the inner vessel wall (Fig. 4), or they may adhere to it (Fig. 5). Tyloses in American beech, white oak, osage-orange, *Maclura pomifera* Raf., and black locust, *Robinia pseudoacacia* L., do not only lie on the inner surface of a vessel, but they appear to grow to it (Figs. 2 and 6). In such cases, the composite walls appear to be double or triple and it becomes difficult to differentiate between cell wall and tylosis wall. For example, a triple wall could consist of a tylosis wall, a vessel wall, and an adjacent cell wall, which may be the wall of another vessel segment, a vasicentric tracheid, or a parenchyma cell.

The triangular space formed at the junction where two tyloses and the inner wall of the vessel meet may be filled with substances possessing both the electron density and the appearance of a normal middle lamella (Figs. 2 and 6), or a semi-intertylosic space may be formed (Figs. 7 and 8). Tyloses lying on the inner surfaces of vessel walls were observed to arch over the borders of pit pairs, thus acting as dividing walls between contiguous pit and vessel cavities (Figs. 6 and 9). The space enclosed by a tylosis and a pit membrane may be filled with substances which appear to be highly amorphous (Fig. 9) or they may remain empty (Fig. 6). When

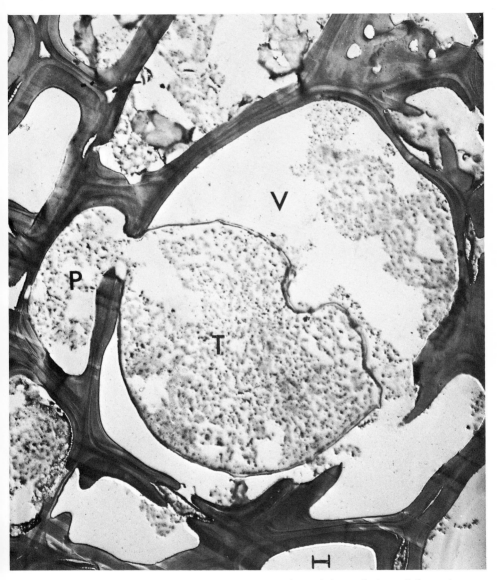

Fig. 3. Ultrathin cross section through an area located five cells inward from the cambial zone in white oak, *Quercus alba* L., sapwood. The developing tylosis in the vessel apparently emerged from the parenchyma cell at the left. V—vessel, T—tylosis, and P—parenchyma cell.

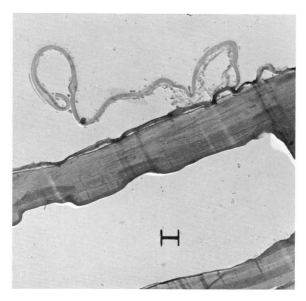

FIG. 4. Cross section through a tylosis lying loosely on the inner surface of a springwood vessel segment adjacent to a ray parenchyma cell in white ash heartwood.

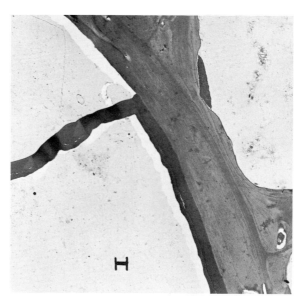

FIG. 5. Portion of a tylosis in a springwood vessel segment of white ash heartwood. This tylosis adheres to the vessel wall, is lamellated, and has unusually high electron density.

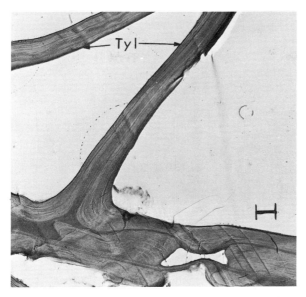

FIG. 6. Portions of two tyloses (upper structures) in a springwood vessel segment of black locust, *Robinia pseudoacacia* L., heartwood. An electron-dense zone can be seen between the tyloses (in a double tylosis wall) and between the tylosis at right and the vessel wall. The pit cavity at the lower right is overarched by the tylosis.

two tyloses come into contact with one another, they appear to grow together and to form a double tylosis wall (Figs. 2, 6, 7, 8, 9, 10).

In electron micrographs of ultrathin sections through double tylosis walls there always appears to be an intertylosic zone similar to the middle lamella separating normal cells. In many instances this zone has an electron density and texture which is typical of intercellular substance. In order to elucidate this point, sections through vessels containing tyloses were treated with ozone according to the method described by Lantican (1964). Separation of the tyloses at the intertylosic zone (Fig. 11) was interpreted to be a preferential attack on lignin, or some other polyphenolic substances, which was the behavior observed by Lantican in gas phase pulping experiments. This separating zone is therefore presumed to be lignin-like and resembles the true middle lamella.

The results of the ozone treatment also showed the tyloses to be of lamellar and microfibrillar construction. However, it could not be determined from ultrathin sections whether the tyloses were of primary- or of secondary-wall type of organization. Direct carbon surface replicas of delignified tyloses were necessary to show that the random arrangement

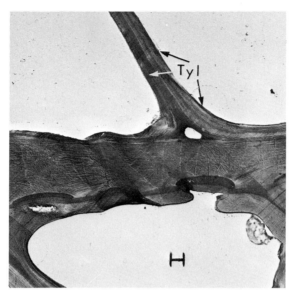

FIG. 7. Double tylosis wall in a cross section of a springwood vessel segment of osage-orange, *Maclura pomifera* Raf., heartwood. A semi-intertylosic space is formed at the junction of two tyloses and the inner vessel wall.

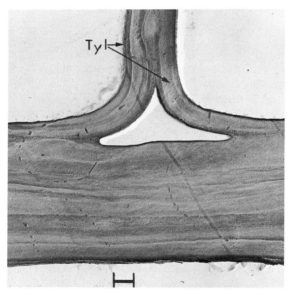

FIG. 8. Portions of two individual tyloses joined to one another and to the inner wall of a springwood vessel segment in black locust heartwood. The vessel wall is at the lower half of the micrograph.

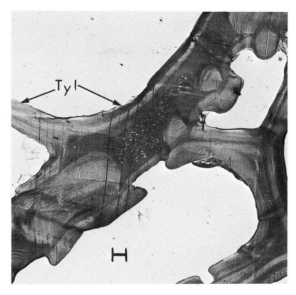

FIG. 9. Part of a springwood vessel segment containing tyloses, upper left, and adjacent parenchyma cells, right, in the heartwood of osage-orange. Several pit cavities are enclosed by the tylosis and they are filled with electron-dense substance.

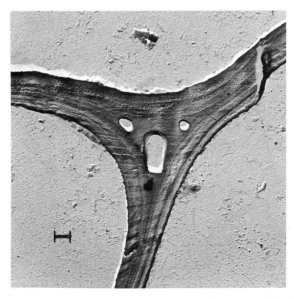

FIG. 10. Junction of three tyloses in a springwood vessel segment of black locust heartwood. Intertylosic spaces are formed where intertylosic substance is lacking.

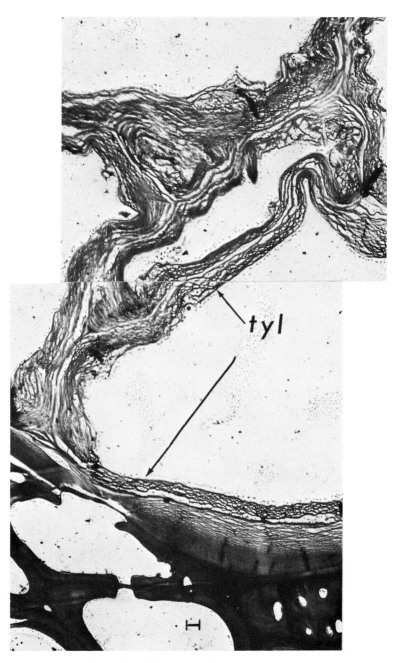

FIG. 11. Cross section of ozonized tyloses in a springwood vessel segment of osage-orange heartwood. The tylosis walls were degraded quite uniformly, as evidenced by the methacrylate-swollen lamellae. The intertylosic zone was attacked sufficiently to separate the tyloses.

of microfibrils, typical of primary walls, was present in some cases (Fig. 12).

In other instances (Fig. 13), the microfibrils were found to be organized into the parallel pattern that is typical of secondary walls. It was not possible to detect whether the secondary walls contained the alternating layers (S_1, S_2, and S_3) found in most wood cells.

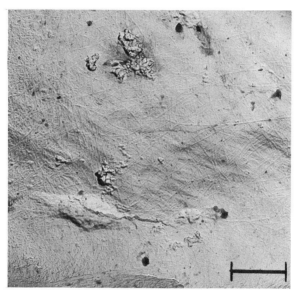

FIG. 12.   Direct carbon replica of the surface of a tylosis in white oak, *Quercus alba* L. Note the random arrangement of microfibrils which is typical of primary cell wall. Specimen was partially delignified before the replica was prepared.

Electron micrographs of these same surface replicas revealed the presence of intertylosic pitting in white oak, osage-orange, and black locust. The surfaces of the pit membranes (Fig. 13) were of the random microfibrillar arrangement observed on normal hardwood bordered pit membranes. Ultrathin sections of the tyloses through the pit area show that they do resemble normal pits (Fig. 14). Pit membranes in tyloses of black locust measured approximately 0.1 μ in thickness and the pits were about 1.5 μ in diameter.

In some micrographs of white ash tyloses it was possible to see lamellar structure without ozonization or other delignification treatment. An example of this is shown in Figure 15.

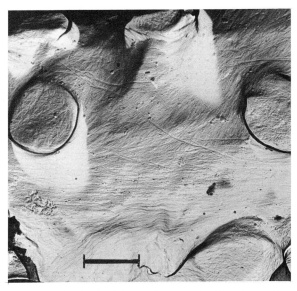

Fig. 13. Intertylosic pitting in black locust heartwood. The pit membranes exhibit randomly oriented microfibrillar structure while the remainder of the tylosis has more highly oriented structure. Specimen partially delignified.

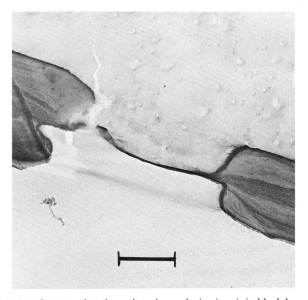

Fig. 14. Cross section through an intertylosic pit pair in black locust.

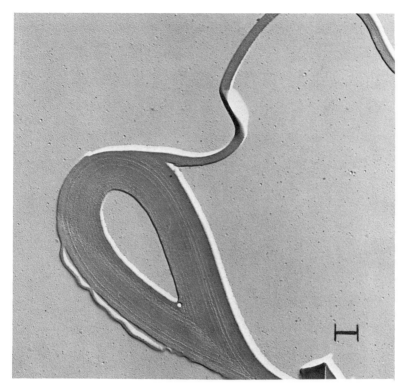

FIG. 15. A multi-layered tylosis in a springwood vessel segment of white ash heartwood. Ultrathin cross section.

Tyloses in the species investigated are variable in thickness as well as in general structure. The thinnest wall measured in the study was 0.05 μ. This was a tylosis of white ash which may be extremely thin and delicate in contrast to the tyloses of white oak, which averaged 2.98 μ in thickness. In black locust the tylosis thickness averaged 0.63 μ. In the greatly thickened and lamellated sclerosed tyloses of some species, their thickness may reach several microns.

ACKNOWLEDGMENT

This study was supported by a research grant from the National Science Foundation (GB1050).

REFERENCES

Alten, H. von (1909) "Kritische bemerkungen und neue ansichten über die Thyllen." *Botan. Z.* 67:1–23.

Beckman, C. H., Kuntz, J. E., Riker, A. J., and Berbee, J. E. (1953) "Host responses associated with the development of oak wilt." *Phytopathology* 43:448–454.

Chattaway, N. M. (1949) "The development of tyloses and secretion of gum in heartwood formation." *Australian J. Sci. Res.*, Ser. B—Biol. Sci., Z 3:227–240.

—————— (1952) "The sapwood-heartwood transition." *Austral. For.* 16:25–34.

Côté, W. A., Jr., Kórán, Z., and Day, A. C. (1964) "Replica techniques for electron microscopy of wood and paper." *Tappi* 47:477–484.

Esau, K. (1948) "Anatomic effects of the viruses of Pierce's disease and phony peach." *Hilgardia* 18:423–482.

Gerry, E. J. (1914) "Tyloses: Their occurrence and practical significance in some American woods." *J. Agric. Res.* 1:445–469.

Gertz, O. (1916) "Untersuchungen über septierte Thyllen nebst anderen Beitragen zu einer Monographie des Thyllenfrage." *Lunds Univ. Arsskr., Avd. 2.* 12:45.

Ghosh, S. S. (1957) "Unusual occurrence of sclerosed tyloses in the wood of *Palaquium*." *J. of Timber Dryers' and Preservers' Asso. of India.* 3:1–2.

Goss, R. W., and Frink, P. R. (1934) "*Cephalosporium* wilt and die-back of the white elm." Nebr. Agr. Exp. Sta. Res. Bul. 70. 24pp.

Hunt, G. M., and Garratt, G. A. (1953) *Wood Preservation.* Second Edition. McGraw-Hill Book Co., Inc., N. Y. 417pp.

I.A.W.A. (1964) *Multilingual Glossary of Terms Used in Wood Anatomy.* Committee on Nomenclature, International Association of Wood Anatomists. Verlagsanstalt Buchdruckerei Konkordia, Winterthur, Switzerland. 186pp.

Isenberg, I. H. (1933) "Microchemical studies of tyloses." *J. Forestry* 31:961–966.

Itō, M., and Kishima, T. (1951) "Studies on the tyloses—their occurrence in the domestic woods." *Wood Research Review, Japan* 3:44–45.

Jorgensen, E. (1962) "Observations on the formation of protection wood." *Forestry Chronicle* 38:292–294.

Jurášek, L. (1956) "Vznik thyl v bukovèm dřèvě" (The origin of tyloses in beech wood). *Drev. Výskum* 1:7–15.

—————— (1958) "Pùsobeni teploty a vlhkosti dřèva na tvorbu thyl u buku" (The influence of wood temperature and moisture content on the formation of tyloses in beech). *Drev. Výskum* 3:5–13.

Kerling, L. C. P. (1955) "Reactions of elm wood to attacks of *Ophiostoma ulmi* (Buism.) Nannf." *Acta Bot. Neerl.* 4:398–403.

Kishima, T., and Hayaschi, S. (1960) "Microscopic observation of the course of water penetration into wood." *Wood Res. (Kyoto)* 24:33–45.

Klein, G. (1923) "Zur Atiologie der Thyllen." *Z. Botan.* 15:417–439.

Kórán, Z. (1964) "Ultrastructure of tyloses and a theory of their growth mechanism." Unpublished doctoral dissertation. State Univ. College of Forestry at Syracuse Univ., Syracuse, N. Y. 95pp.

——————, and Côté, W. A., Jr. (1964) "Ultrastructure of tyloses and a theory of their growth mechanism." *I.A.W.A. News Bulletin,* No. 2.

Lantican, D. M. (1964) "The effect of ozone treatment on the hygroscopicity, permeability and ultrastructure of the heartwood of western redcedar." Unpublished doctoral dissertation. State Univ. College of Forestry at Syracuse Univ., Syracuse, N. Y.

MacLean, J. D. (1952) "Preservative treatment of wood by pressure methods." U.S.D.A., Forest Service, Agric. Handbook No. 40. 160pp.

Meer, J. H. H. van der (1926) "Verticillium wilt of maple and elm seedlings in Holland." *Phytopathology* 16:611–614.

Molisch, H. (1888) "Zur Kenntniss der Thyllen, nebst Beobachtungen über Wundheilung in der Pflanzen." In *Sitzungsber. K. Akad. Wiss. (Vienna), Math.-Naturw. Kl.,* Abt. I. Bd. 97:264–298.

Nečesaný, V. (1955) "Elektronenmikroskopische Untersuchungen der Thyllen und der Kernstoff der Rotbuche, *Fagus silvatica* L." *Bot. Tidsskr.* 52:48–55.

Paclt, J. (1930) "Kernbildung der Buche—*Fagus silvatica* L." (Heartwood formation in beech). *Phytopathol. Z.* 20:255–259.

Parmeter, J. R., and Kuntz, J. E. (1954) "Oak wilt development in bur oaks." Abstract in *Phytopathology* 44:502.

Struckmeyer, B. E., Beckman, C. H., Kuntz, J. E., and Riker, A. J. (1954) "Plugging of vessels by tyloses and gums in wilting oaks." *Phytopathology* 44:148–153.

Vodoz, J. (1957) "Das Verhalten des Holzes während des Trocknung im hochfrequenten Wechselfeld." *Holz Roh- Werkstoff* 15:327–340.

Weber, F. (1954) "Stone tyloses." In *Trans. CSIRO Austr.* No. 2226.

Williams, S. (1939) "Secondary xylary tissues of oaks (*Quercus* spp.) indigenous to the United States." Unpublished doctoral dissertation. N. Y. State College of Forestry, Syracuse, N. Y. 253 pp.

Evidence of Lignin in the
Tertiary Wall of Certain Wood Cells

IRVING B. SACHS

United States Forest Products Laboratory,
Madison, Wisconsin

The walls of wood cells contain many constituents for which a definite distribution pattern has never been described. This obscurity can be attributed to the lack of adequate nondestructive techniques for the identification of these components, which play an important part not only in anatomical relations but also in the utilization of wood. In recent years, investigators have utilized available techniques to picture the location of lignin in the cell wall (Mühlethaler, 1949; Hodge and Wardrop, 1950; Bailey, 1954; Wardrop, 1957; Jayme and Fengel, 1961; Nečesaný, 1962; Sachs *et al.*, 1963; and Lange, 1954).

This paper provides further evidence that lignin is not limited to the compound middle lamella and secondary wall of wood cells, but it is also present in the tertiary wall and warty layer. It is also of interest to compare the picture of lignin location in material subjected to natural cellulosic degradation with specimens chemically treated in the laboratory.

Samples of *Fagus sylvatica* were obtained from a recently uncovered Viking ship and generously contributed to the U. S. Forest Products Laboratory by B. Bronson Christensen of the Danish National Museum, Copenhagen, Denmark. These were dated as being over 2,000 years old, with the cellulose components almost totally hydrolyzed. Chemical assay by Mr. Christensen and his colleagues showed that the samples contained approximately 92.7% lignin.

The method for preparing the material for sectioning was similar to that used previously in this laboratory (Sachs *et al.*, 1963).

Figure 1 shows the appearance of lignin distribution in several cells of the wood specimens that had undergone natural degradation. The lignin in the middle lamella and primary wall appears dense and with no indication that material has been removed. The S_1 and S_2 lignin is dispersed in some cells; however, the random network of lignin after the removal of cellulose is as reported by other investigators (Mühlethaler, 1949; Jayme and Fengel, 1961; Sachs *et al.*, 1963). The lignin in the tertiary wall and warty layer appears quite dense and, in many of the cells, is the only re-

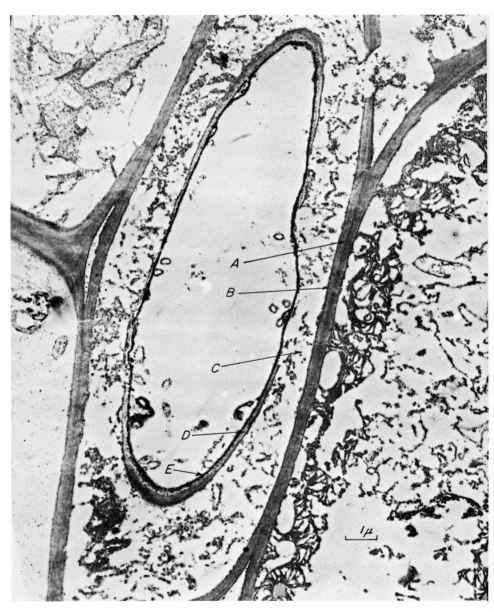

Fig. 1. Cross section of *Fagus sylvatica* after 2,000-year natural degradation, showing lignin location in various cell layers. A—middle lamella, B—primary wall, C—secondary wall, D—tertiary wall, E—wart layer.

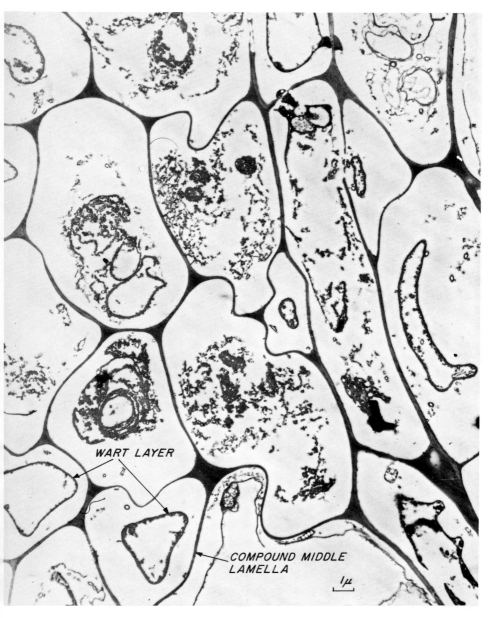

WART LAYER

COMPOUND MIDDLE
LAMELLA

1μ

Fig. 2. Tissue same as in Figure 1 with secondary wall lignin lacking in many cells. Cells, lower left of micrograph, show only wart layer and compound middle lamella.

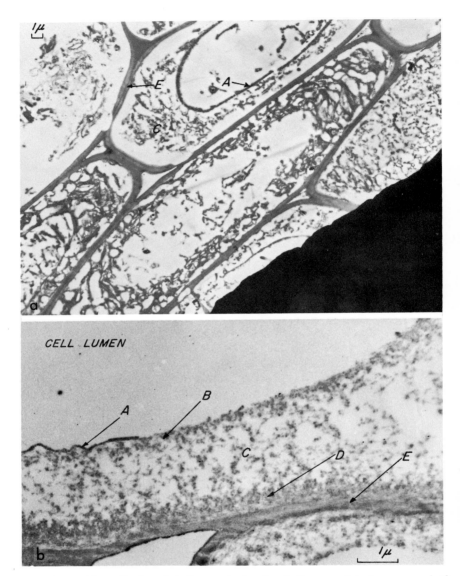

Fig. 3. a. Naturally degraded *Fagus sylvatica* chemically assayed to be composed of 92.7% lignin. ×3,360.

b. *Acer saccharum* after treatment with hydrofluoric acid chemically assays to be composed of 99.8% lignin. ×11,200.

A—wart layer, B—tertiary wall, C—S_2, D—S_1, E—compound middle lamella.

maining evidence of lignin present except for that in the compound middle lamella (Fig. 2).

In addition, warts are still evident on the warty layer, indicating that these structures too are one of the last materials to break down during the natural degradation of wood cells over a long period of time.

Results with the naturally degraded material are compared in Figure 3 with *Acer saccharum* that had been treated with hydrofluoric acid. The resemblance is striking in that the greatest densities of lignin appear in the middle lamella, primary wall, and tertiary wall. In the secondary wall it is evident as a branched network from which the cellulose has been removed.

It is possible that in natural cellulosic degradation of wood, as well as in wood treated with hydrofluoric acid, the lignin may be structurally or chemically modified. Present findings do suggest, however, that not only is the lignin located in the compound middle lamella and secondary wall layers, but also that it is definitely present in the tertiary wall and warty layer. This assumption is in harmony with the recent findings of Jayme and Fengel (1961), Nečesaný (1962), and Sachs *et al.*, (1963), and that assumed by T. Hartig in the seventeenth century as reported by Sanio (1860).

REFERENCES

Bailey, I. W. (1954) *Contributions to Plant Anatomy,* pp. 73–90. Chronica Botanica Co., Waltham, Mass.

Hodge, A. J., and Wardrop, A. B. (1950) "An electron microscopic investigation of the cell wall organization of conifer tracheids and conifer cambium." *Australian J. Sci. Res.,* Ser. B 3:265–269.

Jayme, G., and Fengel, D. (1961) "Beitrag zur Kenntnis des Feinbaus der Fichtenholztracheiden." *Holzforschung* 15:97–102.

Lange, P. W. (1954) "The distribution of lignin in the cell wall of normal and reaction wood from spruce and a few hardwoods." *Svensk Pappertstid.* 57:525–532.

Mühlethaler, K. (1949) "Electron micrographs of plant fibers." *Biochim. Biophys. Acta* 3:15–25.

Nečesaný, V. (1962) "Structural changes of the inner surface of cell walls of wood and its constituents caused by swelling." *Crevarsky Vyskum* 2:85–92.

Sachs, I. B., Clark, I. T., and Pew, J. C. (1963) "Investigation of lignin distribution in the cell wall of certain woods." *J. Polymer Sci.,* Part C 2:203–212.

Sanio, K. (1860) "Einige Bemerkungen über den bau des holzes." *Botanische Zeitung.* 18:201–216.

Wardrop, A. B. (1957) "The phase of lignification in the differentiation of wood fibers." *Tappi* 40:225–243.

Microorganisms and Microbial Enzyme Systems as Selective Tools in Wood Anatomy

ELLIS B. COWLING

School of Forestry, Yale University

INTRODUCTION

Wood anatomists traditionally have sought to attain three major research objectives: (1) to visualize the structural elements of wood cells; (2) to determine the chemical composition and molecular architecture of these structures; and (3) to elucidate the mechanisms by which these structures are synthesized by the protoplast of living cells.

It was stated earlier (Cowling, 1961): "A major justification for fundamental research in the field of wood deterioration is the increasing use of wood-destroying organisms and isolated microbial enzymes in studies of lignin and cellulose structure (Nord and Schubert, 1957; Pew, 1957) and wood anatomy (Asunmaa, 1955; Bailey and Vestal, 1937; Meier, 1955; Reese and Mandels, 1959). The specificity of microbial enzymes, and the very mild conditions under which their reactions proceed, make them potentially ideal reagents for delicate studies of structure (Reese and Mandels, 1959). More complete characterization of the enzymes of wood-destroying fungi, and their effects during decay, would allow these methods to be applied with greater precision and confidence."

Our purpose in the present paper is to direct attention to the usefulness of microorganisms and microbial enzyme systems as selective tools in anatomical investigations. To accomplish this we shall (1) discuss the advantages and limitations of microbiological and enzymological methods in comparison with conventional anatomical techniques, (2) briefly review a few pertinent generalizations and common misconceptions concerning the microorganisms that degrade wood, (3) describe some of our own observations and those made by other researchers on ultrastructural changes in wood caused by decay fungi, and (4) suggest several specific types of studies in the fields of anatomy and wood technology in which microbial or enzymological methods may be useful.

In his introduction to this volume, Dr. R. D. Preston indicated his conviction that progress in science often is achieved through collaboration of specialists in diverse scientific disciplines. Those of us whose special interests and training are in the field of plant pathology agree wholeheartedly with this suggestion. Many pathologists are concerned with the degradation of plant tissues by pathogenic and saprophytic microorganisms. Disintegration of host tissues is an important aspect of pathogenesis (Husain and Kelman, 1959). Without the fundamental contributions many of you have made as specialists in plant anatomy much of all work in plant pathology would be impossible. Anatomical knowledge is essential in understanding how disease spreads through a plant and the mechanisms by which plant tissues break down under the influence of the hydrolytic and oxidative enzyme systems of microorganisms. Similarly, in the course of research on plant diseases, pathologists have made a few observations of properties and developed techniques that we hope have added at least in a small way to the anatomist's understanding of the structure and molecular architecture of plant cell walls.

Earlier in this volume, Dr. Kratzl mentioned the necessity for one's conception of lignin structure to be enlarged or modified as new reactions or properties become known. So in the general field of anatomy—discoveries of new properties of cell walls (be they chemical, physical, or microbiological) may require modification of our traditional concepts of cell wall structure.

One particular contribution of pathologists to plant anatomy we should like to describe in detail because it well illustrates several of the advantages of microbiological tools in anatomical investigations. In 1952, Dr. R. K. S. Wood was working at the University of California together with Drs. Gold and Rawlins of the Department of Plant Pathology on a bacterial soft rot of vegetables caused by *Erwinia aroidae* (Wood, *et al.*, 1952). This organism secretes pectolytic and proteolytic enzymes that break down the constituents of the middle lamella of its herbaceous host plants and permit the cells to separate, giving a watery mass of disorganized tissue. They found that these enzymes were secreted into essentially any medium that would support the growth of the organism. By removing the cells from a culture growing on a simple but chemically defined medium, they obtained culture filtrates with high pectolytic and proteolytic activity but with only negligible cellulolytic activity. Using this culture filtrate as a highly selective mascerating reagent, they were able to visualize in the electron microscope the microfibrils of the primary walls of many herbaceous plants without the rigorous chemical treatments that often are used by anatomists for this same purpose. One of their illustrations is shown in Figure 1.

The procedure used by Wood and his co-workers was elegantly simple —a synthetic medium consisting merely of glucose, asparagin, KH_2PO_4,

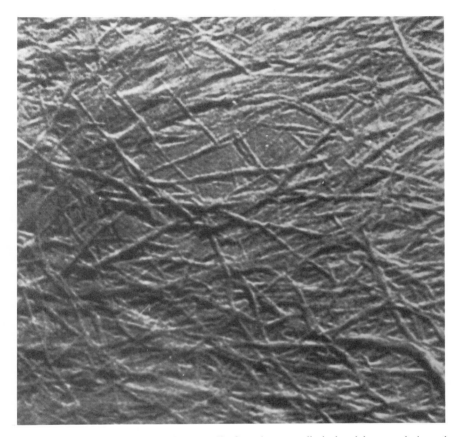

Fig. 1.   Microfibrils of the primary wall of turnip root cells isolated by pectolytic and proteolytic enzymes in culture filtrates of *Erwinia aroidae*. (from Wood *et al.*, 1952).

$MgSO_4 \cdot 7H_2O$, and $CaCO_2$ was sterilized by autoclaving, inoculated with a few cells of the bacterium, and incubated for four days at room conditions. The cells of the bacterium were removed from the medium by centrifugation and 1 mm-thick pieces of plant tissue were placed in this solution. After 15 to 30 minutes the tissues were macerated so completely that single cells were obtained for the most part. These cells were placed directly on grids, dried, shadowed with palladium, and micrographed directly.

The simplicity and specificity of this technique well illustrate several of the advantages of microbiological methods in anatomical investigations.

Advantages and Disadvantages of
Microbiological Methods in Anatomy

An increasingly diverse selection of methods are now used by wood anatomists. Many of these methods involve chemical or physical treatment of the tissue of study prior to microscopic examination. These treatments usually are more or less destructive of certain constituents of the tissue. But by virtue of their specific effects, they are useful in visualizing structural features or determining the chemical composition of a particular structural element. The use of microorganisms or microbial enzyme systems is simply an extension of this general procedure. Many of the chemicals commonly employed in wood anatomy are by no means as selective as we wish they were in removing or reacting with particular cell wall constituents. Many of these chemicals involve exothermic or violent swelling reactions that can create artifacts that obscure native structural features, or worse yet, create new ones. Given the opportunity, we all could probably recite a pet criticism of artifacts created by one of our less astute colleagues in research as a result of unrecognized side effects or other limitations of a particular reagent or treatment. For many purposes microorganisms or their purified or partially purified enzyme systems provide advantages that strongly recommend their use in comparison with conventional chemical reagents.

A major advantage both of microorganisms *per se* and of their isolated enzyme systems is the very mild condition under which their activities and reactions proceed. The cardinal temperatures, pressures, and pH for most microorganisms and enzyme systems are, for all practical purposes, the same physiological conditions under which the cell wall structures themselves were synthesized in the growing plant. Also, water is the solvent in which both synthesis and enzymatic degradation proceed. Thus, it is highly unlikely that unwanted structural modifications will occur as secondary effects of conditions of treatment when microorganisms or their enzyme systems are employed.

The second advantage of enzymes is their specificity. This is one of their most unique attributes. A given enzyme is restricted to catalysis of a particular kind of reaction and that, often, on a given molecular species. Thus, cellulases act on cellulose, pectinases act on pectin, xylanases act on xylan exclusively, and so on. Few if any conventional reagents can match enzymes in specificity of reaction.

Whole microorganisms, of course, are not selective to the point of reacting with a particular molecular species. But many are known that are sufficiently selective to justify their use in anatomical investigations. For example, many fungi will selectively digest the carbohydrates of wood and leave a residue of lignin that closely resembles protolignin in spectographic, elementary composition and other properties (Nord and Schubert, 1957). Other fungi are known that selectively will degrade the S_2 layer of hardwood fiber tracheids (Bailey and Vestal, 1937; Duncan, 1960). Bacteria have been described that will selectively remove the contents and cell walls of parenchyma cells, largely from wood rays (Knuth, 1964).

Microbiological and enzymological techniques also have disadvantages and limitations, just as do all other anatomical methods. Paramount among these, particularly in studies of lignified tissues, is the limited accessibility of wood cell wall constituents to enzyme systems. As shown by the following general reaction sequence, direct physical contact between the enzyme protein molecule and its substrate molecules is essential for catalysis:

enzyme + substrate $\rightleftharpoons$ enzyme-substrate complex $\rightarrow$ enzyme + products

Enzymes are soluble protein molecules of high molecular weight (10,000 to 200,000). Since most wood constituents are insoluble substances of great structural complexity, this initial complex formation can be achieved only by diffusion of the enzyme molecules to susceptible sites on molecular surfaces within the wood cell walls that are accessible to the enzymes. Thus, any structural feature of the cell wall that limits the accessibility of of the constituents or the capacity of the enzyme to diffuse within the structure, will determine the susceptibility of the constituent to enzymatic degradation. Such structural features include the following: (1) the moisture content of the wood; (2) the size and diffusibility of the enzyme molecule involved in relation to the size and surface properties of the gross capillaries, the interstices between microfibrils, and the spaces between cellulose molecules in the amorphous regions; (3) the degree of crystallinity of the cellulose; (4) its unit cell dimensions; (5) confirmation and steric rigidity of the anhydroglucose units; (6) the degree of lignification of the cell wall; and (7) the nature and distribution of substituent groups. The influence of each of these features has been discussed in detail by Cowling (1963).

The problem of accessibility has been minimized in studies to isolate lignin from wood by selective removal of the wood carbohydrates (Pew, 1957). A previous treatment by ball milling wood in a laboratory ball mill will avoid most problems of accessibility. But, on the other hand, ball milling itself is a very rigorous treatment.

A second disadvantage, but not an insurmountable one, is the paucity of commercial sources and the difficulty of obtaining sufficiently pure enzymes for the purpose of a given study. Comparatively few organisms will synthesize and secrete a single extracellular enzyme protein. Thus, culture filtrates or commercial preparations high in concentration of a given enzyme, often contain other enzymes that it may be necessary to inactivate or remove from the system, where high specificity is required. But for many purposes highly purified enzyme systems are not essential. For example, in an attempt to isolate lignin from wood, a mixture of carbohydrases is highly desirable in order to insure that a maximum amount of unwanted carbohydrates will be removed from the lignocellulose complex. Although commercial sources of enzymes are by no means numerous, a steadily increasing array of fairly pure preparations are becoming available. Enzymologists such as Dr. E. T. Reese of the Quartermaster Corps Laboratories at Natick, Massachusetts have made available large numbers of highly purified specific preparations for particular structural studies in recent years (Reese and Mandels, 1959).

A third disadvantage for the anatomist in the use of microorganisms and enzyme systems is psychological—his unfamiliarity with the special techniques involved in sterilization and aseptic handling procedures or enzyme assay methods may alone deter the use of such methods. But these special techniques usually are not complicated and in many cases involve only ordinary laboratory equipment. Also, many anatomists are stationed at institutions whose staff includes microbiological specialists with whom collaboration can be mutually fruitful.

WOOD-INHABITING FUNGI

Before considering in detail how microorganisms and microbial enzyme systems can be used in studies of wood anatomy, we will first review the types of organisms that attack wood and certain of their general properties. Four general types of wood-inhabiting organisms are usually recognized. Each will be described briefly and representative species named.

Wood-Staining Fungi. These organisms are of two types: surface molds such as *Trichoderma lignorum* that develop on the external surface of wood products; and penetrating fungi, of which the so-called blue-stain fungi such as many *Ceratocystis* sp. are most typical, that develop deep within the wood, most conspiciously in the ray parenchyma. Certain species of the latter group characteristically infect trees while the great majority attack fresh-cut wood products. All of these fungi are Ascomycetes or Fungi Imperfecti.

Both groups are restricted to the sapwood, where they inhabit the wood cell lumens and derive nourishment primarily from reserve food materials stored in the longitudinal and ray parenchyma. They do not significantly affect the strength of wood other than its impact resistance. Their hyphae usually are pigmented and characteristically discolor the wood.

Typical Wood-Destroying Fungi. Two groups of these organisms can be distinguished on the basis of the color and texture of the decayed wood: so-called white-rot fungi such as *Polyporus versicolor* that render the wood lighter in color; and brown-rot fungi such as *Poria monticola* that make the wood darker than normal in color. In advanced stages of decay, brown-rotted wood shows a characteristic cubical pattern of checking perpendicular to the grain that is never shown by white-rotted wood. Most of the typical wood-destroying fungi are Basidiomycetes. They affect both living and dead trees as well as wood products. Both groups inhabit the wood cell lumens; brown-rot fungi derive their nourishment solely from the wood carbohydrates, whereas the white-rot fungi utilize all structural constituents of the cell walls. It is very commonly (and incorrectly) assumed that since brown-rot fungi do not *utilize* lignin, that they do not *degrade* it as well. Actually the molecular weight, methoxyl content, and solubility properties of the residue of lignin remaining in brown-rotted wood are altered substantially. White-rot fungi are commonly assumed to degrade lignin preferentially. This also is incorrect. All white-rot fungi studied to date obtain the greater part of their energy from metabolism of the wood carbohydrates, although it has been shown recently that the white-rot fungi vary considerably in the comparative rates of carbohydrate and lignin utilization (Kirk and Kelman, 1964).

Both white- and brown-rot fungi inhabit the wood cell lumens and penetrate from one cell to another via bore holes. In the case of brown-rot, bore holes are the major evidence of cell wall deterioration visible in the light microscope. White-rot fungi in addition cause a general thinning of the wood cells from the lumen towards the compound middle lamella.

Figures 2, 3, and 4 illustrate the progressive changes in chemical composition of sweetgum sapwood caused by the typical white- and brown-rot fungi *Polyporus versicolor* and *Poria monticola*. Notice that both fungi utilized each wood carbohydrate and the white-rot fungus also utilized lignin at rates that were essentially linear in all stages of decay and approximately proportional to the amounts present in the original sound wood. This uniformity in rate of utilization of the various wood constituents by both test fungi is remarkable in view of the diverse chemical nature of the constituents and their heterogenous distribution within the wood cell walls. Rapid utilization of lignin in the early stages of decay by *Polyporus versicolor* is especially difficult to understand since lignin is concentrated in the compound middle lamella between wood cells.

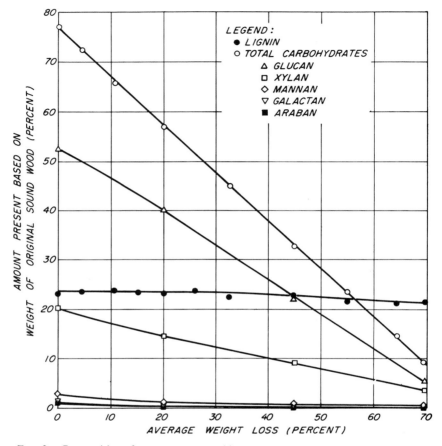

FIG. 2. Composition of sweetgum sapwood in progressive stages of decay by the brown-rot fungus *Poria monticola*. (from Cowling, 1961).

Figure 4 shows the strikingly different patterns of progressive change in average degree of polymerization (DP) of holocellulose induced by the same fungi. *Polyporus versicolor* caused a very slow, gradual change in average DP, whereas the effect of *Poria monticola* was at first very rapid, and then similarly gradual and linear. This striking difference in rate of change of average DP has been shown to account for several other distinguishing characteristics of these fungi: the greater solubility of brown-rotted wood, higher yields and quality of pulp prepared from white-rotted wood, the more rapid rate of strength reduction by brown-rot fungi, and the characteristic cubical pattern of checking of wood decayed by brown-rot fungi.

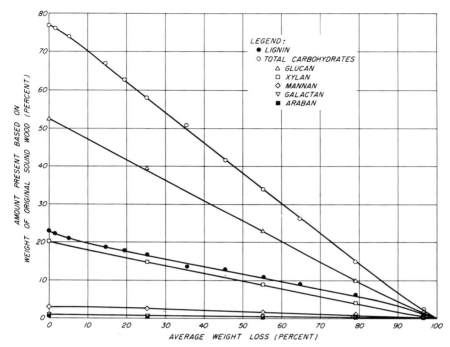

FIG. 3.   Composition of sweetgum sapwood in progressive stages of decay by the white-rot fungus *Polyporus versicolor*. (from Cowling, 1961).

The progressive changes in chemical composition described here provide background for interpretation of changes in ultrastructure in the wood discussed later in this paper. Further discussion of differences in the properties of white- and brown-rotted wood and the comparative biochemistry of the causal organisms is available in the work of Cowling (1961).

Soft-Rot Fungi.   Organisms that cause this unique type of wood deterioration only recently have been generally recognized to be of importance. They are mostly Ascomycetes and Fungi Imperfecti (Barghoorn and Linder, 1944) and attack the exposed surfaces of wood products that are more or less constantly saturated with water. The internal slats of industrial cooling towers and wood floating in sea water are common habitats. In contrast to the typical wood-destroying fungi that inhabit the lumens of wood cells, these fungi are confined to cylindrical cavities they themselves create within the secondary walls of wood cells. In polarized light the cavities are remarkably geometrical in shape, as shown in Figure 5.

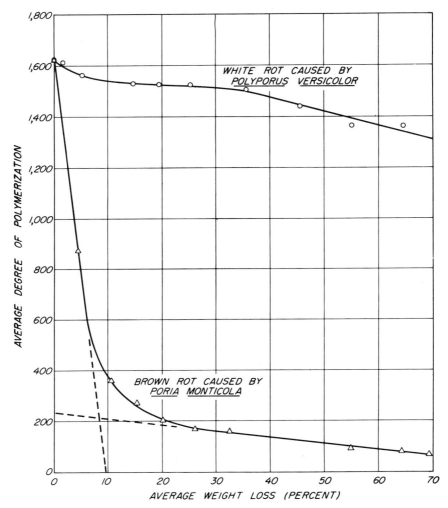

FIG. 4. Average degree of polymerization of the holocellulose of sweetgum sapwood in progressive stages of decay by the white-rot fungus *Polyporus versicolor* and the brown-rot fungus *Poria monticola.* (from Cowling, 1961)

As in so many other aspects of wood anatomy, Dr. I. W. Bailey was one of the first to utilize evidence derived from study of decayed wood to establish previously unrecognized aspects of the structure of wood cell walls. His classical work together with Vestal (Bailey and Vestal, 1937) showed that wood decayed by these soft-rot fungi contain two distinct planes of susceptibility to enzymatic hydrolysis—one parallel to the orien-

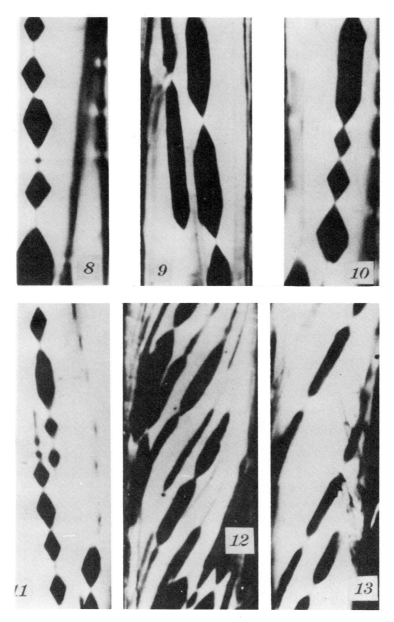

FIG. 5. Longitudinal sections of the xylem of the various wood species photographed in polarized light between crossed nicols, showing enzymatically produced cavities caused by soft-rot fungi. (from Bailey and Vestal, 1937).

tation of cellulose molecules in the secondary wall, and a second also within the secondary walls at an angle of 23° from the fibril axis. He also noted that the angle of intersection of the conical points of the enzymatically created cavities changed with the moisture content of the fiber, indicating that the hydrolysis planes responsible for this particular angle were related to the unit cell dimensions of the crystallites of cellulose in the secondary wall. It is not difficult to explain the first hydrolysis plane, but the conical shape of the ends of the cavities has yet to be explained satisfactorily (Roelofsen, 1956).

Wood-Inhabiting Bacteria.   The significance of bacteria in the degradation of wood has been recognized even more recently than that of the soft-rot fungi. Bacteria have long been associated with bacterial wet wood of living elm trees and a few other species but were considered not to be damaging to the wood. More recently other (as yet unidentified) forms have been associated consistently in northern hardwoods with staining and decay fungi in so-called wound-induced discoloration (Shigo, 1963). An unusually interesting group of sulphur bacteria in certain mill ponds have been shown to cause the rapid and selective degradation of ray parenchyma tissue so that the permeability of the wood to liquids is increased greatly (Knuth, 1964).

ULTRASTRUCTURAL CHANGES IN WOOD DURING DECAY BY TYPICAL WOOD-DESTROYING FUNGI

Two major types of enzymatic effects on wood cell walls by typical wood-destroying fungi are distinguishable: (1) localized dissolution of cell walls at points of contact with the fungal hyphae; and (2) generalized dissolution of cell wall substance at some distance from the hyphae of the organism. The first type is involved in the formation of so-called bore holes as the fungi penetrate from cell to cell within the wood structure. Proctor (1941) prepared excellent light micrographs of these structures and concluded from studies of fungal hyphae in the process of forming bore holes that penetration was achieved by an enzymatic mechanism rather than by application of mechanical forces, as had been proposed earlier.

The highly localized nature of the dissolution involved in formation of these bore holes by the white-rot fungus *Polyporus versicolor* is illustrated in Figures 6 and 7. These direct carbon replicas were prepared according to the procedure of Côté et al., (1964). In these illustrations the hyphae responsible for formation of the holes degenerated autolytically prior to preparation of the replicas.

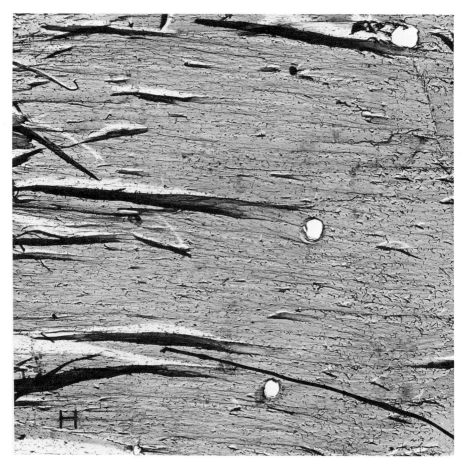

FIG. 6. Replica of a longitudinal surface of spruce tracheid decayed by the white-rot fungus *Polyporus versicolor*. X 4,000.

Figure 8 shows a longitudinal section of sweetgum sapwood in an advanced stage of deterioration by this same fungus. The cell wall in the middle of the micrograph shows three distinct areas from which the cell wall substance was removed at points of contact between the cell walls and the lateral surfaces of the fungal hyphae. A hypha is shown in cross section occupying one of these areas.

Figure 9 shows a similar longisection of sweetgum sapwood with two bore holes. In this case, however, regions of partial degradation show a conspicuous abnormal swelling pattern similar to that observed by Côté

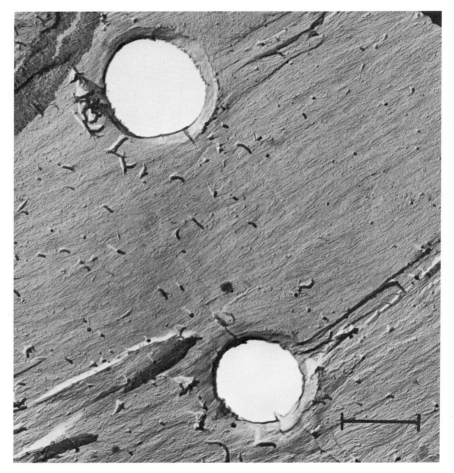

Fig. 7.   Replica of a longitudinal surface of spruce tracheid decayed by the white-rot
fungus *Polyporus versicolor*. X 20,250.

and Day (1962) in the G-layer of tension wood and in wood treated with
gaseous ozone. They considered that abnormal swelling similar to that
shown in Figure 9 resulted from weakening of bonds between microfibrils
during drying in an ethanol series. This weakening then permitted the
methacrylate used as an embedding medium to expand the structure
during polymerization. In common with the G-layer of tension wood and
ozonized wood, the secondary walls of wood decayed by white-rot fungi
contain less than normal amounts of lignin and (presumably), therefore,

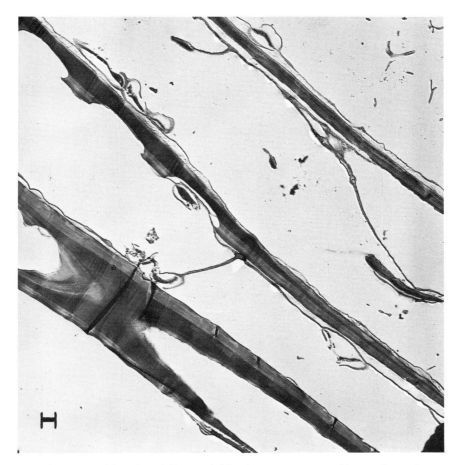

FIG. 8.   Tangential section of fiber tracheids of sweetgum sapwood in an advanced stage of decay by the white-rot fungus *Polyporus versicolor*. X 3,750.

would be less resistant to stresses imposed during drying and polymerization of the embedding medium.

Interpreted in this way, the expanded structure of the wood substance in the vicinity of the bore hole at the right of Figure 9 again confirms the highly localized activity of the enzymes involved in bore hole formation. The expanded structure of the secondary walls of the fiber tracheids at the far left and far right of Figure 9, however, indicates that degradation of cell wall substance also occurs on the surfaces of the lumens of wood cells where no contact with fungal hyphae is involved.

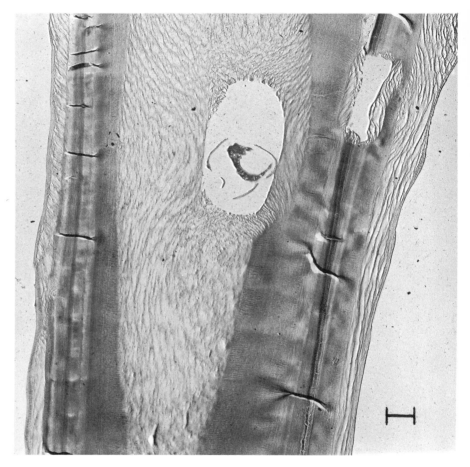

FIG. 9. Tangential section of fiber tracheids of sweetgum sapwood in an advanced stage of decay by the white-rot fungus *Polyporus versicolor*. X 2,700.

These two major types of dissolution indicate that the enzymes of typical wood-destroying fungi are active both when bound to the walls of hyphal cells and when secreted into the medium in which the fungus is developing.

Isolation of Microfibrils by White-Rot Fungi. As indicated earlier in this paper, white-rot fungi cause a general thinning of wood cell walls from the lumen towards the compound middle lamella. Because of this, rapid utilization of carbohydrates which are in greatest abundance in the secondary walls of wood cells can be accounted for readily. Cell wall thinning fails, however, to explain rapid utilization of lignin in the early stages of decay as shown by the chemical analysis in Figure 3. In seeking to resolve this anomaly it was hypothesized earlier (Cowling, 1961) that the lignin-degrading enzymes of *Polyporus versicolor* act first to remove the lignin between microfibrils of the secondary wall, and then, through the channels thus formed, gain access to the bulk of the lignin in the compound middle lamella at a very early stage of decay. This process was consistent with the very gradual change in average degree of polymerization of holocellulose in white-rotted wood (Figure 4) since dissolution of holocellulose could proceed from the surface of microfibrils towards their centers. Both of these processes should tend to isolate individual microfibrils of the secondary wall as decay progresses. It was, therefore, undertaken to determine if this were true. Samples of the same air-dry wood blocks used to obtain the analytical data in Figures 3 and 4 were dehydrated, embedded, sectioned, and shadowed by the procedures of Côté and Marton (1962). The tangential section in Figure 10 shows the appearance of two adjacent fiber tracheid cells and a fungus hypha in cross section at the right. The secondary walls of the wood cells have been expanded somewhat during methacrylate embedding, as discussed above. The general thinning pattern of cell wall dissolution is shown at the left. Short segments of microfibrils isolated during the decay process are apparent in both cell walls.

Relationship of Lignin to the Microfibrils of Wood Cells. Many attempts have been made in recent years to determine the distribution of lignin across wood cell walls. It is now generally accepted that lignin is in greatest abundance in the compound middle lamella and decreases in concentration across the secondary wall towards the lumen. The rate of this decrease is less marked in conifers than in hardwoods. Lignin in the secondary walls is believed to be concentrated between the microfibrils but this has not yet been demonstrated anatomically.

Sachs, *et al.,* (1963) have recently published electron micrographs of wood cell walls from which the bulk of the carbohydrates have been removed by treatment with hydrofluoric acid. Their micrographs, an example of which is shown in Figure 11, show a porous structure within the secondary walls that confirms the gross distribution of lignin but does not reveal the relationship of lignin with the microfibrils, since hydrofluoric acid causes some swelling and distortion of this aspect of the structure. Earlier Meier (1955) published micrographs (see Figure 12) of wood from which the carbohydrates had been removed by brown-rot fungi. His views also confirmed the gross distribution pattern of lignin but the size of the pores shown in the secondary walls also did not correspond with known cell wall structures. Although Meier indicated in personal com-

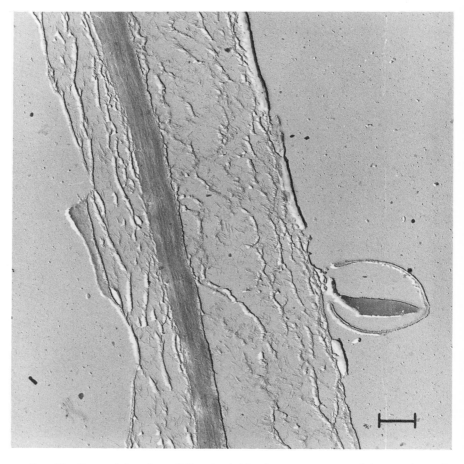

Fig. 10. Tangential section of fiber tracheids of sweetgum sapwood in an advanced stage of decay by the white-rot fungus *Polyporus versicolor.* X 9,750.

munication with us that the pores shown in his micrographs were enlarged somewhat, he agreed that brown-rotted wood, from which the wood carbohydrates have been removed selectively (see Figure 2) and at physiological conditions, provides an almost ideal experimental material for delicate study of this aspect of ultrastructure.

Accordingly, air-dry samples of sitka spruce wood in progressive stages of decay by the brown-rot fungus *Poria monticola* (the same fungus for which the analytical data of Figure 2 was obtained using sweetgum wood) were prepared by the procedure of Côté and Marton (1962) and examined

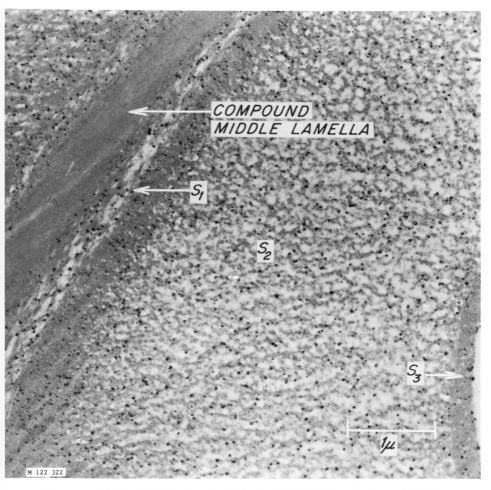

FIG. 11.   Loblolly pine hydrofluoric acid lignin. X 32,000. (from Sachs *et al.*, 1963).

in the electron microscope. Figure 13 shows a typical cross section of undecayed wood. Figures 14, 15, and 16 show similar cross sections of samples that sustained a weight loss due to decay of 65.7%. The section in Figure 16 was prepared and examined without shadowing. Analyses for total carbohydrate and lignin in these decayed wood samples showed that all but 2% of the 65.7% loss in weight was due to removal of the wood carbohydrates. Thus 88% of the original carbohydrates present had

E. B. Cowling

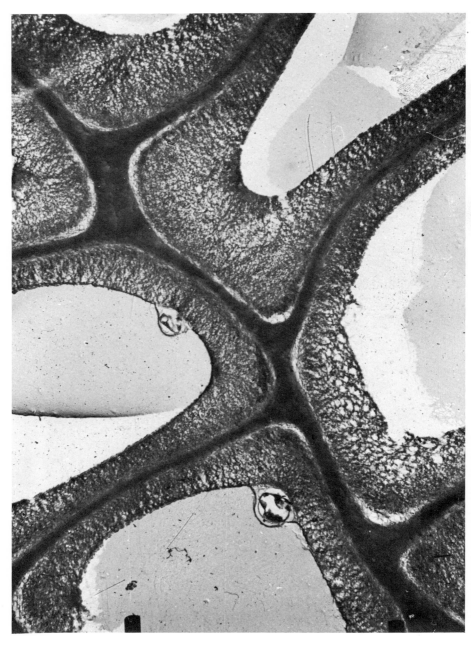

Fig. 12.   Cross section of spruce tracheids decayed by the brown-rot fungus *Merulius domesticus*.   X 5,800.   (from Meier, 1955)

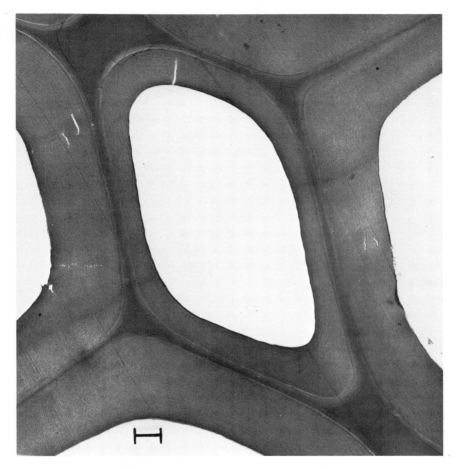

FIG. 13.   Cross section of nondecayed spruce tracheids. X 2,700.

been removed and converted to volatile products (mainly carbon dioxide and water) as a result of the metabolic activities of the fungus.

The decayed wood sections show two distinct changes when compared to the nondecayed sections. During the decay process the distinct contrast shown in Figure 13 between the secondary wall and compound middle lamella gradually decreased so that at 66% weight loss, the various cell wall layers were almost indistinguishable. No discrete openings of any kind were visible showing the lignin framework from which the carbohydrate-rich microfibrils had been removed, even in the unshadowed section in Figure 16, which is shown at a magnification of 26,250 times.

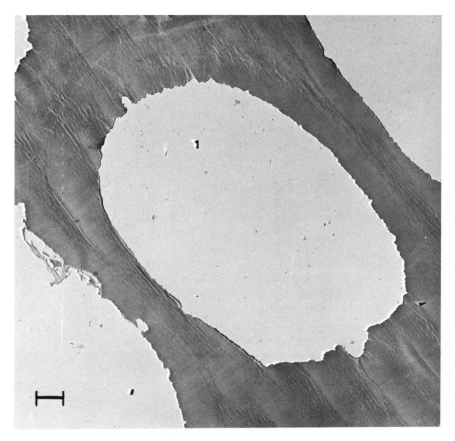

Fig. 14.   Cross section of spruce tracheids in an advanced stage of decay by the brown-rot fungus *Poria monticola.* X 2,700.

Both of these observations were unexpected in terms of our original expectations in examining the sections. We had anticipated that as decay progressed the difference in electron density between the compound middle lamella and secondary wall substance would increase as the carbohydrates were removed, mainly from the secondary walls where they are in greatest relative abundance. We also had anticipated that at some (presumably high) weight loss due to decay the regions of the cell wall from which the carbohydrates were being removed (i.e., the microfibrils) would become apparent as discrete openings in the lignin framework.

The observed diminution rather than expected increase in electron density between the secondary wall and compound middle lamella sug-

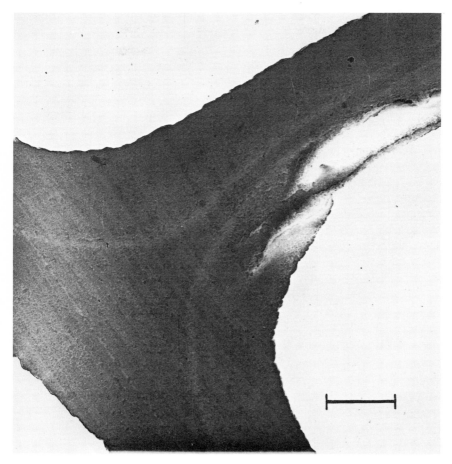

FIG. 15.   Cross section of spruce tracheids in an advanced stage of decay by the brown-rot fungus *Poria monticola.* X 7,000.

gests that the lignin framework of the secondary wall layer might have collapsed during drying of the wood before or during sectioning. Such collapse also would have tended to obscure the outline of the microfibrils from which the carbohydrates were being removed. But the extent of collapse necessary to make up for the loss of 66% of the mass of the wood does not appear to be consistent with the relatively small changes in average cell wall thickness observed in the hundreds of sections examined (cf. Figures 13 and 14).

Further observations on brown-rotted material are needed. It would be desirable to avoid collapse entirely by sectioning freeze-dried or solvent-

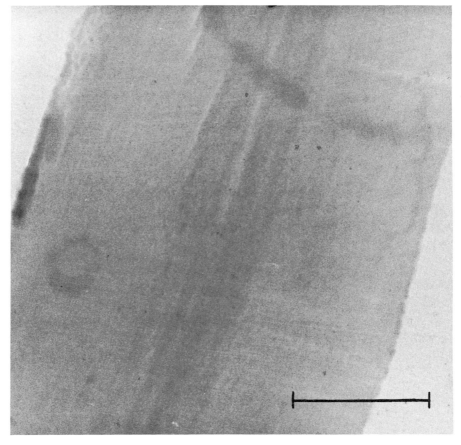

FIG. 16. Cross section (without shadowing) of spruce tracheids in an advanced stage of decay by the brown-rot fungus *Poria monticola*. X 26,250.

exchanged specimens or to prepare replicas of undried material directly. Until this can be accomplished, a complete understanding of the lignin-microfibril relationship will not be available. We continue to believe that brown-rotted wood provides an essentially ideal experimental material for definition of this aspect of ultrastructure. On the basis of evidence accumulated to date, however, it appears that lignin is deposited together with the carbohydrate-rich entities of the cell wall in an extremely fine network and that these entities may be considerably smaller than microfibrils with a cross sectional dimension of 200 Å.

ANATOMICAL PROBLEMS AMENABLE TO MICROBIOLOGICAL OR ENZYMOLOGICAL TECHNIQUES

In this final section we should like to point out a number of past and potential uses of microorganisms and microbial enzyme systems in studies of wood cell wall structure. The pioneering work of I. W. Bailey using the soft-rot fungi to distinguish a hydrolytic plane within the secondary wall does not need to be repeated (see Figure 5).

Determination of Fibril Angles. Many physical properties of wood are related to the so-called fibril angle—the angle between the orientation of microfibrils of the S_2 layer and the axis of the cell. This angle commonly is determined in coniferous woods by measuring the orientation of pit apertures or drying checks that develop in certain species. In many hardwood species, however, determinations using these criteria are difficult or impossible. Particularly for these species, the use of soft-rot fungi may be recommended. These organisms attack hardwood species readily. Techniques for their cultivation on wood have been worked out by Duncan (1960) and others. Examination of longisections in polarized light will give the fibril angle of the wood cells rapidly and with small errors of measurement.

Isolation of Lignin from Wood in an Unaltered Form. Conventional methods for the quantitative or near quantitative removal of lignin from wood involve drastic reagents, such as 72% sulfuric acid, that remove the wood carbohydrates or selectively extract the lignin. These techniques so drastically modify the lignin that studies of the structure of materials so isolated are not relevant to lignin as it exists *in situ*. Bjorkman (1956) has developed a less drastic procedure involving ball milling wood followed by extraction with neutral solvents such as dioxane. But the material so isolated is very high in residual carbohydrate. The preferred method to obtain lignin in as near unaltered form as possible was developed by Pew (1957). His procedure, like Bjorkman's, involves ball milling the wood to increase its accessibility. Rather than extracting the lignin with neutral solvents, however, he treated the ball milled material with a complex mixture of carbohydrases that selectively hydrolized and dissolved the wood carbohydrates, leaving a residue of lignin containing less than 6% residual carbohydrate.

Visualization of Microfibrils in Nonlignified Tissues. The technique developed by Wood *et al.* (1952) and discussed earlier in this paper holds promise of being effective for the visualization of microfibrils without employing rigorous extraction treatments to remove pectic substances in nonlignified tissues, such as those in the meristematic regions of woody plants.

Determination of the Size and Chemical Composition of Microfibrils.
Considerable controversy appears to exist about the cross-sectional dimensions and distribution of amorphous material within microfibrils.
Some of this controversy could be resolved by examining in the electron microscope preparations of isolated microfibrils treated with specific hemicellulose degrading enzymes. If the hemicelluloses in fact are deposited as a paracrystalline sheath surrounding a crystalline core, changes in the cross-sectional dimension of the microfibrils should permit the localization of the hemicelluloses. Since amorphous materials are considerably more susceptible than the highly crystalline cellulose to enzymatic hydrolysis, brief treatments of microfibril preparations with cellulolytic enzymes probably could be used to determine whether or not amorphous materials are deposited around a crystalline core.

Visualization of the Lignin-Microfibril Relationship. Experimentation in the use of brown-rotted wood to visualize the relationship between lignin and microfibrils has been described earlier in this paper.

Determination of the Chemical Nature of the Warty Layer. Liese has shown earlier in this volume that structures resembling cell organelles and the plasma and vacuolar membranes are involved in the formation of the so-called warty layer of wood cells. It should be possible to verify this hypothesis by treating wood sections from developing tissues that only recently have developed a warty layer with proteolytic enzymes. If the membrane can be removed or altered in appearance by such treatments, evidence in support of this hypothesis would be obtained.

Summary

In conclusion we should like to reiterate our conviction that microorganisms and microbial enzyme systems can be of great value as selective tools for anatomical investigations. The specificity of microbial enzymes, and the very mild conditions under which their reactions proceed, make them potentially ideal reagents for delicate studies of structure. The utility of microbiological and enzymological methods will increase as more is learned concerning the metabolic activities of the microorganisms and the mechanisms of enzyme reactions.

In his introduction to this volume Dr. Preston offered the imploration to work together in the interest of increased scientific understanding of ultrastructural aspects of cell walls. Collaboration between anatomists, wood technologists, and microbiologists and enzymologists will surely add substantially to our knowledge of wood cell wall structure.

ACKNOWLEDGMENTS

The research described in this paper is part of a continuing program of research on the biochemistry of wood deterioration being carried out under the direction of the author with the support of the Pioneering Research Program of the Institute of Paper Chemistry at Appleton, Wisconsin.

The research involving electron microscopy (Figs. 6-10, 13-16) and its interpretation was carried out with the cooperation of W. A. Côté, Jr. and A. C. Day, State University College of Forestry, Syracuse, New York.

REFERENCES

Asunmaa, Saara (1955) "Morphology of middle lamella of spruce (*Picea excelsa*)." *Svensk Papperstid.* 58:308–310.

Bailey, I. W., and Vestal, Mary R.   (1937) "The significance of certain wood-destroying fungi in the study of the enzymatic hydrolysis of cellulose." *J. Arnold Arboretum* 18:196–205.

Barghoorn, E. S., and Linder, D. H.   (1944) "Marine fungi: Their taxonomy and biology." *Farlowia* 1:395–467.

Bjorkman, A.   (1956) "Studies on finely divided wood.   I. Extraction of lignin with neutral solvents." *Svensk Papperstid.* 59:477–485.

Côté, W. A., Jr., and Day, A. C.   (1962) "The G-layer in gelatinous fibers—electron microscopic studies." *Forest Prod. J.* 12:333–338.

——Kóran, Z., and Day, A. C.   (1964)   "Replica techniques for electron microscopy." Tappi 47:477–484.

——, and Marton, R.   (1962) "Electron microscopy of white birch heartwood." *Tappi* 45:46–53.

Cowling, E. B.   (1961) "Comparative biochemistry of the decay of sweetgum sapwood by white-rot and brown-rot fungi." U. S. Dept. Agr. Tech. Bull. No. 1258. 79pp.

—— (1963) "Structural features of cellulose that influence its susceptibility to enzymatic hydrolysis."   In *Advances in Enzymic Hydrolysis of Cellulose and Related Materials* (E. T. Reese, ed.), pp. 1–32. Pergamon Press, London.

Duncan, C. G.   (1960) "Wood-attacking capacities and physiology of soft-rot fungi." U.S. For. Prod. Lab. Rept. No. 2173. 28pp.

Husain, A., and Kelman, A.   (1959) "Tissue is disintegrated."   In *Plant Pathology: An Advanced Treatise* (J. G. Horsfall and A. E. Dimond, ed.), Vol. 1, pp. 143–188. Academic Press, N.Y.

Kirk, K., and Kelman, A.   (1964) "Color formation on phenol-containing media as related to lignin breakdown by wood-rotting basidiomycetes." *Phytopathology* 54:897.

Knuth, D. T.   (1964) "Bacteria associated with wood products and their effects on certain chemical and physical properties of wood." Ph.D. Thesis, Univ. Wis., Madison. 143pp.

Meier, H.   (1955) "Über den Zellwandabbau durch Holzvermorschungspilze und die submikroskopische Struktur von Fichtentracheiden und Birkenholzfasern." *Holz Roh-Werkstoff* 13:323–338.

Nord, F. F., and Schubert, Walter J. (1957) "On the mechanism of lignification." *Tappi* 40:285–294.

―――― and ―――― (1958) "Lignin." *Sci. Am.* 199:104–113.

Pew, J. C. (1957) "Properties of powdered wood and isolation of lignin by cellulolytic enzymes." *Tappi* 40:553–558.

Proctor, P., Jr. (1941) "Penetration of the walls of wood cells by the hyphae of wood-destroying fungi." Yale University School of Forestry Bull. No. 47. 31pp.

Reese, E. T., and Mandels, Mary (1959) "Use of enzymes in isolation and analysis of poly-saccharides." *Appl. Microbiol.* 7:378–387.

Roelofsen, P. A. (1956) "Eine mögliche Erklärung der typischen Korrosionsfiguren der Holzfasern bei Moderfäule." *Holz Roh- Werkstoff* 14:208–210.

Sachs, Irving B., Clark, Ira T., and Pew, John C. (1963) "Investigation of lignin dis-tribution in the cell wall of certain woods." *J. Polymer Sci.*, Part C 2:203–212.

Shigo, A. L. (1963) "Fungi associated with the discolorations around rot columns caused by *Fomes igniarus*." *Plant Disease Reptr.* 47:820–823.

Wood, R. K. S., Gold, A. H., and Rawlins, T. E. (1952). "Electron microscopy of primary cell walls treated with pectic enzymes." *Am. J. Botany* 39:132–133.

PART IV

Reaction Wood—*Its Causes, Formation, and Ultrastructure*

The Formation and Function of Reaction Wood

A. B. WARDROP

Commonwealth Scientific and Industrial Research Organization,
Division of Forest Products,
South Melbourne, Australia

Present address: Department of Botany,
University of Tasmania

The discussion by Côté in this volume demonstrates the changes in anatomy and fine structure which accompany the formation of reaction wood of gymnosperms (compression wood) and of angiosperms (tension wood).

In the following survey attention is directed to those factors which govern the differentiation of compression wood and tension wood and to the possible function of these tissues in the plant.

The Occurrence and Distribution of Reaction Wood

The formation of reaction wood is usually, but not always, accompanied by a differential radial growth which results in an eccentric cross-sectional form of the stem or branch concerned. In general this eccentricity is towards the upper side of leaning stems or branches in angiosperms and towards the lower side in gymnosperms (Grossenbacher, 1915; Priestley and Tong, 1927; Rawitscher, 1932; Wergin, 1961). Although this tendency to eccentric development of a stem or branch is usual, a number of workers have noted exceptions to it, especially among the angiosperms (Wardrop, 1964).

From these observations the generalization that eccentric growth is towards the upper side of leaning stems or branches of most angiosperms and towards the lower side in gymnosperms with a well developed arborescent habit, appears justified. It may be noted, however, that when this eccentricity is apparent in only a few growth rings it may not be reflected in the form of the member as a whole. Furthermore, it has been observed (Jaccard, 1938; Wardrop, 1956) that eccentricity of a given growth ring may vary at points along the branch or stem (see below).

According to Jaccard (1938), when a stem or branch exhibited greater radial increment on one side there was a decreased radial increment on the opposite side, i.e., there was a compensation of radial growth, so that the total cross-sectional area of the xylem formed was no greater than when the growth was uniform.

The degree of modification of wood anatomy involved in tension wood formation is extremely variable both between different families and within individual plants. A survey of its occurrence in different families was made by Nečesaný (1955), who concluded that its formation is more common in those families in which the wood is less specialized. Some species, such as *Fraxinus* (Clarke, 1937) and *Tilia* (Jaccard, 1917; Onaka, 1949), are reported to show no great modification in their anatomy although their degree of lignification is reduced (Priestley and Tong, 1927), whereas in species such as *Fagus* and *Eucalyptus* the anatomical modification is very great and is also accompanied by a reduction in the level of lignification.

However, in a recent study of *Lagunaria patersoni*, Scurfield (1964) has reported that the wood on the upper side of bent stems showed no G-layer and the cells were of greater diameter than those on the lower side. In the growth habit of this species, however, positive geotropic growth is not strong.

Although the extent of modification of wood anatomy is variable in compression wood of gymnosperms, the occurrence of this tissue is more regular than is tension wood in angiosperms and so far as the writer is aware no species have been recorded in which it does not occur.

REACTION WOOD FORMATION AND GROWTH MOVEMENTS
IN STEMS AND BRANCHES

In herbaceous plants the orientation in space of a stem or branch may be brought about by differential longitudinal growth on opposite sides of the organ showing response. In woody plants in which secondary tissues have developed, the process by which such movements are effected cannot be brought about by this means, since longitudinal extension growth ceases after the formation of the secondary tissue systems. It has therefore been concluded that tropistic and nastic movements in stems with secondary growth must involve a process of bending. This process was illustrated (Wardrop, 1964) in a young plant of *Tristania conferta* which was placed in a horizontal position and its recovery followed at intervals. The initial response took place in the apex and was followed by a progressive bending of the stem at points of increasing distances from ob-the apex and at which longitudinal growth was no longer possible. Anatomical examination of such a stem showed a considerable development of tension wood along the upper side of the stem, with the exception of the terminal three internodes. Similar observations have been made on large trees of both angiosperms (Jacobs, 1939) and gymnosperms (Büsgen and Münch, 1929).

Other examples of the association between growth responses and reaction wood formation may be seen in the progressive movement of one member of a forked branch following removal of an adjacent branch (Hartmann, 1949) and on the assumption as a leading shoot of the first lateral branch following the removal of the apex of the stem.

Again it was shown by Wardrop (1956) that if stems of *Eucalyptus* were bent into a horizontal position and the cambium was removed from the upper side of the stem no recovery took place in the wounded area, i.e, the region in which reaction wood would be expected to develop. If, however, the cambium was damaged on the lower side of the bent stem, recovery was not inhibited. In a similar experiment with *Pinus radiata*, recovery was inhibited if the cambium was destroyed on the lower side but not if the upper cambium was removed. These observations thus suggest that for the recovery of the stems to occur it was only necessary for the cambium to be active on the side of reaction wood formation and this again indicates a close correlation between the formation of reaction wood and the bending of the stem induced by its experimental treatment.

Perhaps a more convincing demonstration of this point is to be seen in the observation of Wardrop and Davies (1964) in a study of the fine structure of compression wood induced by IAA (indole acetic acid). Thus it was observed that when IAA was applied asymmetrically to vertical stems, compression wood was formed, as demonstrated previously by Wershing and Bailey (1942), but also obvious bending of the stem occurred (Fig. 1).

From observations such as the above it would seem reasonable to explain orientation movements such as those indicated as resulting from a process of bending of the stem or branch which is correlated with the development of reaction wood. However, the fact that some angiosperms do not show the development of a characteristic reaction anatomy yet show orientation movements raises the question whether reaction wood formation is a cause or a result of such movements. In relation to these considerations it is obviously relevant to consider evidence as to the nature of the stimuli giving rise to reaction wood formation, and to survey evidence relating to possible mechanisms by which the bending of stems and branches involved in tropic and nastic movements by the stem and branches may be effected.

FIG. 1. A young tree of *Pinus radiata* to which α-naphthalene acetic acid was applied laterally. The bending of the stem is apparent. Anatomical examination both above and below the point of application (arrow) showed extensive development of compression wood.

FACTORS GOVERNING REACTION WOOD FORMATION IN STEMS

Reaction Wood Formation as a Stress Response. From the observed distribution of reaction wood, it was proposed by Metzger (1908) that reaction wood formation resulted from tension stresses on the upper side of branches and leaning stems of angiosperms and of compressive stresses on the lower side of leaning stems and branches of gymnosperms. The view that reaction wood was a response to stress was supported by the

servation that this tissue was induced in seven to fourteen days when branches were weighted or stems were bent out of their normal vertical position.

Much early work on the effects of tensile stresses on plant anatomy and growth is relevant to the idea that these forces induce reaction wood formation (see Wardrop, 1964).

Evidence such as the above suggests that conditions of tensile or compressive stresses existing in leaning stems or in branches and resulting from their weight could be a factor inducing the abnormal characteristics of the wood now recognized as reaction wood. However, it will be apparent that the weight of the stem and branches is really an indirect manifestation of the influence of gravity and the possibility of a direct gravitational influence was therefore explored by many investigators.

Reaction Wood Formation as a Gravitational Response. Experiments suggesting that gravity may influence the formation of reaction xylem were carried out in gymnosperms by Ewart and Mason-Jones (1906), and in angiosperms by Jaccard (1919, 1938), Onaka (1949), and Hartmann (1949). It was observed that when plants were placed at increasing angles from the vertical, the reaction wood forms consistently on the lower side of the inclined stem of gymnosperms, and on the upper side of stems of angiosperms in similar orientation, and increases in amount up to an angle of inclination of 90° and then decreases again, no reaction wood being formed when the stem is pointing vertically downwards. In a field study it was observed by Berlyn (1961) that the amount of reaction wood formed in stems of *Populus deltoides* was positively correlated with the degree of lean of the trees.

A second type of observation was that made by Ewart and Mason-Jones (1906) and by Jaccard (1938) and by Burns (1942), in which stems and branches were bent into vertical and horizontal loops. In these experiments it was observed that the reaction wood formed on the lower side of vertical loops of gymnosperms, and on the upper side of similar loops in stems of angiosperms, irrespective of whether the wood was placed initially in tension or compression (Fig. 2). These observations were interpreted to mean that gravity is a predominant stimulus governing the formation of reaction wood. Further evidence of the possible influence of gravity on reaction wood formation was obtained by Jaccard (1939, 1940) and by Scott and Preston (1955), who studied the anatomical changes in stems subjected to centrifugal force which could, under the conditions of the experiment, be made to wholly or partially counteract the force of gravity. The plants were placed on the perimeter of a horizontally rotating disk. It was observed that the growth proceeded so that curvature towards the center of the disk took place. In angiosperms

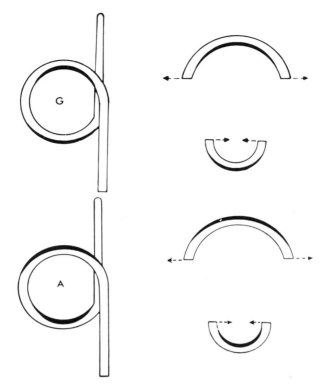

FIG. 2. A diagrammatic representation of the distribution of reaction wood in loops in stems of gymnosperms (G) and angiosperms (A). At the right the movement of the upper and lower segments of the loops observed when they were cut horizontally is shown. (After Jaccard, 1938.)

the tissue formed on the inner surface of the stems was tension wood, and in gymnosperms the wood formed on the outer side was compression wood. Thus characteristic reaction wood was formed when the gravitational force was replaced by a continuous centrifugal force.

Relatively few experiments using horizontal klinostats have been carried out. However, White (1908) observed that compression wood did not develop when conifers were continuously rotated on a horizontal klinostat; and a similar observation was made by Wardrop (1964), using young stems of *Tristania conferta*, although in control stems which were placed horizontally and which underwent geotropic response reaction wood was formed (Fig. 3). It was also observed (Wardrop, 1964) that stems of *Tristania conferta* bent as in Figure 3c showed no reaction wood formation. This observation thus pointed clearly to the conclusion that gravity and not applied stress was effective in inducing reaction wood formation.

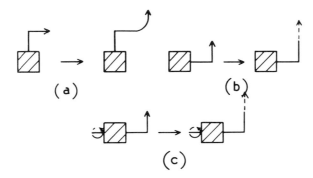

FIG. 3. A diagrammatic representation illustrating various experiments on reaction wood formation in *Tristania conferta*. (a) Stem bent horizontally and allowed to recover: reaction wood was present along the entire upper side of the horizontal regions and both bends. (b) Stem bent so that the apex remained vertical: reaction wood was present along the upper side of the horizontal region to the bend. (c) As (b) but the plant was placed on a horizontal klinostat: no reaction was formed (from Wardrop, 1964).

FACTORS GOVERNING REACTION WOOD FORMATION IN BRANCHES

The observations described above point to the influence of gravity as a major stimulus in governing the formation of reaction wood and the apparent consequent bending response in stems of both angiosperms and gymnosperms. In branches, however, the position appears to be of considerably greater complexity. Indications of this are contained in the observations of the extreme variability of reaction wood distribution in branches compared with that in leaning stems (Jaccard, 1938).

Experimentally this complexity of response is readily apparent and indicates the operation of factors other than, or in addition to, gravity in governing reaction wood formation.

Thus if a branch of either an angiosperm or a gymnosperm is bent downwards, tension wood or compression wood is formed on the upper (adaxial) side or the lower (abaxial) side respectively, as in bent stems. However, if the branches of angiosperms are bent upwards, tension wood is formed on the lower side, whereas in gymnosperms the compression wood is formed on the upper side (Fig. 4) (Jaccard, 1919; Hartmann, 1949; Dyer, 1955; Wardrop, 1956).

Furthermore, it was observed by Münch (1938b) that when *Picea* plants were rotated on a klinostat, although no compression wood was formed in the stem, it was formed in branches on their adaxial side (i.e., nearest the stem) (Fig. 5). This experiment was also carried out by Wardrop (1964), using plants of *Liquidambar styraciflua*. In this instance tension wood was formed on the abaxial side of the branches. It was observed further that

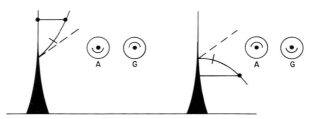

FIG. 4. A diagrammatic representation of the distribution of reaction wood in branches which bent upwards or downwards in a gymnosperm (G) and an angiosperm (A).

there was a consistent downwards movement of the branches during the period of growth, so that the tension wood was formed in a position in which it would effect such a change in branch orientation.

Münch (1938b) interpreted this behavior in terms of the theory of plagiotropism proposed by de Vries. On this view the branches are normally subjected to negatively geotropic and epinastic tendencies. Rotation on the klinostat was considered to eliminate the gravitational influences so that the epinastism alone was effective. Such a view is consistent with that advanced by Hartmann that there is an "intrinsic growth direction" of the branches. This concept has also been advanced by other investigators.

Thus Jost (1907) proposed that there exists for the different organs of the plant "a condition of rest" which, if altered by its own growth or by environmental changes, results in a response by the plant in such a way as to restore this condition. A similar idea is contained in the use by Büsgen and Münch (1929) of the term "reaction norm" of the branches in relation to the stem, and Jaccard's recognition of a "proper spatial setting" of a branch in relation to the stem. It may be noted that Thimann (1964) has attempted a unified interpretation of such phenomena in terms of an hormonal hypothesis (q.v.).

REACTION WOOD FORMATION AND THE MECHANISM OF
GROWTH MOVEMENTS

From the above discussion it is apparent that in general reaction wood formation is associated with growth movements of stems or branches in a manner such that the side on which compression wood is formed tends to become convex and the side on which tension wood is formed becomes concave.

It is consistent with a process of bending of the stem that deformations in the cell wall characteristic of mechanical deformation are recognizable.

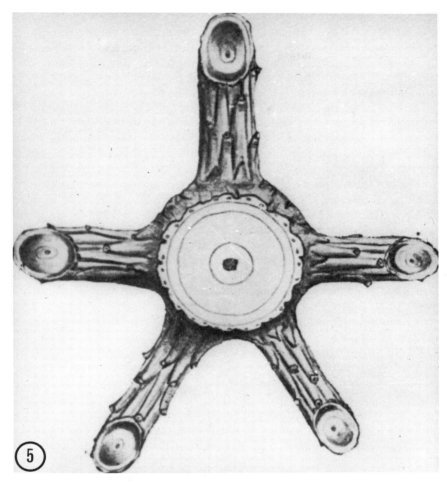

FIG. 5. Illustrating the formation of compression wood on the upper side of branches of a gymnosperm during rotation on a horizontal klinostat (from Münch, 1938b).

Thus slip planes characteristic of the effects of shear and compressive stresses can be seen in the zone internal to zones of compression wood formation (the "susceptible wood" of Green and Yorston [1939]) and in mature tension wood.

In considering mechanisms by which bending of large stems or branches may be effected, it is important to appreciate, as pointed out by Frey-Wyssling (1952), that the stem or branch of a tree should be regarded as a viscoelastic body capable of deformation under stress over prolonged periods of time, i.e., these members undergo creep. Frey-Wyssling pointed out that, this being so, the forces necessary to deform the branch or stem would be very much less than the forces expected on the basis of the strength properties of the wood. He suggested that forces arising in the cambium and acting over a prolonged period would be sufficient to bring about such mechanical bending of the stem.

In relation to the possible mechanism by which bending may be effected, it was demonstrated in investigations of Jaccard (1938), and later those of Münch (1938a) and of Jacobs (1939), that the formation of reaction wood was associated with the development of considerable growth stresses. Thus it was observed in normal vertically growing stems that, if a segment of the stem were removed from the tree and sectioned longitudinally, the outermost sections contracted in length while those passing through or near the center of the stem elongated, so that the center of the stem was in a state of compression relative to the outside of the stem. When stems containing reaction wood were examined in this way, it was found that the contraction of the tension wood was very much greater than that of the tissues adjacent or opposite to it, and when compression wood was present its elongation was greater than that of wood opposite to it. From this it was concluded that the tension wood was in a state of high longitudinal tension and compression wood in a state of extreme compression.

An additional demonstration of the development of growth stresses associated with reaction formation was made by Jaccard (1938). He observed that, when stems or branches were bent in the form of loops and allowed to grow for an extended period, and when these loops were cut, the upper segment extended while the lower segment contracted, presumably as a result of the reaction wood formation (Fig. 2). The existence of such stresses was suggested by Münch to be the cause of movements of orientation in woody stems, and he considered that the longitudinal tensile stress of the tension wood and the longitudinal compressive stresses of compression wood caused a mechanical bending of the stem. Münch (1938a) compared the contraction in woody stems containing tension wood with other known contractile systems in plants, such as the contractile roots of some species. The extent, however, to which such a comparison is valid remains to be demonstrated.

It will be appreciated that the presence of accumulated stresses in growing stems does not necessarily mean that such stresses are effective in governing movements of orientation. However, it was pointed out by Jacobs that if this were so then the asymmetry of stress in asymmetric stems could provide a means by which geotropic recovery could come about, even without the extreme stress accumulation which accompanies reaction wood formation.

In the case of angiosperms, an attempt was made by Wardrop (1964) to test this hypothesis. Thus it will be appreciated that growth stresses demonstrated in mature tissues are present even when the cells are dead, so that if bending of the stem resulted from the operation of such forces then this process would be expected to be a cumulative one, depending on the amount of reaction wood formed, and would be expected to continue at least for a time when the cambium was inactive. Accordingly, a number of stems were bent downwards and held in horizontal position by a spring balance in the manner previously described by Wardrop (1956). The subsequent movements of the stem could be followed by the reading on the balance. The curve obtained for one such tree is shown in Figure 6. The initial decrease in the values of the balance reading resulted

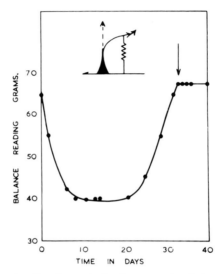

Fig. 6. A graph showing the change in load on a spring balance during geotropic recovery of a young tree of *Liquidambar styraciflua* treated as shown in the diagram. Note the initial stress relaxation in the stem, followed by a period of rapid recovery which was accompanied by reaction wood formation. At the point marked by the arrow the buds were removed and the tree was defoliated, and the stem was artificially loaded to compensate for the loss in weight of the leaves (from Wardrop, 1964).

from relaxation of stress in the stem following the initial bending. With the progressive development of reaction wood, recovery began. After thirty days, when the stem was showing rapid recovery, all leaves and buds were removed, or it was injected with poisons and the leaves were removed. The loss in weight due to this treatment was offset by attaching weights to the stem to give the balance reading recorded before defoliation. After this treatment no further recovery was observed, so it was concluded that the active participation of the differentiating reaction wood was necessary for recovery to occur. This experiment does not preclude the possibility that active stresses causing recovery are generated during differentiation of reaction wood, but suggests that the accumulated stresses demonstrated in mature tissues are alone insufficient to effect movements of orientation. Obviously, however, further experiments of the above type are necessary in assessing this hypothesis.

A further hypothesis was proposed by Frey-Wyssling (1952), who suggested that forces arising in the cambium and acting over a prolonged period could effect bending of the stem, and proposed that the development of reaction wood was to be regarded as a response by the tree serving to maintain the new orientation of the stem (Casperson, 1960, 1961). It was also pointed out that the cell wall organization of reaction wood fibers and tracheids appeared to be an adaption of their normal structure which would resist such compressive and tensile stresses.

In gymnosperms a study of the differentiation of compression wood is consistent with such an hypothesis. Thus, in a recent study by Wardrop and Davies (1964), it was observed that some features of compression wood could be seen early in the differentiation of the tissue. Thus the cells became rounded and intercellular spaces were apparent before secondary wall formation began, although they sometimes appeared to be greater in regions in which the secondary wall had formed. Furthermore, a study of macerated mature tissue showed that the tracheids had greatly distorted and bifurcated tips compared with the smoothly tapered tips of mature cells (Fig. 7). Since the form of the cells is determined before secondary wall formation begins, these features suggest that the tracheids of the compression wood exist in a state of extreme turgidity during differentiation, and their form could reflect deformation arising from the exertion of longitudinal stresses involved in orientation movements. This is also consistent with the observation that geotropic recovery took place when the cambium of the lower side of the stem was intact but not when it had been removed (Wardrop, 1956). The case of tension wood formation in angiosperms, however, appears considerably more complex. The differentiating xylem of tension wood appears identical with normal wood until differentiation of the SG layer begins. The SG layer is first apparent as an unlignified, sometimes convoluted, layer lying adjacent to the layers S_1, S_2, or rarely the layer S_3 of the secondary wall (Scurfield and Wardrop, 1962). The differentiation of fibers containing this layer is prolonged. This is apparent in the persistence of the protoplast in tension wood fibers compared with those on the opposite side of the stem. In fibers in which the SG layer is not convoluted, it shows a progressive thickening until the

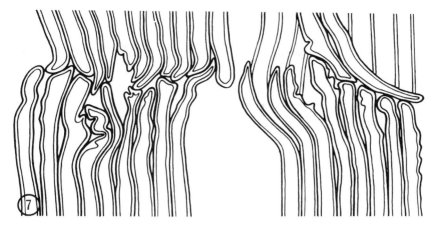

FIG. 7. Illustrating the distorted tips of compression wood tracheids in *Pinus peuce* (from Münch, 1940).

lumen of the cell may be almost completely filled. In fibers in which the layer shows convolution, it is observed to thicken in the convoluted form and then to straighten on to the existing cell wall, and this is then followed by the development of a further convoluted part of the layer which subsequently is also straightened and deposited on the existing part of the SG layer (Fig. 8). In some species, however, such as *Acacia*, the SG layer retains its convoluted form even in mature cells.

It was shown by Scurfield and Wardrop (1962) that before the straightening of the convoluted layer was complete it often showed slight birefringence, which was absent in mature cells and could be reduced or eliminated by dehydration in alcohol. Furthermore, in the differentiating fibers it was observed that the inner part of the SG layer stained more intensely with basic dyes, such as light green (this was also the case with the fibers of reaction phloem), and with Congo red. In mature fibers the intensity of staining with Congo red was greatly reduced.

Now, as stated above, geotropic recovery took place if the cambium forming tension wood was intact. Furthermore, since this tissue is formed on the upper side of the stem, any such bending can only occur by the longitudinal contraction of this side of the stem. Since the differentiating xylem appeared normal until the SG layer was formed, it is difficult to envisage a mechanism by which such contraction could arise in turgid cells, and it is therefore reasonable to seek the source of the forces causing longitudinal contraction in the differentiating secondary wall. One possible source of such forces is the crystallization of cellulose during secondary wall formation (Wardrop, 1964).

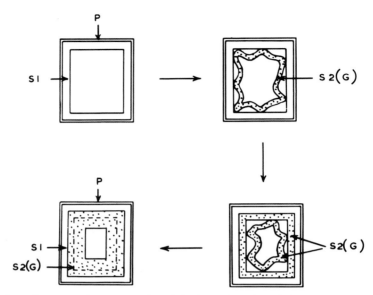

FIG. 8. A diagrammatic representation of the formation of the SG layer of tension wood fibers in *Grevillia robusta* (from Wardrop, 1964).

Thus, if it is accepted that stress accumulation is not responsible for the bending process, the forces responsible would seem to arise from some change during the differentiation process. Since in compression wood the form of the cells is determined before secondary wall formation, it is possible that forces generated in the phase of surface growth of the tracheids may be further enhanced by the subsequently formed secondary wall. During the formation of tension wood, however, it would seem that any source of forces causing longitudinal contraction is most likely to be in the differentiating secondary wall.

In an attempt to reconcile the various views advanced as to the mechanism of bending of stems or branches involved in orientation movements, a provisional hypothesis may be advanced. As background it may be recalled that the degree of lignification of compression wood is greater than that in wood opposite to it in the same growth ring, and the over-all lignification of tension wood is less than that in wood opposite to it in the same growth ring. Thus there is a similar differential lignification of leaning stems and branches in both angiosperms and gymnosperms, such that the lignification is greater on the lower side.

Let it be assumed that during differentiation there is a tendency for the fibers and tracheids to contract in length and also that the degree of any such contraction is less when the lignin content of the cell wall is high.

On these two assumptions, irrespective of the development of the characteristic reaction anatomy, forces would be generated which would tend to cause the stems or branch to become concave towards the less lignified side. When reaction wood is formed, the presence of the virtually unlignified SG layer in tension wood and the heavy lignification of the compression wood tracheids would enhance this bending brought about by a differential lignification alone.

In support of such an hypothesis, several lines of argument may be advanced. Thus there is some evidence that there is a change in physical texture of the secondary wall during its formation. Reference has already been made to the change in the SG layer of tension wood fibers, through which the layer changes from an initial convoluted form and flattens on to existing layers of the wall. During this process minute radial striations appear in the layer when viewed in cross section. A similar development of radial striations was observed in the layered secondary walls of phloem fibers of *Nerium oleander* by Krabbe (1887). It is to be emphasized that these changes occur in walls still saturated with water and are not the result of stresses due to drying, so that it is reasonable to assume that they reflect a change in the state of the wall. It may be noted in both of these instances that the wall is not lignified.

Evidence that lignification can alter the dimensions of the wall has been presented by Alexandrov and Djaparidze (1934), Frey (1926), Preston (1941), and Preston and Middlebrook (1949). It was observed in different cells that lignification caused a change in thickness of particular wall layers so that in effect they became swollen as a result of the lignification process. Although these instances probably represent an extreme effect of lignification, it may be argued that any degree of lignification would reduce the postulated tendency for the wall to decrease in volume. It is readily understandable that lignification should have this effect, since it is well known that lignin is located between the microfibrils (Mühlethaler, 1949) and may even penetrate the interstices within them (Wardrop, 1954).

If we now consider possible sources of this postulated contraction of the cells during differentiation, it was proposed by Wardrop (1956) that during wall formation the cellulose microfibrils are deposited in only a partly crystalline state and that as the cell matures further crystallization occurs. This process is never complete, as is seen by the presence of a peripheral paracrystalline phase around the microfibrils. Now, it was shown by Wardrop (1955) that delignification results in an increase in the degree of lateral order of the micelles within the microfibrils, so that some lignin can be assumed to be closely associated with the paracrystalline phase of cellulose. Furthermore, the degree of lateral order of different celluloses appears to be correlated with the degree of lignification, being greater in the less lignified cells (Wardrop, 1948). Specifically, this may be illustrated for tension wood and wood opposite to it from the same growth ring (Table I).

TABLE I. Breadth of Half-Maximum Intensity (radians) of the 002 Diffraction Line of Normal Wood and Tension Wood of *Eucalyptus regnans* (Wardrop, 1955)

Specimen	Line breadth	
	Untreated	Hydrolyzed[a]
Normal wood	0.070	0.062
Normal holocellulose	0.059	0.052
Tension wood	0.049	0.046

[a] Hydrolyzed with 8% hydrochloric acid for 15 minutes at 100°C.

Thus, in elaborating the above hypothesis, it is reasonable to suggest that lignification serves to inhibit the crystallization of the microfibrils, resulting in a lower degree of lateral order and a reduction in the tendency for the cells to contract in volume.

It may be noted further that the postulated contraction in volume is analogous to shrinkage which occurs on drying, in that a reduction of the volume of the wall is involved. In attempting to explain the anisotropy of shrinkage, it was shown by Preston that if a decrease in length of the helical winding of a wall layer was assumed, then, depending on the initial orientation of the microfibrils to the longitudinal cell axis (θ), the cells would contract in length ($\theta < 40°$) or expand in length ($\theta > 40°$) (Preston, 1942, 1964). In tension wood the microfibrils of the SG layer are at an angle of less than 5° to the cell axis, and in the S_1 layer ca. 40°. In compression wood the angle of orientation in the S_2 layer is 45–50°, and in the layer S_1, 70–90°, so that, insofar as these effects are involved, the cell wall organization in reaction wood is such as to favor a tendency to longitudinal contraction in tension wood and longitudinal expansion in compression wood.

Thus, in terms of the above hypothesis, reaction wood would be regarded as both participating in the process of orientation movements and also serving, through the modification of its structure, to be adapted to maintain the position of the stem or branch concerned.

PHYSIOLOGICAL ASPECTS OF REACTION WOOD FORMATION AND ITS FUNCTIONAL SIGNIFICANCE

In the preceding survey a number of observations which point to the association of reaction wood formation and orientation movements have been described. In some of these and other observations, evidence of correlative response of branch movements has been obtained. Thus Hartmann (1949) and others have shown that the assumption of apical dominance of the first lateral branch following removal of the apical shoot involves reaction wood formation. Furthermore, it was shown by Münch (1938b) that the branch immediately below the region of bark removed in girdled stems behaved in a manner similar to the subterminal shoot in decapitated stems.

It was observed by Onaka (1949) that eccentric growth did not occur in bent stems if the apex was removed or if a circular incision was made around the stem, and, furthermore, that there was no recovery of the stem. Wardrop (1956) observed that if a stem was bent for a period of time and then the apices of the stem and branches were removed, recovery of the stem continued. However, if the apices were removed prior to bending, no recovery took place and no reaction wood was formed until axiallary buds became established.

These observations indicate that the site of the stimuli governing geotropic response lies in the apex, but once this process has been initiated it can continue at least for a time without the participation of the apex.

In gymnosperms, evidence of hormonal control of reaction wood formation and the associated movements of stems and branches is fairly direct. Thus, following the demonstration that IAA induces compression wood in conifers (Wershing and Bailey, 1942) and also induces bending when asymmetrically applied to vertical stems (Wardrop and Davies, 1964), Toda et al. (1963) have shown that if IAA is applied to decapitated stems the first lateral branch does not show geotropic response to become the leader. It has also been observed that when the apical shoot is removed from horizontal stems and replaced by IAA, normal geotropic recovery takes place (Wardrop and Davies, unpublished).

The distribution of auxin in stems and branches undergoing reaction xylem formation under natural conditions does not appear to have been investigated, but Nečesaný (1958) has studied this question in artificially bent tems. Ether extracts were made from the differentiating zone from the upper and lower sides of a bent stem of *Populus alba* following the method of Luckwill (1952), and the effect of chromatographically separated components of the extracts on the extension or inhibition of coleoptiles of *Triticum aestivum* was measured. It was observed that substances stimulating elongation of the coleoptile sections were present mainly on the lower side. IAA appeared to be the most important of the stimulating substances. It will be appreciated that the influence of the substances which enhance or inhibit the elongation of coleoptile sections on the cells of the tissues in which they occur cannot be easily assessed, since their effect on different test tissues may differ. This has been observed in the case of an inhibiting substance extracted from woody shoots by Barlow *et al.* (1959).

It may be noted that Westing (1960) observed a greater concentration of what was probably an indole compound on the lower side of horizontal shoots of *Pinus strobus*. However, Wareing *et al.* (1964) were unable to confirm Nečesaný's results in that they could not detect any consistent difference in the growth promoters and growth inhibitors on the upper and lower side of shoots of poplar or willow.

Evidence was obtained by Nečesaný (1956, 1958) that the substances extracted may be related to both cell division and cell elongation. Thus he observed that the thickness of callus developed in cuttings from horizontally grown branches was less on the side containing tension wood. Furthermore, roots developed on the side opposite the tension wood. Nečesaný considered that the greater development of callus on the side opposite the tension wood could be attributed to a higher concentration of IAA in that region.

Although reaction wood of gymnosperms can be induced by the application of IAA, in experiments performed so far on the application of IAA and other substances it has not been possible to induce reaction xylem formation in angiosperms by this means (Onaka, 1949; Wardrop, 1956). (See the contribution of Kennedy in this volume, in which what appears to be tension wood was induced by the application of tri-iodobenzoic acid.) However, Nečesaný (1958) observed that when IAA was added to the upper side of stems in which tension wood was undergoing formation, the further formation of this tissue was reduced, at least for a time. The application of IAA to the lower side of such stems was without effect on tension wood formation. It was observed further that the fiber length was least on the side of IAA application, so that if it is accepted on the basis of Nečesaný's observations that the formation of tension wood results from a differential distribution of IAA and other growth-regulating substances in the stem, it would be expected that the fiber length would be less in compression wood and greater in tension wood than in the xylem opposite these tissues. This is in agreement with the observations of Onaka (1949), Nečesaný (1955), and Ollinmaa (1959).

As already pointed out, it was proposed by Münch (1938) that the angle which a branch makes with the stem represents the result of the balance between gravity and an intrinsic epinastism, so that if either of these factors were removed, e.g., by decapitation or by growing the plant on a klinostat, a lack of balance between the forces would result and the orientation of the branch would be influenced by the remaining predominant influence.

Thimann (1964) has extended this type of concept to the hormonal level and has postulated that the angle existing between the stem and branch is determined by the balance of forces governing auxin distribution. Thus auxin is derived from the terminal bud and leaves and is diverted to the lower side of the branch and would tend to cause an upward curvature, but this is prevented by a second postulated force governing auxin distribution, for which evidence was advanced by Thimann, and which tends to cause the auxin to move to the upper side of the branch. Thus if, as Nečesaný's experiments suggest, tension wood is formed under conditions of auxin depletion and compression wood under conditions of auxin excess, a hormonal explanation of the distribution of these tissues, at least under simple experimental situations, appears to be possible. Thimann also pointed out that the distribution of peroxidase, studied initially by Wardrop and Scaife (1956), may be significant in such a mechanism, since peroxidase may act as an IAA oxidase and as an oxidizing enzyme involved in lignification.

Such an argument thus provides the basis of a general physiological hypothesis of reaction wood formation, although, as pointed out by Thimann (1964), there are many points yet to be resolved. However, the recognition of the correlative aspects of reaction wood formation and of its participation in tropic and nastic responses by the plant, provides a remarkable instance in which transient physiological influences governing such responses receive anatomical expression.

Since the orientation of the branches to the stem, as well as the extent of their growth, determines the form of the tree, it can be seen that the integrated study of reaction wood formation in woody plants in relation to its ultrastructure and anatomy, as well as its physiological aspects, provides a rare example of the value of these different approaches to the study of this fundamental problem in morphogenesis.

REFERENCES

Alexandrov, W. G., and Djaparidze, L. I. (1927) *Planta* 4:467.
Barlow, H. W. B., Hancock, C. R., and Lacy, H. J. (1959) *Proc. Intern. Conf. Plant Growth Regulators, Ames Iowa*, p. 140.
Berlyn, G. P. (1961) *Iowa State J. Sci.* 35:367–424.
Burns, G. P. (1942) Vermont Agr. Expt. Sta. Bull. No. 492.
Büsgen, M., and Münch, E. (1929) *The Structure and Life of Forest Trees.* Chapman and Hall, London.
Casperson, G. (1960) *Ber. Deut. Botan. Ges.* 73:349–357.
———— (1961) *Naturwiss.* 48:701.
Clarke, S. H. (1937) *Forestry* 11:85–91.
Dyer, D. (1955) *J. Oxford Univ. For. Soc.,* Ser. 4, 4:19.
Ewart, A. C. J., and Mason-Jones, A. G. (1960) *Ann. Botany (London)* 20:201.
Frey, A. (1926) *Jahrb. Wiss. Botan.* 65:210.
Frey-Wyssling, A. (1952) *Ber. Schweiz. Botan. Ges.* 62:583.

Green, H., and Yorston, F. H. (1939) *Pulp Paper Mag. Can.* 40:244–250.

Grossenbacher, J. G. (1915) *Trans. Wisconsin Acad. Sci.* 18:1.

Hartmann, F. (1949) *Das statische Wuchsgesetz bei Nadel-und Laubbaumen. Neue Erkenntnis über Ursache, Gesetzmassigkeit und Sinn des Reaktionsholzes.* Springer, Vienna.

Jaccard, P. (1917) *Rev. Gen. Botan.* 29:225–243.

_____ (1919) *Nouvelles-recherches sur l'accroissement en épaisseur des arbres.* Memoire primé et publié par la Fondation Schnyder von Wartensee à Zurich, Switzerland.

_____ (1938) *Ber. Schweiz. Botan. Ges.* 48:491–502.

_____ (1939) *Ber. Schweiz. Botan. Ges.* 49:135.

_____ (1940) *Ber. Schweitz. Botan. Ges.* 50:279–284.

Jacobs, M. R. (1939) Commonwealth Forestry and Timber Bur. Bull. No. 24, Canberra.

Jost, L. (1907) *Lectures on Plant Physiology.* Clarendon Press, Oxford.

Krabbe, G. (1887) *Jahrb. Wiss. Botan.* 18:346.

Luckwill, L. C. (1952) *Nature* 169:375.

Metzger, K. (1908) *Naturw. Z. Forst-u. Landwirtsch.* 6:249–274.

Mühlethaler, K. (1949) *Biochim. Biophys. Acta.* 3:15–25.

Münch, E. (1938a) *Flora (Jena)* 32:357–424.

_____ (1938b) *Jahrb. Wiss. Botan.* 86:581–673.

_____ (1940) *Flora* N.F. 34:45.

Nečesaný, V. (1955) *Sb. Vysoke Skoly Zemedel. Lesnicke Brne, Rada C* 3:131.

_____ (1956) *Drev. Výskum* 1:17

_____ (1958) *Phyton (Buenos Aires)* 11:117–127.

Ollinmaa, P. J. (1959) *Acta Forest. Fennica* 72:5–8.

Onaka, F. (1949) *Mokuzai Kenkyu* 1:1–83.

Preston, R. D. (1941) *Proc. Roy. Soc. (London), Ser.* B 130:103.

_____ (1942) *Forestry* 16:32–48.

_____ (1964). See "Discussion" of paper by Wardrop, A. B. (1964).

_____, and Middlebrook, M. (1949) *J. Textile Inst.* 40:T715–T726.

Priestley, J. H., and Tong, D. (1927) *Proc. Leeds Phil. Soc.* 1 (Part 5):199–208.

Rawitscher, F. (1932) *Der Geotropismus der Pflanzen.* Fischer, Jena.

Scott, D. R. M., and Preston, S. B. (1955) *Forest Sci.* 1:178–182.

Scurfield, G. (1964) *Australian J. Botany.* In press.

_____, and Wardrop, A. B. (1962). *Australian J. Botany* 16:93–105.

Thimann, K. V. (1964) In *Formation of Wood in Forest Trees.* M. H. Zimmermann, Ed., p. 452 Academic Press, N.Y.

Toda, R., Akasi, T., and Kikuti, H. (1963) *J. Japan. Forestry Soc.* 45:227.

Wardrop, A. B. (1948) "The Submicroscopic Organization of the Plant Cell Wall and its bearing upon the Growth of the Plant Cell." Thesis, Department of Botany, University of Leeds, England.

_____ (1954) *Holzforschung* 8:12–29.

_____ (1955) *Australian J. Botany* 3:177–189.

_____ (1956) *Australian J. Botany* 4:152–166.

_____ (1964) "Reaction anatomy of arborescent angiosperms" *In Formation of Wood in Forest Trees.* (M. H. Zimmermann, ed.), pp. 405–456. Academic Press, N.Y.

_____, and Davies, G. W. (1964) *Australian J. Botany* 12:24–38.

_____, and Scaife, E. (1956). *Nature* 178:867.

Wareing, P. F., Hanney, C. E. A., and Digby, J. (1964) In *The Formation of Wood in Forest Trees.* M. H. Zimmermann, Ed., Academic Press, N.Y.

Wergin, W. (1961) *Faserforsch. Textiltech.* 13:51.

Wershing, H. T. and Bailey, I. W. (1942) *J. Forestry* 40:411–414.

Westing, A. H. (1960) *Forest Sci.* 6:240–245.

White, J. (1908) *Proc. Roy. Soc. Victoria* 20:107–124.

Anatomy and Ultrastructure of Reaction Wood

W. A. CÔTÉ, JR. and A. C. DAY

*State University College of Forestry
at Syracuse University*

In the preceding article, Wardrop discusses the physiological and environmental factors leading to the formation of reaction wood in gymnosperms and angiosperms. This paper deals with the structural aspects of reaction wood, compression wood in conifers and tension wood in hardwoods. Its purpose is to bring together information on the anatomical and ultrastructural features now recognized as characteristic of these abnormal woody tissues. Table I has been prepared to facilitate a comparison of the principal features of reaction wood in hardwoods and softwoods.

In discussing compression and tension wood in terms of structural deviations from what may be called normal wood, it is imperative that one point be stressed. These are characteristcs associated primarily with *pronounced* reaction wood formation. In mild forms, the evidence may be less striking or less overwhelming in character, but nevertheless, careful examination can lead to detection of even mild reaction wood. It is interesting to note that reaction wood occurs in some form much more frequently than realized.

Compression Wood

Gross Features. Compression wood almost always occurs in the eccentric portion of a tree stem or branch cross section, the area that was located on the "underside" of a leaning conifer or of a branch. The growth increments in the eccentric region are wider than those of the same season's growth on the upper side of the stem or branch. A thin disk of this material viewed by transmitted light shows a greater opacity in the compression wood area than in the remainder of the section (Fig. 1) (Pillow, 1941). It has been noted, however, that in some species this effect cannot be found (Dadswell and Wardrop, 1949). The compression wood zone is usually reddish in color; thus the German designation "Rotholz" for coniferous reaction wood.

TABLE I. Comparison of Tension Wood and Compression Wood Characteristics

	Tension wood	Compression wood
Gross and physical characteristics; mechanical properties	Eccentricity of stem cross section: "upper side"	Eccentricity of stem cross section: "lower side"
	Dry, dressed lumber: silvery sheen of tension wood zones in many species; darker than normal in certain tropical and Australian species	Nonlustrous, "dead" appearance
		"Rotholz" darker than normal
	Green-sawn boards woolly on surface	
	Longitudinal shrinkage up to 1+%	Longitudinal shrinkage up to 6–7%
	Particularly high tensile strength in dry tension wood; lower than normal in green condition	Modulus of elasticity, impact strength, tensile strength: low for its density
Anatomical characteristics	Gelatinous (tension wood) fibers present though may be lacking in some species	Rounded tracheids
		Intercellular spaces
	Vessels reduced in size and number in tension wood zones	Transition pattern, springwood–summerwood, altered: more gradual than in normal wood
Microstructure	G-layer present; convoluted or not	Helical checks or cavities in S_2
	Slip planes and compression failures in tension wood fiber walls	Slip planes and compression failures generally absent
	G-layer in secondary wall of gelatinous fibers in 3 types of arrangements: $S_1 + S_2 + S_3 + G$ or S_G $S_1 + S_2 + G$ or S_G $S_1 + G$ or S_G	
Ultrastructure	Primary wall appears normal	S_3 layer absent
	S_1 may be thinner than normal	S_1 may be thicker than normal
	Microfibrillar orientation of G-layer nearly parallels fiber axis; high parallelism within G-layer	S_2 microfibrillar orientation approaches $45°$
		Ribs of cellulose parallel to direction of microfibril orientation; cellulose lamellae parallel with wall surface

Chemical composition	Lignification of tension wood fibers variable; unlignified or slightly lignified Abnormally high *cellulose* content Abnormally low *lignin* content More *galactan* than normal Less *xylan* than normal	"Extra" lignin deposited as a layer between S_1 and S_2 Abnormally low *cellulose* content Abnormally high *lignin* content More *galactan* than normal Less *galactoglucomannan* than normal

FIG. 1. A thin disk of red pine, *Pinus resinosa* Ait., photographed by transmitted light to show the relative opacity of compression wood (dark, eccentric zone) compared with normal wood (light zone).

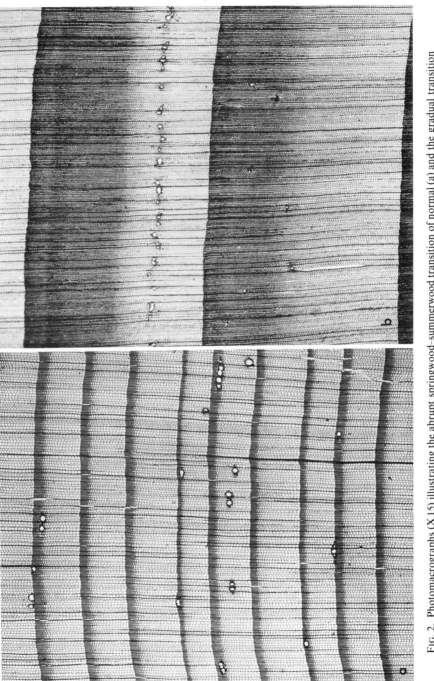

Fig. 2. Photomacrographs (X 15) illustrating the abrupt springwood–summerwood transition of normal (a) and the gradual transition of compression (b) wood in the wood of Douglas-fir, *Pseudotsuga menziesii* (Mirb.) Franco. (from Core *et al.*, 1961).

There is a more gradual transition between springwood and summerwood in reaction wood of conifers than in the unaffected portions of the growth increment (Fig. 2). This characteristic is more obvious in wood species having abrupt transition as a normal feature. In other species, where the transition is generally gradual, the summerwood may appear more pronounced in compression wood zones due to an increased amount of thick-walled cells (Core, et al., 1961).

In lumber, compression wood is recognized by its nonlustrous, "dead" appearance, a decrease in contrast between springwood and summerwood, and its relatively greater density than ordinary wood. In spite of this latter feature, it is nevertheless weaker than normal wood, on a density basis. Compression wood has a lower modulus of elasticity, impact strength, and tensile strength than normal wood (Pillow and Luxford, 1937).

Lumber containing compression wood has a great tendency to bend, twist, and split. This is due to differential shrinkage in the longitudinal direction between normal and reaction wood. Compression wood exhibits exceedingly high longitudinal shrinkage, which may, in extreme cases, reach as high as 6 to 7% compared to the negligible amount of shrinkage (0.1–0.2%) in this direction in normal wood adjacent to it in the same piece. Deep transverse checks occur across the compression wood tissue in severe cases, but they usually terminate at the normal wood (Fig. 3). Rupture occurs in the compression wood tracheids since their tensile

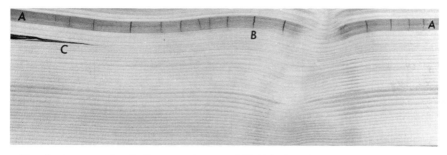

Fig. 3. A narrow band of compression wood (AA) in fir, *Abies* sp.; note the transverse checks (B) limited to the compression wood band. The abnormally high longitudinal shrinkage of the compression wood caused the split to develop at C.

strength is considerably lower than that of normal tracheids. Transverse shrinkage (radial and tangential) was reported by Pillow and Luxford (1937) to be less than normal in compression wood.

Reaction Anatomy. Compression wood tissue is easily recognized when examined with a light microscope. Tracheid cross sections invariably appear rounded rather than square, rectangular, or polygonal as in normal wood. As a consequence, intercellular spaces occur at the junction of four tracheids (Fig. 4). Radial checks can be observed in the secondary wall. When viewed in longitudinal section, these checks appear as helically oriented openings (Fig. 5). They follow the general fibrillar alignment of the S_2 layer and of the pit orifices in the latewood tracheids (Fig. 6).

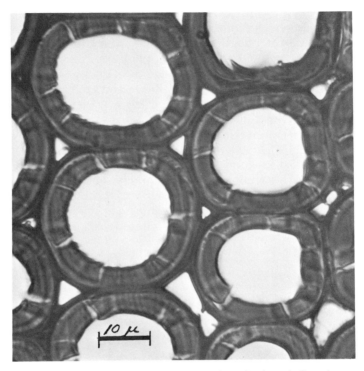

FIG. 4. Compression wood tracheids in a cross section of redwood, *Sequoia sempervirens* (D. Don) Endl. Note their round shape, the intercellular spaces, and the radial checks in the cell walls. Photomicrograph X 1300.

An explanation for a more gradual springwood-summerwood transition in compression wood of species normally exhibiting an abrupt one is to be found in the cell walls of the springwood cells, which are thicker in this case (Fig. 7). The use of polarization microscopy reveals that the inner layer of the secondary wall (S_3) is lacking in compression wood tracheids of species where three layers generally occur (Fig. 8).

The greater longitudinal shrinkage of compression wood has been attributed to the flatter than normal helix in the S_2 layer of these cells

FIG. 5. Longitudinal section of compression wood tracheids in redwood. Note the helical openings in the cell wall. Photomicrograph X1300.

(Wardrop and Dadswell, 1950). The tracheids of compression wood are substantially shorter than normal conifer cells, a fact which correlates with a fibrillar orientation of approximately 45°.

Ultrastructure. Although there is good indication through the application of polarization microscopy that the tracheids of compression wood lack an S_3 layer (Fig. 8), electron microscopy is required to confirm this. In electron micrographs of Figures 9 and 10, the helical checks visible with the light microscope clearly extend from the tracheid lumen to the S_1 layer of the secondary wall, but the usual S_3 layer of a normal tracheid wall is missing. The helical openings are therefore limited to the S_2. It should be noted that in some tracheids, e.g., *Picea,* the S_3 is often lacking. If present, the polarization effect is so weak that it leads to the interpreta-

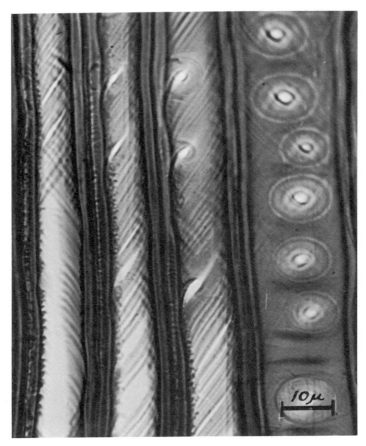

FIG. 6. Radial section of eastern larch, *Larix laricina* (Du Roi) K. Koch, compression wood. Note the absence of helical openings in the springwood tracheid (right). The "checks" follow the fibrillar orientation of the S_2 cell wall layer and the pit orifices in the summerwood tracheids. Photomicrograph X1300.

tion of its absence. Caution must be used in evaluating cell wall layering with this tool alone because fibrillar orientation of the layer in question is very critical. In the case of an S_3 layer that is oriented at only a small angle from that of the S_2, it could easily be overlooked if reliance is placed on birefringence effect alone. At least in the limited number of species examined, the S_1 layer of compression wood tracheids is thicker than normal. Other features of compression wood (listed in Table I) should be considered in any determination of presence or absence of compression wood.

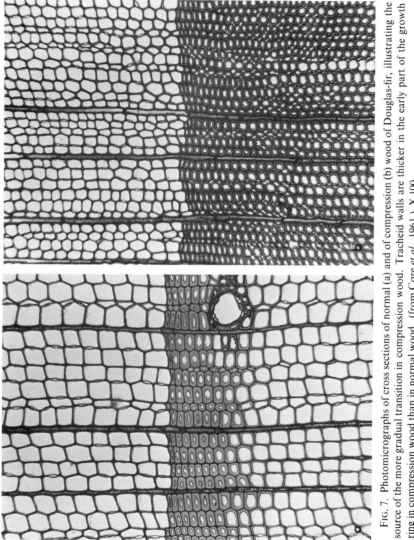

Fig. 7. Photomicrographs of cross sections of normal (a) and of compression (b) wood of Douglas-fir, illustrating the source of the more gradual transition in compression wood. Tracheid walls are thicker in the early part of the growth ring in compression wood than in normal wood. (from Core et al., 1961.) X 100.

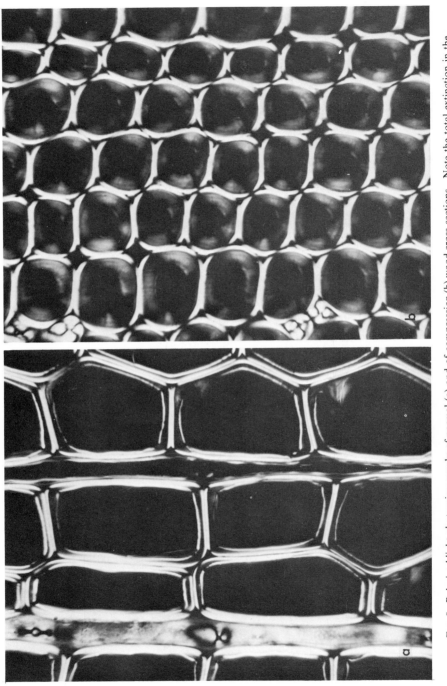

FIG. 8. Polarized light photomicrographs of normal (a) and of compression (b) wood cross sections. Note the total extinction in the S₂ and clear birefringence of the S₃ layers in normal wood. The S₃ layer is lacking in compression wood tracheids (no birefringence) but the fibrillar orientation of the S₂, being flatter than normal, produces a diffuse effect. (a) X 800; (b) X 1050.

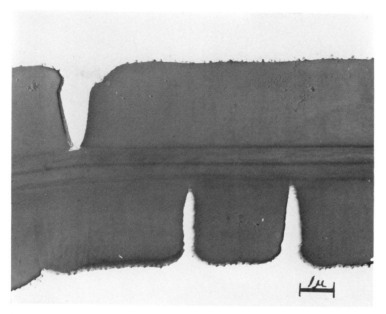

FIG. 9. Electron micrograph of a cross section of a portion of a compression wood tracheid in redwood. Note that the S_3 is lacking and that the helical openings in the S_2 terminate at the S_1 layer. Warts can be detected within the openings as well as on the lumen lining. X8400.

Wardrop and Davies (1964) have shown without question that these so-called "helical checks" are not due to seasoning, but are inherently morphological. They can be observed in electron micrographs of developing cell walls of compression wood tracheids. Since prominent warts are distributed even within these openings (Harada and Miyazaki, 1952; Harada et al., 1958), there can be no doubt that these are characteristic cell wall formations and not artifacts of drying. Ultrathin longitudinal sections through the S_2 layer of compression wood tracheid walls, when examined with the electron microscope, reveal that the openings parallel the fibrillar orientation of this layer (Fig. 11). The branching of the cavities, near the S_1 boundary, can be noted in Figure 12 as well as in cross section (Fig. 10). The ribs of cellulose extending towards the lumen between the helical cavities are oriented parallel to the direction of the microfibrils and the lamellae parallel the wall surface (Wergin and Casperson, 1961; Wardrop and Davies, 1964). It has been suggested that the presence of these helical cavities in compression wood tracheids is un-

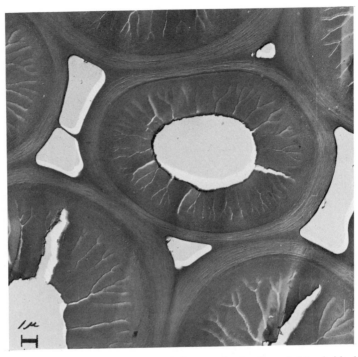

FIG. 10. Compression wood in heartwood of eastern larch. Rounded tracheids, branched "checks," abnormally thick S_1 layer, and absence of an S_3 layer can be observed in this electron micrograph. Note the parent wall where it traverses the intercellular space at upper left. X3200.

doubtedly contributory to high longitudinal shrinkage in coniferous re-action wood (Wardrop, 1964a).

The chemical composition of compression wood is detailed by Timell elsewhere in this volume. In general, cellulose content is lower than nor-mal, as is the amount of galactoglucomannan present. There is much more galactan than in normal wood. Abnormally high lignin content is typical of compression wood and at least part of this increased amount can be accounted for. In Figure 13, an unshadowed, ultrathin cross sec-tion of spruce compression wood, electron-dense zones can be seen be-tween the S_1 and S_2 layers. This was the location suggested by Dadswell et al., (1961) for the excess lignin, on the basis of ultraviolet photomicro-graphs and the nature of pulped compression wood tracheids. Partial delignification with acid chlorite of material from the same specimen as in Figure 13 results in the preferential separation of S_1 and S_2 at this region of lignin concentration (Fig. 14) (Timell and Côté, 1964).

Fig. 11. Longitudinal section through the S_2 of a compression wood tracheid in eastern larch sapwood. The helical openings follow the microfibrillar orientation of this layer (arrow). Electron micrograph X8400.

Tension Wood

Gross Features. Eccentricity of stem cross section is also a general feature of hardwood reaction wood (Fig. 15). In this case the eccentric portion is located on the upper or tension side of a leaning stem or branch. When green logs containing tension wood tissue are sawn into lumber, the surfaces will often be woolly in the tension wood zones (Fig. 16). Tension wood stands out in dressed lumber of many species because of its silvery sheen, the reaction xylem being more reflective than adjacent normal tissue. In certain Australian species tension wood zones are darker than normal wood areas (Dadswell and Wardrop, 1949).

Although not so great as in compression wood, longitudinal shrinkage of tension wood may be as high as 1%, which is considerably higher than the negligible longitudinal shrinkage of normal hardwood. Pillow (1950)

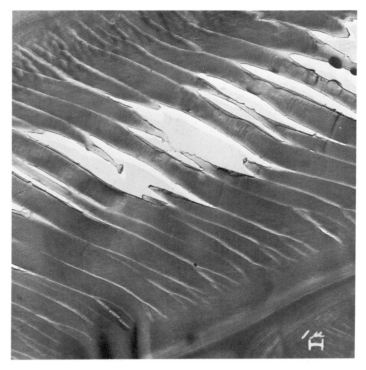

FIG. 12. Same specimen as in Figure 11. Note the branching of the helical "checks" as they approach the S_1. Electron micrograph X3200.

measured longitudinal shrinkages as great as 0.64% in mahogany tension wood. Warping and twisting of lumber containing tension wood is a serious problem of the hardwood industry, particularly when this reaction tissue is found in extensive areas of the material. Collapse is another industry problem associated with the seasoning of tension wood from the green condition (Dadswell and Wardrop, 1955). Some species have a greater tendency for collapse than others, but the presence of tension wood aggravates this condition.

Klauditz and Stolley (1955) found that tension wood is particularly low in tensile strength when tested in the green condition, lower than normal wood. However, when air-dried, its tensile strength is greater than normal wood. They attribute this to increased lateral bonding, G-layer to remainder of the secondary wall, as shrinkage takes place.

Reaction Anatomy. Tension wood anatomy is characterized by the presence of gelatinous fibers, cells containing a gelatinous or G-layer which

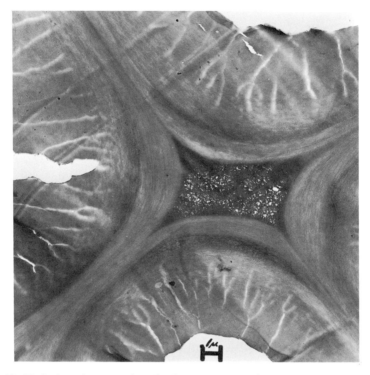

FIG. 13. Unshadowed cross section of red spruce, *Picea rubens* Sarg., compression wood. Note the electron-dense layer between S_1 and S_2, particularly near the thickened tracheid corners. This is interpreted to be the location of the "extra" lignin of compression wood. In this case, the intercellular space contains a deposit of amorphous, electron-dense material. Electron micrograph X4500. (Timell and Côté, 1964.)

appears thick or swollen in cross section (Fig. 17). Scurfield and Wardrop (1962) found that convoluted G-layers in tension wood fibers are representative of various developmental stages during cell wall formation. The looseness of attachment of the G-layer to the remainder of the secondary wall is evidenced by its uniform displacement during microtoming (Fig. 17). Though it is now known that tension wood may be present in certain hardwood species which lack a G-layer in the secondary wall of the fibers (Onaka, 1949), most species contain gelatinous fibers in some form and in some pattern of distribution if tension wood is present. Abnormally low lignin content may be the principal evidence for the presence of tension wood in those species which do not produce gelatinous fibers, although gross features such as eccentricity of stem should also indicate this

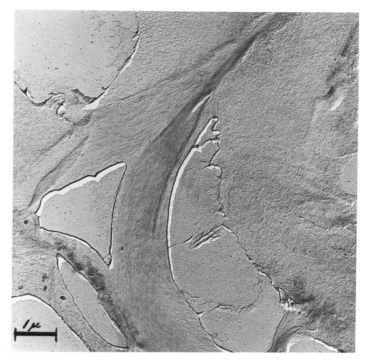

FIG. 14. Specimen from same source as Figure 13, partially delignified by an acid chlorite treatment, separates at the electron-dense zones. Electron micrograph of ultrathin cross section, Pt-shadowed. X11,000. (Timell and Côté, 1964.)

condition. Wardrop (1964b) has suggested that the phloem be investigated for reaction tissue in such cases. This was based in part on the results of Jaccard (1938), who noted that in *Tilia* the usual tension wood fibers are lacking, but bark is greatly modified.

The wall structure of tension wood fibers can be quite variable. Dadswell and Wardrop (1955) reported that three types had been observed. In the first type, the fiber contains the usual three secondary wall layers, S_1, S_2, and S_3, as well as an additional layer designated as G or S_G (Fig. 18). In the second type, the S_3 is lacking, the G-layer occurring immediately after the S_2 (Fig. 19). In a third variation, a G-layer is found adjacent to the S_1, and the S_2 and S_3 layers are absent. It now appears that there is no established relationship between species and the type of tension wood fiber formed. More than one type may appear in a single specimen.

A feature of the gross anatomy of tension wood is in the reduction in size and number of vessels in this abnormal tissue. The remainder of the tissue, including the ray and longitudinal parenchyma, are apparently unmodified (Wardrop and Dadswell, 1955).

Fig. 15. Eccentric stem cross section of American beech, *Fagus grandifolia* Ehrh., containing a large concentration of tension wood (reflective zone).

Polarization microscopy of longitudinal sections of the cell walls of tension wood fibers reveals that many slip planes and compression failures occur in specimens that have not been stressed in any way, for example, in macerated fibers. Though they are common in hardwood reaction wood (Fig. 20), they are not characteristic of the tracheid walls of compression wood (Wardrop and Dadswell, 1947).

Ultrastructure. Since only the fibers undergo modification in tension wood formation, discussion of the ultrastructure of hardwood reaction wood will be limited to this type of element. As indicated above, presence of a G-layer in the fibers is the salient feature of tension wood anatomy. The nature of this layer has been investigated by staining reactions, UV absorption, X-ray diffraction, and electron microscopy, as well as by incidental or indirect observations such as the effect of methacrylate embedding and the effect of shrinkage on the equilibrium moisture content (Wardrop and Dadswell, 1955; Preston and Ranganathan, 1947; Côté and Day, 1962).

FIG. 16. Woolly surface of a green-sawn board of mahogany, *Swietenia mahagoni* Jacq., which contained extensive areas of tension wood.

Staining reactions cannot ordinarily be employed exclusively and, in this case, they have been amply supported by other evidence. The unlignified areas of the tension wood fibers stain green and the lignified layers stain red when safranin and fast green or light green are used (Jutte, 1956). The G-layer invariably takes green stain since it is known to be composed of highly crystalline cellulose and is virtually unlignified. Sharp (nondiffuse) X-ray diffraction patterns provide this evidence. The G-layer absorbs very weakly in UV while the heavily lignified middle lamella absorbs very strongly.

Electron micrographs of longitudinal sections through tension wood fibers (Fig. 21) reveal that the G-layer is made up of cellulose microfibrils oriented nearly parallel to the longitudinal axis of the cell. When specimens of tension wood are embedded in methacrylate for ultrathin

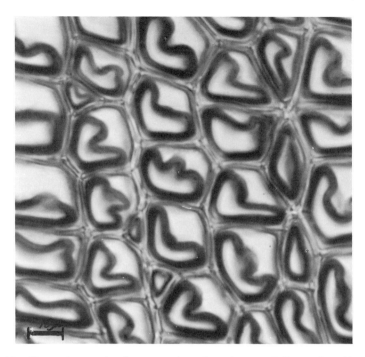

FIG. 17.   Photomicrograph of cross section of tension wood fibers of quaking aspen, *Populus tremuloides* Michx., containing prominent G-layers.   Section stained with fast green and safranin, photographed using a red filter (Wratten 25A).   Note that the convoluted G-layers are all displaced in the same direction, indicating the cutting direction as well as the loose attachment to the remainder of the secondary wall.   X900.

sectioning, the G-layer expands during polymerization but the remainder of the secondary wall does not. This has been interpreted as an indication of relatively weak lateral bonding and lack of incrusting substances in the G-layer.

Cross sections of such a swollen wall (Fig. 22) show lamellation and, if enlarged further (Fig. 23), provide a view of isolated microfibrils. These range in diameter from approximately 200 to 400 Å. Further evidence of lamellation and longitudinal orientation of the G-layer microfibrils can be seen in Figure 24. Finally, advantage can be taken of methacrylate-expanded G-layers in the isolation of zones that are resistant to this phenomenon. A dense, narrow band can often be observed lining the much reduced lumen in such cases (Fig. 25). This zone is apparently analogous to the terminal lamella of normal wood elements.

The primary wall of tension wood fibers is probably of normal composition, but the S_1 may be thinner than in normal wood cells (Wardrop and Dadswell, 1948).

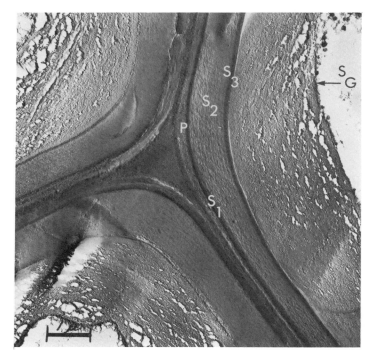

Fig. 18.   Cross section of hackberry, *Celtis occidentalis* L., containing fibers with G-layers. The three normal layers S_1, S_2, and S_3 are present as well as the additional S_G. Note the partially swollen G-layer. Electron micrograph X11,500. (Côté and Day, 1962.)

As with compression wood, tension wood differs from normal wood in chemical composition. Timell, in this volume, points out that abnormally low lignin levels typify hardwood reaction wood. Lignification is variable in tension wood and the fiber walls may be partly or completely unlignified. On the other hand, the cellulose content is much higher than normal and the amount of galactan present is usually, albeit apparently not always, greater than in normal hardwood of the same species. The proportion of xylan found in tension wood is also lower than normal.

REFERENCES

Core, H. A., Côté, W. A., Jr., and Day, A. C. (1961) "Characteristics of compression wood in some native conifers." *Forest Prod. J.* 11:356–362.
Côté, W. A., Jr. and Day, A. C. (1962) "The G-layer in gelatinous fibers—electron microscopic studies." *Forest Prod. J.* 12:333–338.

Dadswell, H. E., and Wardrop, A. B. (1949) "What is reaction wood?" *Australian Forestry* 12:22–23. Also CSIRO (Australia) Div. of For. Prod. Reprint No. 116.

―――― and ―――― (1955) "The structure and properties of tension wood." *Holzforschung* 9:97–104. Also CSIRO (Australia) Div. of For. Prod. Reprint No. 269.

――――, ――――, and Watson, A. J. (1961) "The morphology, chemistry and pulp characteristics of reaction wood." In *Fundamentals of Papermaking Fibres* (Francis Bolam, ed.), pp. 187–219. Tech. Section of British Paper and Board Makers' Asso. (Inc.), London.

Harada, H., and Miyazaki, Y. (1952) "Electron microscopic observation of compression wood." Bulletin of the Govt. Forest Experiment Station, No. 54, pp. 101–108 (Meguro, Tokyo, Japan).

――――, ――――, and Wakashima, T. (1958) "Electron microscopic investigation on the cell wall structure of wood." Bulletin of the Govt. Forest Experiment Station, No. 104 (Meguro, Tokyo, Japan).

Jaccard, P. (1938) "Excentrisches Dickenwachstum und Anatomisch-Histologische Differenzierung des Holzes." *Ber. Schweiz. Botan. Ges.* 48:491.

Jutte, S. M. (1956) "Tension wood in Wane (*Ocotea rubra* Mez)." *Holzforschung* 10: 33–35.

Klauditz, W., and Stolley, I. (1955) "Uber die biologisch-mechanischen und technischen Eigenschaften des Zugholzes." *Holzforschung* 9:5–10.

Onaka, F. (1949) "Studies on compression and tension wood." Bulletin of the Wood Research Institute, Kyoto Univ., Japan. 1:1–83.

Pillow, M. Y. (1941) "A new method of detecting compression wood." *J. Forestry* 39:385–387.

―――― (1950) "Presence of tension wood in mahogany in relation to longitudinal shrinkage." U. S. For. Prod. Lab. Report No. D1763.

――――, and Luxford, R. F. (1937) "Structure, occurrence and properties of compression wood." U. S. Dept. Agri. Tech. Bull. No. 546. 32pp.

Preston, R. D., and Ranganathan, S. (1947) "The fine structure of the fibres of normal and tension wood in beech (*Fagus sylvatica* L.)." *Forestry* 21:92–98.

Scurfield, G., and Wardrop, A. B. (1962) "The nature of reaction wood. VI. The reaction anatomy of seedlings of woody perennials." *Australian J. Botany* 10:93–105.

Timell, T. E., and Côté, W. A., Jr. (1964) Unpublished results.

Wardrop, A. B. (1964a) Personal communication.

―――― (1964b) "The reaction anatomy of arborescent angiosperms." In *Formation of Wood in Forest Trees* (M. Zimmermann, ed.) pp. 405–456. Academic Press, Inc., New York.

――――, and Dadswell, H. E. (1947) "Contributions to the study of the cell wall 5. The occurrence, structure and properties of certain cell wall deformations." CSIRO (Australia) Bulletin No. 221.

―――― and ―――― (1948) "The nature of reaction wood. I. The structure and properties of tension wood fibres." *Australian J. Sci. Res.,* Ser. B 1:3–16.

―――― and ―――― (1950) "The nature of reaction wood. II. The cell wall organization of compression wood tracheids." *Australian J. Sci. Res.,* Ser B 3:1–13.

―――― and ―――― (1955) "The nature of reaction wood. IV. Variations in cell wall organization of tension wood fibres." *Australian J. Botany* 3:177–189.

――――, and Davies, G. W. (1964) "The nature of reaction wood. VIII. The structure and differentiation of compression wood." *Australian, J. Botany* 12:24–38. Also reprint No. 568 CSIRO (Australia) Div. For. Prod.

Wergin, W., and Casperson, G. (1961) "Uber Entstehung und Aufbau von Reaktionsholzzellen." *Holzforschung* 15:44–49.

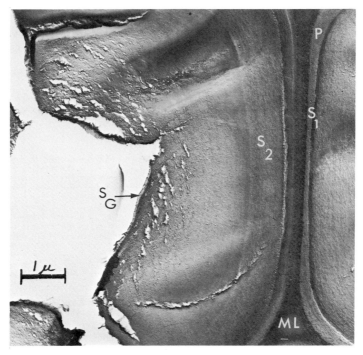

FIG. 19. Gelatinous fiber wall in red oak, *Quercus rubra* L., with S_1 and S_2 layers, but lacking an S_3. Note the partially swollen G-layer. Electron micrograph X11,500. (Côté and Day, 1962.)

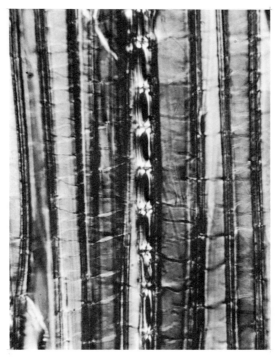

FIG. 20. Slip planes and compression failures in the cell walls of tension wood fibers in poplar, *Populus* sp.; polarized light photomicrograph X800.

FIG. 21. Longitudinally oriented cellulose microfibrils from the G-layer of a tension wood fiber of sugar maple, *Acer saccharum* Marsh. The layer was expanded by methacrylate embedding. Matrix removed. Electron micrograph X6800. (Côté and Day, 1962.)

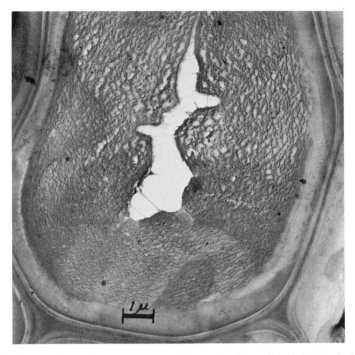

FIG. 22. Cross section of same specimen as Figure 21. The cell wall has an S_2 layer but lacks an S_3. The G-layer is greatly expanded by methacrylate embedding.   Methacrylate matrix not removed. Electron micrograph X7760. (Côté and Day, 1962.)

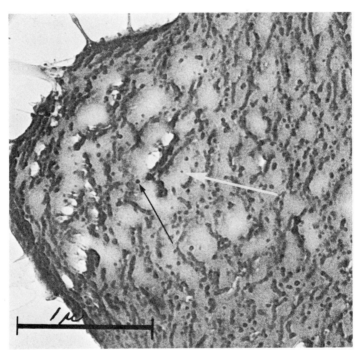

Fig. 23. Portion of Figure 22 enlarged photographically to show the isolation of individual microfibrils in cross section. They range from 200 to 400 Å in diameter. X35,000. (Côté and Day, 1962.)

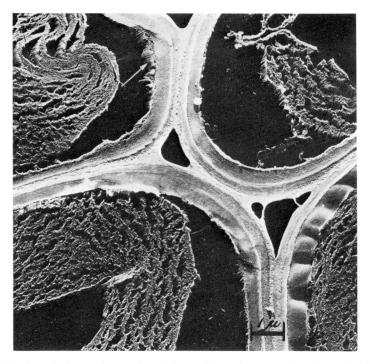

FIG. 24. Lamellation of G-layer in gelatinous fibers of sugar maple. Note also the high degree of parallelism of the microfibrils of this layer (arrow). X7760. (Côté and Day, 1962.)

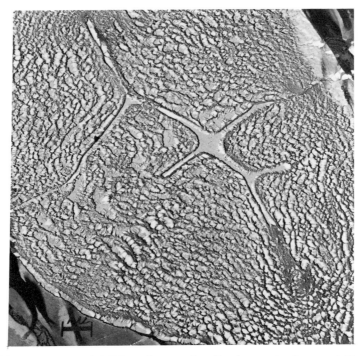

FIG. 25. Greatly expanded G-layer from poplar, *Populus* sp., tension wood illustrating its lamellar organization. Note the compact and electron-dense terminal lamella lining the much-constricted lumen. Ultrathin cross section, electron micrograph X6800. (Côté and Day, 1962.)

Tracheid Development in Tilted Seedlings

R. W. KENNEDY and J. L. FARRAR

Faculty of Forestry, University of Toronto

INTRODUCTION

An examination of wood sections under the microscope shows the great natural variation in xylem anatomy—even within one annual ring. Not only is there "normal" variation from earlywood to latewood, but also there are often bands or arcs of wood where the tracheids and other cells differ in radial diameter, wall thickness, lignification, and general shape. Characteristics of wood behavior reflect differences in cell structure. A better understanding of cell development is therefore of basic interest and practical importance.

Variation in the environment of the growing tree is one cause of differences in the xylem cells (Larson, 1962). This paper presents some preliminary results in connection with a series of investigations on the effects of various environmental features on the formation of wood. The work was carried out with seedlings to permit a high degree of environmental control. However, this does not imply a deprecation of field studies of large trees; more than one approach to the study of wood quality can be justified.

Experimenting with seedlings under controlled environment offers a chance to produce wood in the same annual ring under two or more quite different conditions. Provided that the wood formed during a certain period can be identified, such experiments allow the observer to determine specific effects as brought about by changes in the environment.

This paper describes a method of producing an internal date mark on the wood by tilting the seedlings significantly off the vertical for short periods in order to obtain an arc of reaction wood. Two such marks would serve to delimit the wood formed under certain conditions between specific dates. By the same means, growth rate could be determined in terms of number of days required to initiate one new cell. If the number of immature cells in the cambial zone is known, the growth rate figure could then be used to calculate the time required for differentiation of tracheids to be complete.

It is known that the formation of compression wood on the underside

419

of leaning conifers is in response to gravity (Onaka, 1949; Spurr and Hyvarinen, 1954; Scott and Preston, 1955). It has also been established that the formation of compression wood is due to a supraoptimal concentration of auxin (indole acetic acid) (Wershing and Bailey, 1942; Onaka, 1949; Fraser, 1949; Nečesaný, 1958; Wardrop and Davies, 1964).

As the investigation progressed it became evident that such features of compression wood as round shape, excessive wall thickening, and excessive lignification could occur separately in cells which did not have other features of compression wood. Their occurrence was related to the developmental stage of the tracheid during the tilting period. Tracheids newly derived from the cambium did not respond in the same way as those in later stages of maturation.

A number of experiments were conducted which will be described separately in succeeding sections. Duration of the tilting period was the main variable. It was desirable to obtain the marker arc in as short a time as possible to avoid unduly upsetting the hormone distribution and other physiological balances within the stem. In addition the interaction of tilting with drought treatment was also investigated.

Experiment 1

Duplicate jack pine (*Pinus banksiana* Lamb.) and tamarack (*Larix laricina* [Du Roi] K. Koch) seedlings were selected for each of four treatments described below. These seedlings were about three months old, and several millimeters in diameter, and were grown from seed in individual 250-ml plastic containers employing Perlite as the root medium. The medium was irrigated with a complete nutrient solution. The seedlings were grown in a greenhouse at summer temperatures and a sixteen-hour day using artificial light to extend natural day length.

In this initial experiment the containers were first tilted at 60° to the right of the vertical. A wooden rack was employed to maintain the containers in this position, while the position of the seedlings was maintained by tying them to wooden stakes which were embedded in the Perlite parallel to the long axis of the container. After 1, 2, 3, or 4 days, the containers were moved through a vertical arc of 120° to a position 60° to the left of the vertical. The under side of the stem in the first position thus appeared as the upper side in this second position. Again after 1, 2, 3, or 4 days the seedlings were tilted back to the original position 60° to the right of the vertical. These cycles were continued for a period of 34 to 36 days, after which the seedlings were harvested by reducing the main stem to pieces one inch long for convenience in handling. Therefore, those seedlings whose position was reversed daily had each lateral half of the stem on the under side on 17 separate occasions (17-17). Those seedlings which were allowed to remain tilted in one position for 2 days had one lateral half on the under side on 9 occasions, while the other half was on the under side a total of 8 different times (9-8). For the 3- and 4-day periods, the corresponding figures were 6-5 and 5-4 respectively. The final position in those seedlings tipped for 3-day intervals was held for 6 days (days 31 to 36), thereby producing an unequal number of underside positions. After aspirating the pieces of stem in FAA solution, transverse sections were cut from the hypocotyl region on the sliding microtome, and stained following a safranin-fast green schedule for microscopic examination.

Results. An over-all view of a jack pine stem whose position was changed at 4-day intervals is presented in Figure 1. Reaction arcs are evident as concentric semicircular bands of darker-stained, more heavily

FIG. 1. Transverse section through the hypocotyl of a *Pinus banksiana* seedling tipped 60° to the right and left of vertical at four-day intervals.

lignified tissue. The slightly elliptical shape of the cross section is traceable to increased cambial activity along the two opposite and longest radii which received the maximum gravitational effect of tipping. Opposite sides of the same jack pine are shown in Figure 2, while similarly

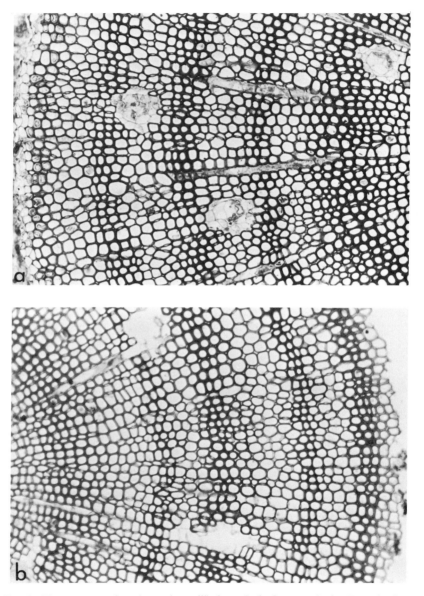

Fig. 2. Transverse sections (opposite radii) through the hypocotyl of a *Pinus banksiana* seedling tipped 60° to the right and left of vertical at four-day intervals. A. Four full arcs, with the inception of a fifth just behind the cambium. B. Four full arcs (the zone of reaction wood nearest the pith is unrelated to treatments).

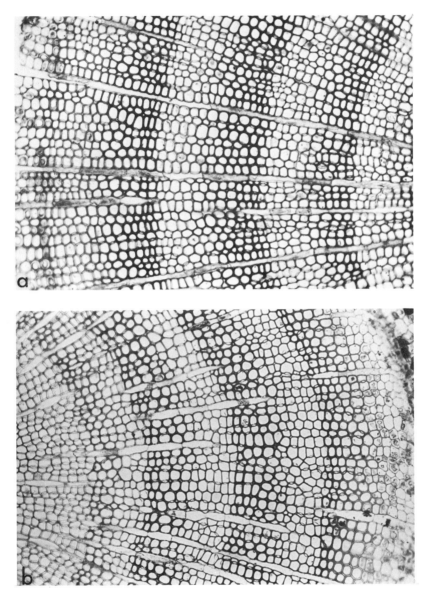

FIG. 3. Transverse sections (opposite radii) through the hypocotyl of a *Larix laricina* seedling tipped 60° to the right and left of vertical at four-day intervals. A. Four arcs, with the inception of a fifth just behind the cambium. Only a portion of the first reaction arc is evident at the extreme right. B. Four full arcs.

treated tamarack are shown in Figure 3. It is evident in both species that only 4 full arcs are present, despite the fact that one half of the stem was in the under position 5 times. Only the inception of the fifth arc can be noted in Figures 2A and 3A. Examination of a portion of the jack pine stem under higher power (Figure 4) revealed that the arcs of heavily

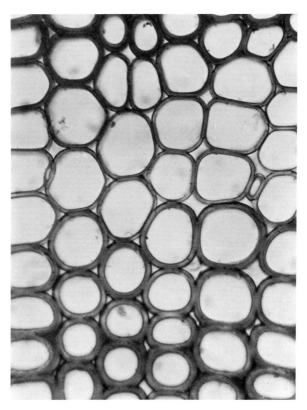

FIG. 4. A portion of Figure 2, showing parts of two heavily lignified arcs (top and bottom) and less lignified intervening tracheids.

stained calls produced by tipping differed from the tracheids between them primarily in degree of lignification. The intervening tracheids between arcs very often were rounded in shape and displayed considerable intercellular spaces—both features of compression wood. Furthermore, the tracheids included in the arcs did not always possess these features to the same extent.

Cell counts along radial files in the middle of the jack pine arcs indicated that there were about 24 cells between the beginning of the first arc and the beginning of the fourth arc. The corresponding time period was 28 days, indicating that one cell was reaching the final stage of lignification every 1.17 days. The corresponding rate for tamarack was one cell in 0.93 days. In both species the normally lignified cells outnumber the excessively lignified cells by a factor of 1.3. This factor may be somewhat controversial, however, owing to the gradual transition from heavy to normal lignification in the outer portion of each arc.

The results of the three-day treatments are shown for jack pine and tamarack in Figures 5 and 6. The number of heavily lignified arcs (six and five) corresponded to the number of tipping cycles. However, the final arc with the same width as the others resulted from tipping for six days.

The results of the two-day treatments in jack pine are shown in Figure 7. A longitudinal section through a reaction arc (Fig. 8) reveals the presence of spiral checking, a feature associated with typical compression wood. The number of arcs (eight and seven) is less than the number of tilt periods (nine and eight). In tamarack no arcs could be distinguished, but the whole area influenced by tilting was lignified more than normal. Tamarack was similarly affected by the daily cycles, whereas jack pine seemed to form normal xylem during the daily cycles.

Discussion. The discrepancy between the number of arcs of excessively lignified wood and the number of periods in the lower position reflected the time required for a cell to reach maturity after it had reached the stage when lignification could be influenced by tipping. Apparently this took place when the cell was about three to four days from maturity. This produced a lag of a like number of days bettwen tipping and the first appearance of an excessively lignified tracheid on the lower side of the stem. Tracheids nearer maturity continued to lignify normally despite the tipping, whereas those in the "susceptible" stage during tilting proceeded to lignify excessively even though they were moved to the upper position three days before lignification was complete. Under this hypothesis and with the further assumption that one tracheid per day is reaching final maturation (i.e., complete lignification), an idealized model can be proposed (Table I) which corresponds closely with the pattern of arcs observed in the seedlings tipped at four-day intervals.

It is apparent that each cell alternated between the upper and lower position as it matured. This explains why the cells in the heavily lignified arcs usually lacked some of the features of typical compression wood, and also explains the frequent presence between the arcs of thick-walled, round tracheids having intercellular spaces.

If a differentiating tracheid were in the "susceptible" stage of lignifica-

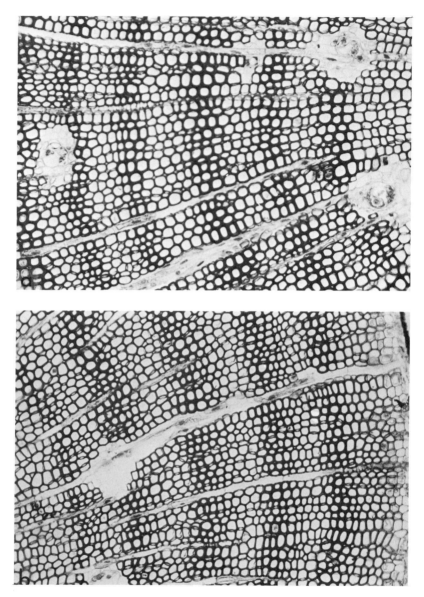

FIG. 5. Transverse sections (opposite radii) through the hypocotyl of a *Pinus banksiana* seedling tipped 60° to the right and left of vertical at three-day intervals. A. Six arcs, the outermost of which was associated with a six-day period of tilting. B. Five arcs.

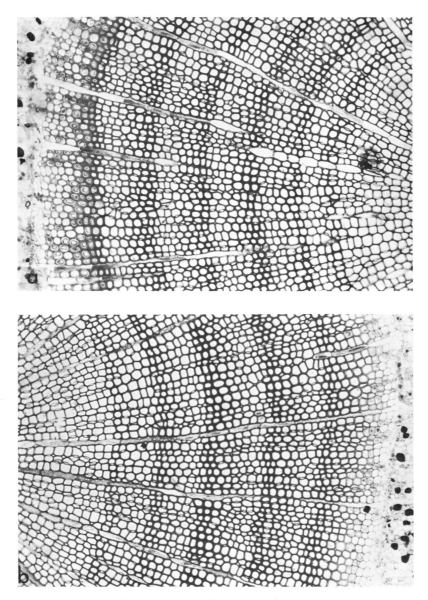

FIG. 6. Transverse sections (opposite radii) through the hypocotyl of a *Larix laricina* seedling tipped 60° to the right and left of vertical at three-day intervals. A. Six arcs, the outermost of which was associated with a six-day period of tilting. B. Five arcs.

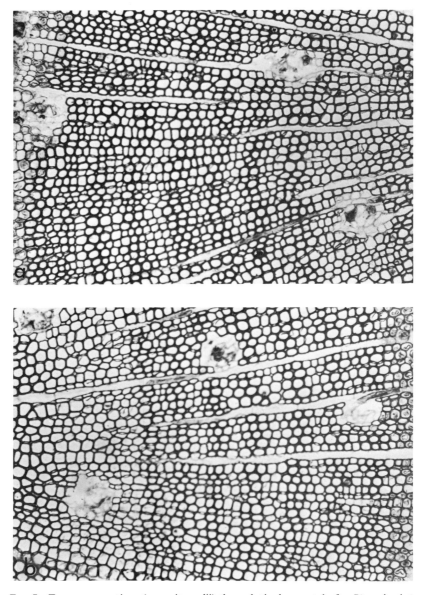

Fig. 7. Transverse sections (opposite radii) through the hypocotyl of a *Pinus banksiana* seedling tipped 60° to the right and left of vertical at two-day intervals. A. Eight arcs. B. Seven arcs.

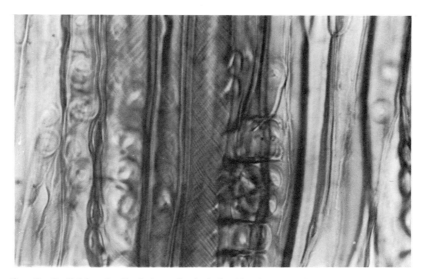

FIG. 8. Radial longitudinal view of spiral checking in a reaction arc of *Pinus banksiana* tipped at two-day intervals.

tion for a total of four days, seedlings tipped in opposite directions every two days would be expected to produce heavily lignified cells exclusively. On the other hand, if an immature tracheid were in this sensitive stage for only two days, reaction arcs alternating with normally lignified zones would be anticipated. The latter supposition seems to apply to jack pine.

Tipping can therefore be expected to affect the differentiating zone as follows. The cambial initial and cells near it will be induced to divide more frequently. This would account for the elliptical shape of the stem. The cells in mid-stage will be induced to become rounded in shape and thicken their walls excessively, while those nearer maturity will be caused to lignify excessively. More information on this will be given in connection with following experiments.

EXPERIMENT 2

A second series of seedlings were selected to test the accuracy of the conclusions drawn from the first experiment. In addition, care was exercised in sectioning so that the cambial zone might remain intact. This enabled counts of the number of immature cells to be made; these in turn were used along with the tipping technique to deduce the time necessary for a tracheid to mature after its inception at the cambium, and allowed

TABLE I. Model for Final Maturation of Tracheids in Seedlings Cycled 60° Right and Left from Vertical at Four-Day Intervals

Day	Position of seedling	Position of lateral half A	Degree of lignification of tracheid maturing on that day on side A
0	vertical	upright	normal
1	60° right	underside	normal
2	"	underside	normal
3	"	underside	normal
4	"	underside	excessive
5	60° left	upperside	excessive
6	"	upperside	excessive
7	"	upperside	normal
8	"	upperside	normal
9	60° right	underside	normal
10	"	underside	normal
11	"	underside	normal
12	"	underside	excessive
13	60° left	upperside	excessive
14	"	upperside	excessive
15	"	upperside	excessive
16	"	upperside	normal
17	60° right	underside	normal
18	"	underside	normal
19	"	underside	normal
20	"	underside	excessive
21	60° left	upperside	excessive
22	"	upperside	excessive
23	"	upperside	normal
24	"	upperside	normal
25	60° right	underside	normal
26	"	underside	normal
27	"	underside	normal
28	"	underside	excessive
29	60° left	upperside	excessive
30	"	upperside	excessive
31	"	upperside	excessive
32	"	upperside	normal
33	60° right	underside	normal
34	"	underside	normal
35	"	underside	normal
36	"	underside	excessive

estimates to be made of the time required for the completion of various stages of differentiation (initiation, enlargement, secondary wall thickening, and lignification).

Method. Duplicate jack pine and tamarack seedlings approximately 6 months old, growing as described in the previous section, were leaned

60° from the vertical for either a 1- or a 2-day period, following which they were returned to the upright position for 4 days. A second 1- or 2-day tipping was followed by 8 days in the normal vertical position. The total treatment was thus either $\underline{1} + 4 + \underline{1} + 8$ days or $\underline{2} + 4 + \underline{2} + 8$ days. At the conclusion of the second vertical period the seedlings were harvested for sectioning in the usual way. In the jack pine, sections were taken not only through the hypocotyl, but at three regular intervals approximately 4, 8, and 12 cm above this location. Only the first height above the hypocotyl was examined in the tamarack.

Results. Figure 9 shows the two heavily lignified arcs formed in the hypocotyl region as a result of exposing jack pine to a $\underline{2} + 4 + \underline{2} + 8$

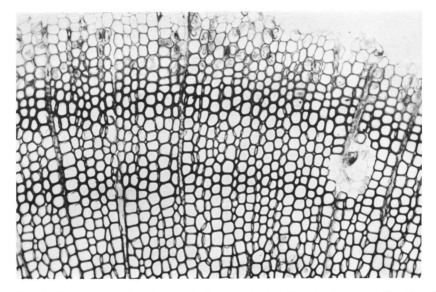

FIG. 9. Transverse section through the hypocotyl of a *Pinus banksiana* seedling tipped 60° for two two-day intervals, separated by four days and followed by eight days in the upright position just before harvest.

treatment. On the average, each reaction arc appears to be three cells wide in a radial direction, and is separated by a zone of three normal cells. Since six cells are present between the start of the first and second markers, one cell was reaching final maturity every day. It is logical to assume that the width of the differentiating zone remained constant; therefore the cambial initial was adding one cell per day.

The cambial zone as it appeared at the time of harvesting the stem is illustrated in Figure 10. Approximately 20 cells are evident between the

432

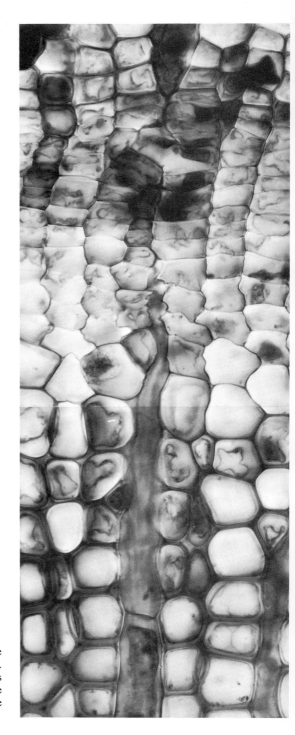

FIG. 10. Differentiating xylem in the *Pinus banksiana* seedling of Figure 9. The cambial initial is four or five cells from the top of the photograph; one fully lignified cell is shown at the bottom.

cambial initial to the most recent fully lignified tracheid. The exact position of the cambial initial is problematical, but was taken to be the longitudinal element in the region of the shortest ray cell, or approximately two cells behind the first readily recognizable phloem cell. The cambial zone was composed of about ten cells in the phase of initiation, corresponding to divisions in the cambial initial itself and xylem mother cells (Bannan, 1962). Cell enlargement seemed to be restricted to those two or three cells immediately before the first full-sized cell. Four cells were found to be in each of the processes of secondary wall thickening and lignification.

The position of the reaction arcs was somewhat different at higher levels in the seedlings. The appearance of the arcs at mid-stem in jack pine is shown in Figure 11A. Here the number of mature cells beyond the later reaction arc had changed from zero to three. This figure was maintained at all higher levels sampled. A similar shift in position of reaction arcs between hypocotyl and mid-stem was observed for tamarack. It appears either that the stimulus responsible for increased lignification may have reached the upper levels of the stem somewhat before the hypocotyl region was affected, and similarly ceased to be operative at an earlier point in time at the higher level, or alternatively, differentiation may have been delayed at the hypocotyl.

At mid-point and higher positions within one of the jack pine trees, a secondary pair of reaction arcs (Figure 11B) were noted in a position diametrically opposite to the initial arcs. Because of their interlocking positions, it was assumed that the secondary pair were formed as a result of returning side B (upper side) to the upright position after tilting. The enigmatic occurrence of these secondary arcs provided the impetus for an additional experimental series (number five) to be described subsequently.

Because of the slightly faster growth of the tamarack seedlings, approximately one additional tracheid was noted both in the first reaction arc and in the intervening normal cells between arcs at the hypocotyl and mid-stem levels. Tipping for one day on two different occasions ($\underline{1} + 4 + \underline{1} + 8$) was generally unsuccessful in producing two well-defined reaction arcs, with the exception of one of the two tamarack seedlings (Figure 12). In this instance, tipping for the two one-day periods resulted in reaction arcs of one and two tracheids.

In jack pine, the average number of tracheids included within the first reaction arc, the intervening normal zone, and the second arc was 2.2, 3.4, and 2.0 respectively. These figures represent the average over-all levels in the pair of seedlings given a $\underline{2} + 4 + \underline{2} + 8$ treatment. Corresponding figures for tamarack were 2.5, 5.3, and 3.0. However, the hypocotyl (Figure 9) and mid-stem (Figure 11A) sections from one of the jack pine

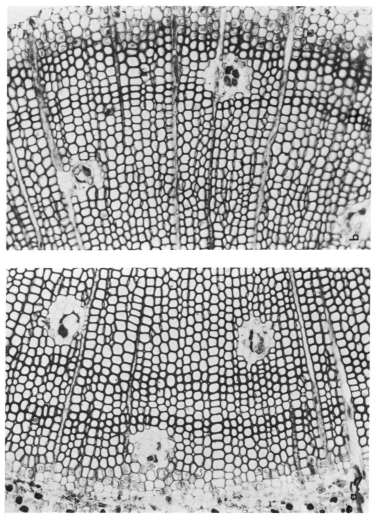

FIG. 11. Transverse sections (opposite radii) at mid-height through the *Pinus banksiana* seedling of Figure 9. A. Primary reaction arcs. B. Secondary reaction arcs.

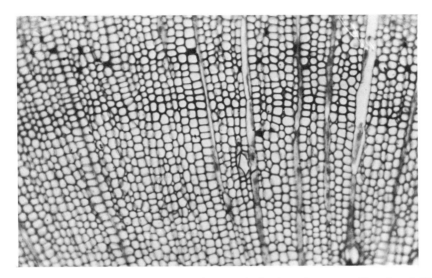

FIG. 12. Transverse section through the hypocotyl of a *Larix laricina* seedling tipped 60° for two one-day intervals, separated by four days and followed by eight days in the upright position just before harvest.

seedlings displayed an equal number of tracheids (three) in each of the various zones.

Discussion.   The clear divisions noted between various stages of maturation have been somewhat simplified for ease of presentation. However, a considerable degree of overlapping exists between the various phases of differentiation (Wardrop, 1957). The number of cells undergoing lignification was determined from observation based on staining reactions. The first cell showing a faint pink tinge at its corners was taken to be the first lignifying tracheid. Nevertheless, the fact that only 4 cells were observed to be lignifying is at variance with the results of Wardrop (1957), who noted 35 out of a total number of 45 cells in the cambial zone of *Pinus radiata* to be in some stage of lignification. However, the much faster rate of growth in his material may explain a large part of the difference, for we have noted increasingly wider zones of lignification in seedlings producing compression wood under the influence of extended tipping periods and growing at a rate twice that of normal. Furthermore, our observations of lignification are based on absorption of safranin stain visible at no more than 360 X, and therefore undoubtedly do not represent the very earliest stage of this process.

If it is assumed that the cambial zone was composed of a constant number of cells during the course of the treatment, a model of the tracheids differentiating on the underside of the seedling given a $\underline{2} + 4 + \underline{2} + 8$ treatment can be proposed (Fig. 13). Six tracheids are known to have reached maturity between the beginning of the first horizontal treatment and the second 6 days later (Fig. 9). Hence it was assumed that one new cell was initiated every day. Since the total number of cells in the cambial zone was about 20 (Fig. 10), approximately 20 days were required for the complete process of differentiation, a figure in reasonable agreement with that of Dadswell (1963), who reported 14 days as a general figure, and Wilson (1964), who found 16–23 days required for *Abies concolor*. The phases of division, enlargement, thickening, and lignification were esti- mated to require 10, 2, 4, and 4 days respectively. Wilson (1963, 1964) has observed 6–10 days for division plus enlargement to be completed, and an additional 10–13 days for thickening and lignification.

The mature cells in the model differ with regard to shape, wall thick- ness, and lignification. These differences were related to the develop- mental stage of these cells when the stem was placed horizontally. For example, those cells in the stage of lignification at the time of the first horizontal treatment, developed into normal tracheids (No. 1 to 4). The first cell to show a response to the horizontal position was No. 5, which was XVII or XVIII from the cambium and just completing its wall thick- ening. It matured four days after treatment began and was normal except for excessive lignification. Cells 6 and 7 also became excessively lignified and in addition became somewhat rounded. These most closely resembled typical compression wood tracheids. Cells 8 to 10 became normally ligni- fied but were somewhat rounded. Cells 11 to 13 were affected by both horizontal periods. Their shape was affected during the first period and lignification during the second. These cells were X to XII from the cam- bium during the first horizontal period and thus were expanding in radial diameter. The younger cells (No. 14 to 20) seemed unaffected by the first horizontal period; the final form of cells 14 to 18 could be explained on the basis of their response to the second horizontal period. Cells 19 and younger seem to have been unaffected by either horizontal period. They were in the unexpanded stage during the second treatment.

EXPERIMENT 3

Because approximately four days were necessary for the completion of each of the phases of wall thickening and lignification, no completely typical compression wood tracheids had thus far been produced. To ac- complish this, seedlings were leaned for an eight-day period in order to encompass both of these phases of differentiation.

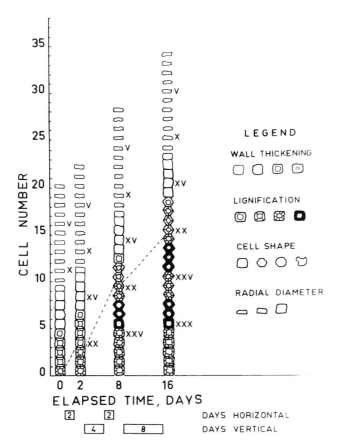

FIG 13. Model of tracheids developing on the underside of a jack pine seedling which was placed horizontally for two 2-day periods, separated by a 4-day period in the upright position, and followed by an 8-day period in the upright position, before harvesting (2 horizontal, 4 vertical, 2 horizontal, 8 vertical). The cells are numbered from the youngest mature tracheid on day 0 to the cambium. Each cell retains the same number throughout its life. The cells are also numbered in the reverse order with Roman numerals to facilitate tracing the development of a particular cell. For example, cell 13 is VIII from cambium on day 0, XII on day 4, and XXII on day 16. The column of cells at day 0 represents a file of tracheids as it appeared at the beginning of the experiment, whereas that at day 16 represents a file of tracheids at the end of the experiment. Only this latter file was actually observed (Figs. 9 and 10); the other files are based on deductions. The dotted oblique line separates the developing tracheids above from the mature ones below.

In the legend, four degrees are shown for thickening of secondary wall and lignification: nil, intermediate, normal, and excessive. Four cell shapes are shown: normal, somewhat rounded, round, and distorted. Three radial diameters are distinguished.

Method.   Jack pine seedlings 8 months old were tipped in their containers for an 8-day period, after which they were returned to the vertical position for 32 days before harvesting. Two seedlings were tipped at each of 45° and 90° in order to investigate the effect of angle of tilting on reaction wood formation. Tilting at 45° offered an advantage in that automatic subirrigation could be continued; watering had to be carried out manually when the seedlings were tipped at greater angles.

The seedlings were sectioned through the hypocotyl and at higher levels approximately 5 cm apart. Some sections were stained in the conventional way, while others were mounted unstained in glycerin. These unstained mounts were examined in a Reichert Zetopan microscope equipped with a mercury-vapor lamp and exciter filter to give a band of light peaking at a wavelength of 410 mμ (near ultraviolet), in order to take advantage of the intrinsic fluorescence of lignin (Frey-Wyssling, 1964).

Results.   The section through the hypocotyl of a jack pine inclined at 90° is illustrated in Figure 14. Figure 15 illustrates a few radial rows of tracheids from two different areas within the widest portion of the reaction arc. The first cell of the reaction arc was different from normal only in its excessive lignification. The succeeding four or five tracheids exhibited the increasingly circular shapes and thicker walls usually asso-

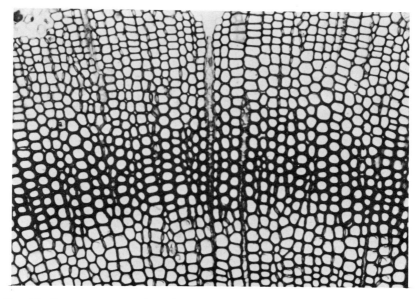

Fig. 14.   Transverse section through the hypocotyl of a *Pinus banksiana* seedling tipped 90° for eight days.

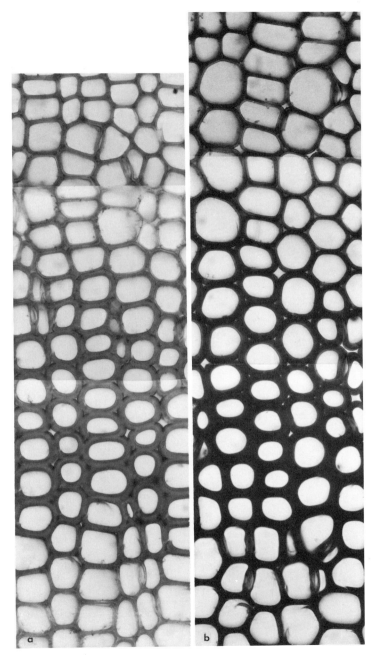

Fig. 15. Typical radial files of tracheids from the widest portion of the reaction arc of Figure 14. In both A and B, the first tracheid of the reaction arc (only excessively lignified) is the third full cell from the bottom of the photographs.

ciated with typical compression wood. Beyond these typical cells, the tracheids gradually returned to normal. Figure 16 illustrates the reaction arc as it appeared in the fluorescence microscope. Here a gradient in lignin content of the tracheids within the arc could clearly be seen, ranging

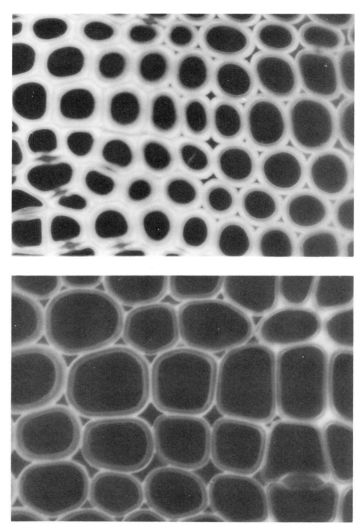

Fig. 16. Portions of the reaction arc of Figure 14 as seen in the fluorescence microscope. A. Initial portion of arc, showing highest degree of lignification in the otherwise normal rectangular tracheids at the beginning of the arc.   B. Outer extremity of arc, showing rounded but otherwise normal tracheids gradually returning to the rectangular shape devoid of intercellular spaces.

from excessive in the initial portion to normal in the middle and outer parts of the arc, where the circular shape of the cells was still clearly evident.

The radial width of the eight-day reaction marker was approximately constant at all heights in the stem. However, a section through the upper root, 2 cm below the level of the medium in the containers, showed only one third the number of reaction cells present in the stem. The seedlings tipped 45° produced a much narrower reaction arc, equivalent only to that found in the root section of those tilted a full 90°.

Discussion. A model of the developing tracheids is shown in Figure 17A. This model is based on observations of the sections shown in Figures 14 to 16. On the day of harvest, 10 immature cells were observed, and the same number has been assumed for the other days. At harvest, 24 mature cells were observed back to the first cell influenced by the treatment (No. 2 to 25). Allowing a lag period for the maturation of cell 1 gives 25 cells reaching maturity in 40 days. From these figures it was deduced that about 18 days were required for a cell to pass from cambium to maturity.

The variation in the form of the cell walls on Day 40 is a reflection of the degree of immaturity of the cells during the horizontal treatment. Tracheid 2 was excessively lignified but otherwise normal. It was horizontal only during the last two days of maturation, and consequently its expansion and wall thickening had been completed before treatment began. Tracheids 5 and 6 came closest to typical compression wood, having excessive lignification and wall thickening, and a round shape. They were horizontal during the last six or seven days of maturation. Hence cell enlargement, wall thickening, and lignification were all affected by treatment. Tracheid 9 was round but otherwise normal; the tree was restored to the vertical position just before wall thickening began. Tracheid 13 was somewhat rounded, but otherwise normal. It was initiated during the treatment, but was II from the cambium when treatment ceased. Finally, tracheid 15 was initated after treatment and was normal.

EXPERIMENT 4

Concurrent with this series of experiments on formation of reaction arcs, another series was conducted on the influence of drought on xylem anatomy. These experiments will be reported elsewhere but some preliminary results are presented here dealing with the effects of drought and tilting combined.

Method. Drought was induced by sealing the surface of the container with molten paraffin and withholding water. A few days of such treatment

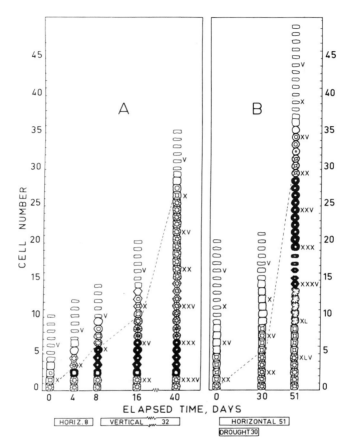

Fig. 17A. Model of tracheids developing on the underside of a jack pine seedling which was laid horizontally for eight days and then returned to the upright position for 32 days before harvesting. The column of cells at day 0 represents a file of tracheids as it appeared at the beginning of the experiment; the column at day 40, the day of harvest; and the other columns are intermediate times.

For the day of harvest (day 40) the file of tracheids is based on an actual section (Fig. 15); the other files are based on tentative deductions. The cells are numbered from the youngest mature cell on day 0 to the cambium. Each cell retains the same number throughout its life. The cells are also numbered with Roman numerals in reverse order to indicate their distance from the cambium. For example, cell 8 is III from cambium on day 0, V from cambium on Day 4, VIII from cambium on day 8, XIII from cambium on day 16, and XXVIII from cambium on day 40. The dotted oblique line separates the developing tracheids above from the mature ones below.

B. Model of tracheids differentiating on the underside of a jack pine seedling which was laid horizontally for 51 days prior to harvest and subjected to drought during the first 30 days of that period. The representation is similar to that in 17A with the exception of the time scale.

brought the soil to the permanent wilting point of sunflowers. A jack pine seedling, about 6 months old, was laid horizontally for 51 days immediately preceding the date of harvest, and subjected to drought for the first 30 days of this period. The seedling was sectioned at mid-height.

Results. The tracheids which were affected by drought and tipping are shown in Figures 18 and 19. The first five tracheids of the reaction arc

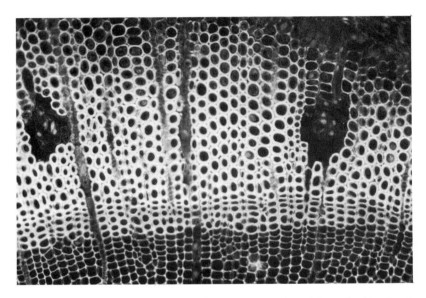

FIG. 18. Fluorescence photomicrograph of a transverse section of the underside of a *Pinus banksiana* seedling laid horizontally for 51 days prior to harvest and subjected to drought during the first 30 days of that period.

showed a gradual reduction in radial diameter with lignification only somewhat above normal, as determined by the differential fluorescence of the earlier and later portions of the reaction arc. The contrast in lignin content between these smaller tracheids and succeeding reaction tracheids is not evident with ordinary light microscopy (Fig. 19). The reaction arc was preceded by four or five cells with intermediate wall thickening, and four or five others with intermediate lignification.

Discussion. A model of the developing tracheids is shown in Figure 17B, based on Figures 18 and 19. The number of immature cells (20) present on the day of harvest was assumed to be the same on the first day. External measurements indicated that there was no diameter growth during the drought, so only one new cell is shown as forming during that

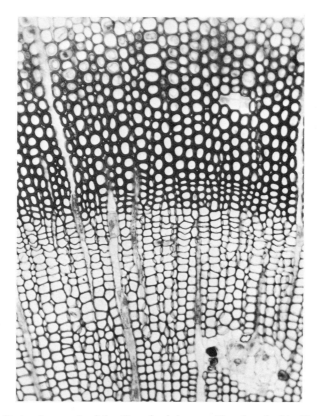

Fig. 19. Photomicrograph of the *Pinus banksiana* seedling described in Figure 18. Differentiation between the first 4 or 5 cells and the remainder of the reaction arc is lacking in this photograph (cf. Fig. 18).

period. The drought is also assumed to have stopped differentiation within a day or two after water was withheld.

It is known from other experiments that the horizontal position would cause all cells younger than No. 3 to differentiate into compression wood if watering were normal. It is assumed that cells 1 to 4 became normally lignified before the drought became effective, but further (excessive) lignification was halted by the drought. Cells 5 to 8 were prevented by drought from reaching even normal lignification. The maturation of cells 9 and younger was interrupted and altered by the drought, but not stopped permanently.

In cells 9 to 13, wall thickening had commenced before drought interrupted differentiation. After water was restored, no further thickening occured, but some lignification did take place. Because of their thin walls, they later became distorted when younger cells ahead of them expanded.

Drought stopped expansion in cells 14 to 18. After water was restored, wall thickening and lignification proceeded almost normally, but their reduced size showed the effects of drought.

Cells 19 to 28 were typical compression wood cells unaffected by drought. Cells 29 and younger were immature cells of compression wood. The round shape appeared at about cell XIV from the cambium when wall thickening began.

EXPERIMENT 5

As mentioned previously, secondary arcs were occasionally noted in a position diametrically opposed to the primary reaction arcs formed on the underside as a result of tipping. The fact that such secondary arcs were in a position closer to the cambium suggested that they may have formed due to the restoration of the stem to the vertical position. In order to test this hypothesis, seedlings representing a number of species were tilted in the horizontal position for a relatively long time, after which they were allowed to remain in the vertical position for a significant period before harvesting.

Method. A single 10-month-old seedling of each of the 6 species listed in Table II was tilted in the horizontal position for a 28-day period, after which it was restored to the vertical for 41 days. Special care was exercised to insure against movement of the seedling in its pot following tipping by tying the seedling at several points to a vertical supporting stake inserted firmly into the soil. After harvesting, each seedling was sectioned transversely through the hypocotyl, mid-point, and upper quarter of its main axis. A radial count was made of the number of tracheids included from the inception of the 28-day primary arc to the final mature cell bordering the cambial zone. Similarly, the number of tracheids from the beginning of the opposite secondary arc (if present) to the most recently matured cell was noted. Reaction tracheids, defined as those cells which showed clearly at least one attribute of typical compression wood, were counted separately from normal tracheids.

Results. Figure 20 shows an over-all view of the interlocking primary and secondary reaction arcs produced in northern white cedar. Table II summarizes the cell counts made from the beginning of opposing arcs in all species sampled. It is evident from Table II that a secondary arc formed in at least one level in all six species, since it was absent only at the upper and lower levels of white pine. Generally in the pines the sec-

TABLE II. Number of Mature Reaction (R) and Normal (N) Tracheids from
the Beginning of Primary and Secondary Reaction Arcs to the Cambial
Zone in Seedlings Subjected to 28 Days Horizontal plus
41 Days Vertical Positioning

| | Height in stem | | | | | |
| | Upper quarter | | Mid-stem | | Hypocotyl | |
Species	Primary side	Second- ary side	Primary side	Second- ary side	Primary side	Second- ary side
Jack pine	19R	8R	14R	5R	17R	7R
(Pinus banksiana)	13N	11N	9N	3N	11N	2N
Red pine	41R	14R	45R	22R	39R	13R
(Pinus resinosa)	25N	16N	30N	10N	29N	18N
Eastern white pine	18R	—	32R	9R	33R	—
(Pinus strobus)	9N	All N	6N	1N	9N	All N
Northern white cedar	44R	43R	42R	48R	48R	42R
(Thuja occidentalis)	28N	10N	32N	6N	47N	7N
Tamarack	20R	33R	46R	15R	44R	20R
(Larix occidentalis)	16N	—	14N	19N	16N	18N
Black spruce	26R	23R	33R	32R	42R	43R
(Picea mariana)	10N	—	12N	6N	23N	5N

ondary arc was less than half the width of the primary arc. Northern
white cedar and black spruce displayed pronounced secondary arcs rival-
ing in number of cells those produced initially. In general, however, the
degree of reaction wood attained in the secondary arcs was less than that
of the primary. Figures 21A and B indicate the varying severity of reaction wood in opposite arcs at the hypocotyl level in tamarack.

After the seedlings were returned to the vertical, the cambium was
generally more active on the secondary side than on the side of the primary arc. This was particularly noticeable in northern white cedar, tamarack, and black spruce, where the number of reaction plus normal cells
on the secondary side often outnumbered the normal tracheids produced
over the same time on the primary side by a factor of two.

The jack pine seedling exhibited a ring of about three slightly less lignified, thin-walled cells immediately before the primary arc. This ring could
also be located on the secondary arc side of the seedling, thereby pro-
viding a reference marker which enabled direct comparisons to be made of
tracheids formed contemporaneously on opposite sides of the stem. The

Fig 20. Primary (left) and secondary (right) reaction arcs in *Thuja occidentalis*, produced by tipping horizontally for 28 days followed by 41 days in the vertical position before harvest.

tracheids formed between this less lignified zone and the secondary reaction arc were thus developed concurrently with the primary arc. These tracheids are obviously fewer in number and reduced in radial diameter compared with those of the primary arc (compare Figs. 22B and 22A). A comparison between the average radial diameter of these tracheids, and those formed concurrently in the initial reaction arc, is given in Table III. Also included in this table as a form of control is the average radial diam-

TABLE III. Average Radial Diameter (Microns) of Tracheids in Various Locations in a Jack Pine Seedling Subjected to 28 Days Horizontal plus 41 Days Vertical Positioning

Location of tracheids	Height in stem			
	Upper quarter	Mid-stem	Hypocotyl	Average
1. Primary arc	20.5	18.3	19.8	19.5
2. Contemporary and opposite to 1.	14.0	14.7	14.1	14.3
3. Preceding 2.	21.0	20.2	21.6	20.9

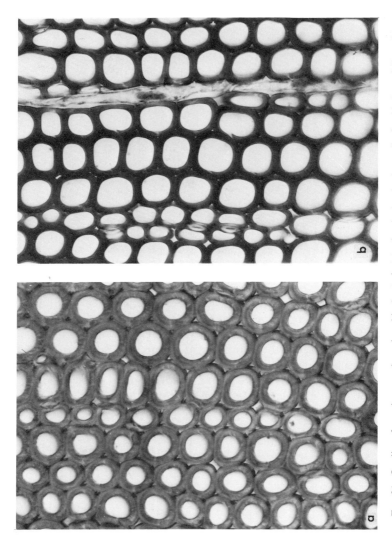

FIG. 21. Quality of reaction wood produced in *Larix laricina* by tipping horizontally for 28 days, followed by 41 days in the vertical position. A. Portion of the primary arc. B. Portion of the secondary arc.

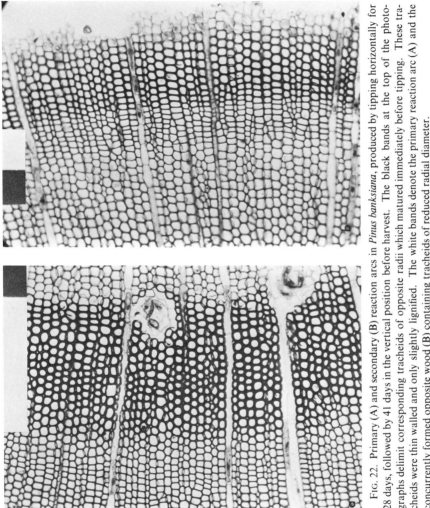

FIG. 22. Primary (A) and secondary (B) reaction arcs in *Pinus banksiana*, produced by tipping horizontally for 28 days, followed by 41 days in the vertical position before harvest. The black bands at the top of the photographs delimit corresponding tracheids of opposite radii which matured immediately before tipping. These tracheids were thin walled and only slightly lignified. The white bands denote the primary reaction arc (A) and the concurrently formed opposite wood (B) containing tracheids of reduced radial diameter.

eter of ten tracheids immediately preceding the less lignified zone on the secondary side.

Discussion. The regular occurrence of the secondary arc in the seedlings suggests a redistribution of auxin upon restoration to the vertical position such that an excess becomes available in the area that had formerly been the upper side. The more rapid growth rate on the secondary side after return to the vertical also supports this contention. However, it is logical to assume only that the *relative* concentration of auxin had increased from subnormal on the upper side to more or less normal when the vertical position was resumed. This relative difference in auxin concentration as a result of changing positions may provide a possible explanation for the wood formed.

During the 28-day period of lean, height growth continued in the seedlings and the leaders showed the usual negative geotropic response by bending up 30° to 90°, with the single exception of the black spruce which showed no response. When the seedlings were replaced upright, the lower side of bent leaders afforded an opportunity for localized collection of supranormal concentrations of auxin. It is conceivable that such concentrations could have been dispersed basipetally, resulting in the formation of the secondary arcs. However, the fact that no bending was noted in black spruce—a species that displayed a remarkably well developed secondary arc—militates against this mechanism as the principal causal factor.

The reduction in radial diameter of the tracheids contemporary but opposite to the initial reaction arc can be explained on the basis of an auxin availability below that of normal when these tracheids were forming on the upper side of the horizontal stem. Larson (1962) has demonstrated the reduction in radial diameter of tracheids due to shortened photoperiod, and likewise has postulated a lower auxin availability as the basic explanation for this phenomenon. Onaka (1949) has also noted a reduction in radial tracheid diameter of wood produced opposite to compression wood. In *Cryptomeria japonica,* springwood tracheids on the upper side were 23% smaller than the compression wood formed at the same time on the lower side. These upper tracheids were 48% smaller than those produced on the same side immediately before leaning began. Corresponding values for *Pinus densiflora* were 22 and 17% respectively. The comparable figures for jack pine taken from the average values in Table III were 26 and 31%.

A smaller zone of 2 to 3 tracheids having reduced radial diameter may be located in Figure 22A, approximately 4 cells beyond the primary reaction arc. This zone appears to have been formed contemporaneously with the secondary arc of Figure 22B, and offers further evidence of an imbalanced hormone distribution following the return of the seedling to the upright position.

General Discussion and Summary

These experiments showed that a definite date mark could be placed on the xylem of coniferous seedlings by tilting for a period of two days. Where growth is slow, this presentation period would have to be extended. The xylem marker consisted of an arc of excessively lignified tracheids, about three cells wide and extending about 180° around the stem.

Two arcs were used to delimit a time interval which in turn could be utilized to determine the growth rate of the seedling in terms of the number of days required to initiate a new cell. This value multiplied by the number of immature cells between cambium and wood allowed calculations to be made of the length of time required for a tracheid to be completely differentiated. One day was generally required to produce a new cell; twenty days were necessary for all differentiation phases to be completed.

In most cases, the first half of the differentiation period was characterized by no obvious change in cell size or shape, but rather by only limited enlargement followed by periclinal cell division. A subsequent period of two or three days was sufficient to complete the phase of enlargement. Wall thickening and lignification both required about four days. Enlargement and wall thickening overlapped in time as did wall thickening and lignification.

The response to tilting varied with the stage of maturation of the cell. During the earliest period, tilting encouraged cell division. Cells affected during the succeeding phases of differentiation had altered shape, wall thicknesses, or degree of lignification. Thus typical compression wood tracheids were formed only when the differentiating cells were on the underside of the stem for the entire period of enlargement, thickening, and lignification.

The response of the differentiating cambial zone to gravity is associated with varying distribution of auxin, which in large amounts is known to promote cell division and excessive lignification. The two-day period required to induce at least one characteristic of reaction wood (excessive lignification) is not short when compared with the upward movement of a growing apex placed in the horizontal position. The relocation of auxin in response to gravity may be related to the movement of statoliths. These organelles may act as perceptors for transmission of the geotropic stimulus by rolling to the lower side of the cell in a matter of minutes following a change in orientation (Steward, 1964; Thimann, 1964).

Drought drastically altered the pattern of maturation. As drought intensified, cell division and subsequent differentiation were brought to a halt. After watering was restored, tracheids in the later stages of maturation did not differentiate to a significantly greater extent; those in the earlier stages resumed the maturation processes, but in a modified way. The results were anomalous in that the tracheids affected by the drought appeared immediately before the first heavily lignified cells of reaction wood, not withstanding the fact that tilting preceded drought by two or three days. Double reaction arcs were used to delineate drought periods. The nature of the drought-affected tracheids will be published elsewhere.

ACKNOWLEDGMENT

This research was supported by a grant from the Ontario Research Foundation.

REFERENCES

Bannan, M. W. (1962) "The vascular cambium and tree-ring development." In *Tree Growth* (T. T. Kozlowski, ed.), pp. 3-21. Ronald Press, N. Y.

Dadswell, H. E. (1963) "Tree growth-wood property inter-relationships. I. Need for knowledge of effects of growth conditions on cell structure and wood properties." In *Proceedings of a Special Field Institute in Forest Biology* (T. E. Maki, ed.), pp. 5-11. School of Forestry, North Carolina State University, Raleigh, N. C.

Fraser, D. A. (1949) "Production of spring wood with β-indole acetic acid (heteroauxin)." *Nature* 164:542.

Frey-Wyssling, A. (1964) "Ultraviolet and fluorescence optics of lignified cell walls." In *The Formation of Wood in Forest Trees* (M. H. Zimmermann, ed.), pp. 153–167. Academic Press, N. Y.

Larson, P. R. (1962) "Auxin gradients and the regulation of cambial activity." In *Tree Growth* (T. T. Kozlowski, ed.), pp. 97–117. Ronald Press, N. Y.

Nečesaný, V. (1958) "Effect of β-indoleacetic acid on the formation of reaction wood." *Phyton* 11:117-127.

Onaka, F. (1949) "Studies on compression and tension wood." Bulletin of the Wood Research Institute, Kyoto Univ., Japan. No. 1 (Translation No. 93, Canada Dept. of North. Affairs and Nat. Res., For. Br., For. Prod. Labs. Div., pp. 1–99.)

Scott, D. R. M., and Preston, S. B. (1955) "Development of compression wood in eastern white pine through the use of centrifugal force." *Forest Sci.* 1:178–182.

Spurr, S. H., and Hyvarinen, M. J. (1954) "Compression wood in conifers as a morphogenetic phenomenon." *Botan. Rev.* 20:551–560.

Steward, F. C. (1964) In *Plants at Work,* p. 158. Addison-Wesley Publ. Co. Inc., Reading, Mass.

Thimann, K. V. (1964) "The role of polar hormone transport in tropisms." Abstract in *Tenth International Botanical Congress,* p. 195. Univ. of Edinburgh, Edinburgh.

Wardrop, A. B. (1957) "The phase of lignification in the differentiation of wood fibers." *Tappi* 40:225–243.

———, and Davies, G. W. (1964) "The nature of reaction wood. VIII. The structure and differentiation of compression wood." *Australian J. Botany* 12:24–38.

Wershing, H. T., and Bailey, I. W. (1942) "Seedlings as experimental material in the study of 'Redwood' in conifers." *J. Forestry* 40:411–414.

Wilson, B. F. (1963) "Increase in cell wall surface area during enlargement of cambial derivatives in *Abies concolor*." *Am. J. Botany* 50:95–102.

―――― (1964) Personal communication.

PART V

Physicochemical Properties of Wood and Wood Fibers— *Relationship to Ultrastructure*

Variability in Wood

CARL DE ZEEUW

*State University College of Forestry
at Syracuse University*

Every piece of wood is unique in structure and properties. This arises fundamentally from the fact that cell walls are variable in chemical composition and in organization on the molecular level. Furthermore, even between the several parts of individual trees there are major differences in the sizes of cells, their wall thicknesses, and the sorting of cells into tissues. All these structural features of wood directly influence its physical behavior and hence the variability extends to these latter characteristics that are of primary importance in the utilization of wood.

Scarcely any person using or studying wood is unaware of the differences which exist in some property between pieces that are supposedly similar. In spite of this familiarity few consider the variety of ways in which variability is expressed in wood. Commonly variability is considered in terms of cell sizes, ring widths, percentages of latewood, or density. However, it should be apparent from the papers given at this conference, as well as from any other selection of recent research, that almost any set of measurements of natural properties of wood will exhibit a range of variation. Papers describing the differences between "normal" and reaction wood cell wall structure and chemical composition are good examples. The controversial questions of microfibrillar dimensions can also be considered in light of the fact that there may be inter-specific differences or other variation basically causing discrepancies which are being reported in current literature. On a grosser scale, the range of values for mechanical properties in a given kind of wood are just as truly an expression of variability in wood as any other.

Anatomical differences between species are perhaps the earliest studied and most obvious of the expressions of variability in wood. Descriptive anatomists have been studying the many kinds of angiosperms and gymnosperms for several hundred years. It is now possible to define qualitatively the expected anatomical structure of many kinds of wood as well as the probable range of variation which may be encountered in the commercially important species. The two-volume work on dicotyledons by Metcalfe and Chalk (1950), with more than twenty-five hundred references, and the work of Phillips (1941), on the gymnosperms, indicate the extent to which this aspect of variability in wood has been pursued. Qualitative descriptions of wood anatomy are satisfactory for purposes of identification, because separations can be made on presence or absence of structures. However, if real relationships are to be drawn between structure and properties then the observations must be quantitative in order to define the gradations and relative influences.

The complex puzzle of variable interrelationships and causative factors in wood is too difficult to understand unless it is broken into segments. A convenient system is to consider first the variation within single trees and then variability between trees. The discussions will cover known information to indicate our present state of knowledge, the areas in need of attention, and some of the unifying concepts. Emphasis will be placed on quantitative studies since these are undoubtedly most useful in defining the relationships between structure and properties that are required in our present evaluation of the qualities needed in wood for specific purposes, and the related definition of specific types of trees to grow.

Within-Tree Variation

The morphological variation within an individual tree arises from the interlocking influences of two primary systems on the cambium and its differentiating tissues. One is the availability of moisture and the other is the influence of crown elongation on the differentiating cambium (Larson, 1962; Zahner, 1963; Zimmermann, 1964).

Earlywood formation is associated with auxin production arising from the actively elongating crown. The auxin is translocated vertically to the cambium and influences radial enlargement of tracheids in conifer stems and possibly also affects the earlywood vessels in hardwoods. The amount of auxin available to the cambium decreases with increasing distance from the active crown so that both magnitude and duration of earlywood formation are lower at the base of the tree than within the upper or crown-related parts of the tree. During the period of high moisture availability or low moisture stress (Zahner, 1963) the crown elongation, auxin production, and earlywood formation continue. As available moisture decreases, the radial cell enlargement decreases, the differentiated cells remain alive longer, and the walls become appreciably thicker than those in the earlywood. This latter period is that of latewood formation.

An additional influence on the morphology of the tree stem lies in the increasing length of the cambial initials with age (Bannan, 1959, 1962; Bosshard, 1951). These initials, and the cells derived from them, are shortest when they are first differentiated from primary tissue. In the first few years after formation the cambial initials increase quite rapidly in length and approach the maximum exhibited by mature trees.

The effects of the growth control systems outlined above can best be shown by reference to specific studies on within-tree variation.

Cell Dimensions. Cell length is the best known aspect of variable morphology in wood. This is traceable to Sanio's (1872) pioneering investigations in tracheid length variation in *Pinus sylvestris* L. Within the present century the matter of fiber length has become important to the pulp and paper industry, with a consequent expansion of information on both conifers and hardwoods. Two excellent summaries and bibliographies of the work on cell length variation exist: Dinwoodie (1961), and Spurr and Hyvärinen (1954).

Definite patterns of cell length changes are evident radially within a growth ring. It has been shown by macerating serial sections that cell lengths decrease following the inception of yearly growth until a minimum length is reached in the first portion of the earlywood. Thereafter the cell lengths increase to a maximum in the latewood, either rapidly or slowly, depending upon the nature of the transition from early- to latewood (Bisset and Dadswell, 1950; Bisset *et al.*, 1950). The reported increases may be as large as 0.5 mm within one ring of Douglas-fir (*Pseudotsuga menziesii* [Mirb.] Franco) according to Bisset and Dadswell (1950). Other studies, using isolated early- and latewood material from the same ring, confirm the results already cited (Bosshard, 1951; Hejnowicz and Hejnowicz, 1959; Scaramuzzi, 1959). Lengths of vessel elements in *Fraxinus excelsior* are reported to follow the pattern of increased length in the latewood (Bosshard, 1951). However, in *Robinia pseudoacacia,* which possesses stratified cambial initials, Hejnowicz and Hejnowicz (1959) report no length variation for vessel elements within a ring from early- to latewood.

Cell length variation vertically within a ring follows a general pattern of gradual increase in length from the base upward to a maximum below the crown and a decrease in length above this height in the trunk. This progression was first defined by Sanio (1872) and since that time by many others for both conifers and hardwoods, notably by Bailey and Shepard (1915), Bisset and Dadswell (1949), Elliott (1960), Jackson (1959), Nicholls and Dadswell (1962).

Cell length variation in the radial direction between successive growth increments also follows a well defined curve, which was first noted by Sanio (1872). A plot of the mean lengths of cells in each of the increments conforms roughly to a logarithmic curve (Bailey and Shepard, 1915, Bisset and Dadswell, 1949; Elliott, 1960). The shortest cells are found near the pith, the longest in the wood formed at the period of tree maturity. In very old trees the length of cells decreases from the maximum, as shown by the diagrams for *Sequoia sempervirens* given by Bailey and Faull (1934). In conifer stems, if curves are drawn separately for the earlywood and the latewood portions of the increments from the pith outward, the cell lengths in the earlywood exhibit a more gradual rise in length in the early years than is shown by the latewood. Furthermore, the variability in length for the earlywood cells is much less than that for the latewood cells (Hejnowicz and Hejnowicz, 1959; Stevens, 1959; Wellwood, 1962).

Cell length variation between trunk, root, and branches of a single tree is incompletely known, and because of this fact, confusing. The most available studies are Bailey and Faull (1934), Fegel (1941), Gleaton and Saydah (1956), and Jackson (1959).

Vessel element lengths in successive increments from the pith outward are known only from a few studies. Bosshard (1951) reports that in *Fraxinus excelsior* the earlywood vessel elements increase in a manner typical of tracheids and fibers, but that latewood vessel elements show almost no change with age. Only minor changes in vessel lengths in the radial direction were reported by Hejnowicz and Hejnowicz (1959) for *Robinia pseudoacacia,* and by Aung (1962) for *Shorea.*

Measurements of other cellular elements are quite scarce. For example, one of the few studies of cell wall thickness and its ratio to lumen diameter within a tree is that of Scaramuzzi (1959) on hybrid poplar. Aung (1962) reports radial variation in percentage of cell wall in *Shorea.* Both of these studies reveal that there is a distinct increase in ratio and wall thickness from the pith outward. Very few measurements of vessel volumes exist. Myer (1922) cites values for a number of kinds of trees but gives no indication of within-tree variation.

Cell Wall Organization. The general nature of the secondary cell wall layering as originally proposed by Kerr and Bailey (1934) has been substantiated by many workers. However, far too little attention has been paid to the variability of this wall layering in terms of the proportionate amounts of layers present both within the tree and between species. This problem is noted by Bailey (1957) and studied by Wardrop and Dadswell (1957).

The presence of reaction wood within a tree stem is one of the most marked causes for variability in cell wall layering. In conifers, the S_2 layer is greatly modified in the form of radial lamellations and is accompanied only by the S_1 (Wardrop and Dadswell, 1950). In hardwoods the usual modification of the cell in tension wood exhibits a special gelatinous layer consisting of highly oriented and crystalline cellulose. The gelatinous layer may appear with the usual three-layered secondary wall or may replace either or both of the S_2 and S_3 layers (Wardrop and Dadswell, 1955). The variability due to reaction wood is increased by the fact that there are gradations in degree of modification of cells within a tree.

The orientation of microfibrils within the cell wall layers is certainly not constant, as has been clearly shown in the summaries by Dadswell and Wardrop (1960) and Liese and Côté (1960). Further variation is also evident if the mean microfibrillar angles of the S_2 layer of conifer tracheids are studied. Wardrop and Preston (1950) in *Pseudotsuga menziesii* and Pillow *et al.* (1953) in *Pinus taeda* show that the microfibrillar angle approaches more nearly to the cell axis as measurements are made in increments from the pith outward. This pattern coincides with that for cell length increase and is tied to it by the relationships between cell length and microfibrillar angle derived by Preston (1934, 1947) and Wardrop and Preston (1950).

Chemical Composition of the Cell Wall. Within individual growth increments Ritter and Fleck (1926) have shown that the cellulose content is highest in the latewood and the lignin conversely higher in the earlywood of three kinds of hardwoods and three conifers. These results are confirmed by Hale and Clermont (1963) for *Pseudotsuga menziesii* and *Pinus resinosa*.

The distribution of cellulose in successive increments from the pith outward has been shown to conform to the curve for tracheid lengths in the radial direction in the stem by Hale and Clermont (1963), working with *Pseudotsuga menziesii*, and by Wardrop (1951), with the same species and *Pinus radiata*. Zobel and McElwee (1958b) report a significant increase in cellulose from juvenile to mature wood in *Pinus taeda*. Schutt and Augustin (1961) show that *Pinus contorta* exhibits some increase in cellulose content in samples taken through the outer rings at breast height.

Evidence that there is a decrease in cellulose content with vertical position in the stem is given by Hale and Clermont (1963) and also by Shutt and Augustin (1961).

X-ray examination of the crystallinity of cellulose from a thirty-three year old stem of *Tsuga heterophylla* (Lee, 1961) has shown that there was a marked increase from the third to the fifteenth increment.

Another major cause of variation in the chemical composition of the cell wall is the presence of reaction wood. In general, it can be stated that compression wood is 20 to 30% greater in lignin than comparable normal wood. In contrast, tension wood exhibits a higher proportion of cellulose and decreased lignin in comparison with normal wood. The cellulose in tension wood is also more highly crystalline. The data in support of these statements appears in a number of scattered sources, which are summarized in tabular form by Panshin *et al.* (1964).

Spiral Grain. Orientation of the axis of cells in the stem is seldom parallel to a plane drawn through the pith. The many investigations relating to variations in the angle of spirality within tree stems are summarized by Noskowiak (1963). He concludes that in conifers the spirality follows a general pattern. In the first ten years of growth the spiral angle is in the left direction. In older trees the left spiral decreases to zero and from this time forward the spiral grain angle increases in the right direction. Within this general pattern there is a great deal of variation between trees in the maximum angle of deviation. Noskowiak also reports differences of angles of one-half to three degress between the early- and latewood zones of a single ring. In hardwoods there is a much greater variety of patterns of spirality and variability so that it is not possible at this time to define a general form of relationship for hardwoods.

Specific Gravity. The amount of wood substance present is closely correlated with the specific gravity of the wood. Thus it is readily appreciated that the specific gravity distribution within a ring is closely related to the early- and latewood components in conifers and to vessel and fiber proportions in hardwoods. The graphs of density change in a ring have the same saw-tooth shape as those quoted for cell lengths (Phillips *et al.,* 1962). Within the stem in conifers the density increases from the pith outward and decreases from the base upward (Spurr and Hsiung, 1954; Göhre, 1955; Zobel *et al.,* 1959; Yandle, 1959). The core of wood near the pith has low specific gravity and is essentially uniform at all heights in the tree (Zobel *et al.,* 1959). In hardwood stems the pattern of specific gravity variation is more difficult to interpret because of the greater variety of tissue patterns and fewer investigations. There is one type of distribution pattern in ring porous hardwoods associated with latewood percentage. This is reported by Hamilton (1961) for *Quercus rubra* and Bethel (1943) for *Quercus prinus* as inversely related to age from the pith and height in the trunk above the base. The distribution in hybrid poplar described by Göhre (1960) is roughly similar to that given for the oak above but no correlation was made with tissue types. In the diffuse porous woods, the density pattern resembles that for conifers in the radial direction in *Liriodendron tulipifera* (Thorbjornsen, 1961) and in *Shorea* (Aung, 1962).

Specific gravity of wood is the best existing index to both mechanical and nonmechanical wood properties. In general the mechanical relationships conform to an exponential function of specific gravity (U.S. Forest Products Laboratory, 1941). However, the relationships are not exact. This arises for one reason because of the variations in lignin and cellulose ratios. Examples can be seen in the tables of mechanical properties for reaction wood in Panshin *et al.* (1964). The increased percentage of lignin in tropical woods has also been shown by Clarke (1937) to relate directly to increased compression strength. The presence of infiltrates of heart-wood substances in general tends to increase the apparent specific gravity with little effect on mechanical properties except for increases in compression strength and hardness. As a result there can be a hidden component of variation when mechanical properties are used as an index of the character of wood.

The general index of specific gravity to strength in wood is useful, but, as was pointed out, there are discrepancies related to the factors affecting specific gravity. This defect can be overcome by such multiple factor studies as Barefoot (1963), relating specific gravity and toughness in *Liriodendron tulipifera* to vessel volume, gelatinous fibers, percentage parenchyma, age from pith, site index, height in tree, and degree of lignification. Such studies are difficult to conduct without a computer, but are necessary if the various elements affecting the variability in wood are to be understood.

Between-Tree Variation

The variability between trees within a species may be greater or smaller than the within-tree variation. Two general influences contribute to this intra-specific variability: growth factors and genetical factors. The first of these influences also affects the within-tree variation and can hardly be disassociated.

Growth Influences There is a large amount of literature relating tree growth conditions to the structure of the wood produced. These studies are summarized by Dadswell (1957), Hildebrandt (1960), and Larson (1957).

Availability of moisture is one of the primary factors causing variability. Previous discussion has related high moisture availability to early-wood production and moisture deficit in the growing season to latewood. In conifers the moisture availability related to dominance in the stand has been shown to produce broad annual rings and reduced latewood percentage, among other effects (Schultze-Dewitz, 1960). Kennedy (1961) has related the latewood in *Pseudotsuga menziesii* to precipitation.

Site quality has a direct effect on the wood produced by conifers. The better sites produce larger volumes of wood with lower specific gravity than the poorer sites (Harlow, 1927; Jayne, 1958).

Differences in soil types apparently have some influence. Wilde and Paul (1959) report that *Populus tremuloides* grown on two soil types varied about 10% in specific gravity and also in chemical composition. When fertilizer is added to soils the specific gravity of the conifer wood produced increases (Wilde and Voight, 1948; Erickson and Lambert, 1958). Tracheid length has also been shown to increase in *Pinus pinaster* after the addition of super phosphate (Bisset *et al.*, 1951).

The effect of geographic location on wood properties has been studied by a number of investigators, among whom are Myer (1930), Echols (1958), Zobel and McElwee (1958a), and more lately Knigge (1962). All these indicate that whereas there are differences between geographical locations, these differences are largely attributable to available moisture, summer temperature, and length of growing season. The most recent information, which appears in the preliminary report of the U.S. Forest Products Laboratory *Western Wood Density Survey*, makes these conclusions even more certain.

Genetic Influences. In recent years it has become apparent that an attempt must be made to influence the type of wood produced in new stands by the genetic improvement of trees. It has been known intuitively from other crop breeding programs that this should be possible and considerable discussion of the problem has been published since 1958 (Browning, 1958; Dadswell and Wardrop, 1960; Duffield, 1961; Jackson and Greene, 1958; Perry and Wu, 1958; Zobel, 1960).

One of the major problems, as yet uncompleted, is the identification of those wood structures and properties which can be classed as inherently different in various individuals of a species. For this purpose it is necessary to isolate the between-tree variation in samples from a number of trees and identify those portions of the variability which can be associated with the environmental factors. The residual variation, if any, can be ascribed to the genetical control. Champion (1933) worked with Indian conifers and identified the heritability of spiral grain by more or less intuitive methods. More recent work using statistics as a primary tool of data analysis has shown that tracheid length is inherited: Echols (1955) for *Pinus elliotii*, Hartley (1960) for *Pinus radiata*, Wellwood (1960) for *Tsuga heterophylla*, and Boyce and Kaeser (1961) for *Populus deltoides.* Specific gravity has been pointed out as an inherited property by Cech *et al.* (1960) in *Populus trichocarpa* and by Zobel (1956) in *pinus taeda*. Cellulose content in *Pseudotsuga menziesii* has been shown to be an inherited factor by Kennedy and Jaworshy (1960), but Cech *et al.* (1960) failed to show this in *Populus trichocarpa*, perhaps due to having tested the wrong factors. A number of other studies have been inconclusive but still indicate that there are good possibilities for genetic control of factors: Kramer (1957) and Buijtenen *et al.* (1961) for tracheid length in *Pinus taeda;* Kloot (1957) for strength in bending and compression in *Pinus radiata;* and Thorbjornsen (1961) for fiber length in *Liriodendron tulipifera.*

The problem of variability enters into the methods for sampling in the selection of trees for breeding programs as well as into the determination of inherited factors. The within-tree variation may be as large as the genetic component so that it becomes important to control this factor (Dadswell *et al.*, 1961). Richardson (1961) and Zobel *et al.* (1960) discuss the matter of proper location of sampling within the tree for comparable results. Wahlgren and Fassnacht (1959) have developed a method of relating breast-height increment core samples to the tree specific gravity. Dadswell and Nicholls (1959) and Hale (1962) have developed systems of standard curves for comparison with data from specific trees to be evaluated.

PHYSICAL BEHAVIOR OF WOOD AS AN INDEX OF VARIABILITY

Our ultimate goal in producing trees for commercial purposes is the use of the wood in those trees. Since the use of wood is directly influenced by its physical characteristics, it becomes important to know the variability and relationships of the latter to the structural features of the wood. Some of the physical properties have been related directly to morphology and the possibility exists that others could also be studied in this way. The most successful of these studies relate the increase in tensile strength of wood to increases in fiber length and corresponding decrease in fibril angle (Wardrop, 1951; Wellwood, 1962). Tensile testing has also been applied to isolated single fibers (Jayne, 1960; Leopold and McIntosh, 1961). The strength of these single fibers has been correlated with the available area of wall cross section and fibril angle in an attempt to characterize their variability.

Dimensional changes in wood are related to cell length and fibril angle, to cell wall thickness, latewood or other tissue bands, and to character and proportion of ray tissue. It can be readily appreciated, therefore, that some of the patterns of variability already described will apply to dimensional changes. Erickson (1958) has demonstrated increases in tangential shrinkage across the ring from early- to latewood. Paul (1939) reports increased shrinkage with age from the pith in *Quercus alba*. Erickson (1949) relates shrinkage to specific gravity in *Liriodendron tulipifera*. Cockrell (1946) has demonstrated that longitudinal shrinkage is dependent upon fibril angle.

The complex problem of anisotropic dimensional changes in wood is still a fertile field for investigation of variability. Numerous studies have related independent factors to transverse anisotropy with limited success except in certain kinds of woods. It is obvious that multiple factor analysis is needed for such studies. Schniewind (1959) has developed a unique study of this kind in which he derives mathematical expressions relating transverse anisotropy for shrinkage, elasticity, and tensile strength as functions of ray and other tissue volumes, early- and late-wood. His theoretical values agree well with experimental results for *Quercus kellogii*.

CONCLUSIONS

The previous discussions have shown that variability in wood can be accounted for on the basis of gross anatomical differences on the one hand, and by cell and cell wall modification on the other. At present we are pursuing studies of all aspects of this problem and perhaps it is just as well that we are. However, it is my own feeling that the really important aspects of variability are those related to cell wall structure, its chemical composition, and growth systems which control the formation of the cell. These areas of interest are relatively new because it has been difficult, if not impossible, to investigate them in the past with tools available.

Analysis of the work in electron microscopy of the woody cell wall to date forces us to acknowledge that we are still in the stage of confirmation of those educated guesses which were made in the past by various brilliant research men on the basis of light microscopy. It is important that observations be extended not only to higher magnifications, but to more extensive sampling of specimens within species and wider representation of species than has been studied previously. A system is also needed for the examination of material in a swollen condition representative of the normal state in the living tree.

One of the great defects of our present methods for studying variability in wood is the enormous amount of labor required to bring forth a few facts. Our methods are too much bound to personal observation. We must use and develop automatic data collection systems so that the labor will be principally expended on the analytical phase of the problem. In addition, modern data processing methods are not only essential because of the mass of information to be handled, but because they allow the use of more effective mathematical methods in the analysis.

As a last point, I wish to stress the fact that a great deal of the investigations in the past have been almost wholly empiric. We will continue to need the collection of data of this empiric nature, but efforts should be made to assemble critical information which can then be tested against some theory and applied to a wide range of similar situations. We must choose the factors to be studied with great care and sample on the basis of the best information so that the total effort available for the study of variability in wood can be extended over the maximum range of problems.

REFERENCES

Aung, M. (1962) "Density variation outwards from the pith in some species of *Shorea* and its anatomical basis." *Empire Forestry Review* 41:48–56.

Bailey, I. W. (1957) "Need for a broadened outlook in cell wall terminologies." *Phytomorphology* 7:136–138.

————, and Faull, A. F. (1934) "The cambium and its derivative tissues. IX. Structural variability in the redwood (*Sequoia sempervirens*), and its significance in the identification of fossil woods." *J. Arnold Arboretum* 15:233–254.

————, and Shepard, H. B. (1915) "Sanio's laws for the variation of size in coniferous tracheids." *Botan. Gaz.* 60:66–71.

Bannan, M. W. (1959) "Some factors influencing cell size in conifer cambium." *Proc. Ninth Intern. Botan. Congress* 2:18–19.

———— (1962) "The vascular cambium and tree ring development." In *Tree Growth* (T. T. Kozlowski, ed.), pp. 3–21. Ronald Press, N. Y.

Barefoot, A. C., Jr. (1963) "Selected wood characteristics of young yellow-poplar (*Liriodendron tulipifera* L.). Part 1. Specific gravity and toughness." *Forest Prod. J.* 13: 233–239.

Bethel, J. S. (1943) "Factors influencing the specific gravity of chestnut-oak wood." *J. Forestry* 41:599–601.

Bisset, I. W. J., and Dadswell, H. E. (1949) "The variation of fiber length within one tree of *Eucalyptus regnans* F.v.M." *Australian Forestry* 13:86–96.

———— and ———— (1950) "The variation in cell length within one growth ring of certain angiosperms and gymnosperms." *Australian Forestry* 14:17–29.

————, ————, and Amos, G. L. (1950) "Changes in fiber length within one growth ring of certain angiosperms." *Nature* (London) 165 (4192):348–349.

————, ————, and Wardrop, A. B. (1951) "Factors influencing tracheid length in conifer stems." *Australian Forestry* 15:17–30.

Bosshard, H. H. (1951) "Variabilität der Elemente des Eschenholzes in Funktion von der Kambiumtätigkeit." *Schweiz. Z. Forstw.* 102:648–665.

Boyce, S. G., and Kaeser, M. (1961) "Environment and genetic variability in the length of fibers of eastern cottonwood." *Tappi* 44:363–366.

Browning, B. L. (1958) "Chemical characterization of wood samples for the forest geneticist." *Tappi* 41:156–157.

Buijtenen, J. P. van, Zobel, B. J., and Joranson, P. N. (1961) "Variation of some wood and pulp properties in an even-aged Loblolly pine stand." *Tappi* 44:141–144.

Cech, M. Y., Kennedy, R. W., and Smith, J. H. G. (1960) "Variation in some wood quality attributes of one-year-old black cottonwood (*Populus trichocarpa*)." *Tappi* 43:857–859.

Champion, H. G. (1933) "The importance of the origin of seed used in forestry." *Indian Forest Record* 17 (5).

Clarke, S. H. (1937) "A comparison of certain properties of temperate and tropical timbers." *Tropical Woods* 52:1–11.

Cockrell, R. A. (1946) "Influence of fibril angle on longitudinal shrinkage of ponderosa pine wood." *J. Forestry* 44:876–878.

Dadswell, H. E. (1957) "Tree growth characteristics and their influence on wood structure and properties." *CSIRO, Australia, 7th British Commonwealth Forestry Conference Australia and New Zealand.*

————, Fielding, J., Nicholls, J. W. P., and Brown, A. G. (1961) "Tree-to-tree variations in the gross heritability of wood characteristics of *Pinus radiata*." *Tappi* 44:174–179.

————, and Nicholls, J. W. P. (1959) *Assessment of wood qualities for tree breeding.* 1. *In*

468 C. de Zeeuw

Pinus elliottii var. elliottii from Queensland. (CSIRO, Australia Div. of For. Prod. Tech. Paper No. 4.

———, and Wardrop, A. B. (1960) "Recent progress in research on cell wall structure." *In Proceedings Fifth World Forestry Congress, Seattle,* pp. 1279–1288.

Dinwoodie, J. M. (1961) "Tracheid and fiber length in timber, a review of literature." *Forestry* 34:125–144.

Duffield, J. W. (1961) "Progress and problems of genetic improvement of tree quality." *Forest Prod. J.* 11:211–213.

Echols, R. M. (1955) "Linear relation of fibrillar angle to tracheid length, and genetic control of tracheid length in slash pine." *Tropical Woods* 102:11–22.

——— (1958) "Variation in tracheid length and wood density in geographic races of Scotch pine." Yale Univ. School of Forestry, Bull. No. 64.

Elliott, G. K. (1960) "The distribution of tracheid length in a single stem of Sitka spruce." *J. Inst. Wood Sci.* 5:38–47.

Erickson, H. D. (1949) "Relation of specific gravity to shrinkage and of these factors to growth in yellow poplar." *J. Agric. Res.* 78:103–127.

——— (1958) "Tangential shrinkage of serial sections within annual rings of douglas-fir and western redcedar." *Forest Prod. J.* 5:241–250.

———, and Lambert, G. M. G. (1958) "Effects of fertilization and thinning on chemical composition, growth and specific gravity of young douglas-fir." *Forest Sci.* 4:307–315.

Fegel, A. C. (1941) "Comparative anatomy and varying physical properties of trunk, branch, and root wood in certain northeastern trees." New York State College of Forestry, Syracuse, N. Y., Tech. Publ. No. 55.

Gleaton, E. A., and Saydah, L. (1956) "Fiber dimensions and paper making properties of the various portions of a tree." *Tappi* 39:157A–158A.

Göhre, K. (1955) "Die rohwichte des Douglasien-holzes, ihre verteilung im Stamm und abhangigkeit vom abstand vom mark, jahrringbreite und spatholzanteil." *Arch. Forstw.* 4:639–661.

——— (1960) "Die Verteilung von Rohwichte im Pappelstamm." *Wiss. Abh. Dtsch. Akad. LandwWiss. Berlin* No. 44:51–79.

Hale, J. D. (1962) "Minimum requirements for defining species norms for quality of variable woods." *Tappi* 45:538–542.

———, and Clermont, L. P. (1963) "Influence of prosenchyma cell-wall morphology on basic physical and chemical characteristics of wood." *J. Polymer Sci.,* Part C 2:253–261.

Hamilton, J. R. (1961) "Variation of wood properties in southern red oak." *Forest Prod. J.* 11:267–271.

Harlow, W. M. (1927) "The effect of site on the structure and growth of white cedar (*Thuja occidentalis* L.)." *Ecology* 13:452–470.

Hartley, W. R. (1960) "Nutrients and tracheid length in seedlings of *Pinus radiata* D. Don." *Empire Forestry Review* 39:474–482.

Hejnowicz, A., and Hejnowicz, Z. (1959) "Variations in length of vessel members and fibers in the trunk of *Robinia pseudoacacia.*" *Acta. Soc. Bot. Polon.* 28:453–460. (Also in *Proc. Ninth Intern. Botan. Congress,* 1959).

Hildebrandt, G. (1960) "The effect of growth conditions on the structure and properties of wood." In *Proceedings Fifth World Forestry Congress, Seattle,* pp. 1348–1353.

Jackson, L. W. R. (1959) "Loblolly pine tracheid length in relation to position in tree." *J. Forestry* 5:366–367.

———, and Greene, J. T. (1958) "Tracheid length variations and inheritance in slash pine and loblolly pine." *J. Texas Forest Service* 4(4).

Jayne, B. A. (1958) "Effect of site and spacing on the specific gravity of wood of plantation-grown red pine." *Tappi* 41:162–166.

————— (1960) "Some mechanical properties of wood fibers in tension." *Forest Prod. J.* 10:316–322.

Kennedy, R. W. (1961) "Variation and periodicity of summerwood in some second-growth Douglas-fir." *Tappi* 44:161–166.

—————, and Jaworshy, J. M. (1960) "Variation in cellulose content of Douglas fir." *Tappi* 43:25–27.

Kerr, T., and Bailey, I. W. (1934) "The cambium and its derivative tissues. X. Structure, optical properties and chemical composition of the so-called middle lamella." *J. Arnold Arboretum* 15:327–349.

Kloot, H. (1957) *Can the strength of radiata pine be improved?* CSIRO (Australia) Forest Products Newsletter, No. 232.

Knigge, W. (1962) "Untersuchungen über die Abhängigkeit der mittleren Rohdichte nord-amerikanischer Douglasienstämme von unterscheidlichen Wuchsbedingungen." *Holz Roh- Werkstoff* 20:352–360.

Kramer, P. R. (1957) "Tracheid length variation in loblolly pine." Texas Forest Service Tech. Rpt. No. 10.

Larson, P. R. (1957) "Effect of environment on the percentage of summerwood and specific gravity of slash pine." Yale Univ. School of Forestry Bull. No. 63.

————— (1962) "A biological approach to wood quality." *Tappi* 45:443–448.

Lee, C. L. (1961) "Crystallinity of wood cellulose fibers studied by X-ray methods." *Forest Prod. J.* 11:8–12.

Leopold, B., and McIntosh, D. C. (1961) "Chemical composition and physical properties of wood fibers. III. Tensile strength of individual fibers from alkali-extracted loblolly pine holocellulose." *Tappi* 44:235–240.

Liese, W., and Côté, W. A., Jr. (1960) "Electron microscopy of wood. Results of the first ten years of research." In *Proceedings Fifth World Forestry Congress, Seattle,* pp. 1288–1298.

Metcalfe, C. R., and Chalk, L. (1950) *The Anatomy of Dicotyledons.* The Clarendon Press, Oxford, England.

Myer, J. E. (1922) "Ray volumes of the commercial woods of the United States and their significance." *J. Forestry* 20:337–351.

————— (1930) *The structure and strength of four North American woods as influenced by range, habitat and position in the tree.* New York State College of Forestry, Syracuse, N. Y., Tech. Publ. No. 31.

Nicholls, J. W. P., and Dadswell, H. E. (1962) *Tracheid length in Pinus radiata D. Don.* CSIRO (Australia) Div. of For. Prod. Tech. Paper No. 24.

Noskowiak, A. F. (1963) "Spiral grain in trees." *Forest Prod. J.* 13:266–275.

Panshin, A. J., de Zeeuw, C., and Brown, H. P. (1964) *Textbook of Wood Technology,* Vol. 1, Second Edition, McGraw-Hill Book Co., N.Y.

Paul, B. H. (1939) "Shrinkage of white oak as affected by position in the tree." *J. Forestry* 37:572–573.

Perry, T. O., and Wu, W. C. (1958) "Variations in the specific gravity of slash pine wood and its genetic and silvicultural implications." *Tappi* 41:178–180.

Phillips, E. W. J. (1941) "The identification of coniferous woods by their microscopic structure." *J. Linnean Soc. of London* 52:259–320.

—————, Adams, E. H., and Hearmon, R. F. S. (1962) "The measurement of density variation within growth rings in thin sections of wood using beta particles." *J. Inst. Wood Sci.* 10:11–28.

Pillow, M. Y., Terrel, B. Z., and Hiller, C. H. (1953) "Patterns of variation in fibril angles in loblolly pine. U. S. Forest Products Lab. Rept. D1935.

Preston, R. D. (1934) "The organization of the cell wall of the conifer tracheid." *Phil. Trans.*, Ser. B 224:131–172.

———(1947) "The fine structure of the wall of the conifer tracheid. II. Optical properties of the dissected walls in *Pinus insignis.*" *Proc. Royal Soc. (London) B134:202–218.*

Richardson, S. D. (1961) "A biological basis for sampling in studies of wood properties." *Tappi* 44:170–173.

Ritter, G. J., and Fleck, L. C. (1926) "Chemistry of wood. IX. Springwood and summer-wood." *Ind. Eng. Chem.* 18:608–609.

Sanio, K. (1872) "Ueber die grosse der Holzzellen bei der gemeinen Kiefer (*Pinus silves-tris*)." *Jahrb. wiss. Botan.* 8:401–420.

Scaramuzzi, G. (1959) "Variazioni dimensionali delle fibre nel fusto in *Populus* x *euramer-icana* cv. 'I 214'." *Pubbl. Cent. Sper. Agric. For., Roma* 2:87–118.

Schniewind, A. P. (1959) "Transverse anisotropy of wood as a function of gross anatomic structure." *Forest Prod. J.* 9:350–359.

Schultze-Dewitz, G. (1960) "Wie wirkt sich der Einfluss der Stellung eines Baumes im Bestand auf seine Holzstruktur." *Holzforsch. Holzverwert.* 12:30–33.

Schutt, P., and Augustin, H. (1961) "Die Verteilung des Cellulosegehaltes im Stamm. Un-tersuchungen über eine Methode der züchterischen Probenahme an 30 jahrigen Murray-kieferen." *Papier* (Darmstadt) 15:651–655.

Spurr, S. H., and Hsiung, W-Y. (1954) "Growth rate and specific gravity in conifers." *J. Forestry* 52:191–200.

———, and Hyvärinen, M. J. (1954) "Wood fiber length as related to position in the tree and growth." *Botan. Rev.* 20:561–575.

Stevens, S. H. (1959) "Tracheid length in *Pinus caribaea* Morelet." In *Rept. Imperial Forestry Inst., Oxford*, 1958/59, pp. 18–19.

Thorbjornsen, E. (1961) "Variation in density and fiber length in wood of yellow poplar." *Tappi* 44:192–195.

U. S. Forest Products Laboratory (1941) "Specific gravity–strength relations for wood." Rept. No. 1303. Madison, Wis.

——— (No date, probably 1963) "Western wood density survey" (preliminary report).

Wahlgren, H. E., and Fassnacht, D. L. (1959) "Estimating tree specific gravity from a single increment core." U. S. Forest Prod. Lab Rept. No. 2146. Madison, Wis.

Wardrop, A. B. (1951) "Cell wall organization and the properties of the xylem. I. Cell wall organization and the variation of breaking load in tension of xylem in conifer stems." *Australian J. Sci. Res. Ser.* B 4:391–414.

———, and Dadswell, H. E. (1950) "The nature of reaction wood. II. The cell wall or-ganization of compression wood tracheids." *Australian J. Sci. Res.*, Ser. B 3:1–13.

——— and ——— (1955) "The nature of reaction wood. IV. Variation in cell wall organ-ization of tension wood fibers." *Australian J. Botany* 3:177–189.

——— and ——— (1957) "Variations in the cell-wall organization of tracheids and fi-bers." *Holzforschung* 11:33–41.

———, and Preston, R. D. (1950) "The fine structure of the wall of the conifer tracheid. V. The organization of the secondary wall in relation to the growth rate of the cam-bium." *Biochim. Biophys. Acta* 6:36–47.

Wellwood, R. W. (1960) "Specific gravity and tracheid length variations in second-growth Western hemlock." *J. Forestry* 58:361–368.

———(1962) "Tensile testing of small wood samples." *Pulp Paper Mag. Can.* 63(2):T61–T67.

Wilde, S. A., and Paul, B. H. (1959) "Growth, specific gravity and chemical composition of quaking aspen on different soil types." U. S. Forest Prod. Lab. Rept. 2144. Madison, Wis.

_____, and Voigt, G. K. (1948) "Specific gravity of the wood of jack pine seedlings raised under different levels of soil fertility." *J. Forestry* 46:521–523.

Yandle, D. O. (1956) *Statistical evaluation of the effect of age on specific gravity in loblolly pine.* U. S. Forest Prod. Lab. Rept. No. 2049. Madison, Wis.

Zahner, R. (1963) "Internal moisture stress and wood formation in conifers." *Forest Prod. J.* 13:240–247.

Zimmermann, M. H., ed. (1964) *The Formation of Wood in Forest Trees.* Academic Press, N. Y.

Zobel, B. J. (1956) "Genetic, growth and environmental factors affecting specific gravity of loblolly pine." *Forest Prod. J.* 6:442–446.

_____ (1960) "Selection and breeding of coniferous trees with superior wood characteristics." *In Proceedings Fifth World Forestry Congress, Seattle,* pp. 1354–1358.

_____, Henson, F., and Webb, C. (1960) "Estimation of certain wood properties of loblolly and slash pine trees from breast height sampling." *Forest Sci.* 6:155–162.

_____, and McElwee, R. L. (1958a) "Natural variation in wood specific gravity of loblolly pine and an analysis of contributing factors." *Tappi* 41:158–161.

_____ and _____ (1958b) "Variation in cellulose in loblolly pine." *Tappi* 41:167–170.

_____, Webb, C., and Henson, F. (1959) "Core or juvenile wood of loblolly and slash pine." *Tappi* 42:345–356.

The Mechanical Properties of Plant Cell Walls: Helical Structure and Young's Modulus of Air-Dried Xylem in *Picea sitchensis*

D. R. COWDREY and R. D. PRESTON, F.R.S.

The Astbury Department of Biophysics,
The University of Leeds

INTRODUCTION

It is now well recognized that the detailed organization of the cellulose in the walls of wood tracheids and fibers (references in Preston, 1952), in common with that of many other elongated cells of both higher (Stern and Stout, 1954) and lower (Frei and Preston, 1961) plants, varies in a fairly regular way with cell dimensions. It is also known that in those cases which have been investigated—such as sisal fibers (Spark *et al.*, 1958) and cotton hairs (Meredith, 1946)—these variations are associated with variations in the mechanical properties of the cells, such as Young's Modulus, breaking strength, and extension at break. In all these cells, the long molecular chains of cellulose, aggregated into microfibrils (Fig. 1), lie in a series of helices round the cell, and it has been shown that when the cells are stretched along their lengths the corresponding Young's Modulus is greater the steeper the helices. This relation between structure and Young's Modulus has been attributed by Hearle (1963) rather to the lateral compression of the cell wall than to the bending, twisting, and slipping of microfibrils when the cell stretched longitudinally, and his arguments have some persuasiveness if the cell could be regarded as a solid cylinder. Since, however, fibrous cells of higher plants are hollow cylinders—a cell 50 μ wide having a wall thickness only of some 5–10 μ—it is difficult to believe that the conditions necessary for his formulation exist, except in the most extreme cases, in natural fibers.

The relationship between structure and physical properties is important not only in industry, for plant materials of commerce (including wood) consisting of elongated cells, but also in all considerations of the growth processes of cells which lead to changes in dimensions, and the situation has already received some attention particularly from this latter point of view. The conclusions which have been reached will be dealt with later.

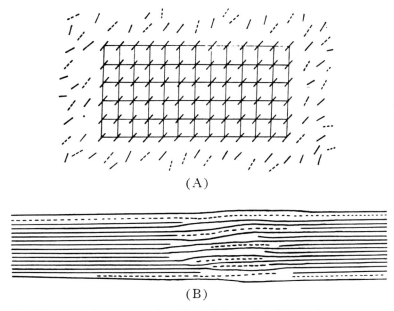

Fig. 1. Diagrammatic representation of a cellulose microfibril, A in transverse, B in longitudinal section. In A, the oblique full lines represent the trace in this plane of cellulose chains, dotted lines represent chains including nonglucose sugars. The central lattice area represents the crystalline core. In B, full lines represent cellulose chains, dotted lines represent chains containing sugars other than glucose.

We merely notice now that they involve the energy of bending and twisting of microfibrils as conditioned by the slope of the helical windings, energies which Hearle discounts in view of the higher energies involved in the concomitant compression of his (erroneous) model cell.

We have for some time been concerned with the measurement of the Young's Modulus of a series of specimens of wood of known structure. The work has now reached a stage at which it is clearly worth while to undertake a more ambitious program with many more individual specimens and using a faster method of structure determination. It is the purpose of this paper to present the preliminary results and to examine them in terms of a model which assumes that resistance to extension is due solely to the bending and twisting of microfibrils. The degree of agreement between observed data and calculations from the model, and particularly discrepancies between the behavior of the real tissue and the model, will then pave the way for improvement of the assumed model. It is quite clear even now that the model proposed, even in the form in which it is subsequently amended, is far too simple. The problem of extension of cylinders with anisotropic elasticity is mathematically very complex and we present this model now only as a preliminary approximation pending a more formal treatment which may later be possible.

Although conifer wood is much simpler in construction than is that of almost any angiospermous tree, it is still too complicated for preliminary theoretical treatment. The first simplification imposed in building a model is to omit the ray tissue. When a piece of wood is stretched parallel to the grain (and therefore to the length of the tracheids), it is clear that the tracheids, with their thick walls, their great length, and their overlapping ends, will bear much the greater part of the stress, and the vascular rays, with their limited height and thinner walls, by far the lesser part. It seems therefore in the first instance justifiable to omit the rays. We now turn therefore to the tracheids themselves.

The structure of tracheid walls is now known in some detail and has been described in outline elsewhere in this book (p. 215). Within each of the three secondary wall layers the microfibrils lie in helices (Fig. 2), rather flat in S_1 and S_3 (some 70° to 50° to the cell length) and steeper in the thicker central layer S_2 (some 40° to 10°) (Frei *et al.*, 1957; Wardrop and Dadswell, 1957). The pitch of the S_2 helices varies with cell length L roughly according to the relation

$$L = A + B \cot \theta$$

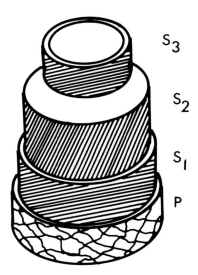

S_3

S_2

S_1

P

Fig. 2. Diagram of part of a fiber or tracheid to show the general direction of the microfibrils in the primary and secondary layers of the cell wall.

where θ is the angle between the helical winding and cell length (Preston, 1934, 1947), and the same condition is thought to hold with the helices of S_1 and S_3 (Wardrop and Preston, 1947). The linear molecular chains of the hemicelluloses, mainly mannan and xylan, are believed also to lie parallel to the cellulose microfibrils in each layer (Liang *et al.*, 1960; Preston, 1964), and the whole is in some way permeated by lignin. Since the advent of electron microscopy it has been shown that the layer S_1 contains two helices, and that the layer S_2 is finely lamellated with the helical direction varying slightly from one lamella to the next (Frei and Preston, 1961; Wardrop and Dadswell, 1957).

When a cell constructed in this way is subjected to longitudinal stress the reaction will clearly be complex. It can be shown, however, and indeed it appears intuitively reasonable, that much the greater proportion of the stress is borne by the S_2 layer, and the S_1 and S_3 layers can therefore be ignored in a first approach as leading to effects of only second order significance. In the wood used in this investigation, in fact, the layer S_3 (in the sense of a layer with a microfibrillar direction different from that in S_2) is absent (Wardrop and Dadswell, 1957) so that only the S_1 layer can contribute to this secondary effect.

In the model, therefore, we replace the whole tracheid by the S_2 cylinder. We further assume the angle θ to be uniform throughout and ignore the sloping tips of the cells. This leaves us with the problem of an anisotropic material, for which we can assume orthorhombic symmetry with the crystal axes tilted at an angle θ to the direction of stress, exactly as assumed by Probine (Probine and Preston, 1961) for the cells of *Nitella*. No solution has yet been given for such a problem. We therefore simplify the model still further by considering the S_2 layer to consist of fibrils lying in helices at the common angle θ, and free to move over each other, taking particular note that the diameter of these fibrils need not be assumed to be the diameter of the microfibrils. The problem then resolves itself into the very much simpler one of the extension of a simple helix by stress applied parallel to the axis. The mechanical constants of the fibrils then depend not only on the constants of the real microfibrils but also on the properties and proportions of the noncellulosic wall constituents and on the interactions between them.

The Helical Spring Model

It may be seen from the electron micrograph (Fig. 3) that the microfibrils are arranged as closely packed helices in the S_2 layer. Successive layers of helical microfibrils may be thought to extend like helical springs,

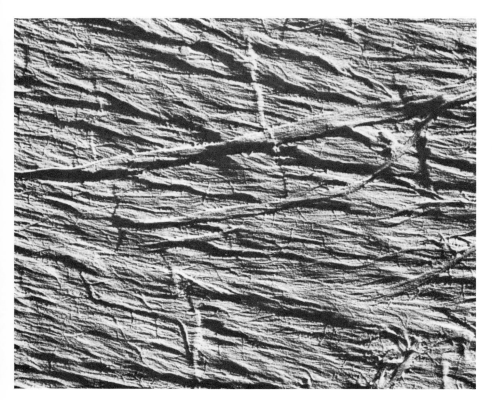

FIG. 3. Electron micrograph of microfibrils in a cell wall of *Picea sitchensis*.   Carbon replica; shadowed Pd-Au. X 21,750.

by bending and twisting, and not by the stretching of individual microfibrils.

The alternative theory of Hearle (1963), involving the concept that the resistance to stretching of the fiber is due to the resistance to radial compression of the inner layers of microfibrils, when the fiber need not have any inherent rigidity, seems particularly unacceptable for tracheids. Not only are the cells hollow but they have a noncircular cross section, so that it seems most unlikely that resistance to buckling will dominate the bending and twisting mechanism of the coils described above.

Consider a small extension of one helix, consisting of one fibril continuous throughout the length of the cell. This can be shown (Champion and Davy, 1948) to be connected with the dimensions and the elastic properties of the material by the relation

$$x = \frac{2fr^2L \sec \theta}{\pi a^4 q n} \ (2n + \overline{q - 2n} \sin^2\theta) \tag{1}$$

where

- x is the extension of the coil
- r is the radius of the helix
- a is the radius of the helical microfibril
- f is the axial load
- L is the length of the fiber, $L \sec \theta$ being the length of the helical winding
- q is Young's Modulus of a fibril
- n is the shear modulus of a fibril
- θ is the helical angle between a tangent to the microfibril and the longitudinal axis of the fiber.

For the same extension per unit length of the fiber, the stress will vary across the fiber according to equation (1), and the total axial load F on the cell will be the product of the stress on the microfibril and the area of an annulus of radius r, integrated from the inside, radius r_i, to the outside, radius r_o, of the S_2 layer (Fig. 4).

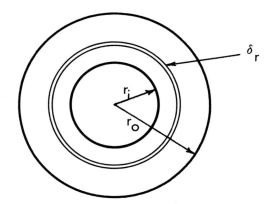

FIG. 4. Cross section of the S_2 layer containing several sublayers of microfibrils.

From Figure 5 this can be seen to be

$$F = \int_{r_i}^{r_o} \frac{f}{\pi a^2 v \sec \theta} \cdot 2\pi r \, dr$$

$$F = \int_{r_i}^{r_o} \frac{x \pi a^4 q n}{2L \sec \theta . \pi a^2 v \sec \theta \, (2n + q - 2n \sin^2 \theta)} \cdot \frac{2\pi r \, dr}{r^2} \qquad (2)$$

where v is a space factor introduced to allow for the fact that the microfibrils do not occupy the whole cross section of S_2.

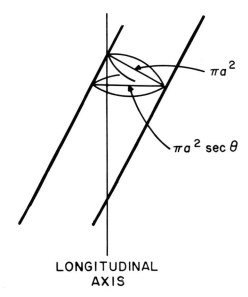

πa^2

$\pi a^2 \sec \theta$

**LONGITUDINAL
AXIS**

FIG. 5. Diagram to illustrate the effective cross-sectional area of a fibril with the stress along the longitudinal axis of the cell.

Equation (2) involves r and θ, which may be related in different ways between and within fibers. The following analysis will take the helical angle to be constant across the thickness of the S_2 as certainly a close approximation to the truth.

Taking θ to be constant, integration of equation (2) leads to the relation

$$F = \frac{xa^2qn\cos^2\theta}{Lv(2n + q - 2n\sin^2\theta)} \cdot \log_e \frac{r_o}{r_i} .$$

The initial value of Young's Modulus for the wood substance is given by

$$E = \frac{F}{\pi(r_o^2 - r_i^2)} \cdot \frac{L}{x}$$

so that

$$\frac{J \cdot \log_e\left(\frac{r_o}{r_i}\right)}{(r_o^2 - r_i^2)} = \frac{v}{a^2qn}(q\tan^2\theta + 2n) \qquad (3)$$

where

$$J = \frac{1}{E} ,$$

the initial compliance. For the apparent value of the initial compliance, i.e., as referred to the total cross section of the experimental piece of wood instead of that of the wood substance,

$$\frac{J \cdot \log_e\left(\frac{r_o}{r_i}\right)}{r_o^2} = \frac{v}{a^2 q n}(q \tan^2\theta + 2n). \qquad (4)$$

This relation between J and $\tan^2\theta$ is linear if the other factors in the equation are constant.

In this case, when $\tan^2\theta = 0$

$$J_o = \frac{2v}{a^2 q} \cdot \frac{r_o^2}{\log_e(r_o/r_i)}$$

$$\text{slope of } J/\tan^2\theta = \frac{v}{a^2 n} \cdot \frac{r_o^2}{\log_e(r_o/r_i)}$$

hence

$$\frac{\text{intercept}}{\text{slope}} = \frac{2n}{q}.$$

It should be noted that the intercept J_o has no precise physical meaning since when $\theta = 0$ L must be infinite. It is used only as a mathematical convenience.

Materials and Methods

The material examined consisted of a disc of *Picea sitchensis* provided by the Forest Products Laboratory, Buckinghamshire. In order to insure that the determination of structure and of mechanical properties refer to as nearly the same group of cells as possible, small specimens were prepared in the following way.

Radial longitudinal sections 100 μ thick were prepared, and from these, strips of wood 100 μ wide were cut by means of two razor blades separated by a metal shim of appropriate thickness. These strips were examined microscopically and only those retained for use in which the edges of the strip lay exactly parallel to the grain. These were then mounted over a hole between two metal clamps (Fig. 6b) held together by a circlip and cemented in place with copper dental cement. When the structure was to be determined by X-ray diffraction, the whole apparatus could then be mounted on an X-ray spectrometer. Subsequently (or in some cases before this) the clamps were mounted on the microextensometer to be described below, the circlip removed, and the extensometer set in operation.

Determination of the helical angle θ was also sometimes achieved under a polarizing microscope. This is a destructive method and, for this rea-

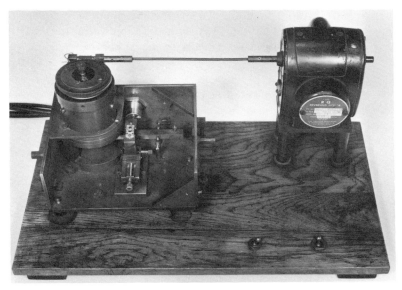

FIG. 6. a. General view of microextensometer. b. A view of the spring, test specimen, and transducer pick-up head.

son, strips 100 μ wide from either side of the specimen were retained for this purpose. In order to eliminate as far as possible variables other than θ, the specimen was always cut centrally to the annual ring in the early-wood.

The Microextensometer

This equipment was designed some years ago for the investigation of the mechanical properties of vegetable fibers and has already been briefly described (Spark *et al.*, 1958). Photographs of the extensometer are seen in Figure 6. The apparatus consists basically of a horizontal spring-loaded beam A, pivoted about a vertical axis O (Fig. 7). The specimen to be extended is held between two clamps B and C, one (B) fixed to the beam

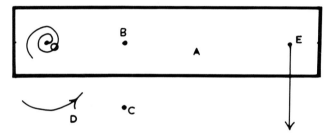

FIG. 7. Diagrammatic representation of the operating principle of the microextensometer. For explanation see text. The inner and outer ends of the clock spring only are shown in this diagram.

and moving with it and the other rigidly attached to the body of the apparatus. The clamps are movable along most of the length of the beam in order to allow for a wide range of extensibility. Application of the load is made by winding a clock spring D in the direction shown by the arrow (Fig. 7), the load applied being directly proportional to the angular movement of the outer end of the spring provided that the movement of the beam is negligible. In practice, the beam never moves through more than 0.5°; this is commonly less than 0.1% of the movement of the outer end of the spring and can be ignored. The extension of the specimen at any load is given by the movement of the beam at the point of attachment of the specimen. In operation, the load is applied at a constant rate by winding the spring at a constant angular velocity by means of a synchronous motor, the rate of loading depending upon the dimensions of the spring.

The spring was calibrated by attaching one end of a thread to the outer end of the beam (point E in Figure 7). The thread passed over a light pulley so that weights could be placed in a small pan hanging freely from the other end. The spring was recalibrated frequently. Movement of the beam was detected by means of a displacement pick-up. The meter readings of the direct-reading measuring bridge for various displacements of the transducer head were checked with a micrometer screw gauge.

In operation, a clamp carrying a specimen as described above was secured to the apparatus and the circlip retaining the two halves was removed. The synchronous motor was switched on and at the same instant a stop clock was started. Meter readings were taken every 10 seconds of time so that the extension rate could be plotted manually after the experimental run. The extension of any specimen rarely exceeded 10 μ so that the strains involved with 2 mm-long specimens were of the order of 0.5%. With the specimen still intact the circlip was replaced and the dimensions of the strip measured with a traveling microscope.

Measurement of Helical Angle

By Polarization Microscopy. The two strips from either side of the strip used in the extensometer were macerated in 5% chromic acid and washed. The tracheids were fixed to microscope slides with albumen and cut down their length with a hand razor, and the mean value of θ was found under the polarizing microscope using the methods described by Preston (1934, 1952). Some 35 to 45 tracheids from each ring were observed. The probable error, $\pm 2\sigma/\sqrt{n}$, was calculated where σ represents the standard deviation of n measurements. The angle determined in this way represents the weighted mean value of θ for S_1 and S_2 layers taken together. It may be taken as the value for S_2 with an error no greater than $\pm 1°$ (Preston, 1947).

By X-Ray Diffraction. The angle θ can readily be determined from an X-ray diagram from the spread of the 002 reflections (Fig. 8) (Preston, 1946). The intensity of this arc, scanned around a circle with center at the center of the diagram and radius equal to the distance from the center to the most intense point in the arc, is, at any azimuth ψ from the equator, proportional to

$$\frac{1}{\sqrt{1 - \cos^2 \propto \cos^2 \psi - \cos^2 \theta}}$$

where θ is the helical angle and $\propto$ is the glancing angle for the 002 planes (11°38'). At the point at which

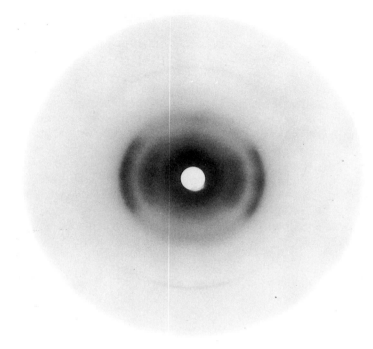

Fig. 8. X-ray diffraction photograph of a test specimen.

$$\cos \propto \cos \psi = \sin \theta$$

the intensity is theoretically infinite. In practice, if θ is sufficiently large this leads to a broad arc, most intense towards each end, the azimuthal angle 2ψ between the points of maximum intensity being given by the above equation. In a real specimen such as a conifer tracheid the angular dispersion of the microfibrils about their common preferred direction presents a complication which cannot fully be allowed for. Empirical intensity distribution curves have been considered by de Booys and Hermans (1941) and the equivalent orientation factors calculated.

Suitable X-ray diagrams of these small specimens can be obtained only in a microcamera with small slits and even then exposure times of the order of twenty hours were necessary. In order, therefore, to reduce background scatter from air the X-ray camera was totally enclosed and filled with H_2. Slits 40 μ in diameter were used, with CuK_α radiation from a Hilger microfocus tube and a flat film.

The resulting diagram was scanned around the 002 ring on a microdensitometer in which the stage could be rotated uniformly around the center of the diagram about an axis parallel to the scanning beam. When the angle θ was so large that the two 002 reflections broke up into two arcs each, the value of θ was calculated as described above. When θ is small these two arcs are fused as shown in Figure 8. Under these circumstances the angle θ was calculated from the angular width of the arc at 40% of the maximum intensity, following standard practice.

The angles obtained in this way were always checked against the values obtained under the polarizing microscope.

Cell Dimensions

The lefthand side of equation (4) involves a term

$$\frac{\log_e \left(\dfrac{r_o}{r_i} \right)}{r_o^2}$$

so that it is necessary to investigate the cell dimensions in annual rings. Only a small proportion of a growth ring is latewood in *Picea sitchensis* and the radial dimensions of cells vary but little in the remainder of a ring.

Transverse sections of specimens taken from the earlywood were mounted on slides and examined with a microprojector. The image was cast on a sheet of drawing paper and the cells outlined with a pencil. An area of the paper was weighed before and after removal of the lumen spaces.

Let W_1 be the weight of an area A of the paper which covers the equivalent of n complete cells, and let W_2 be the weight of the piece of paper when the lumen spaces have been removed, then

$$\frac{W_1}{(W_1 - W_2)} = \frac{n \pi r_o^2}{n \pi r_i^2} = \frac{r_o^2}{r_i^2} \, .$$

Also, a mean outside radius is given by

$$\bar{r}_o = \sqrt{\frac{A}{n \pi}} \, .$$

RESULTS

The results presented in Table I are the measurements of the initial value of Young's Modulus with the corresponding helical angles. Several specimens from each annual ring were stretched and the average for the initial Young's Modulus calculated; each value of E is the mean of ap-

TABLE I. Measurements of the Initial Value of Young's Modulus with the Corresponding Helical Angles

Ring	E	J	θ_1°	θ_2°	$\tan^2\theta_1$	$\tan^2\theta_2$
4	5.09	0.196	–	–	–	–
5	5.43	0.184	–	27.1	–	0.262
6	4.47	0.224	–	–	–	–
7	6.19	0.162	21.8.	20.6	0.160	0.141
8	10.94	0.091	–	21.0	–	0.147
9	12.52	0.080	–	16.3	–	0.0855
10	13.71	0.073	11.8	13.3	0.044	0.0559
11	17.35	0.058	–	10.5	–	0.0343
12	19.96	0.050	9.6	9.4	0.028	0.0274
13	22.12	0.045	–	9.2	–	0.0262
14	19.28	0.052	9.3	8.8	0.026	0.0240
15	26.53	0.038	–	8.2	–	0.0208
16	27.96	0.036	8.9	7.0	–	0.0151
17	–	–	–	6.9	–	0.0146
18	30.43	0.033	–	6.8	–	0.0142
19	26.07	0.038	6.5	6.5	0.013	0.0130

Units of E: 8.315×10^8 dyne cm^{-2}
J: 1.204×10^{-9} cm^2 dyne^{-1}
θ_1 is the helical angle determined by X-ray diffraction.
θ_2 is the helical angle determined by polarization optics.

proximately fifteen measurements. The values of θ_2 represent the mean helical angle of about 45 tracheids (measured under the polarizing microscope); θ_1 is the average helical angle determined from the X-ray diagram of three or four specimens from the same annual ring, E being known for each specimen.

Table II contains the error estimates associated with E and θ for each annual ring. ϵ is the mean deviation from the mean and 2δ is the total spread in $\tan^2\theta_2$ for an error in θ_2 of $\pm\dfrac{2\sigma}{\sqrt{n}}$, where σ is the standard deviation of n measurements.

Table III contains cell dimensions for certain annual rings. Again entries represent the mean of some twelve determinations. The largest value of

$$\frac{\log_e\left(\dfrac{r_o}{r_i}\right)}{(\bar{r}_o)^2}$$

is 7.34×10^4 cm^{-2} (ring 4) and the smallest value is 2.62×10^4 cm^{-2} (ring 19). In the following estimation of q and n the value 5.0×10^4 cm^{-2} represents the order of magnitude of this term for any of the annual rings

TABLE II. Errors Associated with
tan $^2\theta$ and J

Ring	2δ	ε	ε/δ
4	–	0.016	–
5	0.072	0.007	0.19
6	–	0.011	–
7	0.042	0.012	0.57
8	0.046	0.0043	0.19
9	0.022	0.0039	0.35
10	0.012	0.0054	0.89
11	0.017	0.0042	0.48
12	0.016	0.0034	0.43
13	0.010	0.0018	0.35
14	0.0099	0.0039	0.79
15	0.0071	0.0018	0.51
16	0.0070	0.0028	0.80
17	0.0052	–	–
18	0.0051	0.0017	0.67
19	0.0041	0.0018	0.88

TABLE III. Cell Dimensions in the
Immediate Vicinity of the
Test Specimens

Ring	r_o/r_i	$\overline{r_o}$ in μ
4	1.23 ± 0.02	16.8 ± 0.5
8	1.22 ± 0.03	21.2 ± 0.5
9	1.23 ± 0.02	19.6 ± 0.9
12	1.21 ± 0.02	22.1 ± 0.7
15	1.20 ± 0.03	21.4 ± 1.4
19	1.16 ± 0.02	23.8 ± 0.8

measured. It is clear from Figure 9 that E increases rapidly across the annual rings from pith to bark, i.e., along the direction in which both tracheid length is increasing and the helical angle decreasing. A plot of $J(=1/E)$ against $\tan^2\theta$ (Fig. 10) shows that the relation between these is approximately linear, as expressed in equation (4) if r_o, r_i, v, n, and q are either constant or subject to mutually canceling variation. This is a remarkable development considering the variability of wood. Equation (4) can now be taken as a straight line, all the other terms being regarded as constant. Figure 10 makes it clear that J increases as $\tan^2\theta$ increases, as predicted from the model. The intercept and slope of the straight line included in the figure are

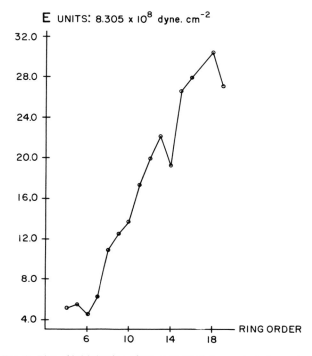

FIG. 9. Plot of initial value of Young's Modulus against ring order.

$$\text{intercept:} \quad 3.61 \times 10^{-11} \, \text{cm}^2 \, \text{dyne}^{-1}$$
$$\text{slope:} \qquad 7.52 \times 10^{-10} \, \text{cm}^2 \, \text{dyne}^{-1}$$

from which $\dfrac{q}{2n} = 20.8$.

q and n can be calculated for any value of fibril diameter.

Discussion

The steady increase in Young's Modulus in passing across the annual rings from pith to bark, i.e., in traversing a zone along which the helix of the S_2 layer is steepening, suggests immediately a direct relation between the helical organization of cells and Young's Modulus. Such a relation would be in harmony with the known effect of orientation on the Young's Modulus of regenerated cellulose fibers and in agreement with the findings of Spark et al. (1958) with individual sisal fibers. Variation in this particular mechanical property of the tracheid wall is clearly a func-

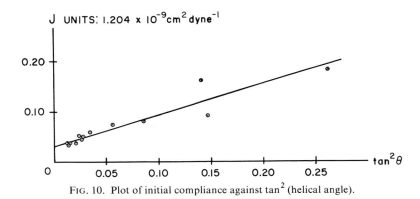

FIG. 10. Plot of initial compliance against $\tan^2$ (helical angle).

tion of the variation in the organization of those components of the wall which are helically oriented, namely the cellulose microfibrils and the associated hemicelluloses. This is not in itself to say that the presence of lignin has no importance for the magnitude of Young's Modulus.

The approximately linear relation between J and $\tan^2\theta$, in agreement with the deductions from a simplified model of the tracheid wall, leads us to suppose that the concept of the mechanical properties of these cells as associated with the bending and twisting of fibrils in the wall, which are relatively free to slip over each other for small extensions of the cell, is worth while pursuing. It leads away from the relation deduced by Hearle $(E = K (1 - \cot^2\theta)^2$ in our terminology), based on the assumption that the major component of resistance to stretch resides in the relative incompressibility of the wall. The spread of the experimental points is to be expected since the relationship between J and $\tan^2\theta$ can be strictly linear only if the other factors in equation (4) can be regarded as constant.

Interpretation of the real cell in terms of the model is not, however, straightforward. The value of the intercept on the ordinate in Figure 10 allows us to set up the equation

$$\frac{2v}{a^2 q} \cdot \frac{r_o^2}{\log_e r_o/r_i} = 3.61 \times 10^{-11}.$$

From this, q, the Young's Modulus of the fibril, can be calculated if a and v are known. Most wood cell walls contain cellulose in amounts of the order of 50%. v may therefore be taken as 0.5 without introducing errors of an order of magnitude. The value to be assumed for a is uncertain. It seems unlikely that, if individual cellulose microfibrils with their associated hemicelluloses are embedded in lignin, they will be free to slip over one another, and it would therefore be unsafe to assume that a should be the radius of a single microfibril. If this assumption is made, indeed, so that $a = 50$ Å, then the value of q turns out to be 8.8×10^{18} dyne cm^{-2}, six orders of magnitude greater than the highest value known for cellulose (*ca.* 10^{12} dyne cm^{-2} [Treloar, 1960]). If the model is to be interpreted literally, then for q to be of the order of 10^{12} dyne cm^{-2}, $a = 5$ μ. It is interesting to note that the cross-sectional area of a fibril 5 μ in radius is about one quarter of the cross-sectional area of an S$_2$ lamella. The results presented here would therefore be consistent with the concept that the microfibrils adhere strongly in large aggregates—which would then be the fibrils of the model—and that slipping takes place only between these aggregates.

It is difficult to see how the high value for q can be harmonized in any other way by modification of the model. If we were to assume, for instance, that the greater part of the energy absorbed during stretching is involved not in the bending and twisting of the microfibrils but in the breaking of linkages or other displacements between the microfibrils, then one would suppose that this energy would be a linear function of the total microfibril surface in a cell. If that were so, since the microfibril length in unit length of cell is proportional to $1/\cos \theta$ and the number of microfibrils in the cell cross section is proportional to $\cos \theta$, then the energy absorbed in this way would be independent of θ since the diameter of the microfibrils is presumably constant. This would mean that the force applied to the cell for any extension (and therefore E) would be independent of θ. The small additional energy involved in bending the microfibrils, yielding the $\tan^2 \theta$ component, would be negligible. Until, therefore, a mechanism can be found whereby deformation of the intermicrofibrillar substances yields a $\tan^2 \theta$ component, it must be taken that the most acceptable model of the wall as far as extension is concerned consists of a number of "fibrils," small in each cell, consisting of some 10^6 microfibrils firmly welded together by the intermicrofibrillar substances but relatively free to slip past each other. It is worthy of note that earlier work on sisal fibers (Preston, 1955) gives a value for $\frac{q}{2n}$ as 84.2 on the basis of the helical spring model. This is the same order of magnitude as that obtained for *Picea sitchensis*.

The lines of weakness in the wall which these considerations suggest may well be associated with the presence of bordered pits. It is somewhat reassuring to note that lines of weakness can readily be seen in compression wood tracheids (p. 403).

In further studies it is proposed to examine the effects of stretching wet specimens and delignified wood. From the latter it may be possible to correct the model for the lignin contribution. That the lignin behaves as a pure viscous liquid or a plastic solid is not yet certain; however, from preliminary hysteresis loops it would appear that even for a small extension, a specimen of wood may exhibit a fractional set as large as 25% of the maximum strain, for a strain of the order of 0.04%. A more formal approach to the problem will be attempted when more data are available; it could then be that the helical spring model in the form proposed here may have to be very seriously modified.

ACKNOWLEDGMENT

This work was carried out under a contract from the Forest Products Laboratory, Princes Risborough, Bucks, England to which our thanks are due.

REFERENCES

Bailey, I. W., and Kerr, T. (1935) "The visible structure of the secondary wall and its significance in physical and chemical investigations of tracheary cells and fibers." *J. Arnold Arboretum* 16:273–300.

Booys, J. de, and Hermans, P. H. (1941) "Zur Ableitung eines 'mittleren Orientierungswinkels' aus dem Rontgendiagramm." *Kolloid-Z.* 97:229.

Champion, F. C., and Davy, N. (1948) *Properties of Matter.* Blackie, London.

Frei, Eva, and Preston, R. D. (1961) "Cell wall organisation and wall growth in the filamentous green algae *Cladophora* and *Chaetomorpha*. II. Spiral structure and spiral growth." *Proc. Roy. Soc. (London), Ser. B* 155:55.

————, ————, and Ripley, G. W. (1957) "The fine structure of the walls of conifer tracheids. VI. Electron microscope investigations of sections." *J. Exp. Botany* 8:139–146.

Hearle, J. W. S. (1963) "The fine structure of fibers and crystalline polymers. III. Interpretation of the Mechanical Properties of Fibers." *J. Appl. Polymer Sci.* 7:1207–1223.

Liang, C. Y., Bassett, K. H., McGinnes, E. A., and Marchessault, R. H. (1960) "Infra red spectra of crystalline polysaccharides. VIII. Thin wood sections." *Tappi* 43:1017–1024.

Meredith, R. (1946) "Molecular orientation and the tensile properties of cotton fibers." *J. Textile Inst.* 37:T205–T218.

Preston, R. D. (1934) "The organisation of the cell wall of the conifer tracheid." *Phil. Trans. Ser. B* 224:131–172.

———— (1946) "The fine structure of the wall of the conifer tracheid. I. The X-ray diagram of conifer wood." *Proc. Roy. Soc. (London), Ser. B* 133:327–348.

———— (1947) "The fine structure of the wall of the conifer tracheid. II. Optical properties of dissected walls in *Pinus insignis*." *Proc. Roy. Soc. (London), Ser. B* 134:202–218.

———— (1952) *The Molecular Architecture of Plant Cell Walls.* Chapman and Hall, London.

———— (1955) "Mechanical properties of the cell wall." *Handbuch der Pflanzenphysiologie* 1:745–751.

———— (1962) "The electron microscopy and electron diffraction analysis of natural cellulose." In *The Interpretation of Ultrastructure* (R. J. C. Harris, ed.), pp. 325–348. Academic Press, New York.

———— (1964) "Structural and mechanical aspects of plant cell walls with particular reference to synthesis and growth." In *The Formation of Wood in Forest Trees* (M. H. Zimmermann, ed.), pp. 169–188. Academic Press, New York.

————, and Cronshaw, J. (1958) "Constitution of the fibrillar and non-fibrillar components of the walls of *Valonia ventricosa.*" *Nature* 181:248–250.

Probine, M. C., and Preston, R. D. (1961) "Cell growth and the structure and mechanical properties of the wall in internodal cells of *Nitella opaca.* I. Wall structure and growth." *J. Exp. Botany* 12:261–282.

Spark, L. C., Darnborough, G., and Preston, R. D. (1958) "Structure and mechanical properties of vegetable fibers. II. A micro-extensometer for the automatic recording of load-extension curves for single fibrous cells." *J. Textile Inst.,* 49:T309–T316.

Stern, F., and Stout, H. P. (1954) "Morphological relations in cellulose fiber cells." *J. Textile Inst.* 45:T896–T911.

Treloar, L. R. G. (1960) "Calculations of elastic moduli of polymer crystals. III. Cellulose." *Polymer* 1:290–303.

Wardrop, A. B. (1954) "The intermicellar system in cellulose fibers." *Biochim. Biophys. Acta* 13:306–307.

————, and Dadswell, H. E. (1957) "Variations in cell wall organisations of tracheids and fibers." *Holzforschung* 11:33–41.

————, and Preston, R. D. (1947) "Organization of the cell walls of tracheids and wood fibers." *Nature* 160:911.

Tensile Stress Analysis of the Cell Walls of Coniferous Tracheids

RICHARD MARK

School of Forestry, Yale University

It has been over thirty years since K. H. Meyer and H. Mark (1930) first calculated the strength properties of the cellulose crystal on a theoretical basis. It has also been more than thirty years since Freudenberg (1932) first described the cell walls of wood fibers as analogous to reinforced concrete, the crystalline cellulose acting as the reinforcing rods, with the other substances of the wall filling a role similar to that played by the cement and aggregate.

At that time, knowledge of the ultrastructure of the wood cell wall was meager, but in recent years it has been elucidated to such a large extent by chemical, biological, and physical means that enough is now known about cell wall ultrastructure to apply mathematical tests to the concepts of the afore-mentioned researchers.

The task has been made somewhat easier by the refinement of mathematical techniques for analyzing stresses in filament-wound structures in recent years. Such structures are of great technical importance in reinforced plastics technology and in the field of space exploration, and a substantial body of engineering and scientific literature has been developed (Rosato and Grove, 1964; Shibley *et al.*, 1962). The most precise approach to stress analysis of filament-wound pressure vessels, fuel cell tanks, rocket-engine cases, and the like has been through the use of the mathematical theory of elasticity, and it is this approach that I have taken to the problem of tensile stress analysis of the tracheid wall. A wood fiber or tracheid is a filament-wound, closed-end spindle of reinforcing filaments of structural carbohydrate in a matrix of amorphous and/or para-crystalline polymers. The method to be shown is generally applicable, with suitable modifications, to any cell type.

The objective of this research is to determine what levels of stress are reached in the various components of the unaltered cell wall as it undergoes tensile loading to failure. Thus, hopefully, the mode of macro-molecular rupture can be deduced.

Required for solution of the problem are the following:

1. The net cross-sectional area of the cell walls, normal to the direction of applied tension.

493

2. The proportions of item no. 1 assignable to the various layers of the walls.

3. The proportions of item no. 2 assignable to structural carbohydrate and to other cell wall constituents.

4. The elastic constants of each of the cell wall constituents of item no. 3, taking into account their isotropic or anisotropic characters.

5. The filament winding angles, i.e., the mean angles formed by the microfibrils within each cell wall layer with respect to the cell axis.
In item no. 5, then, two assumptions are made. One is that the axial direction of the anisotropic structural carbohydrate polymer chains is coincident with the microfibrillar direction. The other is that tension is applied exactly parallel to the fiber or tracheid axis.

There are some other assumptions necessary to the solution of the problem which will be discussed further along.

Figures 1a and 1b show the ruptured ends of a microsection of *Juniperus virginiana* tested in tension. This test specimen was punched out of a radial section of sapwood 0.0214 mm thick using a micromanipulator and a specially designed punch. It was punched from late springwood, an area of the ring statistically different from other areas of the ring, as I will explain further on. The specimen, which has a rather dumbbell-shaped outline, is designed to fail in the constricted neck, where there is no ray tissue. Specimens taken from early springwood show a brash fracture across the neck, with characteristic separation along planes parallel to the S_2 fibrillar orientation. Specimens such as the one in Figures 1a and 1b, from late springwood, characteristically have a tough, splintering type of fracture in which the tracheids appear, upon cursory examination, to have pulled out along the middle lamella. This specimen, tested underwater, sustained a maximum load of 83 grams.

With the epoxy resin embedment technique of Luft (1961) and the sectioning method of Bonga (1961), both specimen ends were embedded and resectioned serially through the rupture area. Figures 1c and 1d are a matched pair of these resections of the test specimen at the position shown by the arrows on Figures 1a and 1b.

It is immediately evident that what appeared to be a middle lamella failure was actually failure in the outer region of the secondary wall, and in the splintering pull-out of the tracheids, S_2 and S_3 separated from the remainder of the cell, indicating failure within S_1. This plane of failure has been repeatedly confirmed on microscopic observations ever since it was first noted by Garland (1939) and has recently been the subject of a detailed electron microscopic study by Wardrop and Addo-Ashong (1963).

These well matched resections of the test specimen were photograph-

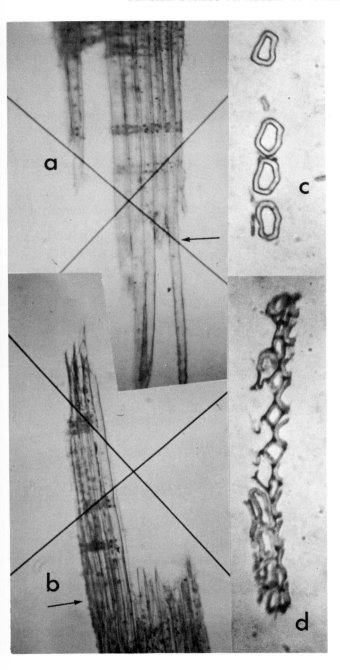

FIG. 1. The ruptured ends of a microsection of late springwood tested in tension are shown in a and b. In c and d, a matched pair of resections are shown. These came from the plane indicated by the arrows in a and b; c is a resection of a and d is a resection of b.

ically reproduced by Dr. Berlyn at an approximate magnification of 6100 X. At the same time a stage micrometer with graduations of 0.01 mm was reproduced in the same way. After conditioning all prints to equilibrium (TAPPI, 1949), the individual cells and cell wall layers were cut out of the prints. The areas of the following components of the test specimen critical area were determined by several weighings in comparison with weights of numerous rectangular areas marked off from the enlarged micrometer scale:

Radial walls of complete cells	*Radial walls of incomplete cells*
PM, S_1, S_2, S_3	PM, S_1, S_2, S_3
Tangential walls of complete cells	*Tangential walls of incomplete cells*
PM, S_1, S_2, S_3	PM, S_1, S_2, S_3

PM stands for components external to S_1, viz., primary wall and intercellular substance. The sum of all areas in the cross section was 0.003174 mm^2. The stress on the gross area was therefore 0.083 kg $\div$ 0.003174 mm^2 = 26.15 kg/mm^2.

Now in proceeding from this point to more precise analysis of stress in the tracheid walls, it is necessary that any assignment of value to one of the variables should be done so that stress levels do not appear to be larger than they actually are. The specimen net cross-sectional area (the first of the items required for problem solution) is a case in point.

There is substantial evidence that slide processing can change wall dimensions of cells, although wood sections mounted by conventional techniques seem to show far more wall distension than by the epoxy procedure (Gladstone, 1964). We cannot say that epoxy embedment eliminates all structural voids in the cell wall, but it does appear to be very effective in approaching the dehydrated dimensions of the wall. We therefore assign the gross cross section of the S_1, S_2, and S_3 layers as equal to the net void-free cross section of these same areas, tacitly assuming all solid-solution structures have closed therein. This approximates the truth in that it is certain the area is no larger than our determined value, and thus the stress we determine will be a minimum.

As for that part of the specimen area which is compound middle lamella, Lange (1958) presented microradiographic and optical evidence that in *Picea excelsa* the packing density of the constituents in this region is *ca.* 80% of that in the secondary wall. On the other hand Asunmaa and Steenberg (1957) claimed a relative packing density in the middle lamella slightly greater than in the secondary wall region. The explanation Lange (1959) offers for the discrepancy is that Asunmaa and Steenberg failed to account for the inorganic matter. I have carried out some calculations on this matter and find that Lange's explanation can be plausible if the bulk of the inorganic matter lies in the compound middle lamella, but Wise (1952) cites several authors to the effect that inorganic matter is distributed throughout the wall.

NET CROSS-SECTIONAL AREA

I have assumed a relative packing density for the middle lamella of my specimen at 90% of that in the secondary wall. Taken together with wall substance specific gravity of 1.48 as determined by pycnometer, and data on chemical constituents obtained for required item no. 3, this reduces the area ascribable to the middle lamella region and to the cross section as a whole by the amount of 0.000039 mm². The net cross-sectional area becomes 0.003135 mm² and the stress on the net area is therefore 0.083 ÷ 0.003135 mm² = 26.47 kg/mm². In subsequent calculations this will be referred to as f_x, the applied tensile stress in the axial direction of the tracheids.

PROPORTIONS OF CROSS SECTION IN VARIOUS WALL REGIONS

For purposes of stress analysis the number of discrete cell wall areas is reduced from the sixteen groups determined from the paper cut-outs to a total of six.

These six areas are listed in Table I, together with the proportion of the total specimen cross-sectional area they occupy respectively. The explanation for this grouping will be given in the mathematical part of this paper.

TABLE I. Proportions of Test Specimen Neck in Various Wall Regions

Part of specimen cross section	Percent of Total net area
All of the area in PM plus S_1	28.689
S_2 radial walls of complete cells	30.688
S_2 tangential walls of complete cells	11.166
S_3 radial walls of complete cells	6.101
S_3 tangential walls of complete cells	1.649
All of the $S_2 + S_3$ area of incomplete cells	21.707

PROPORTIONS OF CHEMICAL CONSTITUENTS IN TRACHEID WALL AREAS

As stated in the introductory paragraphs, our knowledge of the xylem cell wall has greatly increased, but many compromises still have to be made in formulating a mathematical expression for the mechanical properties of the wall because of the remaining information gaps. This statement is especially true when one realizes that the only wood polysaccharide for which theoretical mechanical properties have been calculated is the pure cellulose crystal. The other associated polysaccharides vary not only in their distribution across the wall but also widely in their physical nature, from the relatively unbranched, resistant glucomannans to the highly branched, water-soluble arabinogalactans (Meier, 1964). As for lignin, its exact formula is yet to be fixed. It is clear that some constituents are much more closely associated with cellulose than others, but in what exact manner is not determined. Some noncellulose units may exist as nonglucose linking residues within the cellulose chains, some may be included within the crystallites as short chains of impurity, some may be chemically bonded to the crystallite exterior, and some may be bonded only indirectly via some intermediary; finally, some constituents are just bulked into the wall in an unbonded state. The sugar most closely associated with cellulose appears to be mannose (Nelson, 1961).

Some decision had to be made in this study as to how the filamentous reinforcement should be isolated, literally and figuratively, from the matrix of embedding substances. My decision was to use the fraction which most severely restricts the "resistant" residue content—the Cross and Bevan cellulose fraction of wood. This "resistant carbohydrate" fraction, I believe, most closely approximates Wardrop's (1963) designation of "framework substances." Using Cross and Bevan carbohydrate as framework, and the remainder as matrix, provides the best delineation of what is reinforcement and what is cement in the cell wall. In Cross and Bevan analysis, most of the hemicelluloses are removed with the lignin and minor constituents. Goring (1963) has now shown a great similarity in physical properties of lignin and hemicelluloses. This work further reinforces my conviction that using the Cross and Bevan fraction in the mathematical analysis as the "structural" carbohydrate was the best course.

It should be emphasized that the actual specimens which underwent tensile testing were not modified in any way. They were not even stained for microscopic observation until after the test. The Cross and Bevan analysis was run on wood meal samples from the same tree in order to determine the structural carbohydrate percentage that would be used in the stress analysis.

The method devised for determining Cross and Bevan content of my specimen was one which is probably worthy of mention since it may be useful in other studies. A study of the annual ring that included my test specimen indicated that its cells could be separated into four groups, i.e., parenchyma cells and three types of tracheids, viz., early springwood, late springwood, and summerwood. To determine if these classifications were indeed discrete entities, the following analyses were made.

The differences between the tangential double wall thicknesses of early and late springwood tracheids were found on the basis of 120 measurements to be significant at the 0.1% level by "t" test (Snedecor, 1956).

The lumen diameter in the radial direction of the transition tracheid between late springwood and summerwood, identified by the presence of a pit on just one tangential wall, was measured in comparison with the lumen diameters of the cells radially adjacent to it. These diameters were tested by statistical analysis which showed that 95% confidence intervals around the three population means did not overlap. Further, the average diameter of the transition lumens equalled the average of radially adjacent lumens. Each sample mean was the average of 10 lumen diameters. I thereby had measurement criteria to separate the cell types found in the wood of my specimen tree.

The specimen tree possessed two erect leaders from about six feet up. One leader was greatly suppressed, and whereas a ring from the main stem was about 60 cells wide, the same ring on the suppressed leader was 4 to 5 cells wide. It was possible, with a hand microtome, to section sapwood material in small slivers from wafers of the suppressed leader, which contained different proportions of the four above-mentioned cell types. For example, the outermost sliver contained very suppressed rings, but successive slivers (I made four groups) towards the center of the suppressed stem contained progressively wider rings. How the cell proportions will vary in such samples can be illustrated by the content of summerwood—in a ring 4 cells wide, 2 will be summerwood tracheids (see Figure 2), whereas only 7 of a ring 60 cells wide will be summerwood.

A very accurate semi-microanalytical Cross and Bevan procedure has been worked out for 0.4–0.5 g samples (Watson, 1962). Such analyses were run on the four groups. Then by microprojection onto a grid at 950 X magnification the proportion of wall area for each of the four groups was determined on a number of cross sections from representative slivers of each group. A test devised by Scaramuzzi (1963) for the accuracy of this procedure showed that at least 10,000 determinations were needed for each of the four sliver groups.

Eventually over 50,000 determinations were made, and the data collated for cell wall area of each of the four cell types in each of the four sliver groups. The algebraic data-fitting technique of Huntington and Franklin (1951) was then used to determine from this data and the chemical analyses the Cross and Bevan carbohydrate content of each of the four cell types in the ring (wall densities assumed same for various cell types). The results are shown in Table II.

From this table, it can be seen that about half of the wall substance

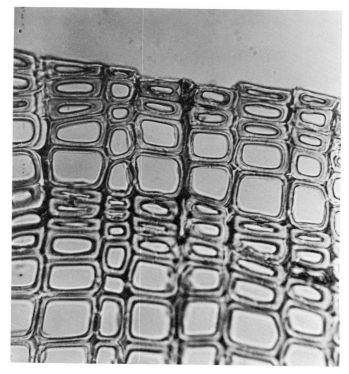

Fig. 2. The last annual ring of a suppressed erect leader from the specimen tree. Part of preceding year is visible. Corresponding ring of main stem was 60 cells wide.

TABLE II. Cross and Bevan Analysis for
Resistant Carbohydrate

Cell type	Cross and Bevan content, %
Early springwood tracheids	45.0
Late springwood tracheids	49.3
Summerwood tracheids	57.7
Parenchyma (axial and ray)[a]	30.0

[a]The value for parenchyma is not reliable, since the volume of cell wall occupied by parenchyma is very small, ca. 2% of total wall volume; large changes in the Cross and Bevan content of parenchyma result in virtually no change in the other three proportions with equally good fitting of data.

by weight is structural carbohydrate and half can be assigned to matrix constituents in the case to be analyzed, a specimen of late springwood tracheids. Based on the packing densities previously discussed, the distribution data of Lange (1958), and the generally accepted values for the specific gravities of cellulose at 1.55 (Frey-Wyssling, 1964), hemicelluloses at 1.49 (*ibid.*), and lignin at 1.40 (Roelofsen, 1959), the proportions of volume and therefore of cross-sectional area occupied by structural carbohydrate have been calculated for each layer of the late springwood tracheid wall. These proportions are 36.4% for S_1 (including PM) and 53.1% for S_2 and S_3. The corresponding values for matrix substances are therefore 63.6 and 46.9% respectively.

ELASTIC CONSTANTS OF CELL WALL CONSTITUENTS

The application of elasticity theory to any problem requires values for moduli of elasticity in the principal directions, the corresponding Poisson's ratios, and the shear moduli. In this particular problem the requirement is for two elastic moduli (parallel and normal to the microfibrils), two associated Poisson's ratios, and one value for shear modulus of rigidity (in the microfibrillar plane) for each layer of the tracheid wall. This need in turn requires that corresponding elastic constants be determined for both the structural carbohydrate and matrix fractions.

We consider first the elastic constants of the structural polysaccharide, which, by virtue of the Cross and Bevan analysis, is restricted mainly to cellulose I and a small amount of tightly held glucomannan. The theoretical constants for the cellulose crystal are either available or calculable, and are used here to determine the elastic values.

Several workers have derived the modulus of elasticity of cellulose in the direction of the polymer chain axis. These theoretical values are given in Table III. Only one calculation has ever been published for the theoretical modulus in the direction normal to the chains (Srinivasan, 1941), and this was based on the anisotropy in the direction of the fiber rather than in the direction of the crystallite. Surprisingly, I can find no theoretical treatment of the very important shear modulus at all in the literature, nor of the relatively unimportant Poisson's ratios. But all of the deformation and strength properties of fibers are influenced by each elastic property.

Since all these elastic constants are needed in the equations, I derived them, utilizing the results of the more recent discoveries in chain bonding modes. I have used as my model the bonding conformation of Liang and Marchessault (1959), based on infrared spectral studies of ramie, *Valonia*

TABLE III. Theoretical Elastic Constants for Crystalline Native Cellulose
(Note: values for E_{FL}, E_{FT} and G_{FLT} should each be multiplied by
10^4 kg/mm²)

Symbol	Meaning	Previous values	Authority	Calculation of this study
E_{FL}	Modulus of elasticity in polymer chain direction	0.79–1.23	Meyer and Lotmar (1936)	1.266 (Note: in computations the 1.37 experimental value of Sakurada et al. [1962] was used.)
		1.20	Meyer (1942)	
		0.908	Meredith (1959)	
		1.837	Lyons (1958, 1959)	
		0.576	Treloar (1960)	
E_{FT}	Modulus of elasticity normal to chains	0.0214–0.0428	Srinivasan (1941)	0.157
G_{FLT}	Shear modulus of rigidity, average for 101 and 10$\bar{1}$ planes	None recorded in literature		0.0369
μ_{FLT}	Poisson's ratio of contraction in the normal direction to extension under stress in the chain direction	None recorded in literature		0.10
μ_{FTL}	Poisson's ratio of contraction in the chain direction to extension under stress normal to chains	None recorded in literature		0.011

ventricosa, and bacterial celluloses. The model is shown in Figures 3
and 4.

Space will not permit each derivation to be printed here, but the derivation for shear modulus will be shown, since it illustrates the procedure and has not been done previously. The results of derivations are shown in Table III. The related calculations for shear strength and chain slippage (uncoupling) for the cellulose crystal are also presented, and these are tabulated in Table IV, together with the calculations of previous authors.

A note here is in order regarding the most important of all the elastic constants, the longitudinal modulus of elasticity. This has now been experimentally observed by measuring cellulose crystalline lattice extensions

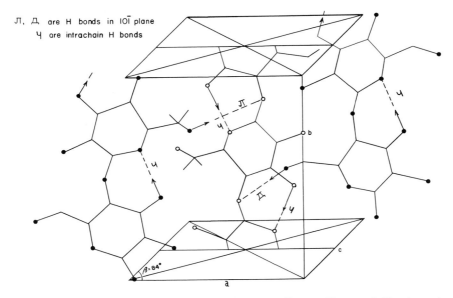

Л, Д are H bonds in 10Ī plane
Ч are intrachain H bonds

FIG. 3. Side view of cellulose crystal bonding, according to Liang and Marchessault (1959).

under constant stress by X-ray diffraction (Sakurada *et al.*, 1962). The average of these observations was $1.37 \cdot 10^4$ kg/mm^2; my calculated value was $1.27 \cdot 10^4$ kg/mm^2, which fell within the range of observations in the above study. I have decided to use the value of $1.37 \cdot 10^4$ kg/mm^2 in the stress analysis.

To calculate shear properties, the longitudinal shear planes must be examined for number and type of hydrogen bonds. In Figures 3 and 4, these bonds are shown. The hydrogen bonds in the 101 plane are shorter than in the 10Ī plane. Marchessault (1964) believes that the $0 - - 0$ distances suggested by Frey-Wyssling (1955), viz., 2.54 Å and 2.80 Å respectively, are good approximations. I have calculated the bond distances of the more angular bonds between adjacent residues in the 002 plane at 2.91 Å.

Consideration of the paratropic planes 101, 10Ī, and 002 for shear within the crystal between residue rows reveals the following numbers of bonds to be shifted or broken:

101 plane - $2n$-2 bonds 2.91 Å long, and n bonds at 2.80 Å
10Ī plane - $2n$-2 bonds 2.91 Å long, and n bonds at 2.54 Å
002 plane - No bonds 2.91 Å long, but $2n$-1 other bonds, half of which
        are 2.80 Å and half 2.54 Å

when n = number of cellobiose residues in one planar row.

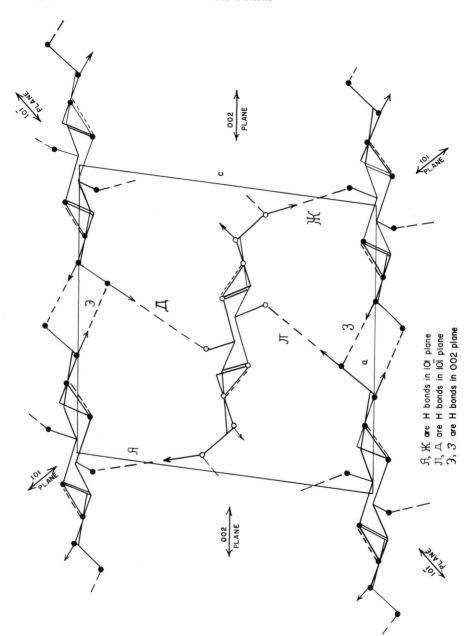

Fig. 4. End view of cellulose chains in a unit cell according to Liang and Marchessault (1959).

TABLE IV. Theoretical Strength Values for Crystalline Native Cellulose
(All values in kg/mm²)

Symbol	Meaning	Previous values	Authority	Calculation of this study
F_{FL-B}	Stress to cause chain scission (cohesive fracture) based on intrachain link bond energies	734.	H. Mark (1943)	766.
F_{FL-P}	Stress to cause chain scission based on potential energy function	2260. 1715.	de Boer (1935) H. Mark (1943)	1775.
F_{FL-V}	Stress to cause separation of chains if ends are all in one transverse plane	28.	H. Mark (1943)	not done (accepted value of 28.)
F_{FL-S}	Stress to cause chain slippage (sliding fracture)	126. 119.	de Boer (1935) H. Mark (1943)	>2037.
F_{FT}	Stress normal to chain axis to rupture H bonds in weakest plane (force ⊥ to 002 plane)	30.	H. Mark as cited by Stamm and Harris (1953), p. 140	43.2
F_{FLT}	Ultimate shear strength in weakest plane (forces ‖ to 002 planes)	None recorded in literature		12.1

Obviously the weakest plane with respect to shear or cleavage is the 002. All other planes (including those not listed above) would have more bonds to overcome.

Lippincott and Schroeder (1955) have presented data for the potential energy, U, of the hydrogen bond related to interatomic distances, R. By computing $\Delta U/\Delta R$ for $\Delta R \rightarrow 0$, I calculated the strength per H bond at $1.97 \cdot 10^{-5}$ dyn. From the angles of the bonds in the crystallites, the component of this strength to resist shear is $0.556 \cdot 10^{-5}$ dyn and $0.506 \cdot 10^{-5}$ dyn for the 2.54 Å and 2.80 Å bonds respectively.

If we consider an arbitrary shear area two cellobiose residues long (20.6 Å) by $n = 12$ residues wide (100 Å), there are a total of $2(2n-1) = 46$ hydrogen bonds therein whose combined resistance to shear is $23(0.556 \cdot$

10^{-5} dyn) + 23(0.506 · 10^{-5} dyn) = 24.43 · 10^{-5} dyn. This strength applies to a shear area of 2060 Å^2, yielding a theoretical shear strength of 118.7 · 10^7 dyn/cm^2 = 12.1 kg/mm^2.

Shear strength *per se* is unrelated to the degree of overlap of adjacent chains. The stress to cause slippage of chains as a mechanism of failure is, however, related to overlap, and also to degree of polymerization (DP) and the positions of overlaps with respect to each other. This can be visualized by considering regularly overlapping chains as interlocked fingers (see Figure 5). Taking Figure 5a, for example, we could have four

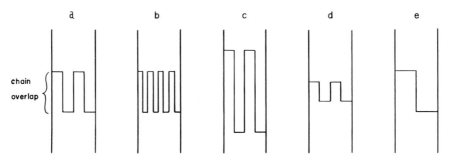

FIG. 5. Modes of chain overlapping in a crystallite.

interlocking fingers (two up and two down). Suppose that in each finger there are two cellulose chains, ending together at the same level. In order to double resistance to slippage, other things being equal, the number of fingers could be doubled (Fig. 5b), wherein there is just one chain to a finger, or the number of fingers could remain at four, but with a doubled overlap distance, as in Figure 5c.

Similarly, resistance to slippage is decreased by a shorter overlap (Fig. 5d) or by decreasing the number of fingers. If the number of fingers is reduced to a single lap, where all the chains end at just two levels only, as in Figure 5e, the weakest overlap situation is created.

I consider the following calculation to give a realistic minimum strength for resistance of chains to failure by slippage. For a DP of 3000 with the Figure 5e type of overlap of 750 cellobiose residues in an element of crystalline cellulose with cross-sectional dimensions of 6 residues by 6 residues = 2228 Å^2, the overlap plane would be 750 residues × 6 residues, an area containing 8250 hydrogen bonds with a total resistance to slip of 4381 · 10^{-5} dyn. The resistance to slip for force applied to the ends of the element is therefore 4381 · 10^{-5} dyn ÷ 2228 · 10^{-16} cm^2 = 1.97 · 10^{11} dyn/cm^2 = 2009 kg/mm^2. Adding to this the forces attracting the ends of chains (Mark, 1943) of 28 kg/mm^2 (these are van der Waals forces at the "fingertips" of the lap), we get a total theoretical value of 2037 kg/mm^2.

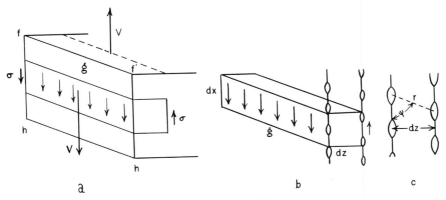

FIG. 6. Shear on a crystal element.

To derive the shear modulus, consider (Fig. 6a) a crystal *ff' hh'* sub-jected to shear forces V so that an element of the crystal is subjected to shear stresses σ. This element (Fig. 6b) has the dimensions $g\ dx\ dz$, where dz is the perpendicular distance between any two polymer chains in a plane and is, therefore, a shear moment arm. As shown in Figure 6c, interchain hydrogen bonds of length r bridge this distance, making an angle Ψ with the chain axis. It can be shown that when bonds of different lengths r_1 and r_2 connect two planes, a shear movement of one plane parallel to the other will cause equal shear strains in the bonds, i.e.,

$$\left(\frac{d\Psi}{\Psi}\right)_1 = \left(\frac{d\Psi}{\Psi}\right)_2. \tag{1}$$

The applied moment on the element is $M = \sigma g\ dx\ dz$. The equal and opposite resisting moment $M = M_1 + M_2$, the sum of the resisting moments due to the different bonds. These are respectively

$$M_1 = n_1 k\ d\Psi_1 \qquad M_2 = n_2 k\ d\Psi_2 \tag{2}$$

where n_1, n_2 are numbers of bonds in the element, k = angular force constant for the hydrogen bond, and $d\Psi_1$, $d\Psi_2$ the angular distortions of bonds. From eqs. (1–2)

$$\frac{M_1}{kn_1\ \Psi_1} = \frac{M_2}{kn_2\ \Psi_2} \qquad M_1 = \frac{M_2 n_1\ \Psi_1}{n_2\ \Psi_2} \qquad M_2 = \frac{M_1 n_2\ \Psi_2}{n_1\ \Psi_1}. \tag{3}$$

Total shearing force on the element, $\sigma g\ dx$, is a summation of the forces on the bond groups. But since shear stress equals shear strain times shear modulus, the total shearing force can be written $Gg\ dx\ \dfrac{d\Psi}{\Psi}$. This force is equalled by the resisting moments divided by their respective moment arms. An equation to express this relation is therefore used to derive G

$$Gg\,dx\,\frac{d\Psi}{\Psi} = \frac{M_1}{(dz)_1} + \frac{M_2}{(dz)_2} \qquad Gg\,dx\,\frac{M_1}{kn_1\Psi_1} = \frac{M_1}{(dz)_1} + \frac{M_1 n_2 \Psi_2}{n_1 \Psi_1 (dz)_2} \qquad (4)$$

and

$$G = \frac{k}{gdx}\left[\frac{n_1\Psi_1}{(dz)_1} + \frac{n_2\Psi_2}{(dz)_2}\right] \qquad (5)$$

Substitution of numerical data for the 101 and 10$\bar{1}$ planes respectively results in two values for G which can be averaged as representative of the cellulose crystal as a whole.

I have calculated the bending force constant for the hydrogen bond at $0.183 \cdot 10^{-11}$ dyn cm rad^{-1}. Considering shear areas of six residues in the 101 or 10$\bar{1}$ plane by one unit cell in the b crystallographic direction, and noting the numbers and types of bonds which must be shifted or broken in each plane, we find

for the 101 plane

$$G_{101} = \frac{0.183 \cdot 10^{-11} \text{ dyn cm rad}^{-1}}{336 \cdot 10^{-16} \text{ cm}^2}\left[\frac{6(1.3125 \text{ rad})}{2.71 \cdot 10^{-8} \text{ cm}} + \frac{10(1.0332 \text{ rad})}{2.50 \cdot 10^{-8} \text{ cm}}\right]$$

$$= 392 \text{ kg/mm}^2$$

for the 10$\bar{1}$ plane

$$G_{10\bar{1}} = \frac{0.183 \cdot 10^{-11} \text{ dyn cm rad}^{-1}}{396 \cdot 10^{-16} \text{ cm}^2}\left[\frac{6(1.2853 \text{ rad})}{2.44 \cdot 10^{-8} \text{ cm}} + \frac{10(1.0332 \text{ rad})}{2.50 \cdot 10^{-8} \text{ cm}}\right]$$

$$= 345 \text{ kg/mm}^2.$$

The average of these values, which is used in the stress analysis, is 369 kg/mm^2.

The values obtained for Poisson's ratios, for which derivations are not shown here, were obtained by combined use of equations from Shaffer (1964a) and Hofeditz (1963), together with some very helpful test data which was kindly obtained for me at the U.S. Forest Products Laboratory (Ethington, 1964).

The modulus of elasticity of the matrix fraction is taken equal to Young's Modulus from tests on rods of electrochemically prepared lignin and molded lignosic precipitate from alkali pulping by Srinivasan (1941). The latter material undoubtedly contained some hemicellulose with the lignin. His value of 204 kg/mm^2 compares with amorphous region elasticity values of 230–615 kg/mm^2 for rigid synthetic polymers (polyesters and polyesteramides) determined by Dulmage and Contois (1958) from birefringence measurements and X-ray diffraction patterns.

Derivation of the matrix shear modulus is simple for an elastically isotropic material. The relation

$$G_M = \frac{E_M}{2(1 + \mu_M)} \qquad (6)$$

holds for such materials, whether they be isotropic by virtue of an inherently amorphous molecular structure, or because of a sufficiently random pattern of small anisotropic units (as in the case of metals). Lignin satisfies both conditions; most hemicelluloses, one or both (Freudenberg, 1964; Frey-Wyssling, 1964; Meier, 1964).

Using the value for E_M (modulus of elasticity) of 204 kg/mm² and a value of 0.30 for μ_M (Poisson's ratio for a rigid laminating resin), the value of G_M, shear modulus of rigidity, is calculated to be 78.5 kg/mm² for the matrix. I believe these matrix elastic constants are reasonable for the underwater state of the test; it should be borne in mind that from the elasticity standpoint the "embedding matrix" includes the solid-solution microvoids as well as the chemical constituents.

FILAMENT WINDING ANGLES

The very evident birefringence of the S_1 and S_3 layers of tracheids and fibers, coupled with the apparent extinction in S_2 of xylem transections studied by polarized light, led many researchers to conclude that in the bright layers the cellulose crystallites were arranged transversely while S_2 micelles had a longitudinal orientation. Wardrop and Preston (1951) showed that in each layer there was actually an inclination of the crystallites. The method they used was to determine the birefringence of a series of sections cut at different angles to the transverse and measure phase difference with a Sénarmont compensator, using the relation

$$n'_\gamma - n'_\alpha = \frac{0.59\theta}{\pi d} \qquad (7)$$

where

$n'_\gamma - n'_\alpha$ = birefringence at the point of observation

θ = half of phase difference, measured by analyzer movement angle

d = thickness of specimen observed

and 0.59 is the wave length of the sodium light in microns in which their observations were made. The maximum birefringence corresponded to the average crystallite angle of inclination from the transverse.

Many electron microscopic studies have now confirmed the conclusion of Preston and Astbury (1937) that the orientation of cell wall microfibrils corresponds with the inclination of crystallites. Further, the microfibrils wind helically in a predominant S or Z sense within a given layer and are continuous, passing over the end of the tracheid and back into the helical pattern (Bucher, 1958).

I have used the method Wardrop and Preston used, with some important modifications which enhance the accuracy of measurement and also yield some additional information.

For one thing, phase difference measurements were made on both the wall closer to the cambium and the wall closer to the heart in tangential wall determinations of every cell measured; correspondingly, measurements were made on both radial walls when sections were made to study them. Another change was to eliminate uncertainty of section thickness, d. I embedded, resectioned, and mounted each of the two transverse, eight radially inclined, and eight tangentially inclined sections, taking at least ten filar micrometer measurements of thickness on each one.

The results are graphed in Figures 7 and 8. Maximum birefringences, corresponding to the mean crystallite orientation, are found to occur at a different angle for each layer. It should be noted that these filament wind-

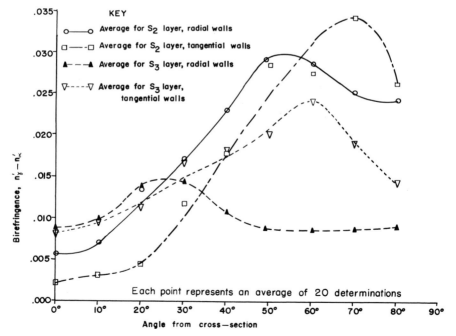

FIG. 7. Birefringences of S_2 and S_3 layers in cell walls of late springwood tracheids from the same ring as the test specimen.

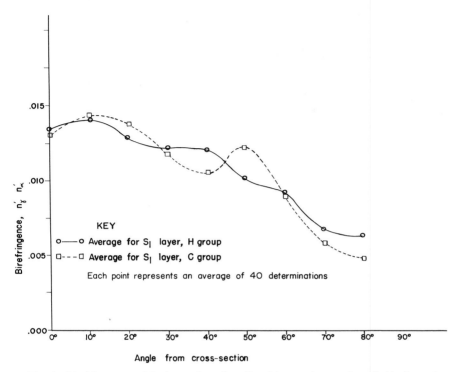

FIG. 8. Birefringences of S_1 layers in cell walls of late springwood tracheids from the same ring as the test specimen.

ing angles are from the transverse; in the mathematical part of this paper, the complementary angles are used, as the equations require the angles from the tracheid axis.

If one considers first Figure 7, the radial walls are seen to be less birefringent and their average crystallites inclined farther away from the cell axes in the S_2 layer. This is not unexpected, and S_2 values compare well with other studies (Preston, 1952).

There is a very large difference in birefringence and crystallite orientation of S_3 walls, which is somewhat surprising. Studies on other conifers do show variations in S_3 helix of this magnitude, but not within the same specimen (Bucher, 1957 and 1958).

In both S_2 and S_3, as sections were examined progressively farther from the transverse, birefringence determinations on the walls opposite those showing brightness increases showed increasing darkness; minimum birefringence values (not shown on graph) were determined for the angles complementary to those showing maxima on the bright walls. This offers conclusive proof that there is little or no crossed fibrillar structure in S_2 and S_3 of this material. Furthermore, since the orientations of the cambial-side and core-side surfaces of the wood as clamped in the microtome were recorded, comparison of this alignment with the walls that became more birefringent (and those that became less so) with angle change enabled the sense of the helix to be determined. In both S_2 and S_3, it is a true Z helix.

The above observations do not hold for the S_1 layer. It was found that increasing section angle from the transverse resulted in similar birefringence patterns for both of the opposing cell walls. Figure 8 illustrates this. The measurements for S_2 and S_3 had shown that the tangential walls closer to the heart of the tree increased in brightness with increasing section angle. These walls, and radial walls which became correspondingly brighter, were designated the "H" group. The other group was designated "C" (closer to cambium). It is seen that for S_1, the walls associated with both groups showed the same trend for birefringence, both with maxima at about 10°. This, as far as I know, is the first determination of crossed fibrillar structure which has been derived entirely from polarized light measurements.

The S_1 layer, then, has both an S and a Z helix and both lie at about 80° from the cell axis. One is tempted to say that the secondary shelf or rise which appears in the two curves of Figure 8 at 40°–50° might represent evidence for a transition angle between S_1 and S_2, but a larger number of specimens would have to be studied before this could be supported.

Lastly, since the birefringence values are about equal, I conclude that the amount of crystalline material in the S helix about equals that in the Z helix in S_1; the S and Z ply thickness totals are equal.

ASSUMPTIONS

Now that all necessary data for the solution of a problem in cell wall stress analysis have been set down, the assumptions of elasticity theory as applied to this problem can be listed as follows:

1. A layer of the cell wall is elastic, i.e., it obeys Hooke's law (stress proportional to strain). This relation ordinarily holds reasonably well for wood tested in tension virtually to the point of failure.

2. A layer of the cell wall is mechanically homogeneous, i.e., the distribution of microfibrils and other structural entities is uniform within the particular layer. The advent of electron microscopy has offered conclusive proof of this.

3. A layer is orthotropic, i.e., its elastic and strength properties can be

resolved along two perpendicular axes. In this case the two axes are the directions parallel and perpendicular to the microfibrils of the layer.

4. Wall layers all deform together under the applied stress. This assumes that wall layers are not slipping past one another in testing. All are stretching together.

5. Buckling does not occur. This is easily satisfied under test conditions of tension applied over a relatively short span.

6. The applied stress creates a condition of plane stress and strain within the walls. This condition is most ideally attained in pure tension of a thin laminate, and is a necessary assumption for the solution of this problem as a two-dimensional problem in orthotropic elasticity.

7. Layers in both radial and tangential walls act together as one deformable laminate.

SIGN CONVENTIONS AND NOTATION

In this paper, tensile stresses and strains are positive and compressive stresses and strains are negative. Angles measured clockwise from the direction in the wall parallel to the axis of the tracheid to the direction parallel to the mean microfibrillar direction of a layer are positive. The directions parallel and perpendicular to the mean microfibrillar direction will be called the "natural axes" of the layer.

One prime on a symbol refers to the cell wall substance in the S_1 layer plus PM; two primes refer to S_2, and three primes to S_3. For example, the symbol E_T'' refers to the modulus of elasticity of cell wall substance in the S_2 layer in the direction transverse to the microfibrils, which is also the mean transverse direction of cellulose chains in that layer.

SOLUTION OF THE PROBLEM

The stepwise analysis of stress in the tracheid walls of the test specimen of Figure 1 will be now carried out.

Step 1. Determination of properties of wall layers in the orthotropic directions which are parallel to their natural axes. The applicable equations are as follows:

$$E_L' = \frac{A_F'}{A} E_{FL} + \frac{A_M'}{A} E_M \qquad E_L'' = \frac{A_F''}{A} E_{FL} + \frac{A_M''}{A} E_M$$

$$E_T' = \frac{E_M E_{FT}}{E_{FT} \dfrac{A_M'}{A} + E_M \dfrac{A_F'}{A}} \qquad E_T'' = \frac{E_M E_{FT}}{E_{FT} \dfrac{A_M''}{A} + E_M \dfrac{A_F''}{A}}$$

$$G'_{LT} = \cfrac{G_{FLT}G_M}{G_{FLT}\cfrac{A'_M}{A} + G_M \cfrac{A'_F}{A}} \qquad\qquad G''_{LT} = \cfrac{G_{FLT}G_M}{G_{FLT}\cfrac{A''_M}{A} + G_M \cfrac{A''_F}{A}}$$

$$\mu'_{LT} = \frac{A_F}{A}\mu_{FLT} + \frac{A'_M}{A}\mu_M \qquad\qquad \mu''_{LT} = \frac{A''_F}{A}\mu_{FLT} + \frac{A''_M}{A}\mu_M$$

$$\mu'_{TL} = \mu'_{LT}\frac{E'_T}{E'_L} \qquad\qquad\qquad\qquad \mu''_{TL} = \mu''_{LT}\frac{E''_T}{E''_L}$$

$$\text{(8)}$$

$$E'''_L = \frac{A'''_F}{A}E_{FL} + \frac{A'''_M}{A}E_M$$

$$E'''_T = \cfrac{E_M E_{FT}}{E_{FT}\cfrac{A'''_M}{A} + E_M \cfrac{A'''_F}{A}}$$

$$G'''_{LT} = \cfrac{G_{FLT}G_M}{G_{FLT}\cfrac{A'''_M}{A} + G_M \cfrac{A'''_F}{A}}$$

$$\mu'''_{LT} = \frac{A'''_F}{A}\mu_{FLT} + \frac{A'''_M}{A}\mu_M$$

$$\mu'''_{TL} = \mu'''_{LT}\frac{E'''_T}{E'''_L}$$

where

$\dfrac{A_F}{A}, \dfrac{A_M}{A}$ = proportions of a cell wall layer in structural carbohydrate framework and matrix, respectively,

E_L, E_T = moduli of elasticity of a cell wall layer parallel and normal to the mean microfibrillar direction of the layer, respectively,

G_{LT} = shear modulus of rigidity of the layer in the plane of the layer,

μ_{LT}, μ_{TL} = Poisson's ratio for a cell wall layer, giving ratio for contraction in the direction indicated by the second subscript to extension under stress in the direction indicated by the first subscript in the plane of the layer.

The derivation of each of the above equations parallels that given by Greszczuk (1964) for composites of fibrous glass in a rigid resin matrix.

Substitution of values from Table III and the last paragraphs of the sections entitled "Elastic Constants of Cell Wall Constituents" and "Proportions of Chemical Constituents in Tracheid Wall Areas" yields the following values:

$$E'_L = 0.51165 \cdot 10^4 \, \text{kg/mm}^2 \qquad E''_L = E'''_L = 0.73704 \cdot 10^4 \, \text{kg/mm}^2$$

$$E'_T = 0.029855 \cdot 10^4 \, \text{kg/mm}^2 \qquad E''_T = E'''_T = 0.037919 \cdot 10^4 \, \text{kg/mm}^2$$

$$G'_{LT} = 0.010996 \cdot 10^4 \, \text{kg/mm}^2 \qquad G''_{LT} = G'''_{LT} = 0.013480 \cdot 10^4 \, \text{kg/mm}^2$$

$$\mu'_{LT} = 0.227 \qquad\qquad\qquad \mu''_{LT} = \mu'''_{LT} = 0.194$$

$$\mu'_{TL} = 0.0133 \qquad\qquad\qquad \mu''_{TL} = \mu'''_{TL} = 0.00998.$$

Step 2. Calculation of properties of wall layers in orthotropic directions applicable to the wall layer as a whole. For the S_2 and S_3 layers these properties are identical with those already calculated parallel to natural axes, but the S_1 layer has a crossed fibrillar structure and must be considered mathematically as a balanced laminate (see Figure 9).

In order to obtain the properties of a balanced laminate, the properties of a single ply must be first determined in the direction of the bisector of

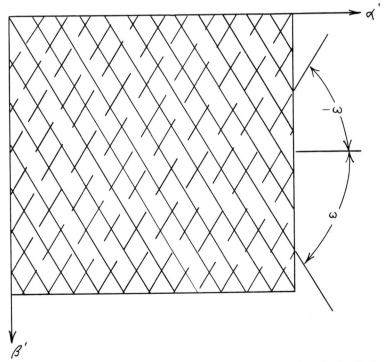

FIG. 9. A balanced laminate, where ω and $-\omega$ are the mean angles of microfibrils from the cell axis, α'.

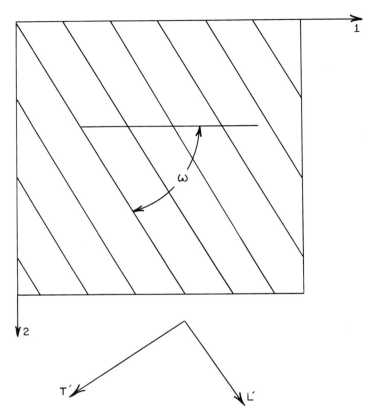

FIG. 10. A single ply of a balanced laminate. The microfibrillar axes are L' and T'; the direction 1 represents the bisector of the balanced laminate and is coincident with the cell axis.

microfibrillar directions and perpendicular to it. In Figure 10 we denote by 1 and 2 the directions parallel and perpendicular to this bisector. The following equations apply to one ply of the S_1 layer (Greszczuk, 1964).

$$\frac{E'_L}{E'_1} = \cos^4\omega + \frac{E'_L}{E'_T}\sin^4\omega + \left(\frac{E'_L}{G'_{LT}} - 2\mu'_{LT}\right)\sin^2\omega\cos^2\omega$$

$$\frac{E'_L}{E'_2} = \sin^4\omega + \frac{E'_L}{E'_T}\cos^4\omega + \left(\frac{E'_L}{G'_{LT}} - 2\mu'_{LT}\right)\sin^2\omega\cos^2\omega$$

$$\frac{E'_L}{G'_{12}} = 1 + 2\mu'_{LT} + \frac{E'_L}{E'_T} - \left(1 + 2\mu'_{LT} + \frac{E'_L}{E'_T} - \frac{E'_L}{G'_{LT}}\right)(\cos^2\omega - \sin^2\omega)^2 \quad (9)$$

$$\mu'_{12} = \frac{E'_1}{E'_L} \left[\mu'_{LT} - \left(1 + 2\mu'_{LT} + \frac{E'_L}{E'_T} - \frac{E'_L}{G'_{LT}} \right) \sin^2\omega \cos^2\omega \right]$$

$$\mu'_{21} = \frac{E'_2}{E'_1} \mu'_{12}$$

$$m_1 = 2 \sin \omega \cos \omega \left[\mu'_{LT} + \frac{E'_L}{E'_T} - \frac{1}{2} \frac{E'_L}{G'_{LT}} - \cos^2\omega \left(1 + 2\mu'_{LT} + \frac{E'_L}{E'_T} - \frac{E'_L}{G'_{LT}} \right) \right]$$

$$m_2 = 2 \sin \omega \cos \omega \left[\mu'_{LT} + \frac{E'_L}{E'_T} - \frac{1}{2} \frac{E'_L}{G'_{LT}} - \sin^2\omega \left(1 + 2\mu'_{LT} + \frac{E'_L}{E'_T} - \frac{E'_L}{G'_{LT}} \right) \right]$$

wherein

ω = angle at which the average microfibril is oriented with respect to the bisector of the balanced laminate,

E'_1, E'_2 = modulus of elasticity of the ply parallel and normal to bisector, respectively,

G'_{12} = shear modulus of rigidity associated with directions 1 and 2,

μ'_{12}, μ'_{21} = Poisson's ratios, giving relative strain in direction of second subscript caused by stress in direction of first subscript,

m_1, m_2 = shear distortion coefficients. (These coefficients give the shear strains due to direct stresses, i.e.,

$$\epsilon_{12} = -m_1 \frac{f_1}{E_L} - m_2 \frac{f_2}{E_L} \tag{10}$$

where

ϵ_{12} = shear strain in the plane of the wall layer,

f_1, f_2 = direct stresses parallel and normal to bisector, respectively.)

Solution of the above equations from the Step 1 results gives

$$E'_1 = 0.02924 \cdot 10^4 \text{ kg/mm}^2 \qquad \mu'_{12} = 0.0596$$
$$E'_2 = 0.2222 \cdot 10^4 \text{ kg/mm}^2 \qquad \mu'_{21} = 0.453$$
$$G'_{12} = 0.01183 \cdot 10^4 \text{ kg/mm}^2 \qquad m_1 = -1.717$$
$$m_2 = 7.248$$

Having obtained the properties of single plies in S_1 parallel and perpendicular to the bisector of its two microfibrillar directions, the properties of the combined S_1 plies are obtained for the same directions. The two plies of S_1 are considered to be of equal thickness. The applicable equations are

$$\frac{E'_L}{E'_\alpha} = \frac{E'_L}{E'_1} - m_1^2 \frac{G'_{12}}{E'_L} \qquad \frac{E'_L}{E'_\beta} = \frac{E'_L}{E'_2} - m_2^2 \frac{G'_{12}}{E'_L}$$

$$\mu'_{\beta\alpha} = \frac{E'_\beta}{E'_L}\left[\mu'_{21}\frac{E'_L}{E'_2} + m_1 m_2 \frac{G'_{12}}{E'_L}\right] \qquad \mu'_{\alpha\beta} = \frac{E'_\alpha}{E'_\beta}\mu'_{\beta\alpha} \qquad (11)$$

$$G'_{\alpha\beta} = \frac{E'_L\lambda'}{\dfrac{E'_L\lambda'}{G'_{12}} - m_1 \dfrac{E'_1}{E'_L}(m_1 + \mu'_{21}m_2) - m_2 \dfrac{E'_2}{E'_L}(m_2 + \mu'_{12}m_1)}$$

in which

E'_α = modulus of elasticity of the S_1 layer parallel to the bisector, i.e., in the tracheid axial direction,

E'_β = modulus of elasticity of the S_1 layer perpendicular to the bisector, i.e., in the tracheid circumferential direction,

$\mu'_{\beta\alpha}$ = Poisson's ratio of S_1 layer, giving relative strain in the α direction caused by stress in the β direction,

$\mu'_{\alpha\beta}$ = Poisson's ratio of S_1 layer, giving relative strain in the β direction caused by stress in the α direction,

$G'_{\alpha\beta}$ = shear modulus of rigidity associated with directions α and β,

$\lambda' = 1 - \mu'_{21}\mu'_{12} = 0.973$.

The results of substitution into these equations are

$$\begin{aligned} E'_\alpha &= 0.02935 \cdot 10^4 \text{ kg/mm}^2 & \mu'_{\beta\alpha} &= 0.694 \\ E'_\beta &= 0.4702 \cdot 10^4 \text{ kg/mm}^2 & \mu'_{\alpha\beta} &= 0.0433. \\ G'_{\alpha\beta} &= 0.02606 \cdot 10^4 \text{ kg/mm}^2 \end{aligned}$$

Step 3. The several layers in the cell wall interact with each other and undergo the same strains. According to the theory of elasticity, the relationship between strains and stresses in a two-dimensional element of cell wall in the directions parallel and perpendicular to the longitudinal axis of the tracheid wall is

$$\begin{aligned} \epsilon_x &= \bar{a}_{11} f_x + \bar{a}_{12} f_y + \bar{a}_{13} f_{xy} \\ \epsilon_y &= \bar{a}_{21} f_x + \bar{a}_{22} f_y + \bar{a}_{23} f_{xy} \\ \epsilon_{xy} &= \bar{a}_{31} f_x + \bar{a}_{32} f_y + \bar{a}_{33} f_{xy} \end{aligned} \qquad (12)$$

where ϵ_x, ϵ_y, ϵ_{xy} are axial, normal, and shear strains parallel to the axial direction of the tracheid (x) and perpendicular to it (y), and f_x, f_y, f_{xy} are the axial, normal, and shear stresses parallel to the x and y axes. The coefficients $\bar{a}$ are related to the properties of the wall layers and their respective orientations.

The inverted form of these equations is

$$f_x = \overline{b}_{11}\epsilon_x + \overline{b}_{12}\epsilon_y + \overline{b}_{13}\epsilon_{xy}$$
$$f_y = \overline{b}_{21}\epsilon_x + \overline{b}_{22}\epsilon_y + \overline{b}_{23}\epsilon_{xy} \tag{13}$$
$$f_{xy} = \overline{b}_{31}\epsilon_x + \overline{b}_{32}\epsilon_y + \overline{b}_{33}\epsilon_{xy}$$

where each $\overline{b}$ term is actually a summation of corresponding b terms for each discrete wall region i, weighted according to the area it occupies in the specimen cross section. That is,

$$\overline{b}_{11} = \Sigma\, b_{11_i}\frac{A_i}{A} \quad \text{and so on.} \tag{14}$$

The subscripts used for the i terms are

o—for the S_1 layer considered as a balanced laminate, in all parts of the test section,

s—for the S_2 layer in the radial walls of complete cells,

t—for the S_2 layer in the tangential walls of complete cells,

u—for the S_3 layer in the radial walls of complete cells,

v—for the S_3 layer in the tangential walls of complete cells,

w—for fragments of S_2 and S_3 layers in incomplete cells which were included in the test specimen critical area.

Each of the coefficients b must be calculated for each of the above six components of the specimen, according to the following equations

$$b_{11} = \frac{1}{\lambda}\,[E_\alpha\cos^4\phi + E_\beta\sin^4\phi + (2E_\alpha\mu_{\beta\alpha} + 4\lambda G_{\alpha\beta})\sin^2\phi\,\cos^2\phi]$$

$$b_{12} = b_{21} = \frac{1}{\lambda}\,[(E_\alpha + E_\beta - 4\lambda G_{\alpha\beta})\sin^2\phi\,\cos^2\phi + E_\alpha\mu_{\beta\alpha}(\cos^4\phi + \sin^4\phi)]$$

$$b_{13} = b_{31} = \frac{1}{\lambda}\,[(E_\beta - E_\alpha\mu_{\beta\alpha} - 2\lambda G_{\alpha\beta})\sin^3\phi\,\cos\phi \\ - (E_\alpha - E_\alpha\mu_{\beta\alpha} - 2\lambda G_{\alpha\beta})\sin\phi\,\cos^3\phi]$$

$$b_{22} = \frac{1}{\lambda}\,[E_\beta\cos^4\phi + E_\alpha\sin^4\phi + (2E_\alpha\mu_{\beta\alpha} + 4\lambda G_{\alpha\beta})\sin^2\phi\,\cos^2\phi] \tag{15}$$

$$b_{23} = b_{32} = \frac{1}{\lambda}\,[(E_\beta - E_\alpha\mu_{\beta\alpha} - 2\lambda G_{\alpha\beta})\sin\phi\,\cos^3\phi \\ - (E_\alpha - E_\alpha\mu_{\beta\alpha} - 2\lambda G_{\alpha\beta})\sin^3\phi\,\cos\phi]$$

$$b_{33} = \frac{1}{\lambda}\,[(E_\alpha + E_\beta - 2E_\alpha\mu_{\beta\alpha})\sin^2\phi\,\cos^2\phi + 2G_{\alpha\beta}(\cos^2\phi - \sin^2\phi)^2]$$

where $\lambda = 1 - \mu_{\alpha\beta}\,\mu_{\beta\alpha}$, and α and β are the orthogonal axes of the component. In the equations just presented, ϕ represents the angle between the orthogonal directions α and β of the component under consideration, and the x and y axes, as shown in Figure 11, which represents a small element under stress. The elastic constants E_α, E_β, $G_{\alpha\beta}$, $\mu_{\alpha\beta}$, and $\mu_{\beta\alpha}$ also refer to the properties of the component.

The six components of the test specimen cross section have been listed previously. In the case of S_1, those areas which are part of complete cells as well as those part of cell fragments are considered as one component because the tracheid axis in all cases is coincident with the bisector of the balanced laminate which S_1 is considered to be. In the cases of S_2 and S_3 layers, radial and tangential walls are handled separately because it has been shown that the average microfibrillar angle is different in the radial and tangential wall areas of both layers.

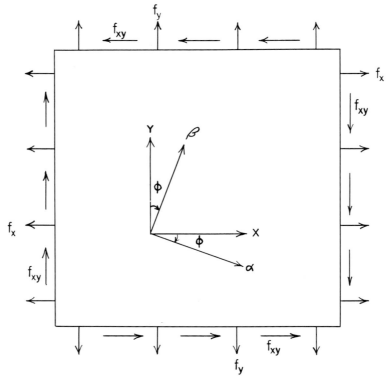

Fig. 11. An element of the cell wall, whose orthogonal axes lie at angle ϕ to the cell axis, under applied stresses f_x, f_y, and f_{xy}.

The last component is a rather special case. Fragments of the S_2 and S_3 layers are handled mathematically as if $\phi = 90°$, i.e., the natural axes of these areas are considered as if the microfibrillar direction were normal to the cell axis.

The reason for this will be evident from Figure 12. The expression for modulus of elasticity E_T of a wall layer in the direction normal to micro-

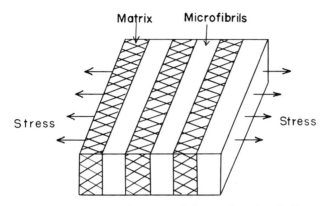

FIG. 12. Stress on an element applied normal to microfibrils.

fibrils is derived from the consideration that stress applied perpendicular to the microfibrils results in equal stress but unequal strain in the two wall layer components, structural carbohydrate and matrix. This is the same as saying that these two constituents are acting as springs in series. The converse is the case for the direction parallel to the microfibrils. Here, applied stress results in equal strain but unequal stress in the layer components, as springs in parallel.

As long as the laminate is very wide, or is continuous as in the case of a full-round tracheid, the elastic constants of a layer in any direction can be expressed as a resolution of these orthogonal elastic properties. But in the case of a severed or split tube of great length compared to diameter, as in these incomplete tracheids where the ratio is approximately 28:1, the necessary boundary conditions for the above resolution do not hold. The problem is statically indeterminate, and under axial stress the areas of structural carbohydrate and matrix interact with each other more as springs in series unless the angle between the microfibrils and the cell axis is extremely small. Since this is not the case, the idealized arrangement of these incomplete cell layers with respect to the tracheid axis is a succession of structural carbohydrate and matrix units acting in series, just as in the idealization of Figure 12, but now with each bar in the picture slanted. The mathematical solution appropriate to this concept is to consider these layers as if the microfibrillar direction were transverse.

The values for $\bar{b}$ may now be obtained through the use of eqs. (14–15), by substitution of the following data from Steps 1 and 2 and the values for proportions of cross section in various wall regions:

$$E_{\alpha_o} = E'_\alpha = 0.02935 \cdot 10^4 \text{ kg/mm}^2$$
$$E_{\alpha_s} = E_{\alpha_t} = E_{\alpha_u} = E_{\alpha_v} = E_{\alpha_w} = E''_L = 0.7370 \cdot 10^4 \text{ kg/mm}^2$$
$$E_{\beta_o} = E'_\beta = 0.4703 \cdot 10^4 \text{ kg/mm}^2$$
$$E_{\beta_s} = E_{\beta_t} = E_{\beta_u} = E_{\beta_v} = E_{\beta_w} = E''_T = 0.03790 \cdot 10^4 \text{ kg/mm}^2$$
$$G_{\alpha\beta_o} = G'_{\alpha\beta} = 0.02606 \cdot 10^4 \text{ kg/mm}^2$$
$$G_{\alpha\beta_s} = G_{\alpha\beta_t} = G_{\alpha\beta_u} = G_{\alpha\beta_v} = G_{\alpha\beta_w} = G''_{LT} = 0.01348 \cdot 10^4 \text{ kg/mm}^2$$
$$\mu_{\beta\alpha_o} = \mu'_{\beta\alpha} = 0.694$$
$$\mu_{\beta\alpha_s} = \mu_{\beta\alpha_t} = \mu_{\beta\alpha_u} = \mu_{\beta\alpha_v} = \mu_{\beta\alpha_w} = \mu''_{TL} = 0.00998$$
$$\mu_{\alpha\beta_o} = \mu'_{\alpha\beta} = 0.0433$$
$$\mu_{\alpha\beta_s} = \mu_{\alpha\beta_t} = \mu_{\alpha\beta_u} = \mu_{\alpha\beta_v} = \mu_{\alpha\beta_w} = \mu''_{LT} = 0.194$$
$$\phi_o = 0° \quad \phi_s = 36° \quad \phi_t = 20° \quad \phi_u = 64° \quad \phi_v = 30° \quad \phi_w = 90°.$$

Solution yields

$$\bar{b}_{11} = 1962.3 \text{ kg/mm}^2 \qquad \bar{b}_{22} = 3728.9 \text{ kg/mm}^2$$
$$\bar{b}_{12} = \bar{b}_{21} = 774.5 \text{ kg/mm}^2 \qquad \bar{b}_{23} = \bar{b}_{32} = -528.9 \text{ kg/mm}^2$$
$$\bar{b}_{13} = \bar{b}_{31} = -963.1 \text{ kg/mm}^2 \qquad \bar{b}_{33} = 832.8 \text{ kg/mm}^2.$$

Step 4. The terms $\bar{a}$ in eqs. (12) are related to the terms $\bar{b}$ by the following

$$\bar{a}_{11} = \frac{\bar{b}_{22}\bar{b}_{33} - \bar{b}_{23}^2}{B} \qquad\qquad \bar{a}_{22} = \frac{\bar{b}_{11}\bar{b}_{33} - \bar{b}_{13}^2}{B}$$

$$\bar{a}_{12} = \frac{\bar{b}_{13}\bar{b}_{23} - \bar{b}_{12}\bar{b}_{33}}{B} = \bar{a}_{21} \qquad \bar{a}_{23} = \frac{\bar{b}_{13}\bar{b}_{12} - \bar{b}_{11}\bar{b}_{23}}{B} = \bar{a}_{32} \qquad (16)$$

$$\bar{a}_{13} = \frac{\bar{b}_{12}\bar{b}_{23} - \bar{b}_{13}\bar{b}_{22}}{B} = \bar{a}_{31} \qquad \bar{a}_{33} = \frac{\bar{b}_{11}\bar{b}_{22} - \bar{b}_{12}^2}{B}$$

where $B = \bar{b}_{11}\bar{b}_{22}\bar{b}_{33} - \bar{b}_{11}\bar{b}_{23}^2 + 2\bar{b}_{12}\bar{b}_{23}\bar{b}_{13} - \bar{b}_{12}^2\bar{b}_{33} - \bar{b}_{13}^2\bar{b}_{22}.$

It is to be noted that in eqs. (12) f_x, f_y, and f_{xy} represent the applied stresses. We are analyzing here the test condition of a uniaxial tensile stress f_x acting alone. Therefore, only the coefficients of the f_x terms need be considered ($f_y = f_{xy} = 0$). The applicable $\bar{a}$ values are

$$\bar{a}_{11} = 1.18949 \cdot 10^{-3} \text{ mm}^2/\text{kg} \qquad \bar{a}_{21} = -0.05709 \cdot 10^{-3} \text{mm}^2/\text{kg}$$
$$\bar{a}_{31} = 1.33934 \cdot 10^{-3} \text{mm}^2/\text{kg}.$$

From eqs. (12), the strains of the tracheid walls are

$$\epsilon_x = \bar{a}_{11}f_x = 11.8949 \cdot 10^{-4} f_x \text{ mm}^2/\text{kg}$$
$$\epsilon_y = \bar{a}_{21}f_x = -0.5709 \cdot 10^{-4} f_x \text{ mm}^2/\text{kg}$$
$$\epsilon_{xy} = \bar{a}_{31}f_x = 13.3934 \cdot 10^{-4} f_x \text{ mm}^2/\text{kg}.$$

Step 5. Solve for shear stresses. Orthogonal strains within each layer are related to the strains undergone by the tracheid walls by

$$\epsilon_\alpha = \epsilon_x \cos^2\phi + \epsilon_y \sin^2\phi - \epsilon_{xy} \sin\phi \cos\phi \qquad (17)$$

$$\epsilon_\beta = \epsilon_x \sin^2\phi + \epsilon_y \cos^2\phi + \epsilon_{xy} \sin\phi \cos\phi \qquad (18)$$

$$\epsilon_{\alpha\beta} = 2(\epsilon_x - \epsilon_y) \sin\phi \cos\phi + \epsilon_{xy}(\cos^2\phi - \sin^2\phi) \qquad (19)$$

and from these strains the orthogonal stresses within the layers are found by the equations

$$f_\alpha = \frac{E_\alpha}{\lambda} \epsilon_\alpha + \frac{E_\alpha \mu_{\beta\alpha}}{\lambda} \epsilon_\beta \qquad (20)$$

$$f_\beta = \frac{E_\beta \mu_{\alpha\beta}}{\lambda} \epsilon_\alpha + \frac{E_\beta}{\lambda} \epsilon_\beta \qquad (21)$$

$$f_{\alpha\beta} = G_{\alpha\beta} \epsilon_{\alpha\beta} \qquad (22)$$

where ϵ_α, ϵ_β, $\epsilon_{\alpha\beta}$ are axial, normal, and shear strains parallel to the orthogonal axes α and β of each component of the cross section, and f_α, f_β, $f_{\alpha\beta}$ are the corresponding axial, normal, and shear stresses.

It is convenient to consider first the relationship for shear stress within a layer, $f_{\alpha\beta}$. This is a planar stress, varying with the shear strain $\epsilon_{\alpha\beta}$ at any point in the cell according to the relationships given by eqs. (19) and (22). Substituting into eq. (19) the values determined for ϵ_x, ϵ_y, and ϵ_{xy} in Step 4, we find

$$\epsilon_{\alpha\beta} = [24.9316 \cdot 10^{-4} \sin\phi \cos\phi + 13.3934 \cdot 10^{-4}(\cos^2\phi - \sin^2\phi)] f_x \text{mm}^2/\text{kg}.$$

The relationship of $\epsilon_{\alpha\beta}$ with ϕ, the angle from the direction of applied stress, is graphed in Figure 13. It is seen that shear strain is zero at approximately 67° and reaches a maximum at 21.04° from the axial direction.

Shear stress, from eq. (22), is also proportional to the shear modulus $G_{\alpha\beta}$ of the particular layer. All of the areas except S_1 have been theoretically shown to have $G_{\alpha\beta} = 134.8$ kg/mm², whereas S_1 has the higher shear rigidity characteristic of a balanced laminate, and $G_{\alpha\beta} = 260.6$ kg/mm² for this layer, according to elasticity theory. The relative stresses reached for identical strains are also graphed on Figure 13. It is seen that a given applied stress will create the largest resultant shear stress in the S_1 layer.

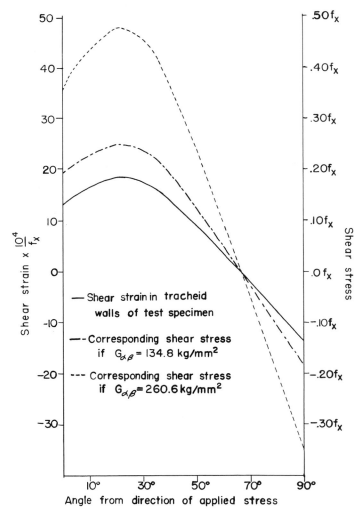

FIG. 13. Relationships of shear strain, $\epsilon_{\alpha\beta}$, and shear stress, $f_{\alpha\beta}$, with angle from direction of applied stress, f_x.

Step 6. Solve for axial and normal stresses. The orthogonal strains, from eqs. (17–18), are related to the orthogonal stresses in each layer by eqs. (20–21).

The values for ϕ used in each case are the clockwise angles from the tracheid axial direction to the axial direction of the microfibrils. These will be mathematically identical to the values of ϕ used previously, except in the case of S_1, where there are two values of ϕ, corresponding to the two plies, at 80° and 100° (see Figure 14). We solve eqs. (17–18) using the respective values of ϕ.

We have stated that the resultant stresses in the structural carbohydrate and matrix are equal in the direction perpendicular to the microfibrils.

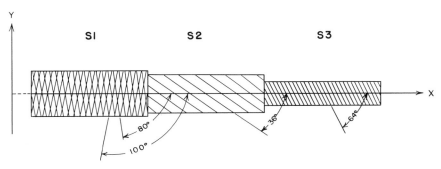

FIG. 14. Microfibrillar directions, with respect to radial walls in the S_1, S_2, and S_3 layers, used in Step 6 of stress analysis.

The values for f_β found from eq. (21) are thus solutions for both components within a layer. These values are

$$f_{\beta 80°} = 0.397 f_x \qquad f_{\beta_s} = 0.393 f_x \qquad f_{\beta_v} = 0.339 f_x$$
$$f_{\beta 100°} = 0.291 f_x \qquad f_{\beta_t} = 0.243 f_x \qquad f_{\beta_w} = 0.448 f_x .$$
$$f_{\beta_u} = 0.536 f_x$$

Parallel to the microfibrils, the strains in both components are equal. The theoretical stresses in this direction are therefore different in the matrix and structural carbohydrate framwork.

The use of the following equations, analogous to eq. (20), provides the theoretical stress analysis for all areas in the fibrillar direction.

$$f_{Mi} = \frac{E_M}{1 - \mu_M^2} \epsilon_\alpha + \frac{E_M \mu_M}{1 - \mu_M^2} \epsilon_\beta$$

$$f_{Fi} = \frac{E_{FL}}{1 - \mu_{FLT} \mu_{FTL}} \epsilon_\alpha + \frac{E_{FL} \mu_{FTL}}{1 - \mu_{FLT} \mu_{FTL}} \epsilon_\beta \qquad\qquad (23)$$

In these equations, the results of eqs. (17–18) are used for each of the respective areas in the test specimen walls, because in these layers the orthogonal strains are coincident with those along the natural axes. Solution of the foregoing equations yields the following.

Stresses in matrix	Stresses in structural carbohydrate
$f_{M_{80°}} = 0.037 f_x$	$f_{F_{80°}} = -3.200 f_x$
$f_{M_{100°}} = 0.109 f_x$	$f_{F_{100°}} = 3.010 f_x$
$f_{M_s} = 0.095 f_x$	$f_{F_s} = 1.824 f_x$
$f_{M_t} = 0.172 f_x$	$f_{F_t} = 8.488 f_x$
$f_{M_u} = 0.022 f_x$	$f_{F_u} = -4.512 f_x$
$f_{M_v} = 0.123 f_x$	$f_{F_v} = 4.211 f_x$
$f_{M_w} = -0.005 f_x$	$f_{F_w} = -0.604 f_x$

EXAMINATION OF EXPERIMENTAL STRESS ANALYSIS

It should be borne in mind that the above stress resultants apply in the strict sense only as long as the deforming body—in this case the test specimen—is behaving elastically. Beyond the elastic region, this analysis may or may not be close to the true stress distribution. It can be said that it is likely to be most accurate for the condition of wood specimens under tension compared with other types of applied traction.

Let us consider the maximum resultant stresses. For a given applied uniaxial tensile stress f_x on the specimen, we have theoretically determined that:

a. Maximum shear stress (from Figure 13) is in the S_1 layer and has the magnitude $0.477 f_x$ in both matrix and structural carbohydrate.

b. Maximum stress normal to the direction of microfibrils is in the radial S_3 area and has the magnitude $0.536 f_x$. This stress applies to both matrix and structural carbohydrate.

c. Maximum stresses within the structural carbohydrate framework in the microfibrillar direction are a tensile stress of $8.488 f_x$ and a compressive stress of $4.512 f_x$ in the tangential S_2 and radial S_3 areas, respectively. None of the matrix stresses in this direction are as high as those in the normal direction.

Substituting the observed value for maximum applied tension of 26.47 kg/mm², the maximum values of stress in the specimen reached 12.63 kg/mm² in shear, 14.19 kg/mm² in normal stress, and 224.68 kg/mm² in the chain direction of the structural polysaccharides.

(See also "Additional note by author" at the end of this paper.)

DISCUSSION

The calculated shear stress of 12.63 kg/mm² in the S_1 layer corresponds almost precisely with the theoretically derived shear strength of 12.1

kg/mm^2 for the cellulose crystal. Since none of the other calculated stresses in the structural carbohydrate fraction attain even one third of the theoretical ultimate values of Table IV, it is reasonable to state that these cells should initially fail by the mechanism of shearing within the structural polysaccharide of the S_1 layer.

This statement can be made not so much because the experimental and theoretical stress values agree (it will be shown that these values are not really so close), but rather because the relative stress levels for axial, normal, and shear stresses maintain a constant ratio within the elastic range. Clearly, at any point in this range, the shear stresses are much closer to exceeding tolerable limits for the structural framework than are the others. Initial yield, slip, or fracture must be in shear.

As soon as an initial failure occurs, there is a redistribution of stress and final separation of the specimen ends may be through some other rupture mechanism.

As for matrix stresses, we lack a theoretical value with which to compare these results. On the molecular level, matrix constituents may be capable of sustaining very high stresses. What we can deduce from this analysis is that the strength of the matrix was sufficiently great to allow cell wall stresses to reach a failure level in the framework. This, of course, is not the same as saying that the matrix is the stronger component, as it does not in general undergo nearly as high stresses.

Similar statements can be made for the strength of the middle lamella. Although a detailed study has been made of the principle of fiber-to-fiber strength transfer via the middle lamella and the effect in theory of varying fiber length (Ahlborn, 1957), I believe this question has been settled to reasonable satisfaction by the researches of Klauditz (1952 and 1957), who found that the interfiber bonding effect of residual pecto-polyuronides in the middle lamella after lignin removal was still sufficient to yield dry tensile strengths even higher, on a net cell wall area basis, than the strength of the undelignified wood. Middle lamella strengths are sufficient to allow stresses within the tracheids to reach a failure level.

Although test and theory seem to be in agreement, there are a number of reasons for suspecting that stresses within the test specimen were actually higher than calculated. These are as follows:

1. The fact that absolutely perfect axial alignment of the tracheids in the section is very unlikely.

2. The likelihood that the resection of specimen ends did not provide the absolute minimum cross-sectional area.

3. The possibility that microvoids are not evenly distributed across the wall, and may aggregate in places.

4. The possibility of unknown damage to the section at some point in processing, loading in grips, etc.

5. The breaking of secondary bonds which must have occurred at some points due to the water-saturated test condition.

6. The increase of stress in the crystalline polysaccharide which probably takes place as amorphous materials yield from their support positions under the slow rate of loading (0.002 inches/min).

7. The possibility of imperfect grip alignment.

8. The fact that Cross and Bevan residues include a small amount of residual noncellulose which has been treated as if it had the mechanical properties of cellulose in the analysis.

9. The fact that the ML areas have been treated as if their fibrillar orientation is as distinct as S_1.

10. The presence of pits, and the fact that a tracheid wall deviates at points from the axial direction of the cell as a whole, combine to disrupt axial stress transfer.

Each of the above factors tends to concentrate stresses or add to them. There are also some factors which would tend to reduce stresses. These are as follows:

1. In the nonlinear deformation shown by the load-strain diagram (Fig. 15) stresses do not rise in proportion to strains.

2. The Cross and Bevan method of structural carbohydrate determina-

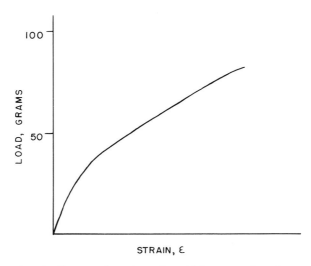

FIG. 15. Load-strain diagram of specimen for which stresses have been analyzed. No units for strain are shown because of the irregular outline of the specimen.

tion may possibly be too severe, resulting in calculations based on less cellulose than is actually present.

3. There probably exists a small number of axially oriented microfibrils in the primary wall (Wardrop, 1963).

It is my opinion that the factors tending to augment stresses are considerably more potent than those tending to decrease them. I therefore conclude that calculated actual stresses, as high as they are, are still not as high as those which were actually attained.

Another area in which test results are less than satisfactory is the subject of load-strain behavior. From Figure 15 it is evident that a nonlinear relation throughout occurred. Not all of this can be explained by time-dependency. Changes in load-strain or stress-strain behavior of oriented filamentous structures have been observed for some time; a mathematical explanation for this behavior has recently been offered by Shaffer (1964b). In my own work, further testing in regard to this problem has been conducted and will be the subject of a future paper.

The calculations which have been presented will be refined as we gain more knowledge of the elastic properties of cell wall constituents. But from what has already been done here, I should like to discuss briefly some of the implications I feel result from this stress analysis.

First, it seems to me that in order for stresses to reach the magnitude shown, the structural carbohydrate as determined by the Cross and Bevan method must be aggregated into continuous extended-chain filaments of nearly perfect crystallinity. I am especially convinced of this when considering the results of Jayne (1960) on pulped, unbeaten tracheids. These showed individual dry strengths as high as 137 kg/mm^2, over 5 times the strength of my wet specimens. Although crystallinity measurements on my specimen material showed the usual low values for wood, Bonart et al. (1960) have pointed out the numerous factors which tend to produce underestimations of crystallinity from X-ray data. They suggest 80–95% as a reasonable range for true cellulose crystallinity.

Second, to satisfy qualitatively the viscoelastic properties of wood, it would be entirely consistent with the above data to suppose that crystallites of pure cellulose can be synthesized in the cell by end addition, to their limit of thermodynamically stable size (Fürth, 1955), and then subsequently "linked up" by short coupling chains or single sugar units of some nonglucose monomer such as mannose. It would be these short coupling regions, capable of transmitting axial tensile stresses to provide good mechanical strength, that would at the same time serve as the sites for hydrolytic breakdown into the short micellar units observed after severe chemical treatment (Rånby, 1958; Wardrop, 1963). These same less-ordered coupling regions would appear amorphous in a diffraction pattern.

Lindenmeyer (1964) has shown that the same polymer can exist in the extended-chain or folded-chain configuration, depending on the conditions of crystallization. The extended-chain conformation is the most thermodynamically stable and there always exists a potential driving force to change the morphology to this more stable form. The condition in which extended-chain morphology is most likely to occur is the case wherein each "bundle" of chains is segregated in such a way that its component molecules are associated with other molecules of about the same length. This state can be most logically achieved by end addition in the cell.

Last, a mechanism of wall synthesis could be postulated to satisfy these conditions which is something between apposition and intussusception. That is, short crystallites could be deposited in the wall during growth and "tacked together" lightly by transversely deposited molecules. Then, during the lignification phase or at some other appropriate time, the linkage of these short micellar rods could proceed, probably with improved crystallization, into long microfibrils. A stress analysis of a growing wall could probably shed light on this.

It should be emphasized that while this stress analysis method can be applied generally to tests of wood and textile fibers and other biological material, the results for any specific case will depend on the filament winding angles and other variables. The theory of elasticity has been extensively and very successfully used for stress analysis of many composite materials, including fibrous glass reinforced plastics (Erickson and Norris, 1955; Fischer, 1960), plywood and wood (on the gross scale) (Hearmon, 1948 and 1962), and now seems to offer many possibilities in cell studies.

Acknowledgment

A large number of individuals and institutions have accorded me valuable assistance and information in this study. At this time I wish to express particular appreciation to the members of my doctoral committee and the School of Forestry, and also to the National Science Foundation, which was kind enough to aid this research with a Cooperative Graduate Fellowship granted through the Yale University Graduate School.

(*Additional note by author, 2/65:* In connection with subsequent work in this area, I noted an error in the solution for $G_{10\bar{1}}$ which however has very little effect on the results. The denominator should be $373 \cdot 10^{-16}$ cm^2. I have recalculated the entire stress analysis and find little change in any of the resultant internal stresses. The new maxima are: 12.88 kg/mm^2 in shear; 14.23 kg/mm^2 in normal stress and 224.85 kg/mm^2 in the chain direction of the structural polysaccharide.)

REFERENCES

Ahlborn, M. (1957) *Beiträge zur Kenntnis der Festigkeitsausbildung des Festigungsgewebes einheimischer Laubhölzer und des Einflusses der Länge der Sklerenchymfasern auf die Ausbildung der Zugfestigkeit.* Dissertationsverlag Pöhling, Braunschweig.

Asunmaa, S., and Steenberg, B. (1957) "Relative scattering densities in pine heartwood, pine sapwood and spruce." *Svensk Papperstid.* 60:751–761.

Boer, J. H. de (1935–36) "The influence of van der Waals' forces and primary bonds on binding energy, strength and orientation, with special reference to some artificial resins." *Trans. Faraday Soc.* 32:10–38.

Bonart, R., Hosemann, R., Motzkus, F., and Ruck, H. (1960) "X-ray determination of crystallinity in high-polymeric substances." *Norelco Reptr.* 7:81–87, 96, 97.

Bonga, J. M. (1961) "A method for sectioning plant material using cellulose tape." *Can. J. Botany* 39:729.

Bucher, H. (1957) "Die Struktur der Tertiärwand von Holzfasern." *Holzforschung* 11:97–102.

——— (1958) "Discontinuities in the microscopic structure of wood fibres." In *Fundamentals Papermaking Fibres, Trans. Symp. Cambridge, Engl., 1957* (F. Bolam, ed.), pp. 7–26.

Dulmage, W. J., and Contois, L. E. (1958) "A study of the elastic modulus and extensibility of the crystalline regions in highly oriented polymers." *J. Polymer Sci.* 28:275–284.

Erickson, E. C. O. and Norris, C. B. (1955) "Tensile properties of glass-fabric laminates with laminations oriented in any way." U. S. For. Prod. Lab. Rept. No. 1853.

Ethington, R. L. (1964) Personal communication.

Fischer, L. (1960) "Design of glass-reinforced plastic structures." In *Proc. Soc. Plastics Ind. Conf., Reinforced Plastics Div.,* Sect. 3-D.

Freudenberg, K. (1932) "The relationship of cellulose to lignin in wood." *J. Chem. Educ.* 9:1171–1180.

——— (1964) "The formation of lignin in the tissue and in vitro." In *The Formation of Wood in Forest Trees* (M. H. Zimmerman, ed.), pp. 203–218. Academic Press, N. Y.

Frey-Wyssling, A. (1955) "On the crystal structure of cellulose I." *Biochim. Biophys. Acta* 18:166–168.

——— (1964) "Ultraviolet and fluorescence optics of lignified cell walls." In *The Formation of Wood in Forest Trees* (M. H. Zimmerman, ed.), pp. 153–167. Academic Press, N. Y.

Fürth, R. (1955) "Fundamental lengths in physics and biology." *Exptl. Med. Surg.* 13(1):17–21.

Garland, H. (1939) "A microscopic study of coniferous wood in relation to its strength properties." *Ann. Missouri Botan. Gard.* 26:1–95.

Gladstone, W. T. (1964) "The use of epon and methacrylates for woody tissues." Unpublished paper, Yale School of Forestry.

Goring, D. A. I. (1963) "Thermal softening of lignin, hemicellulose and cellulose." Pulp and Paper Res. Inst. Can., Tech. Rept. No. 335.

Greszczuk, L. B. (1964) "Elastic constants and analysis methods for filament wound shell structures." Douglas Aircraft Missile & Space Systems Div., Rept. SM-45849.

Hearmon, R. F. S. (1948) "The elasticity of wood and plywood." Dept. Sci. Ind. Res. (U.K.), Forest Prod. Spec. Rept. 7.

—— (1962) "The theory of elasticity of orthotropic materials." In *Proc. Conf. Mech. Behavior of Wood* (A. P. Schniewind, ed.), pp. 84–95. Univ. of Calif., Berkeley.

Hofeditz, J. T. (1963) "Structural design considerations for fiber glass pressure vessels." In *Proc. Soc. Plastics Ind. Conf., Reinforced Plastics Div.,* Sect. 7-C.

Huntington, E. V. and Franklin, P. (1951) "Solution of simultaneous equations." In *Mechanical Engineers' Handbook* (L. S. Marks, ed.), Fifth Edition, pp. 117–120. McGraw-Hill, N. Y.

Jayne, B. A. (1960) "Some mechanical properties of wood fibers in tension." *Forest Prod. J.* 10:316–322.

Klauditz, W. (1952) "Zur biologisch-mechanischen Wirkung des Lignins im Stammholz der Nadel-und Laubhölzer." *Holzforschung* 6:70–82.

—— (1957) "Zur biologisch-mechanischen Wirking der Cellulose und Hemicellulose im Festigungsgewebe der Laubhölzer." *Holzforschung* 11:110–116.

Lange, P. W. (1958) "The distribution of the chemical constituents throughout the cell wall." In *Fundamentals Papermaking Fibres, Trans. Symp. Cambridge, Engl., 1957* (F. Bolam, ed.), pp. 147–185.

—— (1959) "The morphology of hardwood fibers." *Tappi* 42:786–792.

Liang, C. Y., and Marchessault, R. H. (1959) "Infrared spectra of crystalline polysaccharides. I. Hydrogen bonds in native cellulose." *J. Polymer Sci.* 37:385–395.

Lindenmeyer, P. H. (1964) "The relationship between crystallization and deformation processes in crystalline high polymers." *SPE Trans.* 4:157–164.

Lippincott, E. R., and Schroeder, R. (1955) "One-dimensional model of the hydrogen bond." *J. Chem. Phys.* 23:1099–1106.

Luft, J. H. (1961) "Improvements in epoxy resin embedding methods." *J. Biophys. Biochem. Cytol.* 9:409–414.

Lyons, W. J. (1958) "Theoretical values of the dynamic stretch moduli of fiber-forming polymers." *J. Appl. Phys.* 29:1429–1433.

—— (1959) "Theoretical value of the dynamic stretch modulus of cellulose." *J. Appl. Phys.* 30:796–797.

Marchessault, R. H. (1964) Personal communication.

Mark, H. (1943) "Molecular factors affecting mechanical behavior." In *High Polymers,* Vol. 5: *Cellulose and Cellulose Derivatives* (E. Ott, ed.), pp. 990–1015. Interscience Pub., N. Y.

Meier, H. (1964) "General chemistry of cell walls and distribution of the chemical constituents across the walls." In *The Formation of Wood in Forest Trees* (M. H. Zimmerman, ed.), pp. 137–151. Academic Press, N. Y.

Meredith, R. (1959) "Mechanical properties of cellulose and cellulose derivatives." In *Recent Advances in the Chemistry of Cellulose and Starch* (J. Honeyman, ed.), pp. 213–239. Interscience Pub., N. Y.

Meyer, K. H. (1942) *High Polymers.* Vol. 4: *Natural and Synthetic High Polymers.* Interscience Pub., N. Y.

——, and Lotmar, W. (1936) "Sur l'élasticité de la cellulose." *Helv. Chim. Acta* 19:68–86.

——, and Mark, H. (1930) *Der Aufbau der hochpolymer organischen Naturstoffe.* Akademische Verlagsges., Leipzig.

Nelson, R. (1961) "The use of holocellulose to study cellulose supermolecular structure." *J. Polymer Sci.* 51:27–58.

Preston, R. D. (1952) *The Molecular Architecture of Plant Cell Walls.* John Wiley, N. Y.

——, and Astbury, W. T. (1937) "The structure of the wall of the green alga *Valonia ventricosa.*" *Proc. Roy. Soc. (London), Ser. B* 122:76–97.

Rånby, B. G. (1958) "The fine structure of cellulose fibrils." In *Fundamentals Papermaking Fibres, Trans. Symp. Cambridge, Engl., 1957* (F. Bolam, ed.), pp. 55–82.

Roelofsen, P. A. (1959) *The Plant Cell Wall.* Gebrüder Borntraeger, Berlin.

Rosato, D. V., and Grove, C. S. (1964) *Filament Winding: Its Development, Manufacture, Applications and Design.* Interscience Pub., N. Y.

Sakurada, I., Nukushina, Y., and Ito, T. (1962) "Experimental determination of the elastic modulus of crystalline regions in oriented polymers." *J. Polymer Sci.* 57:651–660.

Scaramuzzi, G. (1963) Personal communication.

Shaffer, B. W. (1964a) "The influence of filament orientation on the material properties of reinforced plastics." In *Proc. Soc. Plastics Ind. Conf., Reinforced Plastics Div.,* Sect. 6-E.

————— (1964b) "Stress-strain relations of reinforced plastics parallel and normal to the internal filaments." *AIAA J.* 2:348–352.

Shibley, A. M., Peritt, H. L., and Eig, M. (1962) "A survey of filament winding: materials, design criteria, military applications." Plastec Rept. 10. Plastics Tech. Eval Ctr., Picatinny Arsenal.

Snedecor, G. W. (1956) *Statistical Methods.* Iowa State Coll. Press.

Srinivasan, P. S. (1941) "The elastic and thermal properties of timber." *Quart. J. Indian Inst. Sci.* 4:222–314.

Stamm, A. J., and Harris, E. E. (1953) *Chemical Processing of Wood.* Chemical Publ., N. Y.

Tech. Assoc. Pulp and Paper Ind. (1949) "Conditioning Paper and Papers for Testing." TAPPI Std. T 402, m-49.

Treloar, L. R. G. (1960) "Calculations of elastic moduli of polymer crystals. III. Cellulose." *Polymer* 1:290–303.

Wardrop, A. B. (1963) "Morphological factors involved in the pulping and beating of wood fibres." *Svensk Papperstid.* 66:231–247.

—————, and Addo-Ashong, F.W.(1963) "The anatomy and fine structure of wood in relation to its mechanical failure." In *Proc. Melbourne Univ. Eng. Dept. Symp. on Fracture,* 32pp.

—————, and Preston, R. D. (1951) "The submicroscopic organization of the cell wall in conifer tracheides and wood fibres." *J. Exp. Botany* 2:20–30.

Watson, A. J. (1962) "A semimicro procedure for estimating the resistant carbohydrate material in wood." *Tappi* 45:722–724.

Wise, L. E. (1952) "Miscellaneous extraneous components of wood." Ch. 16 in *Wood Chemistry* (L. E. Wise & E. C. Jahn, eds.), Vol. I, Second Edition, pp. 638–660. Reinhold Publ., N. Y.

The Piezoelectric Effect in Wood

WILLIAM L. GALLIGAN and ARTHUR F. NOSKOWIAK

Division of Industrial Research, and Department of Forestry and
Range Management, Washington State University

The salient feature of a piezoelectric material is the interrelationship between its mechanical and electrical properties. These permit a charge to be developed when the material undergoes strain and, conversely, a strain to be produced when a charge is placed on the specimen. Traditionally, piezoelectric materials have been considered as those demonstrating the characteristics of monocrystals such as quartz. Based on the work of Shubnikov (1940), however, a concept of "piezoelectric texture" has been developed in which crystalline regions may be present in a matrix of material which is noncrystalline. Shubnikov suggested that wood could be placed in this category.

Although wood may indeed qualify as a piezoelectric texture, its extreme heterogeneity adds an imposing array of features which can potentially influence the piezoelectric effect. It is appropriate, therefore, to be concerned about the implications of the piezoelectric effect in regard to study techniques and the ultimate understanding of wood in the molecular, as well as in the histological and gross senses.

The principal investigators reporting research on piezoelectricity in wood have been Shubnikov (1940) and Bazhenov (1960, 1961) in Russia, Fukada (1955, 1957) in Japan, and Galligan and Bertholf (1963) at Washington State University. Bazhenov was the original investigator of the piezoelectric effect in wood. He employed both small wafers and cubes of wood to generate a charge which he measured with an electrometer. Bazhenov demonstrated that a mode of stress application tending to produce a shear strain between the wood fibers was required to yield the piezoelectric charge. Through the use of selected fungal attack on wood and with experiments on noncellular products such as cellophane and viscose rayon, he also demonstrated that the basic unit of the piezoelectric texture of wood must be the cellulose. Bazhenov then argued intuitively that the crystalline areas in the S_2 layer are the sites of the piezoelectric charge development because only in these areas is the ultrastructure suitably ordered and aligned to produce the resultant piezoelectric charge.

Fukada carried out a research program with results parallel to those of Bazhenov. In addition, he examined the effect of the degree of crystallinity by using samples of old temple timbers of differing levels of crystallinity. He found that the piezoelectric charge was directly proportional to the degree of crystallinity as shown by X-ray diffraction techniques. Fukada's work was also extended to textures of other high polymers, including silk fibers and collagen, and demonstrated the existence of the piezoelectric effect in these materials.

Research at Washington State University has emphasized the measurement of piezoelectricity in relatively large specimens using impact loading. Objectives of the research program include more complete examination of the role of cellulose crystallinity, study of the effect of noncellulosic constituents, investigation of the effects of macroscopic wood variables, and finally, exploration of the practical usefulness of the piezoelectric moduli of wood.

CAUSAL STRAIN—RESULTANT PIEZOELECTRIC CHARGE

In general, relative displacement between local electrical charges must take place in a piezoelectric material in order to produce a *net* electrical charge. In wood, as mentioned previously, the only suitably ordered areas appear to be the crystalline regions of cellulose, and it is therefore conjectured that, in the S_2 layer, the necessary displacement takes place between cellulose molecules *within* crystallites.

According to present understanding, stress must be applied which is specifically oriented to produce a shear strain between fibers. Apparently, only that component of the displacement (strain) which is aligned in the longitudinal direction of a fiber contributes to the resultant electrical charge in the fiber. In the transverse directions, any charge caused by strain components at a position in the fiber wall apparently is canceled by the charge generated in the same manner but in the comparable position on the opposite side of the fiber. This reasoning follows from the spiral orientation of the cellulose in the fiber walls.

Within the fiber wall, the S_2 layer is believed to be of principal importance because the cellulose chains in this layer are aligned nearly parallel to the axis of the fiber and thus are most responsive to axial shear. The cellulose in the primary wall and in the S_1 and S_3 layers of the secondary wall presumably does not contribute significantly to the observed piezoelectric effect because the crystalline alignment in those layers is almost normal to the fiber axis.

More understanding of the basis for the piezoelectric effect from the standpoint of ultrastructure is desired, particularly since the particle displacement at this level is responsible for an organized polarity which seemingly overrides the massive heterogeneity of wood.

Polarity of the Piezoelectric Effect

Since the piezoelectric effect is caused by a net imbalance of charges in the material subjected to strain, there is a polarity associated with the effect. In wood, this polarity originates where the charge imbalance occurs (presumably in the crystallites) and is displayed in a definite orientation on the surface of macro-wood specimens when these are subjected to strain. Thus, even though heterogeneous at almost every level of organization, the wood exhibits a resultant polarity. More research is needed in order to understand both *why* the polarity is developed in the local crystalline region, and *how* the resultant measurable polarity is affected by the heterogeneous nature of wood.

Interpretation of Mechanical-Electrical Effects

The interrelated nature of the mechanical and electrical aspects of piezoelectricity is a matter of basic definition. In the case of wood, it is difficult to describe the strain and electrical charge development at the ultrastructure level. It is suggested that spacial model techniques and tensor description be combined to produce a mechanical-electrical model of the ultrastructure. Such a model could yield valuable clues to the nature of the development of the electrical charge.

REFERENCES

Bazhenov, V. A. (1960) "The piezoelectric effect of wood." In *Proceedings Fifth World Forestry Congress, Seattle*, Vol. 2, pp. 1323–1326.
———— (1961) *Piezoelectric Properties of Wood.* Consultants Bureau Enterprises, Inc., N. Y.
Fukada, E. (1955) "Piezoelectricity of wood." *J. Phys. Soc. Japan* 10:149–154.
————, Yasuda, S., Kohara, J., and Okamoto, H. (1957) "The dynamic Young's modulus and the piezoelectric constant of old timbers." *J. Appl. Phys., Japan* 26:25–28.
Galligan, W. L., and Bertholf, L. D. (1963) "Piezoelectric effect in wood." *Forest Prod. J.* 12:517–524.
Shubnikov, A. V. (1940) "On the tensor piezoelectric moduli of non-crystalline anisotropic media." Report in the Division of Physical-Mathematical Sciences of the Academy of Sciences of the USSR, April 26. (From Bazhenov, V. A., *Piezoelectric Properties of Wood*, 1961.)

Intra-Increment Physical Properties of Certain Western Canadian Coniferous Species

R. W. WELLWOOD

Faculty of Forestry, University of British Columbia

G. IFJU

*Department of Forestry and Wildlife,
Virginia Polytechnic Institute*

J. W. WILSON

*Faculty of Forestry, University of British Columbia
and Pulp and Paper Research
Institute of Canada*

The physical behavior of wood results from the interaction of cell wall material — type, orientation, mass, juxtaposition — test environment and nature of applied or induced stresses. Great differences occur between and within a species, and within a single stem, all of which are described in voluminous literature.

An obvious feature of coniferous growth increments is large specific gravity difference between early- and late-formed wood. Specific gravity is a physical property known to affect other properties, and uses, of wood since it is a measure of the amount of cell wall material present. Where growth increments are wide, as in fast-growth material, usual techniques are adequate for measurement of single-increment specific gravity. In particular, the maximum moisture method of Smith (1955) is readily applicable to excised whole increments. Where increments are narrow or where it is desirable to trace specific gravity patterns across a growth increment, however, individual samples must be small and chances of experimental error increase with usual techniques. A new method has been developed whereby micro-specific gravity determinations have been made on individual specimens having a volume of only 0.025 cm^3 and a weight of 5–18 mg (Ifju *et al.*, 1965a). Thereby, the same authors, and Worrall *et al.* (1963) have developed specific gravity profiles across several adjacent growth increments of five western Canadian species. A wide range in earlywood–latewood values was shown by Douglas-fir (0.2–0.7) and

539

western redcedar (0.12–0.6), while Pacific silver fir (0.25–0.6), Sitka spruce (0.2–0.5), and western hemlock (0.2–0.5) showed smaller differences. It would seem from these results that broader specific gravity range accompanies woods with abrupt earlywood–latewood transition. Besides describing magnitude of intra-increment variation, the micro-specific gravity values have given valuable correlations with wood microtensile strength and elasticity (Ifju *et al.*, 1965b), as well as with microphotometer (Green and Worrall, 1963) measurements of cell wall area (Worrall *et al.*, 1963).

For such studies specific gravity is determined on sample coupons cut from water-saturated, serial tangential microsection blanks with a specially made precision die. Green volume is calculated from thickness and area measurements. Samples are rolled in gauze containers, solvent extracted, if required, and conditioned to desired moisture content. Following equilibrium to weighing room conditions, precision weighings are done on a Mettler or other microbalance (10^{-6} gm) over short time with the samples collected in weighing bottles according to time of weighing, species, growth zone, or other characteristics. Moisture contents of the composite are determined and initial air-dry weights are corrected for moisture content according to their appropriate group. Oven-dry weight is divided by green volume to give specific gravity. Typical values, with associated dispersion, of nonextracted Douglas-fir ruptured test specimens are given in Table I.

Physical properties have been intensively studied within and between three consecutive growth increments of a 150-year-old Douglas-fir tree from the University Research Forest, Haney, B. C. (Ifju *et al.*, 1965b).

TABLE I. Comparison of Ultimate Stress (Green) within a Douglas-Fir Growth Increment with "Necked-Down" and Rectangular Test Specimens, and Associated Micro-Specific Gravities
(Ifju et al., 1965a)

| Position within increment % | Ultimate tensile stress, psi | | | | | | Micro-specific gravity (green volume) | |
| | "Necked-down" specimen | | | Rectangular specimen | | | | |
	Mean $\overline{X}$	Standard deviation (S.D.)	Coefficient of variation (C.V.) %	$\overline{X}$	S.D.	C.V. %	$\overline{X}$	S.D.
18	4,254	623	14.7	4,338	375	8.6	0.199	0.005
46	7,746	1,505	19.4	8,331	698	8.4	0.255	0.009
60	12,387	1,995	16.1	14,059	1,527	10.9	0.528	0.010
74	17,895	2,896	16.2	18,982	1,585	8.4	–	–
88	20,049	2,272	11.3	22,229	1,682	7.6	0.624	0.012

Twelve or more points were sampled per increment along each of four adjacent radii. A new rectangular test specimen design allowed stressing 40% of the specimen volume in tension parallel to grain and provided means for direct reading of an elasticity function, which was shown (Ifju et al., a) to be modulus of elasticity. The new test specimen gives higher tensile strength values (2–12%) and lower coefficients of variation than obtained with typical "necked-down" specimens, as demonstrated in Table I. It is noted in this regard that Douglas-fir latewood "necked-down" specimens almost invariably fail in longitudinal shear initiating from the specimen shoulder. Using these techniques, Douglas-fir ultimate tensile strength varied from 2,000 psi in earlywood to 22,000 psi in late-wood, while elasticity was 150 to 1,500 × 10^3 psi. Both properties showed abrupt transition from earlywood to latewood zone and were constant within zone as was specific gravity, except that strength and elasticity increased slightly across the earlywood. Plotted values of specific gravity for the four positions on the three growth increments are shown in Figure 1. Highly significant correlations ($r = 0.92$) were found between strength properties and specific gravity determined on individual broken test specimens. Tangential variation in physical properties was minor in comparison with radial differences.

A mathematical model having the following form was derived for expression of radial variation in physical properties:

$$Y = a + b \arctn \; [(X - 95 + L)/c].$$

where:

Y = specific gravity (G), tensile strength, psi (T) or elasticity, 10^3 psi (E),

a, b = regression coefficients as calculated by the least squares method,

X = percentile position in the increment, %,

L = latewood percentage, %,

c = a constant dependent on the property (G, T, or E) and relative width of the transition zone between earlywood and latewood [1.0 for width of the transition zone between earlywood and latewood] (1.0 for specific gravity, 10.0 for tensile strength and elasticity in the three increments tested).

All radial-increment series and within-increment combinations gave highly significant correlation coefficients ($r = 0.90–0.98$) between the model and actual test values. Conversely, the equation of the model may be solved for percentage latewood, thereby introducing a new physico-mechanical definition of latewood through these results.

Lack of linearity between tensile strength and specific gravity was further examined by transformation of values to specific strength (tensile strength/specific gravity). Values ranged from 1.0 to 4.0 × 10^4 psi. Al-

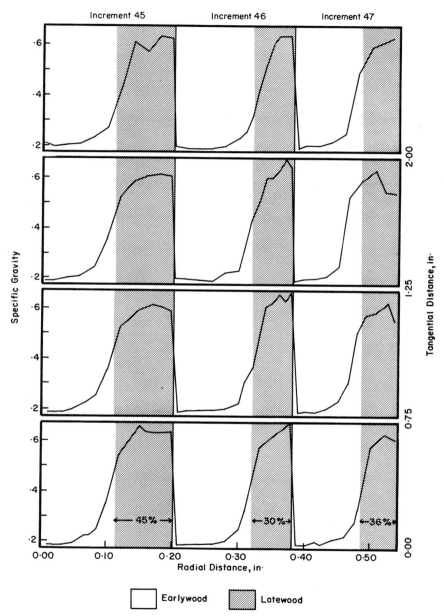

Fig. 1. Within- and between-increment variation of specific gravity for four contiguous tangential positions across three growth increments of Douglas-fir.

though lowest values occurred in the first-formed early-wood, peak values were not in the latewood, but were associated with its initiation. Parabolic curves fitted to individual and combined data showed highly significant correlations ($R = 0.72$–0.87) and explained 51 to 75% of the variation on the basis of position within ring. Specific stiffness (elasticity/specific gravity) calculations gave the same result. It is noted that position of maximum specific strength values correspond with maximum carbohydrate content within increments (Wilson and Wellwood, this volume).

Properties of this same Douglas-fir tree are being surveyed by sampling at regular intervals across radial sections at five equally spaced vertical levels. Analyses are not completed, but range in nonextracted earlywood and latewood specific gravity has been 0.19 to 0.79, in tensile strength 1,850 to 24,540 psi, and in elasticity 106 to 2,370 $\times$ 10^3 psi. These data will provide further test of the above mathematical model.

Another recent study involved investigation of changes within a 35-year-old western redcedar stem following the application of a commercial, high nitrogen content fertilizer (Wellwood *et al.*, in preparation). Samples were selected at six vertical levels to test intra-increment properties before and after treatment. Plotted values for the properties discussed above followed the same patterns noted for Douglas-fir, as illustrated in Figure 1. Average values of tensile strength for the ten to twelve positions across individual growth increments varied from a minimum of 4,000 to a maximum of 14,000 psi. Individual specimens showed a correspondingly greater range. Modulus of elasticity averages were 200 to 1,000 $\times$ 10^3 psi and specific gravity following hot water extraction, 0.24 to 0.36. The most obvious results of fertilizer application were an accelerated growth rate and a general decrease in specific gravity, tensile strength, and stiffness, as well as mean tracheid length. Effects were most marked in the lower portions of the tree, becoming negligible in the upper, crown-formed wood.

Multiple regression analyses were made to test the effect of nine independent wood characteristics on tensile strength and on modulus of elasticity of the western redcedar data. As expected, tensile strength and elasticity were each highly dependent upon specific gravity which accounted for 50% of the variance in the former and 61% in the latter. Total variance was 70.7% in the case of tensile strength and 79.5% in that of modulus of elasticity. Many of the independent variables were highly significantly correlated with each other. Among the highest associations were specific gravity with position in the growth increment (0.728), growth rate with per cent summerwood (0.597), position within growth increment with fibril angle (-0.546), tracheid length with fibril angle (-0.437).

A previous study of microtensile strength within and between growth increments of western hemlock (Wellwood, 1962) provided analyses of the effects of earlywood and latewood considered together and separately (see also Panshin *et al.*, 1964). Tensile strength was highly associated with specific gravity ($r = 0.904$), position of sample within the growth increment (i.e., whether earlywood or latewood, $r = 0.829$) and fibril angle ($r = 0.618$). The multiple correlation coefficient (R) of the five independent variables tested was 0.95.

As with western redcedar, many of these independent variables were themselves highly correlated. In both species, as in European and Japanese larch (Pearson and Fielding, 1961), and in Douglas-fir (Phillips, 1960, as shown in Panshin *et al.*, 1964), earlywood was at maximum specific gravity near the pith. Earlywood of western hemlock and the larches also exhibited maximum tensile strength near the pith. Strength of latewood in western hemlock was not significantly correlated with age of the growth increment although a trend of increasing tensile strength with increasing age from the pith is shown for these data by Panshin *et al.* (1964).

In another investigation of intra-increment variation, physical properties of purposely degraded Douglas-fir earlywood and latewood have been examined in relation to moisture and temperature dependence (Ifju, 1964 and Ifju and Wilson, in preparation). Gamma irradiation, done by Atomic Energy of Canada Limited, was used to provide random scission of cellulose chains in 80-μ thick, water-saturated wafers. It is thought that other major wood components were not affected, and that no constituent was removed or repositioned by the procedure. The treatment (0.1, 1.0, 10.0, and 15.0 megarad dosage) gave materials with cellulose nitrate/acetone intrinsic viscosity range from 35.0 to 2.3 dl/gm (5600 to 160 DP). Microtensile tests on moisture-free, air-dry, and water-saturated sections, at three temperatures (25, 50, and 70°C), provided measurements of ultimate tensile strength, ultimate strain, elasticity, and work to maximum load. Typical earlywood and latewood microtensile failures of nonexposed and exposed (irradiated) specimens are shown in Figure 2. It should be noted that latewood failures at the highest dosage resembled, in many respects, the normal, abrupt failure of nonexposed earlywood.

Mean values for four associated specimens, tested in the saturated condition at 25°C, are shown in the table below. The legend is that of Figure 2.

Degradation was the most important main effect, followed by moisture

	DP $\times 10^3$	Ultimate stress, psi	Ultimate strain, $\times 10^{-2}$ in./in.	Elasticity $\times 10^3$ psi	Work max., $\times 10^2$ in. lb/in.^{3}
A,E	5.25	4,700	1.42	401	0.36
B	5.66	19,200	1.52	1670	1.63
C	0.16	1,400	0.48	296	0.04
D,F	0.16	8,500	0.61	1610	0.26

content and temperature. Interestingly, the most sensitive measurement of degradation was the work function, which showed decrease by a factor of 10 across the experimental range. This compared to factors of 2–3 or less with other test values. Elasticity is a measure of creep in early stages of test and this was little affected by random degradation, suggesting that crystalline cellulose areas are strongly enough bonded to resist severe scission without contributing to increased slippage. This contrasts with lower elasticity values obtained when degradation is produced by hydrolytic attack on amorphous cellulose areas. Several differences in intensity of response were noted between earlywood and latewood.

Micro-compression perpendicular to grain tests have been made by Wilson (1964) across increments of three western Canadian coniferous species. The procedure includes tangential sectioning of water-soaked wood blocks at 100-micron thickness, die-cutting 1×1 to 15×15 mm squares from serial sections, placing single squares (or multiple squares crossbanded) between several micro-slide cover slips, applying a standard compression test to the assembly with close setting of machine limit switch, and making comparison with the system minus the wood specimen(s). Preliminary results showed that fiber collapsibility among the three species examined might be divided by interval according to stress at failure. For example, western redcedar earlywood failed at 1000–1500 psi, while Douglas-fir latewood failed at 6000+ psi. Of interest is the fact that western hemlock earlywood, western redcedar latewood, and Douglas-fir "transition wood" all failed at about the same value (2500–4000 psi). The suggestion is that these three could show some similarities in raw fiber properties. Further, relationship was shown between deflection and thickness of the same type of material. Whole increments dissected from standard cores gave an integral compressibility curve which is believed to be related to the composite of values from thin sections.

Intra-increment specific gravity variation has been correlated with cell wall area (Worrall et al., 1963), as determined on matched cross sections by Scanning Microphotometer measurements (Green and Worrall, 1963). Comparisons were made at eight points across each of three adjacent growth increments in five western Canadian coniferous species. Each species gave almost perfect linear correlation ($r = 0.99$) between these measurements. The same high correlation was had when data between species were grouped. In addition, the latewood fraction was determined by linear measurements as the classic percentage by volume and as the percentage by weight through calculation of area under photometer curves. This quantitative resolution of intra-increment density could relate to some fundamental fiber property. Observations on earlywood–latewood strength variations have shown similar patterns.

Further analysis by Worrall et al. of specific gravity and cell wall vol-

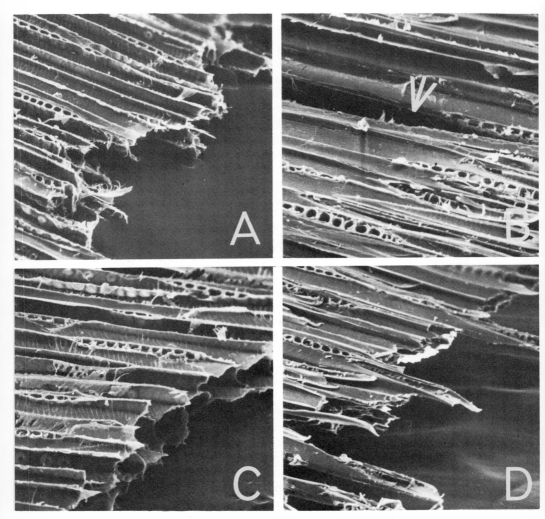

FIG. 2. Scanning electron photomicrographs of typical earlywood and latewood microtensile test failures (courtesy of Pulp and Paper Research Institute of Canada). A. Nonexposed earlywood section, showing combined failure of cell wall and middle lamella. × 150. B. Segment of nonexposed latewood failure, showing terminus (arrow) of "finger-like" fault through apparent yield of middle lamella. × 150. C. Earlywood section following 15 megarad gamma irradiation, showing entire failure through yield of cell wall. × 150. D. Latewood section following 15 megarad gamma irradiation, showing combined failure of cell wall and middle lamella. × 150.

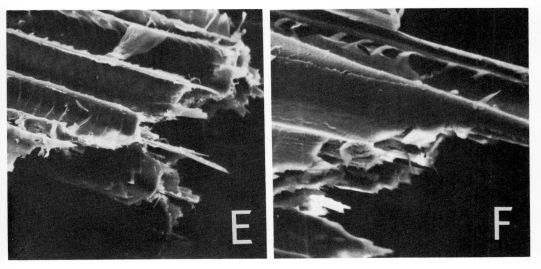

FIG. 2 (continued). E. As 2A. ×450. F. As 2D. ×450.

ume data indicated that cell wall density varies directly with wood density. Earlywood cell walls had a specific gravity of about 0.75 gm/cm³, while latewood cell walls had a specific gravity of about 0.85 gm/cm³. The early-wood cells appeared to have a larger microporosity within the cell walls, in addition to larger lumens. Re-analysis of data from various sources in the literature (Ifju and Kennedy, 1962; Jayme and Krause, 1963; Kellogg and Ifju, 1962) showed the same effect. Similar phenomena have been reported (Jayme and Krause, 1963; Smith and Miller, 1964; Yiannos, 1964) for gross wood segments and for pulp fibers. The term "packing fraction" has been introduced by Worrall et al. (1963) to describe this property of cell wall porosity. It is defined as the ratio of wall density to wall substance density, the latter being the classic 1.53 gm/cm³. If present data, and data derived from the above-listed sources, are extrapolated to high wood density values, it then appears that the cell wall density approaches that of cell wall substance. This variable wall porosity may relate to varying behavior of different wood types in chemical and physico-chemical processing dependent on the accessibility of the cell wall components. Other work on intra-increment variation suggests that "packing fraction" may correlate with the more finite level of chemical organization.

CONCLUSIONS

1. Major specific gravity differences exist in coniferous species across an annual growth increment. Within three growth increments of one

Douglas-fir stem these were found to have a range of 0.20 to 0.62 $\pm$ 10%, based on green volume. Similar ranges exist for other species.

2. Tensile strength and modulus of elasticity parallel to grain for thin wood samples can best be determined by use of a narrow, rectangular specimen. Specific gravities can be successfully determined on the same specimens after rupture.

3. All physical properties studied showed abrupt transition from early- to latewood zone, with variation across increments (radial) much larger than along increments (tangential). Radial stem analysis of western hemlock showed maximum earlywood specific gravity and tensile strength values near the pith, whereas latewood values increased with age.

4. Within-increment patterns were similar for all properties of both Douglas-fir and western redcedar, except that specific gravity was constant across earlywood, whereas both tensile strength and elasticity increased progressively. This anomaly led to nonlinear relationships between strength and specific gravity. A mathematical model has been used for Douglas-fir to express relationships between physical properties and per-centile position within increment.

5. A second anomaly was observed with Douglas-fir in that specific strength (property/specific gravity) values were highest at points of late-wood initiation. This corresponds to position of maximum carbohydrate content within increments.

6. Purposely degraded micro-specimens of Douglas-fir showed greatest sensitivity in strength reduction to loss of cellulose chain length, followed in order by increase in moisture content $(0-28^{+}\%)$ and temperature $(25-70°C)$. Work functions were the most sensitive measure of treatment effects.

7. Micro-compression perpendicular to grain tests showed comparable variation in strength between early- and latewood within single increments.

8. Intra-increment specific gravity variation is strongly correlated with cell wall area as determined by Scanning Microphotometer $(R = 0.99)$. Earlywood cells, in comparison with latewood cells, appear to have a larger microporosity within cell walls, as well as larger lumens. The term "packing fraction" has been introduced to describe this property of vari-able cell wall density.

Acknowledgment

Acknowledgment is made to the Canada Department of Forestry, the National Research Council of Canada, and the Pulp and Paper Research Institute of Canada for financial assistance in the conduct of this work.

REFERENCES

Green, H. V., and Worrall, J. G. (1963) "Wood quality studies. Part I. A scanning micro-photometer for automatically measuring and recording certain wood characteristics." Pulp and Paper Res. Inst. Can. Tech. Rept. No. 331; *Tappi* 47:419–427.

Ifju, G. (1964) "Tensile strength behavior as a function of cellulose in wood." *Forest Prod. J.* 14:366–372.

———, and Kennedy, R. W. (1962) "Some variables affecting microtensile strength of Douglas-fir." *Forest Prod. J.* 12:213–217.

———, Wellwood, R. W., and Wilson, J. W. (1965a) "Improved micro-technique for wood tensile strength and related properties." *Forest Prod. J.* 15:13–14.

———, ———, and ——— (1965b) "Relationship between certain intra-increment physical measurements in Douglas fir." In press. *Pulp Paper Mag. Can.*

———, and Wilson, J. W. (In preparation) "Wood tensile strength behavior as a function of cellulose degree of polymerization."

Jayme, G., and Krause, T. (1963) "Über die Packungsdichte der Zellwände in Laub-hölzern." *Holz roh- Werkstoff* 21:14–19. Pulp and Paper Res. Inst. Can. Trans. Ser. No. 50. CSIRO (Australia) Trans. No. 6544.

Kellogg, R. M., and Ifju, G. (1962) "Influence of specific gravity and certain other factors on the tensile properties of wood." *Forest Prod. J.* 12:463–470.

Panshin, A. J., deZeeuw, C., and Brown, H. P. (1964) *Textbook of Wood Technology.* Vol. I, Second Edition, pp. 210–211. McGraw-Hill, N. Y.

Pearson, F. G. O., and Fielding, H. A. (1961) "Some properties of individual growth rings in European and Japanese larch and their influence upon specific gravity." *Holzforschung* 15:82–89.

Smith, D. M. (1955) "A comparison of two methods for determining the specific gravity of small wood samples of second-growth Douglas-fir." U. S. For. Prod. Lab. Rept. No. 2033.

———, and Miller, R. B. (1964) "Methods of measuring and estimating tracheid wall thickness of redwood (*Sequoia sempervirens* [D.Don] Endl.)." *Tappi* 47:599–604.

Wellwood, R. W. (1962) "Tensile testing of small wood samples." *Pulp Paper Mag. Can.* 63:T61–T67.

———, Jurazs, P. E., and Wu, Y-t. (In preparation) "Response to fertilizer application of intra-increment properties within a western redcedar stem."

Wilson, J. W. (1964) "Wood characteristics. III. Intra-increment physical and chemical properties." Pulp and Paper Res. Inst. Can. Res. Note No. 45.

Worrall, J. G., Green, H. V., and Wilson, J. W. (1963) "Relationship between fractional void volume and wood quality in western Canadian conifers." In preparation. (See Worrall, J. G., B.S.F. Thesis, Fac. For., Univ. B. C.)

Yiannos, P. N. (1964) "The apparent cell-wall density of wood and pulp fibers." *Tappi* 47:468–471.

Intra-Increment Chemical Properties of Certain Western Canadian Coniferous Species

J. W. WILSON* and R. W. WELLWOOD

Faculty of Forestry, University of British Columbia

There is an extensive literature on wood quality differences between species and between members of a single species grown under different environmental conditions or from different seed source. Similarly, variation within a single stem has been much studied in regard to radial and height patterns, as well as wood zones (corewood, heartwood, and sapwood). Further intensive examination has occurred at the individual cell level, including, in particular, wall physical organization and chemical composition. Little is known, however, about incremental growth zones (earlywood and latewood) and how physical and chemical variation at this level influences processing and properties of wood products.

The individual growth zone provides a unique material for examining fundamental physical and chemical behavior, since variability introduced by genetic and environmental differences, age, and distance from pith are controlled within narrow limits. Certain problems arise, however, in sampling within growth increments, since the bulk or mass of material required for most standard tests exceeds the amount easily available. For example, tracheid length or cell wall thickness distribution within a growth increment may be obtained from a small amount of wood material. In contrast, a standard chemical test, such as that for holocellulose, requires an amount of wood meal not readily available from within a particular part of a single growth zone. Strength tests, in turn, are normally performed on specimens of substantial length and cross section, again not readily obtainable within normal growth zones. It is frequently necessary, therefore, to modify existing procedures or to develop new ones when examining intra-incremental properties. Several such modifications or newly developed tests are noted, as are results obtained by their use during investigations on five western Canadian coniferous species.

Chemical constituents and properties of wood have been intensively studied. In spite of this, relatively little has been published on properties or behavior related to intra-increment differences in chemical composition. References in the literature relate, logically, to the pulping industry. It is understood that chemical pulps prepared from earlywood exhibit

**and Pulp and Paper Research Institute of Canada

higher bursting strength, tensile strength, and fold endurance, but lower yield, tear resistance, and bulk, than pulps made from excised latewood. In view of this widely different behavior, the earlywood–latewood ratio might be considered the most important single influence on coniferous chemical pulp yield, behavior in processing, and pulp or cellulose derivative characteristics. As one example, among southern pines it was shown by Chidester *et al.* (1938) that variation of 10% in earlywood content of any one species gave greater differences in pulp quality than were exhibited between four different species. More recently it was noted by Hedin *et al.* (1963) that sulphite dissolving pulps enriched with either earlywood or latewood fibers (tracheids) behaved differently in viscose processing. The addition of earlywood fibers caused less gels and thereby gave better filtration.

Holocellulose is the principal constituent of wood. Standard methods of determining this or similar carbohydrate fractions require 2 gm of wood meal per sample (TAPPI, 1955). A micro-method is therefore required if tests are to be made *within* individual growth increments. Four micro-methods have been advanced for determination of holocellulose or similar carbohydrate fraction. Zobel and McElwee (1958) and Erickson (1962) applied chlorite, Watson (1962) used chlorine-sulphite, and Leopold (1961) followed sodium borohydride reduction with peracetic acid. All worked with 0.5 gm samples. Publication of these methods has not been accompanied by guidance on the critical minimum number of replicates necessary to meet statistical definition of a determination, although Watson (1962) does give data on some replicate determinations. In addition, only Erickson (1962) treats the effect of residual lignin, but no technique is given for this determination on a micro scale. Our interest has been in finding a statistically sound measurement of holocellulose as corrected for lignin residual and as replicated a reasonable number of times. Examination has shown that no method reported does this satisfactorily (Wilson, 1964).

A micro-KAPPA procedure has been applied for lignin correction of holocelluloses. This is calibrated against Klason lignin determined on wood meal chlorited to different levels (Wilson, 1964).

Carbohydrate distribution within growth increments of Douglas-fir was studied following preparation of holocelluloses by the Zobel and McElwee (1958) method. Six points were sampled in each of three adjacent rings having 0.2-inch width and 30–45% latewood. Patterns were identical for all increments. Results showed peak chlorite holocellulose (77–78%, corrected for lignin) occurring at the point of latewood initiation, while the first- and last-formed parts of increments had lower values (72.5–73.5%). Quantitative chromatographic analysis of constituent sugars has shown a similar profile for glucan plus mannan (88–94% based on holocellulose).

On the same basis, galactan increased (2.5 to 6.0%) across each increment, while pentosans decreased from earlywood to latewood (xylan 8.0 to 4.5, araban 0.6 to 0.2%).

Wilson (1964) further postulates that consideration of intra-increment glucan (C) distribution, in combination with micro-specific gravity (G) values and cell wall fibril angle (ϕ), suggests a much sought unifying hypothesis for cellulose tensile strength (T) in that:

$$T \propto \log (GC \operatorname{Ctn} \theta).$$

Projection of present data, as well as values calculated from the literature (Ifju and Kennedy, 1962; Wardrop, 1951), provides close approach to theoretical tensile strength of the cellulose molecule. This basic concept needs further examination.

In other work by Ifju and Wilson (in preparation), it was shown that the average cellulose chain length of Douglas-fir latewood is 6% higher than that of earlywood. This, in combination with variable earlywood–latewood cell wall density (Jayme and Krause, 1963; Worrall et al., 1963; Yiannos, 1964) and differences in degree of crystalline order in wood (Lindgren, 1958) and holocelluloses (Lee, 1961), suggests that longer chain length, better packing, and high crystallinity accompany higher cellulose levels within wood growth increments.

It has been proposed that aromatic nuclei of naturally occurring wood lignin and extractives partially "protect" wood cellulose from degradation by high energy irradiation, similar to styrene in styrene-isobutylene co-polymers. Evidence used to support the proposal includes viscosity measurements on irradiated wood compared to separated holocellulose (Smith and Mixer, 1959), and differences in dilute acid hydrolysis rates of irradiated wood, wood pulp, and cotton (Saeman et al., 1952). Studying response of growth zone tissues to irradiation provided a new experimental method for examining the proposal. Since Douglas-fir earlywood contains 3 to 4% more lignin than comparable latewood (Fig. 1), increasing disparity in number of chain scissions should occur between the two materials as irradiation severity is increased if lignin has protective influence. Wilson and Ifju (in preparation) showed that both earlywood and latewood celluloses were equally degraded across a 0.1–15.0 megarad range of gamma irradiation treatments which gave materials with cellulose nitrate/acetone intrinsic viscosities from 36 to 2 dl/cm. This suggests that aromatic nuclei in wood, which are mostly separate from the cellulose, do not provide protection against irradiation as do benzene rings incorporated as part of a polymer structure.

Micro-lignin determinations have been made across increments of five western Canadian coniferous species by Wu (1964). The acetyl bromide-acetic acid digestion and spectrophotometric method of Johnson et al.

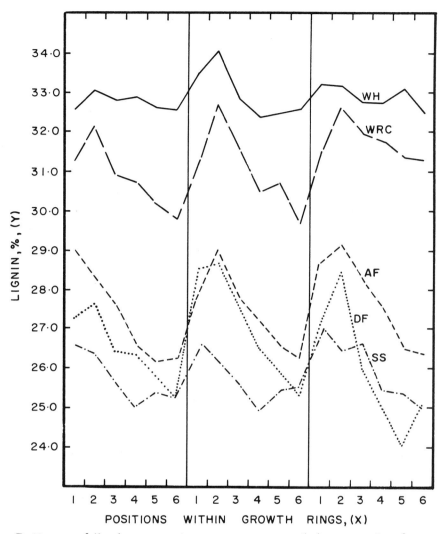

Patterns of lignin percentages across growth increments of
five coniferous species·

WH – Western hemlock (56–58 yr·)
WRC– Western red cedar (72–74 yr·)
AF – Amabilis fir (78–80 yr·)
DF – Douglas–fir (64–66 yr·)
SS – Sitka spruce (69–71 yr·)

(Position 1 ,first formed earlywood ; Position 6, last formed latewood)

FIG. 1.

(1961) has been used with 0.1 gm samples of extracted wood meal. Results are computed from comparative absorbance of digested wood meal for which standard Klason lignin is known. Statistical reliability required two or more replicates. Lignin contents, as illustrated in Figure 1, were found to be highly significantly different within increments of Sitka spruce (25.8 ± 1.1%), Douglas-fir (26.5 ± 2.3%), Pacific silver fir (27.5 ± 1.0%), and western redcedar (31.2 ± 1.5%), but nonsignificant in western hemlock (32.8 ± 1.0%). Except for western hemlock, earlywood was regularly 2–3% higher in lignin than latewood. Significant differences were found between growth increments of Douglas-fir and western redcedar, but not between those of other species, although a slight increase in average lignin values with age was noted. These results extend other earlywood-latewood studies, by Hale and Clermont (1963) and Ritter and Fleck (1926), based on gross samples.

Further study of Figure 1 shows that while minimum lignin occurred regularly in the last formed latewood, maximum lignin was not found usually in the first formed earlywood, but more often somewhat later in the season's growth. This suggests that initial earlywood tissue arising from "overwintered" cambial mother cells has some chemical predisposition towards the preceding season's latewood.

Intra-increment wood methoxyl contents were measured on the same samples examined for lignin (Wu, 1963). Microspecimens (0.2 gm) were treated according to a modified TAPPI procedure (1960) including iodine back titration. Accordingly, a statistically satisfactory determination was provided by three replicates. Two patterns emerged from statistical analyses of the methoxyl data. Sitka spruce (4.8 ± 0.1%) and western hemlock (5.5 ± 0.1%) showed constant values within and between increments. In contrast, Douglas-fir (5.1%), Pacific silver fir (5.1%), and western redcedar (6.0%) repeat a within-increment pattern which is 0.5% higher methoxyl in earlywood than in latewood. Distribution of these values within and between increments are illustrated for the five species in Figure 2.

Further examination of wood methoxyl and lignin data by Wu (1964) showed a highly significant relationship between these values in Douglas-fir ($r = 0.90$) and Pacific silver fir ($r = 0.97$), but no correlation for other species. These species differences demonstrate one cause of widely varying opinion in the literature, and suggest some undescribed lignin-carbohydrate bond complex (Wilson, 1964).

The distribution and composition of Douglas-fir resinous extractives have been examined across a mature seasoned stem (Campbell et al., 1965). Preliminary study of sample size, seasoning, and solvent effects on statistical reliability provided definition of a single determination as average value from ten 0.5 gm replicates. Wood zone differences appeared

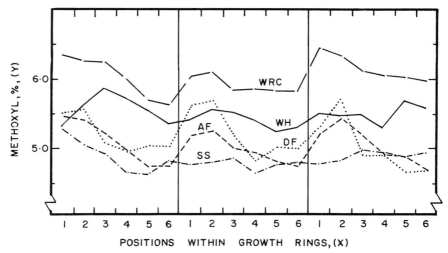

POSITIONS   WITHIN   GROWTH   RINGS, (X)

Patterns of methoxyl percentages across growth increments of
five coniferous species·

```
──────   WH  – Western hemlock  (56–58 yr )
── ──   WRC– Western red cedar (72–74 yr·)
── ──   AF  – Amabilis fir (78–80 yr·)
········   DF  – Douglas-fir (64–66 yr·)
─·─·─   SS  – Sitka spruce (69–71 yr )
```

(Position I , first formed earlywood; Position 6, last formed latewood)

FIG. 2.

with ethanol-benzene (1:2) extraction in that corewood contained 6%,
mature heartwood 5%, and sapwood 2% solubles. Earlywood diethyl
ether solubles were constant across the stem at the 2% level, while latewood ether solubles increased, but without abrupt demarcation by wood
zone, from 2% in sapwood to 4% in corewood. These results suggest some
undisclosed effect of biological activity. Growth zone differences were
evident with both solvents, in that latewood values were consistently
higher than those of earlywood. Comparison of canal and parenchyma
resin components was made by analysis of growth zone extracts. Excised
latewood containing most of the vertical resin canals yielded almost all
of the free resin acids. Conversely, earlywood ether solubles consisted
of mixed fatty acids and unsaponifiables. This gives experimental confirmation to earlier hypotheses (Back, 1960; Mutton, 1962) on differences
between coniferous canal and parenchyma resins.

Multiple-point examination of dihydroquercetin (3,3',4',5,7 pentahy-
droxyflavanone) distribution within several growth increments of

Douglas-fir by Squire (1963) showed a straight-line decrease accompanying progressive seasonal growth. Experiments have been started to locate position of polyphenolic extractives in woody tissues. To do this new methods have been developed, wherein wood extractives are eluted directly from minute wood specimens (0.02–0.04 cm^3) on to chromatographic paper. In one study positions within growth increments of Douglas-fir are being extracted with 50:50 methanol-acetone. Preceding extraction wood rays are excised by micro-dissection, or ray cell contents are otherwise excluded from extracts by chemical complexing *in situ*. Extracts are being examined by a new two-dimensional, three-solvent chromatographic technique.

CONCLUSIONS

1. Properties of earlywood and latewood tracheids differ markedly, as evidenced in pulp properties.

2. Methods available for determining within-increment holocellulose distribution require refinement. Micro-KAPPA and spectrophotometric procedures have been applied for lignin correction of holocelluloses.

3. Within three growth increments of Douglas-fir, peak chlorite holocellulose occurred at the point of latwood initiation, while the first- and last-formed parts of increments had lower values. Similar patterns were shown for glucan plus mannan. Galactan increased, whereas pentosans decreased across growth increments.

4. Average cellulose chain length in Douglas-fir latewood was found to be 6% higher than in earlywood.

5. Lignin contents within increments were highly significantly different in Sitka spruce, Douglas-fir, Pacific silver fir, and western redcedar but nonsignificant in western hemlock. Except for the latter, earlywood was regularly 2–3% higher in lignin than latewood. Significant differences were found between growth increments of Douglas-fir and western redcedar.

6. Wood methoxyl content was constant within and between growth increments of Sitka spruce and western hemlock. Douglas-fir, Pacific silver fir, and western redcedar repeated a within-increment pattern which was 0.5% higher methoxyl in earlywood than in latewood.

7. Intra-increment methoxyl contents were highly significantly correlated with lignin contents in Douglas-fir and Pacific silver fir, but not in the other species tested.

8. Resinous extractives in a Douglas-fir stem were lower in earlywood than latewood.

9. Dihydroquercetin content diminished progressively across growth increments of Douglas-fir.

10. Earlywood and latewood tissues have provided materials for basic study of cellulose tensile strength, protective effect of lignin during high energy irradiation, variable composition of canal and parenchyma resins, and location of polyphenolics in wood.

ACKNOWLEDGMENT

Acknowledgment is made to the Canada Department of Forestry, the National Research Council of Canada, and the Pulp and Paper Research Institute of Canada for financial assistance.

REFERENCES

Back, E. (1960) "On the relative composition of canal resin and ray parenchyma resin in *Picea abies* (Karst.) stemwood." *Svensk Papperstid.* 63:647–651.

Campbell, J. W., Swan, E. P., and Wilson, J. W. (1965) "Comparison of wood and growth zone resinous extracts in Douglas fir." *Pulp Paper Mag. Can.,* April 1965 issue.

Chidester, G. H., McGovern, J. N., and McNaughton, G. C. (1938) "Comparison of sulphite pulps from fast-growth loblolly, shortleaf, longleaf and slash pines." *Paper Trade J.* 107:36–39.

Erickson, H. D. (1962) "Some aspects of method in determining cellulose in wood." *Tappi* 45:710–719.

Hale, J. D., and Clermont, L. P. (1963) "Influence of prosenchyma cell-wall morphology on basic physical and chemical characteristics of wood." *J. Polymer Sci. Ser.* C2:253–261.

Hedin, T., Lalm, E., and Wennerblom, A. (1963) "Comparison of springwood and summerwood enriched dissolving pulps." *Tappi* 46:548–550.

Ifju, G., and Kennedy, R. W. (1962) "Some variables affecting micro-tensile strength of Douglas-fir." *Forest Prod. J.* 12:213–217.

————, Wellwood, R. W., and Wilson, J. W. (In press) "Relationship between certain intra-increment physical measurements in Douglas-fir." *Pulp Paper Mag. Can.*

————, and Wilson, J. W. (In preparation) "Wood tensile strength behavior as a function of cellulose degree of polymerization."

Jayme, G., and Krause, T. (1963) "Über die Packungsdichte der Zellwände in Laubhölzern." *Holz Roh- Werkstoff* 21:14–19. Pulp and Paper Res. Inst. Can. Trans. Ser. No. 50. CSIRO (Australia) Trans. No. 6544.

Johnson, D. B., Moore, W. E., and Zank, L. C. (1961) "The spectrophotometric determination of lignin in small wood samples." *Tappi* 44:793–798.

Lee, C. L. (1961) "Crystallinity of wood cellulose fibers studied by X-ray methods." *Forest Prod. J.* 11:108–112.

Leopold, B. (1961) "Chemical composition and physical properties of wood fibers. I. Preparation of holocellulose fibers from loblolly pinewood." *Tappi* 44:230–232.

Lindgren, P. H. (1958) "X-ray orientation investigations on some Swedish cellulose materials." *Arkiv. für Kemi.* 12:437–452.

Mutton, D. B. (1962) In *Wood Extractives and Their Significance to the Pulp and Paper Industries* (W. E. Hillis, ed.) p. 337. Academic Press, N. Y.

Ritter, G. J., and Fleck, L. C. (1926) "Chemistry of wood. IX. Springwood and summerwood." *Ind. Eng. Chem.* 18:608–609.

Saeman, J. F., Millett, W. A., and Lawton, E. J. (1952) "Effect of high-energy cathode rays on cellulose." *Ind. Eng. Chem.* 44:2848–2852.

Smith, D. M., and Mixer, R. Y. (1959) "The effects of lignin on the degradation of wood by gamma irradiation." *Radiation Res.* 11:776–780.

Squire, G. B. (1963) "Distribution of dihydroquercetin within growth zones of a Douglas fir tree." Unpub. report, Fac. For., Univ. B. C.

TAPPI (1955) "Cellulose in wood." T-17m-55.

TAPPI (1960) "Methoxyl groups in wood." T-2m-60.

Wardrop, A. B. (1951) "Cell wall organization and the properties of the xylem. I. Cell wall organization and the variation of breaking load in tension of the xylem in conifer stems." *Australian J. Sci. Res.,* Ser. B 4:391–414.

Watson, A. J. (1962) "A semimicro procedure for estimating the resistant carbohydrate material in wood." *Tappi* 45:722–724.

Wilson, J. W. (1964) "Wood characteristics. III. Intra-increment physical and chemical properties." Pulp and Paper Res. Inst. Can. Res. Note No. 45.

――――, and Ifju, G. (In preparation) "Response of Douglas-fir earlywood and latewood cellulose to degradation by gamma irradiation."

Worrall, J. G., Green, H. V., and Wilson, J. W. (In preparation) "Relationship between fractional void volume and wood quality in western Canadian conifers." (See Worrall, J. G., B.S.F. Thesis, Fac. For., Univ. B.C., 1963).

Wu, Y. T. (1963) "Intra-increment methoxyl content of five western Canadian coniferous woods." Unpub. report, Fac. For., Univ. of B. C.

――――― (1964) "Intra-increment lignin content of five western Canadian coniferous woods." M.F. Thesis, Fac. For., Univ. B.C.

Yiannos, P. N. (1964) "The apparent cell-wall density of wood and pulp fibers." *Tappi* 47:468–471.

Zobel, B. J., and McElwee, R. L. (1958) "Variation of cellulose in loblolly pine." *Tappi* 41:167–170.

Wall Structure of Loblolly Pine Summerwood Holocellulose Fibers in Relation to Individual Fiber Strength

D. C. McINTOSH

*The Mead Corporation, Central Research
Laboratories, Chillicothe, Ohio*

INTRODUCTION

Previous investigations in this laboratory have shown that the tensile strength of individual loblolly pine fibers can be varied by alkali extraction of fibrous holocellulose (Leopold and McIntosh, 1961) or by cooking wood to different yield levels by the kraft process (McIntosh, 1963). In extending the study on the effects of various mechanical and chemical treatments on individual fiber structure and properties, and eventually on sheet properties, it was necessary to obtain fresh wood in log form for preparation of a large volume of chips for experimental pulping.

The effects of pulp treatment can be better studied on fibers of inherently high strength since slight changes in fiber strength produced by treatment of fibers with low average tensile strength can be masked by fiber-to-fiber variations within the sample. It was therefore decided to prepare fibrous holocellulose from the summerwood portion of a test tree, since previous work has always shown summerwood fibers to be at least twice the strength of springwood fibers, both in breaking load and in tensile strength, based on cross-sectional area. The aim was to select a summerwood holocellulose sample with an average fiber breaking strength of 50 grams and a tensile strength of about 90 kg/mm^2—strengths which were previously obtained for loblolly pine summerwood peracetic acid holocellulose (Leopold and McIntosh, 1961).

A freshly cut green loblolly pine bolt, taken at breast height, was obtained from the vicinity of Macon, Georgia. Specifications for wood quality were that the bolt should be free of compression wood, summerwood proportion about 50% by volume, diameter of about twelve inches, and of relatively fast growth—the last specification for ease in separating springwood and summerwood during careful hand chipping.

Peracetic acid fibrous holocellulose pulp was prepared from the summerwood portions of the outer annual rings. However, results for the

561

first bolt showed that the strength of summerwood fibers was extremely low. A bolt from another loblolly pine tree was obtained, and determinations showed that the fiber breaking strength was higher than that of the first tree, but still below that of the original sample. Summerwood fibers from an additional tree were tested and found to be stronger than any fibers previously tested.

This article records fiber strengths for the trees investigated, along with strength data for fibers from loblolly pine compression wood and Virginia pine normal wood and compression wood. Strengths are reported on a cross-sectional area basis with cross-sectional areas determined by direct microscopic measurements on one hand, and a calculated value, derived from fiber length per gram measurements, on the other. Comparisons of both area measurements are made which yield data on the apparent density and porosity of fiber walls.

EXPERIMENTAL

Wood. The following green loblolly pine bolts were tested. These bolts were cut at breast height vicinity in each tree.

Log 1—9″ diameter; 11 rings; 2.5 rings/inch.
Outer rings chipped.

Log 2—11″ diameter; 25 rings.
Inner core—juvenile wood with fast growth of 3 rings/inch.
Outer 2½″ tested—about 6.5 rings/inch.

Log 3—10″ diameter; 24 rings.
Inner 11 rings—juvenile wood with fast growth rate. Outer 4 years with narrow rings. Rings 11 to 20 (approximately 1.75″ wide) chipped. 5.7 rings/inch.

Log 4—10″ diameter.
Relatively well developed compression wood in one sector.

In addition, tests were carried out on Virginia pine normal wood and compression wood. These samples were from a fully air-dried 1″ disc which had been stored in the laboratory for about two years. The "normal" wood sample came from selected areas from the same disc that provided the compression wood.

Pulp Preparation. The loblolly pine logs were cut into discs 1″ thick.

Chips were very carefully cut by means of a knife from the springwood and summerwood portions of the annual rings for separate cooking. The chips were matchstick size, measuring about ⅛″ × ⅛″ × 1″.

Preparation of fibrous peracetic acid holocellulose pulps was carried out according to the method used previously (Leopold, 1961).

All pulp samples were classified in a Clark Classifier and fibers retained in the No. 2 compartment were used for experimental work. This gave much more uniform samples of shive-free pulp, the shives remaining in the No. 1 compartment.

Individual Fiber Strength. Fiber strength was determined on a modified analytical balance as described previously (Leopold and McIntosh, 1961).

Perimeters and Cell Wall Thickness. The external and internal (next to the lumen) perimeters were measured with a map reader on tracings of fiber cross-sections at a magnification of 3500X. Cell wall thickness was determined by dividing the average of the external and internal perimeters into the cross-sectional area of the fibers. The validity of this method was previously substantiated by direct measurement of wall thickness on tracings of cross sections at twelve randomly located points per fiber cross section.

Fiber Length per Gram of Pulp and Denier. Small samples of wet pulps were diluted and divided into two equal portions and the dry weight of one portion was determined. The other portion was dyed with 4% Congo red and diluted to the desired consistency. Aliquots (5 cc) of the suspension were dried on $3\frac{1}{4}''$ × $4''$ lantern slides. Fibers were observed against a grid through a dissection microscope and measured with an eyepiece micrometer. Ten slides were prepared for each pulp representing 50 ml of the pulp suspension.

This method of examination gives data on number of fibers per gram, total length of fibers per gram, fiber length distribution, and average fiber length.

Fiber denier was computed from the fiber length per gram determination, and is the weight in grams of 9000 meters of fiber length.

Cross-Sectional Area. Cross-sectional area was measured on projected images of photomicrographs of cross sections of fibers which had been broken in tension. Fibers were embedded in sheet cellulose acetate, partially dissolved with acetone, prior to sectioning with a razor blade on a microtome. The area of the lumen was deducted from all cross-sectional area measurements.

Calculated cross-sectional area was determined in the following way:

Specific gravity of cellulose = 1.5

1 gram of cellulose occupies $\dfrac{1}{1.5}$ = 0.660 cc = 660 mm^3

Fiber cross-sectional area (solid) =

$$\frac{660}{(\text{fiber length/gm in km})} \times \frac{10^9}{10^9} \text{ square microns}$$

Apparent Density of Fiber Walls. This was determined from the difference between the measured and calculated cross-sectional areas of the fiber walls on the assumption that the cell wall material had a specific gravity of 1.5 and that the difference between the two areas was due to void volume.

RESULTS AND DISCUSSION

Data on pulp yield and denier of fibers are given in Table I. Cross-sectional dimensional characteristics of the fibers are given in Table II, and results on strength measurements are presented in Table III.

TABLE I. Yield and Denier of Pine Summerwood Pulp Fibers

Bolt no.	Yield of pulp based on wood (%)	No. of fibers per gram (millions)	Total fiber length per gram (km)	Denier
1 (fast growth)	62.8	1.00	2.45	3.68
2 (slow growth)	54.9	0.84	3.22	2.80
3 (intermediate growth)	59.9	0.55	2.03	4.47
Previous test (peracetic acid holocellulose)	71.7	0.89	1.55	5.82
Previous test (chlorite holocellulose)	60.0	–	2.34	3.85

It must be pointed out that although pulp yield figures are included in Table I, they apply to the whole pulp and not necessarily to the fibers tested. All pulps, before fiber classification, contained some shives which were higher in yield than the single fibers examined. This difference in extent of cooking on shives and on fibers was determined by color reactions to "cooking" stains.

Results show that for loblolly pine summerwood pulps from logs 1, 2, and 3, large differences in average breaking load per fiber exist—log 1 being of the order of 20 grams, log 2 about 40 grams, and log 3 about 70 grams. Cross-sectional areas of fibers from logs 1 and 2 were small and similar, but fibers from log 3 had a substantially larger area which was more in line with that of fibers used for previous tests. Strength of fibers per unit area from log 1 was abnormally low, that of fibers from log 2 intermediate, while log 3 produced fibers with the highest tensile strength.

TABLE II. Cross-Sectional Dimensions of Pine Summerwood Pulp Fibers

| Bolt no. | Perimeter measured on fiber cross-sections | | Cell wall thickness (microns) | Cross-sectional area | | Apparent density of fiber wall (gms/cc) |
	Outer (microns)	Inner (microns)		Measured (square microns)	Calculated (square microns)	
1	85	41	6.7	410	270	0.98
2	103	58	5.5	437	200	0.70
3	106	38	8.7	609	326	0.80
Previous test (peracetic acid)	100	44	7.8	568	425	1.12
Previous test (chlorite)	–	–	–	504	282	0.84

TABLE III. Fiber Tensile Strength Properties

				Tensile strength	
Bolt no.	No. of fibers tested	Fiber breaking strength (gms)	strength (gms/denier)	Based on measured cross section (kg/mm^2)	Based on calculated cross section (kg/mm^2)
Loblolly pine summerwood					
1 (fast growth)	40	18	4.9	45	66
2 (slow growth)	38	39	13.8	92	189
3 (intermediate growth)	37	66	14.8	109	203
Previous test (peracetic acid)	42	50	8.6	88	118
Previous test (chlorite)	23	51	13.2	101	181
Compression wood (kraft cook)	17	13	–	38	–
"Normal" wood (kraft cook)	20	32	–	77	–
Virginia pine					
Compression wood (holocellulose)	18	19	–	42	–
"Normal" wood (summerwood holocellulose)	16	54	–	116	–

The difference in thickness of the walls of fibers is normally due to variations in thickness of the S_2 layer, S_1 and S_3 remaining thin and relatively constant in thickness. It is evident therefore that properties which are influenced by the orientation of the cellulose molecules will be influenced by the proportion of the cell wall occupied by the S_2 layer, depending, in turn, on the fiber wall thickness. Since tensile strength of cellulose is greatest in the direction of molecular alignment, it would be expected that longitudinal tensile strength of thick-walled fibers would be greater per cross-sectional area than that of thin-walled fibers.

However, an anomaly exists in the present data. Fibers from log 1 (fast growth) which were intermediate in cell wall thickness were extremely weak in breaking strength and in tensile strength on an area basis. Microscopic examination showed that although their walls were relatively thick, they resembled springwood fibers in that they were pitted with well developed bordered pits—a morphological feature which is rare in summerwood fibers. It is thought that the presence of large bordered pits in this sample is associated with the fast growth rate and the fact that the wood was "juvenile"—i.e., wood laid down in the early years (eight to eleven years in this case) of the tree's life. From past studies it has been noted that the fibril orientation of the fiber wall tends to curve around such pits. Tensile strength of cellulose is lowest in a direction perpendicular to the molecular orientation. If the fibril orientation deviates within the cell wall so that it is perpendicular to the fiber axis, as is the case in the vicinity of the bordered pit, a zone of weakness will occur at this point when tensile stress is applied to the fiber, resulting in low tensile strength. Examination of broken springwood fibers has shown that the rupture line does not occur through the bordered pit but rather follows the fibrillar orientation around such pits.

In addition to the presence of bordered pits, it was noted that the fibers of log 1 showed considerable twist about their axes when drying, indicating a large fibrillar angle of the S_2 layer. The large angle would further decrease the tensile strength of the fibers. This is evident from results of tests on compression wood fibers of Virginia pine which were very low in tensile strength compared to normal summerwood fibers from the same air-dry disc. Loblolly pine compression wood fibers cooked by the kraft process were very weak in tension—considerably weaker than normal loblolly pine from a low yield kraft cook. Compression wood is well known for its low tensile strength in wood form. Probably the most obvious reason for low strength is the typical 45° fibrillar orientation in the fiber wall, and the splits normally found in the fiber wall following this orientation.

It will be noted that fibers of log 2 (slow growth) with a wall thickness of only about 5.5 μ are nearly as strong on a measured cross-sectional area basis as those of log 3 (intermediate growth) with a thickness of the order of 8 to 9 μ. No explanation is readily apparent for this deviation from the wall thickness—fiber strength relationship thought to exist. It is probable, however, that when the S_2 layer reaches a certain thickness, the effect of the relatively small proportion of the total area occupied by S_1 and S_3 is minor and cannot be detected.

It is felt that the low strength of springwood fibers compared to summerwood fibers, on a cross-sectional area basis, is due to presence of large bordered pits, the smaller proportion of S_2 layer, and the larger fibrillar angle of the S_2 layer.

THE POROUS NATURE OF THE FIBER WALL IN WOOD

There is increasing evidence that the fiber walls in wood contain substantial void volume, as recently reviewed (Stone, 1964). Results of studies (Jayme and Krause, 1963) place the density of cell walls of five species of hardwoods between 0.71 and 1.27, while investigations on western conifers (Worrall, 1963) show a cell wall density for summerwood of 0.80 and springwood 0.45.

Measurements carried out in this laboratory on the three bolts of loblolly pine have given the results shown in Table IV.

TABLE IV. Density of Fiber Walls in Wood

	Measured basic density of wood	Lumen area (% of total)	Calculated density of cell wall
	Summerwood		
Log 1 (fast growth)	0.634	23	0.83
Log 2 (slow growth)	0.660	40	1.10
Log 3 (intermediate growth)	0.756	22	0.97
	Springwood		
Log 3	0.270	73	0.97

These results indicate that variability exists from tree to tree in the density of the fiber walls. They also indicate that in loblolly pine, the walls of springwood fibers in wood are no more porous than those of summerwood.

CONSIDERATION OF AREA DETERMINATION
FOR COMPUTING TENSILE STRENGTH

From previous studies on holocellulose fibers extracted with alkali of increasing concentration, and kraft pulps cooked to different yields, it was found that cross-sectional area showed less decrease than that expected from decrease in yield. The walls of pulp fibers therefore are of a porous nature and the void volume within the wall can vary from one pulp to another. It is thus felt that tensile strength calculated on a measurement of cross-sectional area as observed with a light microscope can be misleading in comparing different pulps. Therefore, tensile strength in kg/mm^2 has been computed in Table I, using the fiber breaking strength and the calculated cross-sectional area (solid wall material). On this basis, fibers of log 2 are roughly equal in strength to those of log 3.

This computed figure for tensile strength of pine summerwood holocellulose fibers (200 kg/mm^2) is extremely high considering the ultimate tensile strength of a good grade of regular steel (70,000 psi or 50 kg/mm^2). The tenacity of some well known synthetic fibers (Carroll-Porczynski, 1961) is compared to the strength of loblolly pine summerwood fibers in Table V.

TABLE V. Conditioned Tenacity of Fibers

Type of fiber	Gms/denier
Viscose rayon (high tenacity)	3.2– 5.0
Nylon 6,6 (high tenacity)	6.0– 9.5
Dacron (high tenacity)	6.3– 7.8
Glass	7.5 –
Pine summerwood holocellulose (logs 2 and 3)	13.8–14.8

It is surprising to find that the tenacity of wood pulp fibers can be well above that of man-made so-called high tenacity polymer fibers.

In Table III once more, it is shown that the previous sample of pine holocellulose fibers, made and tested three years ago, had an "inherent" strength of only 118 kg/mm^2 compared to 200 kg/mm^2 for fibers from log 3. This is due to the larger calculated cross-sectional area. The measured yield was high compared to the present samples, and this is indicated by the comparatively small difference between the measured area and calculated area. This could be taken as an indication that the cell wall components which are removed by cooking to a lower yield by the holocellulose method are not contributing to the strength/unit weight of the fibers. This is supported by comparison of strength on a calculated cross-sectional area basis of summerwood chlorite holocellulose at 60% yield (181 kg/mm^2) and the previous summerwood peracetic acid holocellulose at 72% yield (118 kg/mm^2). In previous work in which fiber strength was determined on kraft pulps cooked to different yields (McIntosh, 1963), it was found that strength computed on a yield basis was relatively constant. Stone and Clayton (1960), investigating the zero-span tensile strength of microtome sections of spruce springwood, cooked by the kraft process to different yields, found that the fibers were weakened with reduction in yield, although their tensile strength per unit weight increased.

Van den Akker et al. (1958) measured external maximum and minimum diameters of fibers for an estimation of cross-sectional area. Jayne (1959) estimated the cross-sectional area of the fiber wall by viewing the fiber "end-on" at the break. Work at this laboratory in the past has been based on the area measured on cross sections. None of these methods take into account the submicroscopic void volume of the fiber wall. Kellogg and Wangaard (1964) embedded fibers in methyl methacrylate, but recognized the existence of a swelling effect of the embedding material on the fibers. The effect of embedding fibers in cellulose acetate with acetone as the solvent as used in this laboratory on the cross-sectional dimensions of the fibers is at present not known.

SUMMARY AND CONCLUSIONS

From the data presented it is evident that the density of cell walls in wood is close to unity but that variations in cell wall density can occur from tree to tree. After cooking the wood to liberate fibers to form pulp, the porous nature of the fiber wall is again evident and varies within relatively wide limits from sample to sample. Careful preparation of holocellulose at high yield would not be expected to increase wall porosity, since the holocellulose method is designed to remove lignin which is concentrated in the middle lamella and to retain the hemicelluloses. Preparation of holocellulose of lower yield will remove more components which are present within the fiber wall, creating a more porous structure. This is indicated in the data reported. On further treatment of holocellulose with alkali, or in alkaline cooking methods of pulping, hemicelluloses are removed from the framework of the fiber wall, which results in a more porous but still strong structure.

Experimental data, with one exception, show that holocellulose fibers cooked to a high yield are weaker in grams/denier than holocellulose pulps cooked to lower yields, and that extraction of additional wall components by the holocellulose method produces a more porous fiber structure but does not substantially influence fiber strength based on a measured cross-sectional area. The exception occurred with fibers from a young fast-growth tree which were extremely weak in tension, and it was concluded from microscopic examination that the presence of large bordered pits with the associated deflection in fibrillar orientation, and large fibrillar angle were the probable causes of the low strength.

The amount of porosity of the fiber wall is of importance not only to the determination of fiber strength but also the stiffness of the fiber. This is an important property affecting both the formation of the paper sheet and the properties of the sheet itself. Fiber stiffness is known to depend on the weight of fiber per unit length, and, at a given weight per unit length, the stiffness will be influenced by the distribution of the cellulose in the walls of the fiber. Micro-pores within the fiber wall will reduce the apparent density of the wall and, therefore, increase the cross section at constant weight per unit length. Increased porosity therefore could lead to greater fiber stiffness.

It is readily apparent that, in comparing properties of single fibers from different pulps, some measurement of void volume of the fiber walls should be made so that mechanical properties can be compared on the basis of amount of solid cell wall material and void volume. Work is being carried out on the electron microscopy of ultrathin sections to note differences in compactness of fiber walls.

ACKNOWLEDGMENTS

The author is indebted to R. L. Tippie and L. O. Uhrig of Mead Central Research Laboratories for the experimental work and to The Mead Corporation for permission to publish this paper.

REFERENCES

Carroll-Porczynski, C. A. (1961) *Manual of Man-Made Fibers*. Chemical Publishing Company, N. Y.

Jayme, G., and Krause, T. (1963) "The packing density of cell walls in deciduous woods." *Holz Roh- Werkstoff* 21:14–19.

Jayne, B. A. (1959) "Mechanical properties of wood fibers." *Tappi* 22:461–467.

Kellogg, R. M., and Wangaard, F. F. (1964) "Influence of fiber strength on sheet properties of hardwood pulps." *Tappi* 47:361–367.

Leopold, B. (1961) "Chemical composition and physical properties of wood fibers. I. Preparation of holocellulose fibers from loblolly pinewood." *Tappi* 44:230–232.

————, and McIntosh, D. C. (1961) "Chemical composition and physical properties of individual fibers from alkali extracted loblolly pine holocellulose." *Tappi* 44:235–240.

McIntosh, D. C. (1963) "Tensile and bonding strengths of loblolly pine kraft fibers cooked to different yields." *Tappi* 46:273–277.

Stone, J. E. (1964) "The porous structure of wood and fibers." *Pulp Paper Mag. Can.* 65:T3–T12.

————, and Clayton, D. W. (1960) "The use of microtome sections for measuring the change in strength of spruce fibers due to pulping." *Pulp Paper Mag. Can.* 61:T475–T484.

Van den Akker, J. A., Lathrop, A. E., Voelker, M. H., and Dearth, L. R. (1958) "Importance of fiber strength to sheet strength." *Tappi* 41:416–425.

Worrall, J. G. (1963). "The relationship between fractional void volume and wood quality in western Canadian conifers." BSF Thesis, University of British Columbia.

Aspen Holocellulose and Morphology of Interfiber Bonding—An Electron Microscope Study

S. K. ASUNMAA and D. W. SCHWAB

Owens-Illinois Technical Center, Toledo, Ohio

INTRODUCTION

Ultrastructure and Paper Properties. The strength of plant fibers is attributable to the molecular, supermolecular, and botanical structure of the cell wall. One of the most advanced methods of utilizing the inherent properties of wood polymers, mainly those of native cellulose, is paper-making.

During pulping, the ratios of the chemically distinct wood polymers—cellulose, nonglucanic polysaccharides, and lignin—are modified. The structural components of the fiber wall are somewhat rearranged by mechanical action in refining. The surface properties of the ultrastructural units, on the other hand, are altered only slightly during the various treatments; some irreversible intrafiber bonding may be observed as a hardening, called drying-rewetting hysteresis. The hydrophilic carbohydrate hydroxyl groups remain the significant functional groups, capable of bridging adjacent chains through hydrogen bonds. It is well established that the interfiber bonding is a significant contributor to paper strength, as are component strength and bonding efficiency, both related to pulp characteristics. Conceivably, the integral mechanical properties of the pulp body, paper, can point out interesting materials suitable for study of the significant ultrastructures of the raw material.

The holocellulose pulp produced by Thompson and Kaustinen (1964) and the paper of unusually high physical properties made from it suggest exciting and complicated problems. It is the purpose of this discussion to present an explanation of the optimized macroproperties based upon the fine structural features of some holocellulose pulps. The discussion will be limited to aspen holocellulose because the role of hemicelluloses as ultrastructural units and binding materials is intriguing.

Holopulp as a Material for Ultrastructural Studies. Thompson and Kaustinen prepared the "holopulp" under carefully controlled conditions,

573

under which the diffusion-controlled delignification was greatly enhanced by the initial removal of hydrophobic incrustants. Treatment of relatively large blocks of wood (one-inch cubes) at room temperature with $NaClO_2$ oxidant minimized mechanical and chemical damage to the native structural components. The pulps were never allowed to dry before formation of fiber-to-fiber bonds.

The minimal damage to the fibers is not sufficient to account for the superior strength properties exhibited by the holopulp papers. Surface properties, such as an increased number of hydroxyl groups and atomic distances per unit area between adjacent bonding surfaces, are believed to be important. A logically designed study of ultrastructural components should provide more information on the prerequisites of bonding: interface phenomena, wetting, promoted adhesion, and sticking. A holopulp preparation developed on the basis of optimized macroproperties and a subsequent mild defibration of the product provides a more sophisticated starting material for fine structural and surface studies than samples produced by a maceration which employs drastic oxidations. The isolation of submicroscopic components for appropriate electron micrograph specimens was obtained by mild ultrasonics treatment in aqueous suspensions of known pH. Satisfactory detachment of more cohesional units was achieved without drastic degradation of the delicate growth laminae and membranes.

Experimental Material and Discussion

Surface Properties and Fine Structure. Fragments were collected after mild ultrasonics agitation at the instant of detachment before solvation of the more hydrophilic components had proceeded sufficiently to result in molecular dispersion. These optimum conditions were satisfied in a solution of pH 6.0 after delignification at about pH 4. A hypersonics generator, Model BU-204 from The Brush Development Company, Cleveland, Ohio (with output of 250 watts and operating in the range of 100 to 1000 kc), was employed with a cathode current of 130 ma at several five-minute intervals.

Microfibrils, about 100 Å wide, are shown locally detached from the fibril bundles in Figure 1. (The scale line in the electron micrographs indicates one micron.) The detached but adhering microfibrils carry a surface charge and remain as individual units during the drying procedure, in spite of produced strains and stresses. The fibrils collected from the buffered solutions display a well defined contact angle between the carbohydrate fibril and the substrate, a nitrocellulose film, which also contains some residual hydroxyls.

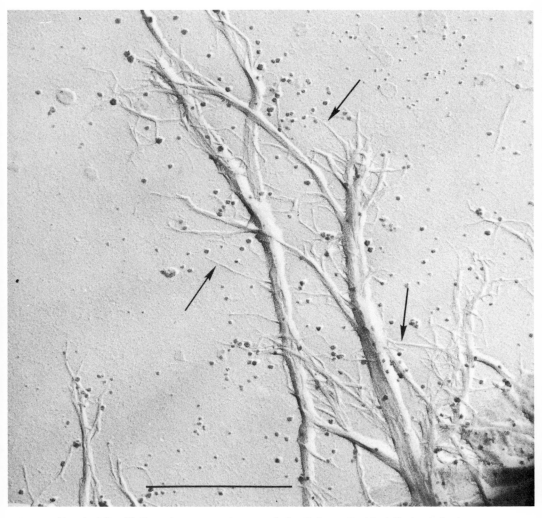

FIG. 1. Microfibrils and aggregates in aspen holocellulose. Residual lignin derivatives show high electron density. Klason lignin less than 1%. X 39,000.

The contact angle may be estimated from the photographic contrasts and definition of the dividing line. This shows as a sharp discontinuity between the substrate and the particular fibril surface that received the maximum amount of the Pt + C shadowing deposit in regions showing an angle of incidence of approximately 90°. The increasing contact angle indicates low adhesion to the substrate and high cohesion in the deposited material. Reproducible conditions of image formation and constant electron optical resolution are prerequisites for correct evaluations. Residual amounts of decomposition and oxidation products of lignin are seen as electron opaque particles 200 to 1000 Å in diameter. The high electron contrast indicates that inorganic components are incorporated in the lignin derivatives.

It is interesting to compare this electron micrograph with Figure 2, showing a similar pulp sample dried from a suspension in distilled water.

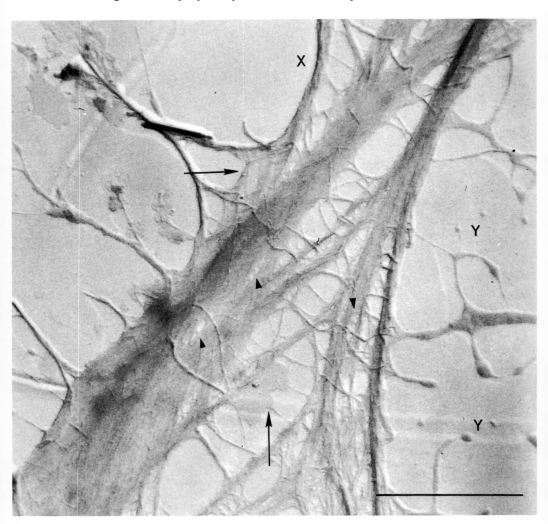

Fig. 2. Good substrate adhesion is promoted by swollen low DP components adhered onto fibrils. Triangles point out indicated network structure. X 39,000.

Similar short microfibrils are seen as bridging units between isolated growth laminae but the contact angle is remarkably low, indicating good wetting of the substrate surface by the components with low degree of polymerization (DP), which apparently adhere to the fibril surfaces but remain mobile and capable of modifying the fibril surface to conform to any adjacent substrate with low surface free energy. In some areas, noted by X, less perfect adhesion to the supporting membrane is indicated. Local uniform surface coating without revealed fine structure is shown in several regions. It is conjectured that the easily water-suspended pulp fractions, β- and γ-cellulose, low DP components, remain attached to the microfibrils but retain mutual adhesion and migrate along the substrate surface as a planar aggregation that finds a sufficient number of bonding sites to promote a uniform spreading. Transition from a fibril structure to a flexible, conforming, and less ordered fraction, can be studied in the area pointed out by a vertical arrow. The gel type film shows a constant physical thickness as far as can be evaluated from the transmitted intensity. The contact angle indicates good adhesion but the rigidity of the broadening microfibril (from 100 to 4000 Å) refers to some basic structure not revealed at this resolution. Contamination of the substrate surface apparently causes reduced adhesion of the less ordered and mobile fraction to the substrate in area Y. Formation of liquid-type droplets with increasing contact angles is indicated here. High viscosity and some cohesion in the adsorbate overrule the substrate adhesion.

A distinct 200–400 Å porosity is revealed in large areas over the entire fibril laminate in Figure 2. Some of the pores are marked by black triangles. It is believed that this kind of ultrastructure is related to inherent nonlinear molecular aggregates. They have not been previously shown in electron micrographs of plant cell walls. It is conceivable that the aspen holopulp contains a variety of morphologically individual hemicelluloses. The porosity, high light scattering data, discussed by Giertz (1950), and local high accessibility, shown by Asunmaa (1955, 1956), of aspen pulps have been demonstrated by various methods and imply some nonlinear aggregation of chain molecules.

Fine Structural Network. A closer study of several specimen areas showing a planar spreading of the deposited material reveals interesting detail in Figure 3. The interconnecting, thinner laminae appear between ridge-like surface elevations consisting of typical fibril bundles. A network structure is observed consisting of segments of rather constant length, less than 1000 Å, but widths varying from 100 to 400 Å. An enrichment of adhered low DP carbohydrate polymers or branched chain molecules is conjectured as a basis for the patterns. The dimensions, specifically the segment width, may indicate some drying effect in accord with substrate adhesion. Because of the high content of nonglucanic

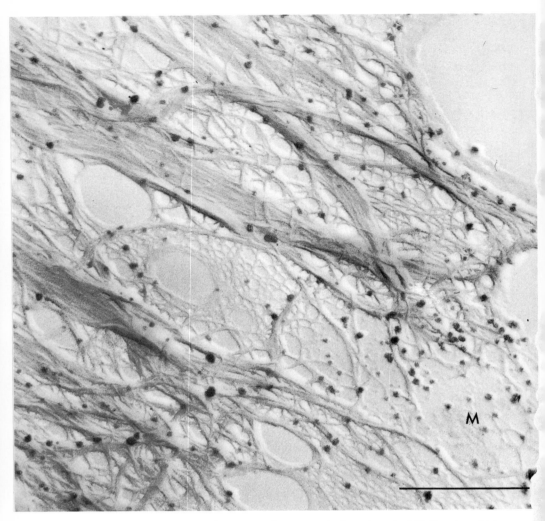

FIG. 3. Regions of well defined network structure indicate branched fibrils. Area M has been damaged in preparation. X 34,000.

carbohydrates in aspen holocellulose, it is believed that branched chains are involved, perhaps in the form of heteroglucanes which are known from the work of Adams (1964), Bowering *et al.* (1961), Bowering and Timell (1960), and Tyminski and Timell (1960). The network structure apparently is rather fragile and easily disintegrated, as shown in area M, where the ultrasonics field has produced stress concentration. The severe

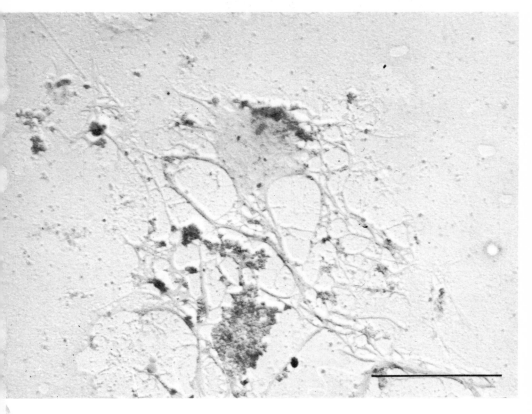

FIG. 4. Network fragments covered with low DP components adhere to residual oxidation products. X 34,000.

mechanical attack is further illustrated in Figure 4, showing a residual fragment from a somewhat similar area. The fine detail can be obscured, and an impression of a uniform deposit of amorphous material obtained, if only low magnification and inferior resolution are available of specimens where less perfect shadowing has been performed and the samples dried on substrates giving a decreasing contact angle. The network character of the branched carbohydrate skeleton with high cohesion and low accessibility is also emphasized in a similar holopulp sample given a negative staining as in Figure 5. Great variations in fibril thickness, specifically at branch points, are apparent. Sodium tungstate solution is used to give the uniform, electron dense background, when the sprayed dispersion is collecting in the drying droplets. From the viewpoint of interfiber bonding, it can be concluded that well preserved low DP frac-

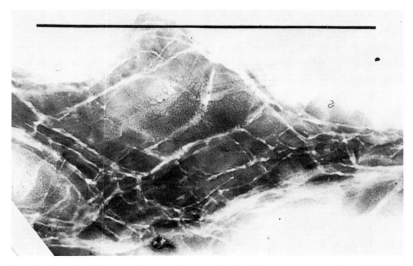

Fig. 5. Branched fibrils and network are emphasized by negative staining. X 90,000.

tions enhance both the interfiber adhesion on the molecular level and good geometric contact between pulp fibers because of bridging flexible fragments of the interconnecting network.

An assumed backbone structure of branched heteroglucanes can explain the observed submicroscopic network. Diffuse X-ray patterns indicate a lack of crystallinity or uniformity. Solubility experiments with dimethylsulfoxide are not considered significant because even short exposures to the electron beam may cause changes in solubility in spite of low beam intensities and negligible heating effects. Partly ordered hemicellulose components, individually existing or adhered on fibril surfaces, on the other hand, will explain the large fraction, 50%, of inaccessible hemicellulose hydroxyls in various holocelluloses calculated from infrared measurements by Rånby (1962).

Ultrastructures. The structure of the individual microfibrils and their mode of aggregation suggest ultrastructural factors influencing the inherent strength of an individual fiber rather than the bonding efficiency. A helical aggregation of two or more microfibrils is shown in Figure 6 in areas A, B, and C. The spiral pitch of 700 Å is measured as a repeating interval in electron contrast in Figure 7. Additional fine structural details are obvious in the form of branching sites pointed out by arrows in Figure 6, dislocations marked by short bars, and an apparent splitting of the 100 Å microfibril in Figure 7 to two components in area S. The observed regular intervals of rotation do not occur as a most common feature in

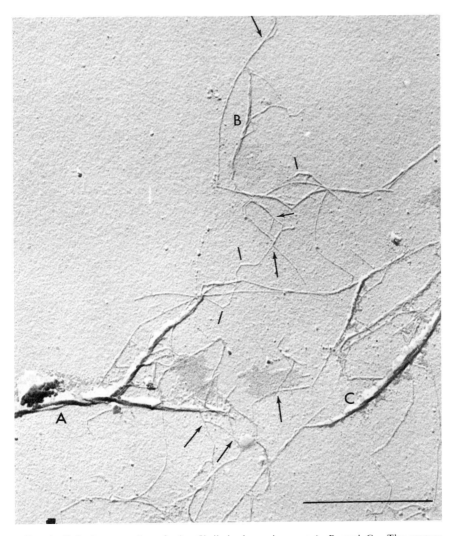

FIG. 6. Helical aggregation of microfibrils is shown in areas A, B, and C.   The arrows mark obvious branching sites of microfibrils, the bars point out dislocations.   X 34,000.

each fibril accretion but the arrangement has been observed as a frequent growth form and recorded in high resolution electron micrographs.   A helical aggregation of microfibrils has been proposed in fibrils of non-glucanic algae by Preston (1962).

The observed, dislocation type changes in growth angles probably

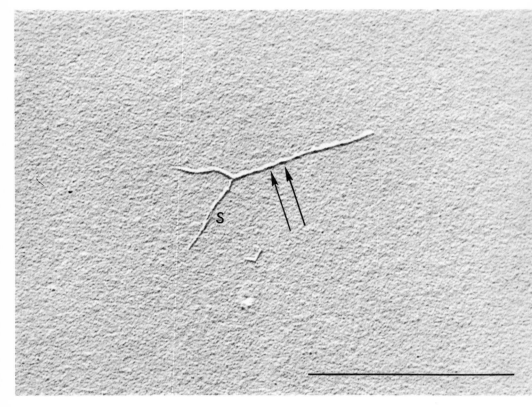

Fig. 7. A helical aggregation of two microfibrils shows a pitch of 700 Å revealed as variations in electron contrast. Elementary fibrils are shown in region S. X 54,000.

originate at certain operative defect sites. A multiplication of dislocations can be initiated by high energy radiation in solids but is not known
at the employed frequencies. The "dislocations" observed by Iwasaki
et al. (1962) refer to structural displacements in the cell wall rather
than to actual crystallographic dislocations.

The existence of branched microfibrils is established by a critical study
of numerous specimens. It is proposed that some primary reason for the
structural anomalies lies in the dimensional range of microfibrils. It is
very unlikely that the β-glucopyranose-cellulose chain would be able to
produce abrupt changes in bond angles. A resolvable molecular discontinuity as a reason for branching, on the other hand, would also produce mechanical discontinuity, strength decrease, and possibly reduced
fibril thickness. These properties have so far not been recorded. There-

fore, it is believed that heteroglycans are involved. The short length, one or two sugar units, of the chemically detected branch chains does not necessarily suggest similar limitation of the supermolecular branches. A branch as a defect site may catalyze physical aggregation or deposition of additional chain molecules through oriented overgrowth, epitaxy. Orientation of accessible and reactive fibril surfaces has been indicated by Preston in a series of wood impregnation studies. Similar orientation of reaction products on pulp surfaces has been verified occasionally in our studies using electron diffraction; however, so far only in certain fibers.

Bond Area. After studying the ultrastructural aspects of the two most significant factors in interfiber bonding, the morphology of the bond area provides a difficult but fascinating subject. A variety of bonding types has been demonstrated in previous work by Emerton *et al.* (1957), Jayme and Hunger (1962), Asunmaa (1957), and Asunmaa and Steenberg (1958). Fractional bonding in a bond area has been illustrated in ultrathin sec-

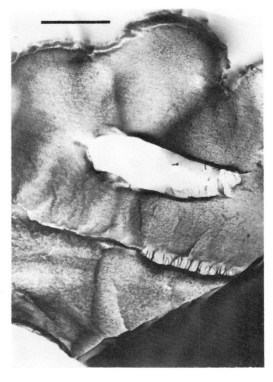

FIG. 8. Cross section of two bonded fibers in paper of semichemical hardwood pulp. X 18,000.

tions and in replicas of fracture faces. Quantitative evaluation of a satisfactory contact and, in all probability, of an actual bonding has been
approached by Page *et al.* (1962 a, b), Nordman *et al.* (1954), and Nordman (1961), using optical methods. A new type of fractional bonding is
illustrated in Figure 8. The sample is not from aspen holocellulose, but
from a hardwood semichemical pulp used for formation of handsheets
under wet pressure and subsequent drying at 110°C. The low magnification print is included in order to point out the lumen areas and emphasize
the well delignified, yet unattacked, shape of the individual fibers, shown
here as cross sections with an interconnecting bond area. No residual
middle lamella is shown; that is, we are dealing with an essential fiber-to-
fiber bonding between carbohydrate components. The left area of the
field in higher magnification in Figure 9 shows an intimate contact with
obscured detail; the field at the right gives an impression of stretched
microfibrils as connecting bridges between the two component fibers. The

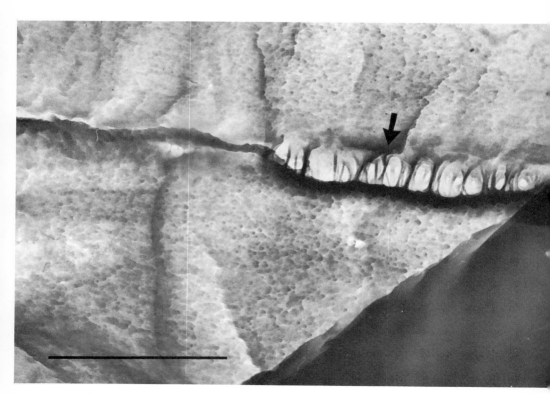

FIG. 9. Detail magnification of the bond area in Figure 8 shows bridging microfibrils,
indicating an interfiber bonding between carbohydrate components. X 47,000.

reproduction of three layers of connecting microfibrils indicates a specimen thickness of about 200 to 300 Å. An interesting fine structure of the fiber wall and cross sections of individual and aggregated microfibrils is depicted in the large areas of the fiber sections. Some variations in orientation and surface elevation are probably caused by the more or less perfect adherence between the drying sections and the substrate. The undamaged fiber walls have prevented penetration of the methacrylate embedding medium into interfiber voids and have so facilitated the definition of detail in the bonding area. A dilute solution of potassium dichromate was used as a contrast material; possibly oxidation and disintegration of easily accessible fractions on fibril surfaces has been initiated in spite of the short available reaction time and the low temperature, 25°C. The structure model, the distinct microfibrils observed as cross sections, supports the early concepts of amorphous and crystalline fractions in the pulp cellulose and in fiber walls. Apparently the oxidized polar groups enhance the intrafibril bonding and promote the adhesion of oxidized interconnecting material to fibril surfaces.

It is not implied that the fibril-bridge bonding in Figures 8 and 9 should represent the only type of actual bonding in a fractional bond area. For instance, the bond region in Figure 11 shows considerably larger voids between areas of firm fiber-to-fiber contact and obvious bonding in a paper prepared without applied wet pressure. Figure 9 rather gives a view of a contact region where spacings between the bridging microfibrils facilitate an electron microscope study of ultrastructure. The dimensions of the bridging fibrils, widths from 70 to 130 Å, offer satisfactory evidence of the fact that the recorded fibrils are actual cellulose microfibrils. The wider units are shown to split up into two- or three-component fibrils of the same characteristic size, as is clearly shown in Figure 10 in areas marked by arrows. Conceivably, the aggregation of component microfibrils to compound fibrils, 200 to 300 Å wide, illustrates the often emphasized intrafiber bonding yielding hardening hysteresis, and its effect on ultrastructure. A firm adherence between component microfibrils results in some rearrangement, deformation, and collapsing of the compound fibril. Rounded-up corners are observed in some areas, as are always obtained in macroscale when single strands from a given area are collected to form a "braid." The decreasing photographic densities, particularly in the upper part of the contact region, indicate that the fibrils are an actual part of the section and the adjacent fibers. They run at a certain angle to the specimen plane and form a part of the relatively thin specimen in areas marked by small arrows. The dimensions, 70 to 130 Å, suggest that we are dealing with an actual carbohydrate bonding where cellulose microfibrils form the supermolecular structure. The probability is very low that a perfect coincidence in fibril size could be obtained in residual

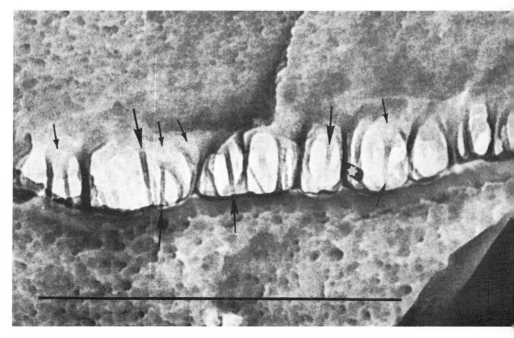

Fig. 10. Detail magnification of fractional bonding in Figure 9 shows single microfibrils, 70 to 130 Å wide, and aggregated compound fibrils with two or more resolved components. The black polygon shows a defect in the photographic emulsion. X 96,000.

fragments of embedding material that does not contain any basic fibril structure. This comment is made with reference to the preparation artifacts occasionally presented by other research groups in low power electron micrographs as a result of poor sectioning. It is also emphasized that the specimen contamination was negligible; several photographic records of the same and consecutive sections repeated the same respectively similar structures.

One significant reason for formation of fractional bonding may be some residual lignin in the outer layer of the hardwood fiber from the semi-chemical pulp. It is well established that lignin in hardwood is concentrated in the middle lamella. The morphology of the studied fiber couple indicates that the middle lamella has been removed, as far as can be determined from the characteristic morphology. The lignin content consequently is very low in the two bonding fibers. Nevertheless, the residual lignin may account for the formation of the observed fractional bonding instead of an extended contact region.

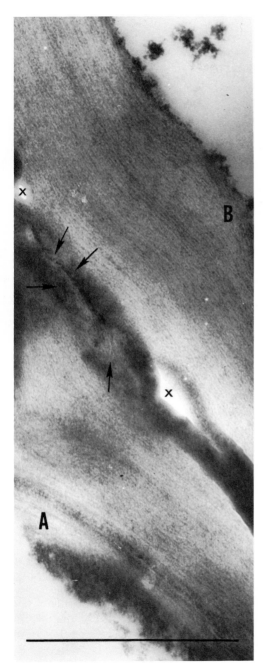

FIG. 11. Bond area between fiber fragments (A and B) with less pronounced refining action. Bridging elements show low photographic density; presumably 90% bonding in area → , 50% in area ↑ , no bonding in voids x, illustrate the bonding efficiency.   X 55,000.

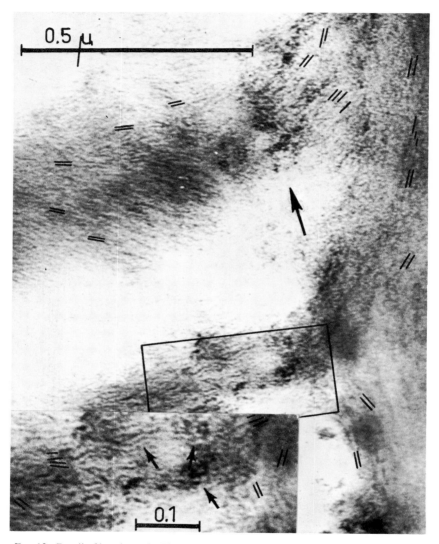

FIG. 12. Detail of bond area in Figure 13. Several spacings between adjacent microfibrils show deposited electron opaque osmium and therefore less perfect bonding, that is, lacking atomic distances. The areas inaccessible to the electron stain indicate firm bonding. A few well resolved microfibrils are emphasized by black line extensions to the osmium filled spacings. The arrows point to regions of meeting microfibrils. X 124,000. The inset analyzes meeting microfibrils as known from serial sections. X 170,000. (from Asunmaa, 1957)

For further detailed interpretations, it is necessary to take into account the laws of image formation in an electron microscope. Both elastic and inelastic scattering are involved, the latter producing a diffuse background especially in thicker specimens and specimen areas. A microscope with good resolving power (at least 10 Å) was used for the present investigation. This made possible a distinct imaging of specimen detail. The dimensional data presented are, therefore, more accurate than the data published in the early electron microscope studies when a routine resolution approximated 50 to 80 Å, the discontinuity lines were not well defined, and the half-width readings of the photometer tracing could differ considerably from the measurements made without proper consideration of the definition of detail. The main cell wall in Figure 9 also reveals fibrils of 200 to 300 Å diameter, the dimensions known from some early references. In the present sample, the anticipating chemical treatment has caused aggregation of single microfibrils to compound fibrils.

The paper-technologically significant data for the semichemical hardwood pulp (Figs. 8, 9, and 10) are as follows: yield, 63.7%; refining, 110 sec. in a Mead laboratory refiner; Williams slowness, 57.7 sec.; basis weight, $127 \text{ gm/m}^2 = 26 \text{ lb}/1000$ square feet.

Figure 11, and Figure 12, a detailed study of the bond area shown in Figure 13, illustrate additional material relative to fiber-to-fiber bonding studied in ultrathin sections through contacting fibers in an experimental paper having a basis weight of 3.2 gm/m^2, prepared on a teflon surface without application of wet pressure, and made from so-called Husum sulfate pulp of pine. A mechanical refining of 16,000 revolutions in a PFI beater, resulting in a degree of beating of 62°SR, was employed. Possible formation of hydrogen bonds between adjacent microfibrils from fibers A and B is indicated by observed intimate contact. The adhesion between microfibrils has prevented penetration of the contrasting osmium tetroxide (reduced *in situ* to metallic osmium) to large areas and made possible the revealing of a limited number of microfibrils in the contact area. From the electron optical point of view, the specimen has been satisfactorily thin to allow resolution of microfibrils as small as about 50 Å diameter and spacings of 25 Å and less. The instrumental resolving power for Figures 11, 12, and 13 was about 20 Å.

SUMMARY

There has been a critical information gap between the evaluated 20 to 90% actual bonding (Page *et al.*, 1962 a, b) in an interfiber bond area

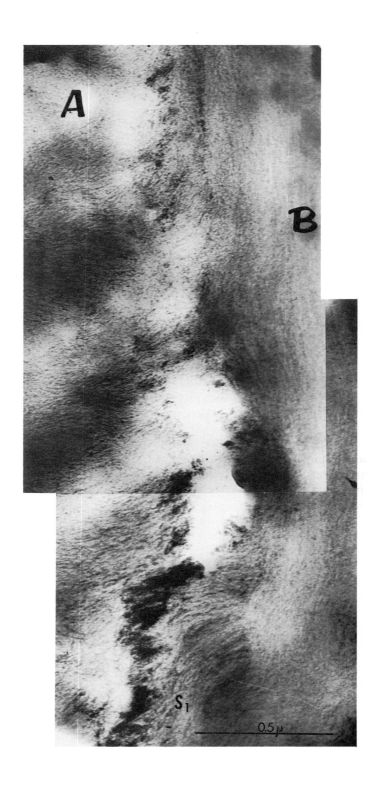

and the statistical evaluations of hydrogen bonds and van der Waals' forces in paper by Nissan (1962) and Sternstein and Nissan (1962).

Some of the sensitive interface phenomena anticipating the formation of an actual bonding have been demonstrated in the present investigation. The importance of the adhered but swelling and thus mobile low DP components for the surface properties of aspen holopulp has been discussed on the basis of good resolution electron micrographs and observed changes in ultrastructure. The 3 Å hydrogen bonds are not resolvable but a distinct imaging of units 7 Å apart is obtained, approaching the range of van der Waals' forces. The significance of fiber chemistry for bonding has been known as an empirical experience in paper technology. Surface adhesion and the role of primers are generally attributed to functional groups that are frequent in wood polyoses. The surface activity of nonfibrillar fractions has been indicated as a decreasing contact angle in this investigation. The observed hemicellulose action is in agreement with the conclusion of Leopold and McIntosh (1961) that the xylan content is an important factor governing the tensile strength of individual fibers.

Some regular nonlinear growth features and fibril ultrastructures are reported to have been found in aspen holopulp. The customary statistical strength evaluations express paper structure in terms of tracheid anatomy and cell wall deformations in the torsional fields of drying, fracturing, and so on. The nonstatistical fractions can be equally important for binding as the more uniform tracheids and fibers with high inherent strength are for tear and tensile strength.

The aspen holopulp contains too many anatomical components to be suitable for statistical strength analysis. On the other hand, for studying bonding properties and their variations as a function of conditions, the aspen holopulp is the most excellent material because of its large nonglucanic fraction and because of its never dried, pristine surfaces.

ACKNOWLEDGMENTS

The authors wish to express their thanks to N. S. Thompson and O. Kaustinen of The Institute of Paper Chemistry, Appleton, Wisconsin, for the sample of aspen holopulp and to P. J. Pochay for several specimen preparations.

FIG. 13. Survey picture of bond area between two fibers, A and B, in the thin experimental paper of 3.2 gm./m^2 basis weight of pine sulfite pulp. Note the S$_1$-wall in the lower part of the section. X 72,000. (from Sikorski, 1960)

REFERENCES

Adams, G. A. (1964) "Water soluble polysaccharides of sugar maple (*Acer saccharum*)." *Svensk Papperstid.* 67:82–88.

Asunmaa, S. (1955) "Electron microscope studies on sections of aspen sulfite pulp fibers." *Svensk Papperstid.* 58:33–34.

_____ (1956) "Impregnation and embedding of cellulose fibers for electron microscopy." *Svensk Papperstid.* 59:527–530.

_____ (1957) "Contact region between two fibers." In *Electron Microscopy, Proc. Stockholm Conf, 1956* (F. S. Sjöstrand and J. Rhodin, ed.), pp. 293–294. Almqvist and Wiksell, Stockholm.

_____, and Steenberg, B. (1958) "Beaten pulps and the fiber-to-fiber bond in paper." *Svensk Papperstid.* 61:686–695.

Bowering, W. D. S., and Timell, T. E. (1960) "Synthesis and characterization of 2-0-(β-D-Glucopyranosyluronic acid)-D-xylopyranose." *J. Am. Chem. Soc.* 82:2827–2830.

_____, Marchessault, R. H., and Timell, T. E. (1961) "Preparation and properties of a 4-0-methylglucoxylan from the wood of white birch." *Svensk Papperstid.* 64:191–194.

Emerton, H. W., Page, D. H., and Watts, J. (1957) "Further reflection electron microscopy of pulp fibers and paper." In *Electron Microscopy, Proc. Stockholm Conf., 1956* (F. S. Sjöstrand and J. Rhodin, ed.) pp. 287–289. Almqvist and Wiksell, Stockholm.

Giertz, H. W. (1950) "The opacity of paper pulps. I. Measuring methods." *Svensk Papperstid.* 53:673–680.

_____ (1951) "The opacity of paper pulps. II. General viewpoints." *Svensk Papperstid.* 54:267–274.

Iwasaki, T., Lindberg, B., and Meier, H. (1962) "The effect of ultrasonic treatment on individual wood fibers." *Svensk Papperstid.* 65:795–816.

Jayme, G., and Hunger, G. (1962) "Electron microscope 2- and 3-dimensional classification of fiber bonding." In *Formation and Structure of Paper, Trans. Symp. Oxford, 1961* (F. Bolam, ed.), Vol. 1, pp. 135–170. Technical Section of British Paper and Board Makers' Association (Inc.), London.

Leopold, B., and McIntosh, D. C. (1961) "Chemical composition and physical properties of wood fibers. III. Tensile strength of individual fibers from alkali-extracted loblolly pine holocellulose." *Tappi* 44:235–240.

Nissan, A. H. (1962) "General principles of adhesion with particular reference to the hydrogen bond." In *Formation and Structure of Paper, Trans. Symp. Oxford, 1961* (F. Bolam, ed.), Vol. 1, pp. 119–130.

Nordman, L. S. (1961) "Bonding in paper sheets." In *Fundamentals Papermaking Fibers, Trans. Symp. Cambridge, Engl., 1957* (F. Bolam, ed.), pp. 333–347.

_____, Gustafsson, C., and Olofsson, G. (1954) "The strength of bondings in paper. II." *Paperi ja Puu* (Paper and Timber) 36:315–320.

Page, D. H., Tydeman, P. A., and Hunt, M. (1962a.) "A study of fiber-to-fiber bonding by direct observation." In *Formation and Structure of Paper, Trans. Symp. Oxford, 1961* (F. Bolam, ed.), Vol. 1, pp. 171–193.

_____, _____, and _____ (1962b.) "The behaviour of fiber-to-fiber bonds in sheets under dynamic conditions." In *Formation and Structure of Paper, Trans. Symp. Oxford, 1961* (F. Bolam, ed.), Vol. 1, pp. 249–263.

Preston, R. D. (1962) "The microfibrillar structure and the coherence of plant cell walls." In *Electron Microscopy, Fifth International Cong. Philadelphia, 1962* (S. S. Breese, Jr., ed.), p. BB-1. Academic Press, N. Y.

Ränby, B. G. (1962) "Summing up." In *Formation and Structure of Paper, Trans. Symp. Oxford, 1961* (F. Bolam, ed.), Vol. 2, pp. 901–910.

Sikorski, J. (1960) "Studies of fibrous structures." In *IV Internationaler Kongress für Elektronenmikroskopie,* Vol. 1, p. 686. Springer-Verlag, Berlin.

Sternstein, S. S., and Nissan, A. H. (1962) "A molecular theory of the visco-elasticity of a three-dimensional hydrogen-bonded network." In *Formation and Structure of Paper, Transactions of the Symposium Held at Oxford, Sept., 1961* (F. Bolam, ed.), Vol. 1, pp. 319–349. Technical Section of British Paper and Board Makers' Association (Inc.), London.

Thompson, N. S., and Kaustinen, O. A. (1964) "Some chemical and physical properties of pulps prepared by mild oxidative action." *Tappi* 47:157–162.

Tyminski, A., and Timell, T. E. (1960) "The constitution of a glucomannan from white spruce (*Picea glauca*)." *J. Am. Chem. Soc.* 82:2823–2827.

AUTHOR INDEX

A

Acerbo, S. N., 170, 171, *179*
Adams, E. H., 462, *469*
Adams, G. A., 578, *592*
Adams, M. F., 140, *152*
Addo-Ashong, F. W., 494, *533*
Adkins, H., 161, *179*
Adler, E., 159, 174, 175, 177, *178*
Ahlborn, M., 527, *531*
Ahrens, L. H., 184, *188*
Akasi, T., 387, *390*
Alexandrov, W. G., 385, *389*
Altermatt, H., 144, *152*
Altman, P. L., 182, *188*
Amos, G. L., 459, 464, *467*
Aspinall, C. O., 138, 142, 151, *152*
Astbury, W. T., 509, *532*
Asunmaa, S., 91, *95*, 145, *152*, 229, *231*, 235, *248*, 341, *367*, 496, *531*, 577, 583, *592*
Augustin, H., 461, *470*
Aung, M., 460, 462, *467*
Axelrod, B., 144, *155*

B

Back, E., 556, *558*
Bailey, A. J., 146, *152*, 158, *178*, 420
Bailey, I. W., 9, 30, *30*, 36, *49*, 62, 66, 95, 216, 217, 222, *231*, *232*, 235, 237, *248*, 254, *268*, 271, 272, 276, 278, *288*, *289*, 297, *304*, 305, 306, 307, 309, 316, *316*, *317*, 335, *339*, 341, 345, 350, 351, *367*, 373, 387, *390*, *453*, 459, 460, *467*, *469*, *491*
Bamber, R. K., 95, *96*
Bandurski, R. S., 104, *123*
Bannan, M. W., 62, *96*, 433, *452*, 458, *467*
Barber, G. A., 144, *153*, 210, *212*
Barefoot, A. C., Jr., 463, *467*
Barghoorn, E. S., 148, *152*, 349, *367*
Barkley, G., 99, *123*
Barlow, H. W. B., 388, *389*
Barskaya, E. I., 93, *96*
Bassett, K. H., 148, *154*, 476, *491*

Bauch, J., 284, 286, *290*
Bayley, S. T., 104, *123*, 211, *212*
Bayly, I. L., 62, *96*
Bazhenov, V. A., 535, *537*
Beaman, T. C., 104, *123*
Becker, W. A., 52, *59*
Beckman, C. H., 319, 321, *332*, *333*
Beer, M., 51, *60*, 104, *123*
Berbee, J. E., 319, *332*
Berlyn, G. P., 375, *389*
Bertholf, L. D., 535, *537*
Bethel, J. S., 462, *467*
Bhattacharjee, S. S., 142, 143, *152*
Billek, G., 128, *154*, 162, 166, *178*, *179*
Bisset, I. W. J., 459, 464, *467*
Björkman, A., 365, *367*
Björkqvist, K. J., 159, *178*
Bland, D. E., 91, 92, *97*, 128, *156*, 158, *180*
Bloch, R., 47, *49*, 99, *124*
Bloss, F. D., 5, *30*
Blyth, Amélie, 38, *49*
Boer, J. H. de, 505, *531*
Bonart, R., 197, *197*, 529, *531*
Bonga, J. M., 494, *531*
Bonneville, M. A., 106, *123*
Booys, J. de, 484, *491*
Bosshard, H. H., 251, 267, *268*, 271, 274, 285, *289*, 291, *304*, 306, 307, 310, *317*, 458, 459, 460, *467*
Bouck, G. B., 103, 106, *123*
Bouveng, H. O., 138, *152*
Bowen, H. J. M., 185, *188*
Bowering, W. D. S., 578, *592*
Boyce, S. G., 464, *467*
Bradford, G. R., 181, *189*
Bradway, K. E., 261, *268*
Branton, D., 54, 57, *60*
Brauns, D. A., 128, *153*
Brauns, F. E., 128, *153*
Brenner, S., 192, *197*
Brickman, L., 161, *178*
Brode, W. R., 184, *188*
Brown, A. G., 465, *467*
Brown, A. M., 201, *212*
Brown, H. P., 461, 462, *469*, 544, *549*

595